Marine Investigations

by

David H. Pascoe

Marine Investigations

Published by D. H. Pascoe & Co., Inc.
Destin, Florida, USA
www.yachtsurvey.com

First Printing October 2004
Second Printing 2006
Third Printing 2015

ISBN 0-9656496-5-2

LCCN 2006279937

Text, photographs, illustration, layout and editing: David H. Pascoe
Layout and editing: Junko A. Pascoe

Introduction

My inspiration for producing this book derives from several important factors. First is that there are presently no books currently exist on the subject. This is mainly because I would estimate that there are probably less than one thousand full-time professional marine investigators. Secondly – and all aspiring investigators will be glad to hear this — there is a great need for more qualified investigators from all aspects of the marine industry.

On approaching this task I found myself somewhat intimidated by it since this is very wide-ranging subject about which even a half-dozen books could hardly begin to cover it all. So it was that I had to reconcile myself to the fact that this necessarily had to be an introductory text, combined with the fact that it is highly unlikely that anyone is ever going to expend on it. This is simply because there isn't any money to be made in producing books for such a very limited audience.

Marine investigators as a group cover numerous types of investigations involving many technical specialties, so many that no one investigator can possibly be expert at them all. Therefore, in planning this book I decided to choose and give a bit more elaboration on the most common types, such as sinking, fire, machinery damage and fraud. By necessity it was necessary to omit others such as collisions and structural failures, subjects on which entire volumes could be devoted. Certainly the same can be said for the chapters on fire losses and machinery damage cases to which are devoted as many as forty or fifty pages but still barely scratches the surface. My intent is not to be all-inclusive, but to demonstrate the vast complexity and difficulties associated with such investigations.

As an introductory text, its purpose is to acquaint the reader and student with the individual subjects and to provide direction for continued study and self-education. Marine investigators are largely self-educated owing to a lack of educational opportunities for marine professionals. But, there is another, less flattering reason: anyone who can afford the cost of advanced engineering degrees has little motivation to engage in a career of dirty and uncomfortable work crawling around through wrecked boats. There are more pleasant ways of earning a good living with a degree in engineering, so we find few, if any, engineers in our profession.

Perhaps another reason for this is that the marine investigator has a lot in common with police investigators; our work is as much about people as it is boats. Most casualties occur as a result of the actions of people, so if you don't like investigating people, chances are you won't be pleased with a career in marine investigations. The reader will find that at least a third of this book is devoted to investigation techniques with human beings, not just boats. Many people find this to be an unpleasant task because they don't like questioning the motives of others or risking the prospects of confronting the frailties of human integrity.

A good investigator is half cop, half technician. It is important for the student to recognize that, like the homicide detective who partly relies on crime scene specialists, so too does the marine investigator make use of, and rely on, many other technical specialists. He is a lot like a family doctor who is a general practitioner; there is much he doesn't know himself, but he does know those who do know.

Perhaps the most important talent that the marine investigator possesses is his people skills. The investigator's stock in trade is information and as every experienced investigator knows, people are often reluctant to talk to investigators. The investigator who develops the skill of extracting information from reluctant witnesses finishes far ahead of those who don't.

As any fan of the TV series *Columbo* can appreciate, good investigators are not ordinary people. There is something in their nature and character that sets them apart. Normal people are usually satisfied with safe and superficial explanations of things, whereas the investigator is a person who, for whatever reason, is not satisfied with superficial appearances but is compelled to dig deeper. A good investigator is a cynic and a skeptic; he doubts the easy explanation. Good investigators have trouble with the idea of letting sleeping dogs lie because they may be covering up something important. They are prone to kicking the dog to see what it is laying on. What makes them good is that internal motivation to find out. Like the kid who's given a watch for his birthday, he has to take it apart to find out what is inside.

Investigators are also unusual in that they are not get-along, go-along Charlies, the type of person who is not afraid to rock the boat and make waves. He will overturn the apple cart just to inspect the apples at the bottom of the pile. The idea of investigating the behavior of people and events carries with it a certain social stigma: it's not nice to go prying into the affairs of other people, yet that is the business of the investigator. An investigator is not a person for whom social acceptance is a high priority because his occupation makes others view him with caution and distrust.

An additional area of expertise that the investigator must possess is a working knowledge of law. Investigations frequently result in litigation and thus an omnipresent theme throughout this book is the fact that his work will be subject to extensive scrutiny by other experts. His work product must be able to stand up to this scrutiny. He will frequently be subjected to merciless interrogation in depositions and occasional court testimony, thus making it imperative that he have a solid understanding of how to write a proper investigation report that isn't vulnerable to being discredited by the opposition.

While the emphasis is on insurance claims investigations, the same basic principles apply to all investigations regardless of why or for whom they are conducted. Thus, the reader who does not intend to do insurance work should not be put off by frequent reference to insurance matters.

Of the thirteen chapters, fully half are dedicated to learning the fundamentals such as issues of law, insurance contracts, evidence collection and handling, giving testimony and writing reports. The remainder is given over to the specific areas of investigation such as fire or fraud. The reader should understand that none of these chapters are intended to be definitive essays on the individual subjects, about which an entire book could be written. Instead, each chapter presents a broad outline of what is involved in each type, for which the individual investigator must ultimately seek to continue his education by other means.

David H. Pascoe
Destin, Florida
September, 2004

Contents

Chapter 1

The Marine Investigator

An incident that causes loss or damage to a vessel, or injury to persons, is referred to as a "casualty" or "loss" by the insurance industry, regardless of how it occurs. Anyone that is making a claim for loss or damages, whether an insured or not, is referred to as a "claimant". Historically, the marine surveyor has been the preferred expert for the investigation of marine casualties by insurance companies and other interests. This is by virtue of the marine surveyor's long and practical experience with boats and the kinds of things that happen to, or go wrong with, boats.

A fundamental presumption of this book is that reader has a background in marine surveying which is the main prerequisite for becoming a marine investigator. Lacking this, there is no basis upon which an individual can be considered an expert. The prepurchase surveyor, for example, acquires a large body of knowledge during his daily work of inspecting yachts for prospective buyers, as does the claims surveyor, who spends much of his professional life examining one casualty after another for insurance companies. The question the would-be surveyor and investigator invariably asks is how one comes to the point of acquiring this body of knowledge and expertise. This question is as difficult to answer and satisfy as that of describing how one comes to be a marine surveyor.

Nation-wide there are, as of this writing, probably not more than 2,000 practicing, full-time marine surveyors, though there are far more persons who dabble at it, attempting to be professionals without adequate training or experience. The very small size of this profession means that there are no schools or colleges offering degree programs on the subject due to insufficient demand for such a program. Historically, marine surveyors have approached casualty investigations on an ad hoc basis. Fortunately, as recreational boating has grown over the years, so has the degree and sophistication of casualty investigations.

The point of view of this book is primarily from the vantage point of the claims surveyor, for marine insurance claims are, by far, the most frequent reason marine surveyors are hired to investigate losses. There are, of course, many other interests that hire surveyors regarding losses such as banks (lenders), attorneys, boat builders, dealers as well as individuals, among others.

The yacht surveyor as a professional began appearing on the scene immediately after WWII as the boating industry began a long period of rapid and sustained growth. Most of these were men who had small craft experience either in the Navy, Coast Guard or in boat building. During the 1950's, a fledgling group of surveyors formed the Yacht Safety Bureau which evolved in 1962 into what is now the National Association of Marine Surveyors.

Today, marine casualty investigation has grown into a rather sophisticated combination of art and science, employing skills and techniques to a degree not unlike that of the police detective. The good casualty investigator not only possesses an extensive knowledge of boats, but also the skills of a detective; his positive traits include knowledge, persistence, determination and patience. Such skills are necessitated by the fact that when costly accidents occur, litigation often follows.

What is a Vessel?

That probably sounds like a dumb question until such time as one runs across an instance where that definition is in question. A vessel is any type of floating structure that is intended as a *conveyance* on water. A vessel is *not* anything that is permanently affixed to the landmass or attached to the bottom. A vessel is not a dock, but a vessel is a floating house. A floating dock is not a vessel, but a raft is. Anything that is towed becomes a vessel at the time it is being towed. Is a jet ski a vessel? How about a surf board or wind surfer? Because they are conveyances the answer is yes to all.

Though the subject of this book is pleasure craft, it is recognized that many surveyors work in both the commercial and pleasure craft realm, so that the definition of pleasure craft can be just as murky as to what constitutes a vessel. Fortunately, the principles for any type of investigation are the same, so once we learn the basics we can expand our horizons as far as we wish. We distinguish pleasure craft from commercial vessels for two reasons, (1) commercial vessels may be operated in interstate or international commerce, which brings it under cognizance of Admiralty jurisdiction. Commercial vessels are operated by professional mariners (usually), and are *insured quite differently than pleasure craft*; (2) pleasure craft are usually operated by non professional mariners but subject to the same body of law but different insurance contacts. An entire body of law has grown up around commercial marine insurance but not for pleasure craft owing to the diversity of jurisdiction, either federal, state or local that may apply to pleasure craft issues, whereas commercial marine has only one proper jurisdiction, Admiralty.

Moreover, the marine investigator will find it difficult to stay solely within the bounds of pleasure craft because pleasure boats are so often used as commercial craft, including charter, rental, dive charter and so on. All issues of marine salvage, whether commercial or pleasure craft, fall exclusively within Admiralty jurisdiction. Therefore, the investigator will find it useful to have a background in Admiralty as well as the rules and precedents of the lower courts, for the law always exerts an influence over our work whether we are aware of that influence or not.

What Is An Investigation?

For our purposes an investigation is an effort to determine the cause or circumstances leading up to a casualty. The majority of insurance investigations are so mundane as to not be even referred to as such, as nearly all claims are investigated to some degree. Some marine surveyors assigned by the insurer to handle a boat or yacht claim may understand their role only to assess damages and create an estimate. Others will understand their role to determine the facts that lead to the cause of the casualty, particularly when such claims where the cause may be questionable.

There are hundreds of insurance companies that provide insurance for boats, but only a relative handful that specialize in marine insurance. The effect of this means that there are very many company claims people that assign claims to marine surveyors who themselves know little or nothing about marine losses. In all too many cases, these claims personnel don't know what to expect from the surveyor they hire, and vice versa. This leads to the all too common situation of the blind leading the blind, leading to subrogation cases later offered up for litigation in which an adequate investigation was not performed. With large dollar losses, the need for a good investigation is more obvious, but with smaller losses, this point is frequently overlooked.

At this point it is important to realize that the laws of many states specifically require that the insurance company conduct a "reasonable investigation" of questionable losses. This is mandated as much for the protection of the policy holder as it is for the insurer since the payment of claims ultimately affects all policy holders whose premiums pay those claims. It is a gross misunderstanding of the general public that it is "insurance companies" that pay claims. True, insurance companies write the checks, but the money comes from policy holders.

Since most marine casualties are referred to surveyors, it naturally follows that only the surveyor is in a position to make judgements about investigations, whether a loss requires only a cursory or major effort. Throughout my career I have found myself in the position of having to make judgements about whether I thought a cause of loss was worth pursuing or not. Such judgements come down to a matter of whether the dollar amount of loss justifies the additional cost of investigating, combined with a judgement of whether there appears to be promising evidence. In other words, there are always those cases in which it becomes apparent that there is unlikely to be any good evidence available at a reasonable cost, and if the dollar value of the claim is low, then it is probably not worth making much of an investigation.

In actual practice, most claims work is assigned for the purpose of appraisal of damage since in many cases the claims adjuster is not aware that the cause of loss is not ordinary, or that an investigation may be needed. If the surveyor is uncertain about what his client expects, or he is pretty certain that his client doesn't know, then it becomes his job to educate the client. When the client is not an insurer, but perhaps a boat owner or some other interest, it becomes even more critical that the investigator fully brief the client about what should or should not be done, what he can and cannot do. Marine surveyors are not always the right choice for all types of losses, particularly fire and theft of vessel claims where someone with specialist expertise is needed, someone who may or may not be a surveyor. In fact, very few surveyors are qualified to conduct fire investigations, and very few building fire investigators are qualified to investigate boat fires. This will be discussed in detail in Chapter 8 Fire Investigation.

What distinguishes ordinary claims work from an investigation is when it becomes necessary to deal with causation in a separate report. While most surveyors do not do it this way, it is my opinion that casualty investigations should always be addressed in reports separate from those that deal with damages. Standard property adjuster reports typically include issues of cause in one report. The marine investigation is a specialty and reports can be lengthy and complex, so it is best that they be kept separate.

Types of Casualties

The most common types of casualties or case work the marine investigator encounters include, in no particular order:

Sinking	Latent defect
Fire	Structural failure
Collision	Ship repairer's legal liability
Grounding	General liability
Lightning	Personal injury
Windstorm	Vandalism
Theft	Arson
Machinery damage	Warranty claims

As one can see from this list, there is no shortage of opportunities. Of course no investigator can be expert in all these area and his own personal preferences will lead him toward those areas to which he is best suited. Some types of work naturally support others, or lead to other types. In addition, the investigator is often led into new areas by the needs of clients so that over time, and by necessity, he has been motivated to educate himself on a broad range of issues. Our knowledge is also greatly expanded by what we learn from those experts we hire to assist with investigations such as metallurgists, chemists and engineers of all sorts, the same way as police investigators do.

Fraud is such a common element in insurance investigations that, did it not exist, there wouldn't be much need for investigators. Estimates range anywhere from 20 to 50% of most types of claims that are wholly or party fraudulent, resulting in losses up to a hundred billion dollars annually[1]. Furthermore, it is usually wrongly stated that these losses are born by the insurance industry; it is not the insurance companies that suffer 90% of these losses but you and me and everyone who pays insurance premiums, for the cost of this fraud is passed directly onto the policy holders through higher costs.

There are many elements of fraud and the following is a short list:

> Insuring of a non existent vessel
>
> Willful misrepresentation of the insured vessel or false statements on an insurance application.
>
> Willful misrepresentation of service, such as pleasure vs. commercial
>
> Willful destruction of a vessel such as arson and scuttling.
>
> False theft reports
>
> Reporting false cause of loss
>
> Intentional inflation of damages through fraudulent estimates
>
> Collusion with repairers
>
> Fraudulent third party claims against liability coverage

Qualifications

Ultimately, testifying in court as a qualified expert provides the basis for qualification of the investigator in that venue, but that is only a partial answer. An expert is defined as one who has special skills derived from training or experience. Note that the dictionary definition specifically includes experience as a basis for expertise, so we need not feel insecure about being challenged on the lack of formal training. As I point out in a later chapter, experience precedes the university professor who, in most instances, is only parroting what he learned from his teachers and so on. Somewhere along the line, someone has to gain the personal experience that is later taught to others.

Insurance companies, attorneys and others go to the expense of hiring bona fide experts to investigate casualties either for the purpose of determining the cause of loss, whether insurance coverage applies, and who, if anyone, is responsible for the loss. Or simply due to anticipation that litigation may be forthcoming. Thus the overriding concern of the one who hires an investigator is that the investigator possesses the requisite expertise. And because litigation is always a possibility, the expertise of the investigator must be demonstrable.

Before an expert is accepted as such in a court of law he has to be qualified to the court. Qualification means the presentation of sufficient evidence of qualification as to satisfy all parties to the litigation, as well as the judge, that the witness is qualified. This comes in the form of questioning from both sides. Lacking proof of qualification, the opposing counsel will challenge the expert's credentials and probably have him disqualified. In some cases, even the judge may question the assertion that the witness is qualified and subject the witness to his own questioning. Thus, anyone who approaches casualty investigation as something anyone with a bit of knowledge can do, he's likely to have a rude awakening when that investigator ends up in deposition or court.

The author's motivation for writing this book is based on the fact that there are so few opportunities available to obtain the necessary training or experience, yet there is a great need for more qualified experts. The maritime attorney, rightly so, will usually seek a much higher degree of experience than the insurance company, the later of which serves as the primary training ground for those who seek to perform this kind of work.

Fortunately, it is not necessary to present a university diploma in order get qualified as an expert, for the author's experience is that the courts are fairly liberal in civil cases as to what constitutes an expert. The fact is that experts abound in a huge array of subjects, the vast majority of which there are no collegiate degree programs for the subject matter. But for a handful of seminars, virtually all marine investigators are self-taught to one degree or another. The overriding criteria is whether the investigator can demonstrate that he or she posses superior knowledge and experience on the subject. Here we can see that a college diploma can provide one with a lot of secondhand information, but never real world experience.

Even so, formal training in any allied subject such as engineering is certainly beneficial, but it is very rare to find a surveyor that has a degree in engineering. So why aren't there more engineers working as surveyors? The answer probably lies in the fact that there are more comfortable opportunities for employment at higher starting salaries. The prospect of starting one's own business in this line of work does not appear to be widely appealing to engineers. The marine investigator probably has more in common with the police detective than he does with the typical engineer.

Forensics

The marine surveyor is an expert, but he is also a generalist in the same way as a family doctor is. Surveyors know a lot about boats generally, but boats are assemblages of materials, systems, hardware and other components, some of which he has expertise about, others not. Like the police detective, the marine expert often makes use of other experts.

The dictionaries define forensics as follows: "1: belonging to the courts of judicature or to public discussion and debate 2: used in legal proceeding or public discussions 3: the art and study of argumentative discourse; *broadly*: argumentative, rhetorical."

While the term forensic is Latin in its root, its meaning as defined in the dictionary only bears a small resemblance to the way the term is used today. Perhaps our dictionaries are a bit behind the times, because the term forensic is today taken to mean just about any kind of technical investigation for any purpose, whereas in the past it meant mainly the theory of debate whether judicial or not. Today the term is used in conjunction with specific disciplines of physical investigation not only relating to criminal and civil proceedings but also to many other areas of organized human contention such as dispute resolution, insurance claims and so on.

Therefore, forensic investigation can be taken to mean *the evidence obtained by means of the physical investigative sciences and its application toward the discovery of truth.* The important point to understand about the term concerns evidence that is used as the basis of an argument to arrive at the truth of an issue.

Today the forensic investigator is a person equipped with specialty knowledge and training, as in ballistics, medical, pathology, chemistry and even accounting and computers. In the strictest sense of the term, the marine surveyor who investigates sinking casualties is performing a forensic service, the collection and analysis of evidence leading to the determination of the cause of an event that may ultimately be litigated, and therefore *belonging to the courts of judicature.*

That the work of the marine surveyor has a high probability of ending up as a *forensic argument* should remain foremost in the investigator's mind.

Establishing a Business

The marine surveyor student and beginner, of course, is constantly plagued with the problem of how to obtain that training or experience. The beginning surveyor inevitably finds himself in the unenviable position of not being able to get work because he is inexperienced, and can't get experience because he can't get work. One of the most common questions I am asked is that of how to establish a business. As with most professions, that is not an easy proposition and there are no easy answers.

To hold oneself out as an expert, it is first necessary to establish a marine surveying business of some type. There is really no other way to gain the needed knowledge, expertise and experience. Marine *investigation businesses usually evolve out of surveying businesses since that is a logical extension.* However, in terms of mixing different types of surveying work with investigations, this does not always work out well. Pre-purchase survey work does not mix well with either claims work or investigations due to the inevitable scheduling conflicts. By far, the best mix is general insurance claims work and investigations because these are mutually supporting. A surveyor will achieve the highest degree of universal expertise when has the opportunity to perform all types of work. Should he later wish to go for expert witness work, this will best prepare him for the wide variety of subjects that expert witnesses are hired for.

Some people are naturally good at being rain-makers or getting clients, while others are predisposed toward being technocrats. The sole proprietor has to wear both hats equally well to survive. Business generation is a never-ending task that anyone who becomes good at it is going to regard as a trade secret. In reality, there doesn't seem to be any common denominator for success other than persistence and determination. While the daily bread of a survey business may be the repeat client, the difference between surviving and real success is referrals, which are often the largest and best paying jobs that push us over the top of mere business survival.

Referrals mean that the quality of one's work has been noticed, or that one has attained sufficient contact with those people who are in a position to make referrals, that word is getting around, however that may be achieved. It can happen through attendance at business and social functions, or simply diligent effort to meet people during the course of daily work. Over the years I have found that direct efforts to sell one's services has been spectacularly unsuccessful; people do not hire professionals based on sales calls. That said, it does not mean that there is not a time and place for sales calls, either cold or appointed, for there is. But sales calls must be low-key efforts mainly to make the prospect aware of your existence and availability; it is merely an effort to "show face".

The best place to show face is at business or industry functions, and most particularly taking any opportunity to be a speaker or participate in a forum where attention is directed to you. Mere frequent attendance at such functions will eventually lead to getting to know prospective clients, but obviously takes time, as does the whole process of marketing your service.

So who are the people that are most often in the position of making referrals? This is a tough question to pin down, but there are a few obvious choices that include insurance agents, boat yard or marina owners and managers, boat captains, former clients, and other marine industry businessmen. If there is a local marine trade association, so much the better. Even a local Chamber of Commerce can be helpful when other marine trades are represented.

One of the best books directed at the small businessman is Jay Conrad Levine's *Guerilla Marketing*. I highly recommend it.

Licensing

To the best of my knowledge there is no state that requires the licensing of marine surveyors, but most surveyors don't do investigations. Marine investigations may be confined strictly to boats, or may become more wide ranging, involving the investigations of people and their activities. Because of this the question of licensing has been at issue in the laws of the various states, an issue which I have been following for decades.

While I certainly don't know the laws of all 50 states, I have followed those of three major states, Florida, California and New York. The basic intent of the legislatures of these three large states is that those who handle and *settle* insurance claims should be licensed adjusters, while those engaged in certain specialties should not. Over a period of 30 years, the laws of these states have liberalized considerably. New York specifically excludes marine surveyors from licensing. Florida is silent on the subject and California is vague. The intent seems to be that these states do not want to get involved in licensing specialists, nor to include them in broader licensing requirements.

However, none of these states seems to take cognizance of the surveyor as a more wide ranging investigator and thus the laws seem to default on the subject. Every investigator should make a point of studying those parts of their state insurance laws to determine whether licensing seems to be mandated. I started out by making calls to all three states to see if I could get an answer to this question, but could find no one in any state insurance office that had the slightest idea. That's why I recommend that you study the law yourself.

Some surveyors obtain insurance adjuster's licenses and there is a good reason for this. The state *all-lines adjusters license* permits the holder to engage in a broad range of investigation, including the taking of statements as well as obtaining financial records. This license is nearly as broad as that of the private investigator. Holding such a license leaves little doubt as to what the investigator is permitted to do. That is reassuring when one is testifying in court because there is no possibility of being attacked for being unlicensed. This license has proved invaluable to me as it can open many doors that otherwise remain closed.

Ordinarily there would be no way for someone without an insurance education to obtain this license. Fortunately, in nearly every large state there are private tutors that offer reasonably priced tutoring designed to help one pass the state exam one has to take. Typically these tutors rotate around major cities with their six week courses of three nights per week.

Advertising

The question about advertising is not whether it works, but how to make it work and can it be afforded? One shot, one-time ad placement definitely does not work. Advertising is something that has to be done over the long term. To understand this, all one has to do is examine how you react to ads. If you ever purchased any service based on an ad, chances are that it is an ad that you have been seeing for a long time, or have knowledge of the company and so on. The universal rule of advertising is that the less the cost, the less likely it will produce results even with a well-planned program.

The best sources charge more. Naturally. One of the most successful ads I know of by a marine surveyor involved ads on the Junior Chamber of Commerce's bus bench project with benches situated near marinas.

Anyone who wishes to become a marine expert has an advantage over most marine surveyors in the field today. That is because most surveyors merely seek to earn a living without making much of an effort to acquire knowledge. Anyone who wishes to enter this field should do so with the idea of constantly working to improve one's knowledge. This is not difficult because the surveyor is immersed in an ocean of facts and details on a daily basis; he has only to train himself to be inquisitive and observant.

Among the most important skills that any investigator possesses, excepting strictly forensic investigators, are people skills and linguistic skills. An investigator who lacks good people skills is severely crippled in his abilities, for most evidence is obtained by the power of persuasion, the ability to motivate others to cooperate with the investigator. Some people just seem to have a natural talent toward working with others while others have to work at it and acquire that talent by force of habit. No matter, if you don't truly enjoy this work you're not going to be very good at it. The remainder of this book leans heavily on the need for good people skills.

People skills and linguistic skills go hand-in-hand. The linguistic skill is the ability to use language to its best effect; this does not mean to become a good liar. Rather, it means the recognition that a question asked one way is unlikely to produce results, while asked another way will. These are much the same as leadership skills, which includes the ability to motivate another person to cooperate. The good investigator becomes a good teacher because his role is one of constantly explaining things. Unless he learns the art of making difficult subjects understandable to ordinary people, he is unlikely to do well.

Serving Clients

Obligations to the Client

The first obligation to the client is to be the expert one claims to be, and to perform a thorough job. Investigations can be lengthy so that the matter of being paid adequately for one's work can be a major factor. It should be obvious that if the investigator is not being paid adequately, there is substantial incentive to not put in all the time required to do a thorough job. This naturally leads to the issue of payment.

Getting paid by insurance companies is rarely a problem, but working for individuals and lawyers and getting paid at all is a major problem for surveyors because we have long-standing problems of getting paid by these people. Especially lawyers who often are working cases on a contingency basis with no, or very little money up front, thus creating a built-in problem for getting paid. Most experts finally learn the hard way that the only way they're going to get paid is by getting payment *up front*. One has only to consider what it is like trying to collect from a lawyer.

Maintaining objectivity proves difficult for many surveyors to do because it is the client that is paying him. The problem with taking a position of advocacy on behalf of the client is the distortion of truth this inevitably causes. And while this might not seem to be a problem at the time of slanting one's findings on behalf of the client, the presentation of a less than truthful report in a case that ends up in litigation more often than not ends up with the surveyor being discredited in open court, a situation that can cause acute embarrassment, among other things.

The beginner should be aware that the manipulation of facts for the benefit of the client usually ends up becoming painfully obvious to everyone but the persons doing the manipulating. Bias is easy to detect by those who are not involved, though it is hard for one who is involved to appreciate this. It is something the beginner learns over time as he gains experience and having had the opportunity to review the work of other experts who have manipulated facts or evidence to suit their needs. The beginner will do himself a big favor by quickly learning to avoid clients who want the surveyor to manipulate evidence for him.

The vast majority of the surveyor's work will end up in a written report. The obligation to the client is to present a clear, precise and factual report as succinctly as possible. Learning to write good reports is not easy unless one has had college level training in report writing. A poorly written report is a disservice to the client because such reports do not present the case as well as it should be presented. In legal situations, a poorly written report can, by itself, end up losing the case for the client. For that reason I have devoted an entire chapter to report writing. See chapter 13.

Maintaining Objectivity

During the course of writing this book I was involved in a number of cases in which investigators produced investigation reports that were not only biased, but were downright falsified. It was obvious to anyone reading those reports that the investigator was clearly trying to manipulate evidence in favor of his client. With insurance cases especially, the investigator has a duty to be objective and to present fair and unbiased evidence. In the above mentioned cases the investigators included in their reports "evidence" that was unsupported by documentation, unsupported allegations, omission of obvious facts, and irrelevant pejorative commentary. One report was so biased that it was readily apparent that it demonstrated a willful intent to defraud the insured by presenting only evidence in support for denial of the claim, while ignoring evidence that was obvious.

The investigator was obviously not a seasoned professional and was utterly unaware of the severe risk to himself and his client that he posed by committing this fraud. Perhaps he though that in helping his client not pay a claim, that would endear his client to him. It didn't help him much when the insured slapped him and the insurance company with a host of civil complaints including but not limited to libel and fraud based on willful misrepresentation as well as violation of numerous insurance statutes such as bad faith, unfair trade practices and others subject to punitive damages.

The reader has likely observed, from watching televised trials, that there are those expert witnesses whose testimony is "bought," or perhaps more charitably we might say are zealously loyal to their clients. So loyal, in fact, that they clearly are attempting to craft their testimony favorably toward their client. When this happens, it is usually obvious to everyone but the one testifying. It is a mistake to think that juries can't see through this. And if it is evident in the spoken word, so too, is it evident in written reports. Unfortunately, far too many who seek to derive income from involvement in litigation fall into this trap. Highly experienced trial attorneys tell us that biased witnesses tend to hurt, not help their cases. Good lawyers don't want witnesses that are dishonest or even shade the truth, for they know that this is likely to backfire. If a lawyer doesn't have good evidence, he will want to know that before he goes to trial. The purpose of trials is to determine truth, and while it is an imperfect system, the fact remains that the truth is usually revealed in the vast majority of cases.

We should all recognize that every one has bias that derives from our unique position and viewpoint of the world around us. As hard as we might try, we can't rid ourselves of bias completely, but that doesn't mean that we shouldn't try. In the chapter on report writing I discuss some techniques for recognizing and rooting the inevitable bias out of our work. In the meantime, we must avoid manipulative clients because no matter how much they pay us, it can't ever be enough.

For the beginner, it is especially important to resist the urge to "go to bat" for the client With insurance companies this is easy because they expect the unvarnished truth from their experts. But when it comes to other clients, that may not be the case, and the surveyor will find it necessary to advise the client that he will let the chips fall where they may during his investigation.

Obviously, there will be those cases where maintaining one's integrity becomes particularly difficult when the results of the investigation end up being very unfavorable to the client. At the outset, it should be apparent to the surveyor that such an outcome is possible. He can avoid future difficulties by informing the client straight out that he will not manipulate the facts in favor of the client. At some point during the investigation it will likely become increasingly obvious that things aren't going the client's way. At this point it may be wise to advise the client of this and to terminate your employment as a simple matter of being a non-cost effective endeavor.

Win-Win, Not Win-Lose

My experience over the course of a long career is that about a third of all investigations do not produce conclusive, actionable results, or at best will alter anticipated action. Either a cause is not found or the evidence is too weak to merit any kind of action. This becomes particularly troublesome when an investigator is working the defense side of a case. Of course, the investigator is likely to take pride in his ability to determine causes so that his determination to do so may end up with his determination coloring the facts. We're all aware of how this sort of thing comes back to haunt overzealous prosecutors and police detectives. The actions that we are least able to judge objectively, of course, are our own.

The best way to avoid falling into this bias trap is to avoid viewing an investigation as a win or lose situation, while constantly being aware of the consequences of our actions. Maintaining a scrupulous integrity isn't possible when we view an investigation as win or lose, success or failure, the motivation for which usually stems from a misplaced loyalty to the client. We have to avoid the notion that because the client is paying us the investigation must be successful.

In the end, the client we should be serving is the truth. In some cases the truth is hidden and cannot be found. When that happens, the truth is that the truth can't be found, it is not a reflection on our competence when we know that all reasonable avenues of investigation have been exhausted. Our egos will be far less challenged and threatened when we are prepared to lay out all that we have done, and from that draw a conclusion that the cause or truth can't be determined.

Clientele

There are an estimated 22 million registered pleasure boats in the U.S., the vast majority of them under 20 feet in length, and probably many more that are not registered. The size of boats that marine investigators become involved with is usually in the over 20 foot category. Fortunately boat owners are not the only potential clients for his services, and fortunately for us boats tend to generate lots of trouble for both their owners and others who come in contact with them, for boats are status symbols that their owners often cannot afford. And there the trouble begins. The number of potential clients is greatly expanded by those who have legal claims against boat owners.

Insurance Companies

Insurance companies comprise the largest group of clients for marine investigators. While some of the larger marine insurers have staff surveyors, the majority of insurance companies that insure boats do not have marine claims specialists on staff; therefore, they hire independent marine surveyors who are located in proximity to where the casualty occurred. Obtaining the business of major insurers is not easy, for the competition is fierce. Once a company becomes satisfied with the work of a surveyor, they tend to remain partial to that surveyor. Like all of us, they prefer to "know" the person they are working with. Gaining an account with an insurer, particularly a large one, usually means a steady flow of work, something highly prized by surveyors. Insurance companies usually look for a surveyor to be certified by one of the two surveyor societies, NAMS or SAMS.

Traditionally, the role of surveyor-as-investigator is to perform "without prejudice." That simply means that his obligation is to conduct his investigation without regard to the interest of the client or any other interests that may be involved. This phrase is rooted in traditional commercial marine survey practice that is no longer relevant to pleasure craft issues. Despite the fact that the term is widely used, it does not have any legal standing. Insurance companies expect their surveyor/investigators to be unbiased. Do not assume that insurance claims supervisors take steps to attempt to avoid paying claims; in the author's 35 years of experience, he has *never* seen that happen. This, despite lawyers and politicians attempts to paint insurance companies otherwise.

Unfortunately, too many supposedly unbiased marine surveyors and investigators take advocacy positions, essentially becoming advocates for hire. This is especially prevalent with surveyors who represent owners. The consequences for the investigator is a reputation as a hired mouthpiece for those who advance illegitimate claims. While one can carve out a profitable career as a professional advocate, he will never obtain a reputation of credibility and fairness, and will never be able to profit as an expert witness, for only a fool of a lawyer would want to hire a liar, and there aren't many of those regardless of what we might think of lawyers generally. Good lawyers prefer an honest witness over a pliant one, because the liars are almost always exposed in court. It's funny thing about lying in court: Only the perjurer seems unaware that no one believes him.

The insurance company has an obligation to pay legitimate claims and to deny those that are either illegitimate or not covered. This impartiality is reflected in the laws of most all states that require insurers to make "reasonable" investigations, though a few states have laws that are stacked against insurer. When we understand that insurance is a form of socialism wherein participants willing pool their resources (premiums) in return for a guarantee of indemnification for certain losses, we begin to see that insureds who abuse the system do not merely injure the insurance company, but also *all those who participate*. This is why so many companies contain the word "mutual" in their names, for it denotes that the cost and degree of risk is indeed, mutual of all contract holders. Keep this fact in mind and you won't go wrong by way of allowing bias to influence your work. Objectivity is the name of the game.

Lawyers

Attorneys are another common employer of marine investigators. Maritime lawyers tend to concentrate in the major metropolitan areas, or major boating centers, though attorneys tend to be a bit more picky about whom they hire than do insurance companies. Most seek out experts on the basis of referral from someone familiar with the surveyor's work, such as other lawyers. Lawyers may hire surveyors as investigators shortly after a casualty occurs, or as experts to review cases, provide advice and often testimony. Of course, when an insurance case goes to litigation, the insurance company's lawyer will be making use of the company's surveyor so that the surveyor ends up with two jobs out of one.

When it comes to litigation, the surveyor's work is normally guided by the attorney on the basis of what the attorney sees as relevant to the case. Because of this, the surveyor's view may end up differing from that of his client. He should therefore avoid being too assertive about his own views and accept guidance from the attorney. Above all, one should not become so egocentric as to believe that he knows better than the lawyer. Perhaps he does, but the investigator is not trying the case, so his opinion isn't relevant.

The community of maritime lawyers is a small one, not only locally but even on the national scale. Lawyers are always on the lookout for good experts, and they discuss this amongst themselves, which means that reputations spread like wild fire, both pro and con.

Boat Owners

Occasionally surveyors are called upon by boat owners, often at a time when the boat owner perceives that he may have a problem with his insurer, a boat yard or perhaps a warranty issue. A surveyor can work both sides of the street, i.e. for insurers and insureds, without conflict of interest so long as he does not take cases against his client. However, a word to the wise: taking a case against an insurer may preclude him from ever getting any work from that insurer in the future. Thus, when taking work from insureds or boat owners it's best to find out who the insurer is before accepting the case. Never take a case against a current client.

Working both sides of the street can accrue to the benefit of the investigator. Prior to his testimony, either in deposition or on the witness stand, one side will attempt to qualify him while the other will attempt to disqualify him. Opposing lawyers often try to paint the insurance company's surveyor as being biased in favor of the insurer on the basis that he only works for insurance companies. That is an understandable, but uninformed view of the insurance surveyor whose job is to act independently of the insurer's interest. This charge is largely defeated when the surveyor can testify that he has worked for both boat owners and insurers.

Unresolved Warranty Claims are another source of clients for marine investigators particularly in the areas of structural failure and machinery damage. The marine expert can often provide the critical element that motivates manufacturers to settle rather than litigate warranty issues and thus provide a valuable service to boat owners.

One problem with working for individual boat owners is that occasionally we run across one who thinks that because he is paying the surveyor, the surveyor should write anything that the client asks him to. It is best for the surveyor to get an understanding up front with the client that he will report his findings as he finds them. One way to handle that is to ask the client straight out how he will feel if the investigation findings go against the client's interest.

Other Clients

From time to time the surveyor is called on by banks, boat yards, builders, brokers, dealers, even governments and other interests when boats they own or are involved with suffer casualties. At one time a department of the Federal government was one of my best clients and I never found out how they got my name. Local governments that have large marine interests are also potential clients. Some of the most bizarre cases I've ever had have come from these. Such clients are usually not amenable to direct solicitation, but are usually gained by referral. As with boat owners, such clients may seek to have the surveyor represent their interest. Each of these clients will have a different perspective and one needs to be cognizant of that fact and prepared to deal with the issues that arise from it. For example, private individuals are far more prone to want his expert to be a mouthpiece for his views than, say an insurance company or bank that is very unlikely to attempt to influence the expert. I have never run across a bank or insurance company that tried to influence my opinion, but I've had innumerable boat owners, brokers, builders, boat yards and dealers who go to extremes to attempt to edit my findings and opinions.

Arbitration and mediation are increasingly being used as a means of avoiding the terrible costs of litigation. These two terms are often used as synonyms, but are actually to very different processes. Mediation is the effort to resolve a dispute by means of attempting to bring the two parties to agreement. Arbitration is a matter of review and judgement, either by a panel or individual, in which case the outcome is considered final. Binding arbitration is usually included in a contract in lieu of litigation. Increasingly purchase agreements have arbitration clauses in them. Mediation of marine disputes is becoming increasingly common of attempting to resolve differences. As far back as twenty years ago I have been hired by boat builders to mediate warranty claims. The mediator performs the same function as the arbiter, but then attempts to persuade the parties to come to an agreement based on the understanding that a less than perfect settlement is bound to be better than risking a loss in court. Binding arbitration is finding it's way into ever more contracts including insurance policies and this offers yet another avenue of business, since arbiters are usually well paid.

The Insurance Investigator

Marine surveyors hired by insurance companies usually end up playing a dual role. First comes the investigation, and if the loss proves to be covered, then follows an assessment of damages. In neither case is he acting as an agent of the company, but as an independent investigator and advisor. The insurance company is his client, but his role is not to represent the client's interest in any way, only to perform the service requested.

When hired by an insurance company to investigate a loss, the insurance company expects him to act without prejudice to the various interests involved in the case, which may be more than one or two, as when a third party is involved. His job is to discover the truth. As far as the investigation goes, his client is neither the company nor the insured; his client is the *truth*. That is his job and that is what the insurance company expects him to discover, no matter how it turns out. The surveyor's job is to provide the claims adjuster with the most accurate information possible by which the adjuster can come to a fair and proper decision. He should have no other motivation.

Knowledge of Insurance Contracts

Over the years there has been considerable debate over the question of whether the surveyor should be conversant with the insurance policy, its coverages and limitations. Some say that the surveyor should go into an investigation completely blind as to coverage so that he is not influenced in any way by what he knows about it. The other side of the argument is a bit more persuasive, for if he isn't familiar with the coverage, he may end up failing to address certain issues simply by virtue of being unaware that they exist.

Historically, surveyors have been highly knowledgeable about policy coverages, a fact that has served their clients well. Issues such as what constitutes latent defects, wear, tear and gradual deterioration, what constitutes inherent vice, and issues of internal versus external causation will prove critical to the investigation. To this end, surveyors often attend seminars that expressly deal with issues of coverage, and more importantly, how the courts have interpreted a variety of cases involving these issues.

Problems can only arise when the investigator attempts to usurp the role of the claims adjuster, as when he becomes emotionally involved in the outcome and attempts to steer the outcome in one direction or the other. If the surveyor maintains strict neutrality, as he must, his knowledge about coverage's will have no impact on the outcome other than to insure that all aspects of the case have been covered.

Roughly 30 percent of all investigations fail to yield conclusive evidence. One of the more critical skills an investigator develops is the wisdom to know when to terminate an investigation because it isn't producing results; even more importantly, the ability to know when the available evidence is insufficient to support a theory of causation. Every surveyor is faced with clients that have cost restraints and that are unwilling to spend larger sums in search of elusive evidence. When unfamiliar with a client, as with a new client, this is an issue that is best raised at the outset.

The issue of doubt normally accrues to the benefit of the insured; if one can't prove that the cause of loss is not covered, then it is covered. Note that this is not the same as saying that undiscovered causes are covered. Some insurance contracts are worded in such a way that coverage does not apply if a cause of loss can't be determined. This is all the more reason that the investigator should discuss these points with the client before proceeding. Knowing how far you can go and how much you can spend is important to setting investigation priorities, particularly when investigations threaten to be complex and time-consuming.

In nearly all cases, the surveyor ultimately has to make a judgement as to the strength of the evidence he has collected. For example, let's say that a particular investigation is producing some evidence that the cause of loss is likely to lead to a denial of coverage. His client, usually a claims supervisor, is usually not an expert and will therefore rely upon the surveyor to make a judgement as to the strength of his evidence. No claims supervisor wants to issue a coverage denial based on weak evidence, for this is likely to initiate a legal challenge which is something that most insurance companies seek to avoid. Thus, he or she expects the investigator to evaluate the strength of evidence and advise him accurately. For more about the strength of evidence, see Chapter Three.

In fact, the experienced surveyor will run across many instances when his client either has little or no knowledge about boats, let alone the intricacies of technical and legal issues. In such instances the supervisor will be relying on the surveyor's every word and he will ultimately be making coverage decisions by default, whether he intends to or not. This places a heavy responsibility on the surveyor to make the right decisions because, if he makes the wrong one, ultimately the ungainly bird of consequence comes home to roost on his shoulder, as when his advice comes to be tested in litigation and is found to be wanting.

Subrogation

In insurance parlance, subrogation simply means that if an insurer pays a loss that is caused by a third party that is legally liable for causing those damages, the insured assigns the right to attempt to recover those damages to the insurance company; the rights of the insured are *subrogated* to the insurer. Subrogation is an issue that the insurance investigator is constantly aware of and is working with because the issue of third party liability arises frequently.

The investigator handles subrogation issues exactly the same ways as he would any case that is likely to go to litigation. That is, he becomes keenly aware of the need for his conclusion as to causation be rock-solid. However, subrogation cases are slightly different from direct litigation cases in that subrogation is most often a claim of one insurance company against another, though it may just as well be company against an individual or other business.

A very significant percentage of apparently ordinary marine insurance claims — by that I mean perhaps five or ten percent — become subrogation cases, nicknamed Subro Claims. Once again this points out the need for all investigations to be carried out with care. Most subro claims are not litigated but settled between insurance companies, most of which have subrogation departments. The claim file will go from the adjuster to some person in the Subrogation Department that processes these claims against others, a person that we rarely, if ever, hear from. That person will then have to review and process the Subro claim based almost entirely on the investigator's report. This, once again, points up the need for reports to be clearly and precisely written in such a way that someone who has no first hand knowledge about it can understand and make decisions based on a single reading.

The Expert Witness

From having watched TV criminal trials, the reader is no doubt familiar with the expert witness, typically the forensic pathologists of TV fame. There are people who become experts in almost every field of endeavor and who find a way to create a business for themselves as expert witnesses. There isn't a large demand for legal experts and only a few will even manage to be able to create a part time business of it. Even so, part time work can be quite lucrative as it pays very well.

An expert witness is hired based exclusively on a high degree of *demonstrable* expertise to be used in direct court testimony at trial. It is an area of professional service in which some surveyors come to specialize. Being hired as an expert witness is not exactly the same thing as testifying as an expert. An expert witness may be hired who has no direct involvement with the investigation in contrast to the actual investigator who testifies as an expert. Both are experts but they perform different functions. An expert witness may be hired to present his technical knowledge as well as knowledge of techniques and procedures, and to render an opinion. For example, an attorney may hire an expert for the sole purpose of evaluating the work of another expert on the other side. Here the distinction is made between being an expert and being an expert witness; one is a material witness while the other renders opinions.

Surveyors hired as experts may or may not end up testifying. It all depends on how the attorney views the expert's advice. Thus, not every job that we are hired as an expert do we end up with actual court testimony. Indeed, the vast majority of cases settle before going to trial. But for the majority of cases we will end up giving depositions.

Expertise on boats and their systems is not the only thing a trial lawyer looks for in an expert witness. It should be understood that being an expert witness is not something that should be sought after by the beginner or amateur. The larger part is the expert's experience and adeptness at testifying. Trial lawyers desire above everything else, an expert who can handle himself well on the witness stand, bearing in mind that lawyers themselves are well-trained in the art of trying to make witnesses look bad. Much of the expert witness work that I perform for clients involves searching for weakness in the work of other experts and witnesses. Should one desire to become an expert witness, this fact should be kept foremost in mind, for this work can involve some rough treatment of the expert. One should also be aware that one's personal life is not out of bounds. The character of any witness is very much fair game for attack.

The reader is probably aware that a major tactic of opposing lawyers at trial is to attempt to discredit opposing witnesses, a tactic that usually involves attempts to fluster and intimidate the witness. Skilled lawyers are usually pretty good at this and it takes a witness with similar skills and experience to successfully handle these tactics. Thus, the first few times one testifies as an expert are not likely to be pleasant experiences. The opposing side goes over the expert's work with a fine tooth comb, usually in consultation with other experts, looking for ways to attack and discredit that expert witness.

Defense Versus Plaintiff Cases

While it might appear that there are important differences between plaintiff and defense case, in reality there is very little so far as the marine expert is concerned. The essence is the same regardless of which side we are working for. Our job is to arrive at the truth; if there is no truth in the client's case, would that be a case we want to be involved with? If there is any difference at all, it lies primarily in the fact that the burden of proof likes with the plaintiff. This means that we must be even more diligent about both the veracity of the evidence we present, and the way we present it. Otherwise, it really doesn't matter which side we are working for.

It will matter to the investigator who feels that he owes his client some loyalty for the fee he is paid by shading the truth or even outright falsification, but to the truthful expert it matters not the least. Many experts are reluctant, once they've got a retainer, to present their clients with bad or unfavorable news. If one can't stand up to telling the client the truth, and possibly losing the job, then one ought to engage in some other line of work. Any plaintiff or defendant with an ounce of sense does not want to go to trial with a skewed report and false testimony. If he doesn't have a good case he's better off settling it before trial. He deserves to know that his case is not good. This is rather like being an oncologist and having to tell patients they have cancer. If an investigator doesn't have the fortitude to tell him that . . . well, you can finish this sentence yourself.

In fact, I have found working both types of cases to be very beneficial, for I have had lawyers attempt to cast doubt on my credibility by attempting to paint me as someone who is loyal to insurance companies. That tactic fails when I say that I have conducted numerous plaintiff investigations. Therefore, it's a good idea to try to vary the types of work one does so that the issues can be seen and experienced from both sides of the fence.

It is true that there will be some few insurance claims managers who will take umbrage over having taken a case against them, but you know and I know that it isn't smart. A smart manager will recognize that a good investigator tells the truth, and will not hold it against him that he's working for the other side. Of course, one cannot hold an active account with an insurer and take a case against him at the same time, for that truly is a conflict of interest. However, most companies will not be adverse to hiring you on an as-needed basis at other times. As long as you are any company's *regular surveyor*, you cannot take cases against them.

There are occasions where this situation is unavoidable, particularly on issues of subrogation. Subrogation is a term that means that an insurance company, though it's insurance contract, obtains certain of the insured's rights. One of these is the right to recover damages caused by others because the insurer has sustained that loss by virtue of paying the damage cost. An investigator likely holds more than one insurance account, and sometimes the paths of the two companies cross in subrogation and litigation. There is no need to worry about these situations, but you do have an obligation to inform the unknowing party that you are on the other side of the issue. One cannot, of course, handle both sides of the same case.

(Footnotes)

1. Based on Insurance Industry Association estimates.

Chapter 2

The Nature of Investigations

Marine investigations bear distinct similarities to criminal investigations of police professionals. Throughout this book I stress the similarities to police work for reasons that will become self-evident. The similarities are:

1. Important decisions will be made based on the results.

2. The results of investigations have a high probability of being litigated.

3. A similar degree of professionalism is required to be credible.

4. Competence and technical skills required are similar.

5. People's lives may be affected by the outcome.

6. The investigator exposes himself to a degree of risk in the form of civil liabilities.

7. Some investigations become linked to criminal actions.

Marine investigations are unlike criminal investigations in the following ways:

1. In-court application of investigation results is civil, not criminal action.

2. Rules for evidence handling are less stringent.

3. With insurance cases the subject is a customer of our client and not an adversary.

4. The investigator is performing a business service and not a police function.

5. Investigator has no official authority.

The very word "investigator" probably conjures up all kinds of inaccurate notions about the marine investigator. Detective, private eye, and too may TV shows and movies are likely to come to mind, but the marine investigator is nothing so glamorous, though occasionally our work involves spectacular and/or costly casualties such as major fires, collisions and even fatalities.

The subjects of investigation begin with marine casualties either in the form of property loss, damage, warranty claims, structural failures, other plaintiff actions, personal injury and the issue of general liability — who or what is responsible for the loss or injury. The number one client for marine investigators is, of course, the insurance companies that insure boats. Since boats function in a risky environment this inevitably means that there is no shortage of casualties to be investigated.

The types of casualties that marine investigators become involved with are wide ranging and can encompass the unusual. The maxim that truth is stranger than fiction certainly applies to the subject of marine investigations. From the person who is thrown out of a boat and then is run down by the runaway boat, to a husband and his mistress found dead aboard a boat, locked in amorous embrace — victims of carbon monoxide poisoning. The variety of casualties that we work with is not infrequently bizarre and challenging.

Marine investigators are most often independent, self-employed businessmen, or sometimes insurance company employees. The only reason that most companies do not employ their own staff of investigators is because it is generally less costly to employ independent contractors at the time of need, since the number of major marine casualties is not that great. A few of the larger companies have special investigative divisions (SID) and often employ ex cops but mostly in the area of fraud investigations.

The fact that marine investigations are a business and not a police activity exerts a very strong influence on the way we must conduct ourselves; we possess none of the authority that police investigators do. To get things accomplished we have to rely on the powers of persuasion rather than police powers. With insurance claims work, it is often the insurance contract itself that guides our actions. And yet we must always perform our work with the awareness that every case involves the possibility of ending up in litigation. The reasons why our investigations may end up in litigation and even in court stems from (1) insurance claims may be denied based on our work, and (2) casualties usually involve the question of responsibility or liability — who's at fault?

The range of cases that we are called on to investigate is nearly limitless but the majority are grouped amongst a much smaller number of more common incidents listed below in general order of frequency:

Insurance Related	Other
Sinking	Vessel owner
Third party claims	Expert witness case review
Machinery damage	Liability defense
Collision	Warranty cases
Wake damage	General plaintiff work
Latent defect	
Structural failure	
Fire	
Personal injury	
Theft	
Fraud	
Fatality	

The statistics (**Fig. 2-1**) on next page for Miami-Dade County prepared by the State of Florida for the 2002 are typical of accident rates for major metropolitan boating centers. These, of course, are only those that are recorded by official agencies. Experience shows that the vast majority of casualties are not officially recorded and probably run at least ten, and probably more, times higher. For example, only four cases of sinking were recorded for the entire year when probably that many actually occur every day! Only one grounding and one struck submerged object incidents were recorded, but such incidents do not require an official report.

Nearly all fatalities involve an official report and investigations so that the official figures provide a better representation of both the numbers of boats as well as casualties in a given state.

Throughout boating literature we see endless references to rankings of states by the number of registered boats they have. Most of these rankings present a very skewed picture of where the major boating centers are, for they do not take into account the types or size of boats. Michigan and Minnesota rank near the top, as does California in shear numbers. However, these rankings include huge numbers of dinghies, ski boats, inflatables, and small fishing boats such as bass boats. For our purposes of assessing where the major marine business is located is reflected by where the marine surveyors are. On that basis, Florida tops the list by a large margin, followed by Michigan, Maryland, California, Texas, Washington, Louisiana and Maine, not necessarily in that order.

Accident Rank:	4
Population (from Census):	2,253,362
Registered Recreational Vessels:	55,252
Number of Boating Accidents:	79
Number of Injuries:	26
Number of Fatalities:	4
Accident Rate:	1:699

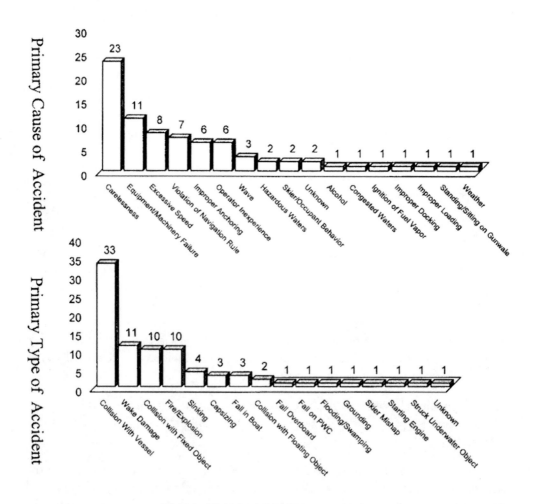

Fig. 2-1. 2002 Miami-Dade Boating Accidents

State registration rankings are also misleading due to numerous multiple state boating areas referred to as "tri-state area" like NY- CT-RI and MD-VA, FL-AL-GA and CA-AZ-NV. Florida has more out-of-state and Federally registered vessels than any other state (a number equal to a third of all registered boats) making it by far the state with the largest number of boats in it. If we look at it from an economic standpoint, the amount of boating business conducted in Florida is twice as much as in the next highest state, California. Similarly, there are more than 1,000 marine surveyors advertising as doing business in Florida, so the competition is pretty steep. The Chesapeake Bay area involves three states and a huge number of boats in a fairly small area, whereas Florida covers 1500 miles of coastline.

It may be more enlightening to look at it from the basis of why investigations are commissioned, for these break down into a smaller number of categories.

Determination of insurance coverage

Determination of insured liability

Determination of potential subrogation.

Determination if fraud has been committed

Litigation defense - any client

Plaintiff's case - any client

Warranty dispute

Already we begin to see how inevitably involved with litigation the marine investigator becomes. And because of the omnipresence of legal issues the investigator must necessarily be reasonably well versed in those areas of law that come to bear on his work. Among these are insurance law, maritime law and certain areas of consumer protection law including fitness for merchantability and product liability. Investigators may have as clients insurance companies, lawyers, governments, boat owners, banks, and boat yards among many others. With each type of client, his perspective of work will be different and he may be working under a different area of law. With insurance work the investigator need be familiar with both insurance policies and insurance law.

With warranty work he will be dealing with warranty contracts and consumer law such as the Magnuson - Moss Warranty Act when working on behalf of the vessel owner. Sometimes surveyors are engaged by boat builders to try to mediate warranty disputes, not in terms of mediation or arbitration, but rather as a sort of independent reviewer. In such instances the surveyor is naturally seen as being a hireling of the builder and not the unbiased third party the builder tries to present him.

Some surveyors have long argued that, as investigators, they need not have any knowledge of insurance contracts nor of law; that their only job is to report the facts of the casualty. This is a rather myopic viewpoint that fails to take into consideration of how contractual and legal knowledge can usefully guide investigations in the right direction. Knowledge of law assists us in determining whether there is an adequacy or insufficiency of evidence, of whether an investigation is worth pursuing or not and, most importantly, whether procedures being followed are proper or not. In another example, a latent defect is essentially a term of insurance and maritime law; how could we write an accurate report if we don't know what a latent defect is, or seaworthiness?

When engaged by insurance companies, marine surveyors often end up wearing three hats. Typically he's hired to assess the damages, but also because of his expertise he's called on to investigate causation and, finally, he often ends up becoming a witness in litigation. In cases of sinking, he is likely to be charged with being a salvage master where he runs head-on into the sticky issue of salvage contracts and oil pollution laws. A surveyor who is not well-versed in these legal issues is of little benefit to his clients.

Each of these issues could be the subject of an entire book, but in this one I try to cover the basics to an essential degree, but the reader should recognize the need for further study on many of these issues.

Tools Needed

Investigations require a wide variety of tools and testing instruments, none of which taken alone is very expensive, but the total cost of all does add up to a tidy amount. The majority of tools needed are those found in any well equipped home workshop, along with a few others not found. By far, the most used and useful is the battery powered drill or screw driver that is needed for removing panels and fasteners. I suggest avoiding the large, heavy higher voltage units such as 14 and 18V tools and go for the less expensive and smaller 9.6 V or 12V units that I have found to be more than adequate. Instead, spend the extra money on the best quality tool available because bargain tools simply won't stand up. My 9.6 V compact Panasonic T-handle fits in my briefcase tool kit whereas my 12V DeWalt unit will not. The Panasonic cost twice as much but is now 12 years old and worth every penny because I haven't had to replace it.

You will also want a rugged, high capacity fan for those blazingly hot summer days, especially in the south.

> Quick change driver set plus extender
>
> Socket and ratchet set, both metric and English
>
> Adjustable crescent wrench, small & large
>
> Vice grips
>
> Channel lock
>
> Screw driver assortment

Heavy duty 2" scraper

25' tape measure

100' tape

6' folding carpenters rule

Dial calipers

Assorted screw drivers, scrapers

Mechanics mirror

H.D. wire cutters

9.6V cordless screw driver (for panel removal)

Assortment of drill bits, hole cutter

VOM multimeter

4 - 15' jumper wires

Moisture meter

Extra batteries for everything battery powered

Digital and film cameras

Rags & waterless hand cleaner

Paper jump suits

Face masks for fire jobs

100' extension cord

25' extension cord

Portable flood light

Large and small flashlights - rubber coated are best because other types don't take well to being frequently dropped

All of these tools, not including fans, lights and cords, fitted into one case will weigh about fifty pounds and chances are you won't want to have to haul them around every job. For that reason I have them divided up into two cases, the primary one containing those tools that are most often needed while most of the time the other, heavier case remains in the car.

For fire investigations an electric saber saw is indispensable for clearing debris and creating access and removing structures that have collapsed.

Dragging a lap top along on a trip might seem worthwhile but I've found it more trouble than it's worth. It's too valuable and one has to expend too much effort protecting it because one can't ever turn his back on the thing or risk dropping it. When it comes to baggage, it's exhausting to be lugging loads of stuff through miles of airport terminals; I want my hands to be as free as possible so I check everything except a single carry-on that contains camera equipment that one dare not send in the cargo hold. If you're going to be travelling a lot, get a high end travel case that is intelligently and sturdily designed; the larger the wheels the better because you'll be taking these things across a lot of gravel parking lots, uneven docks and other bad terrain. A bag with 17 zippered pouches will help keep us occupied looking for things when we should be working. Setting up a special tool kit suitable for travelling is well worth the effort. I use a hard body fiberglass carry-on size case with tools snugly fitted in foam.

Communication with Insured and Insurer

Relations with the Insured and Insurer

As an insurance investigator, one cannot behave like a cop with an authoritative demanding, arrogant attitude. An insured is a customer of the insurance company with whom the company may continue to do business. Though one may not be a representative of the company, he will be seen as such, and need to behave accordingly The proper attitude is one of professionalism, polite and courteous yet decidedly neutral. One should not become overly familiar nor overly distant and remote. A surveyor or investigator is like a warrant officer in the army; he has rank but little power, so he needs to have above average diplomatic skills.

If your skills in this area aren't as good as they should be, you can refine them by taking the time to consciously review how you should behave when making each phone call or meeting with an insured. With just a little practice, your "bedside manner" will improve dramatically. Think about all those doctors you've encountered who displayed an attitude as if they were doing you a favor by allowing you to see them. The insured is a customer, even if he is a crook, and should be treated deferentially at all times; we are not the judge, merely the collectors of evidence.

Because some claims involve falsity perpetrated by the insured or others, issues of the insured's behavior frequently come into play. How the investigator handles these problems is of critical importance both to his continuing relationship with the client insurer as well as possible litigation. Numerous insurance defense cases have been defeated as a result of improper behavior by the investigator taking an adversarial position with the insured, from which frequently emanates unfortunate commentary that ends up in written reports or duly noted by the insured.

The cardinal rule for all written reports is that reports are to contain factual information ONLY and NEVER supposition, speculation, innuendo or biased commentary concerning the behavior of the insured. The report should not have a pejorative tone, but be strictly factual and neutral. Even in the presentation of negative facts, and particularly anything relating to the insured's behavior, should be scrupulously free of condemnation or "attitude" such as a moralistic or condemnatory tone. If there is the need to discuss issues of character and behavior, do it over the phone:

> For example, the insured may be abusive and use foul language with you and generally be uncooperative. The investigator will encounter insureds that will intentionally try to get the investigator riled up, and one can be sure that sooner or later he'll encounter an individual so crafty as to attempt to provoke the investigator's anger because he knows the matter is going to litigation and he is already preparing to scuttle your case by getting you to do or say something inappropriate.

One of the most common plaintiff tactics is to attempt to paint the investigator as the insurer's hired gun whose job is to find a way to avoid paying the claim. Expect to encounter it often, and be alert to the pitfalls and snares of getting emotionally involved.

Avoid the temptation of moral judgements; it is very easy for some people when dealing with the darker side of human nature to become emotionally involved and view themselves as a crusader for truth and righteousness because it is a process that starts subconsciously. There are insurance companies that will pay losses no matter how fraudulent they are simply because their policy is to avoid litigation at all costs. Such a policy may be morally reprehensible, but that is not our judgement to make. The proper attitude to take is one of uncaring whether the loss is paid or not.

The vast majority of insurance companies will expect you to be fair and honest; of course there will be the occasional company that is the exception to the rule, one that may lean to either side. If a client's policy runs contrary to your own morality, the match up between you and them is not a good one and is likely to end badly in any case.

Never get into an argument with the insured or anyone else for that matter. If you find yourself being antagonized, or in a situation that is becoming emotionally heated, the best reaction is to promptly remove yourself from the scene. Cut the discussion short with anything you can think of and leave; do not permit yourself to be dragged into an argument where you may end up saying something you regret. As an investigator, you will encounter many people who are adept at provocation, people who know what they're doing (despite appearances) and why they're doing it. Take note of the very difficult situations cops find themselves in and realize that occasionally you will find yourself in similar situations. To deal with trouble effectively, one needs to be prepared for such probabilities.

Investigator as Adversary

It inevitably follows that the investigator, more often than not, finds himself in an adversarial position. Many people in his local or regional marine community will come to see him as an enemy and hold grudges against him. They will say nasty things about him behind his back, and may even seek to harm his business, particularly if it involves work other than investigation. Those who seek to establish a business in this line of work should be prepared for the inevitable hostility that will be directed his way. In the end, however, the investigator who is scrupulously honest, who holds to the highest levels of professionalism, will end up garnering the respect even of those of whom he has made enemies. Only a fool does not respect a worthy adversary.

Some people are just plain unscrupulous and will do just about anything to protect their interests. Anyone who hasn't had much experience in this business should be aware that sooner or later he will run across some of these characters who, rather than disputing the evidence, will do his best to discredit the investigator with dishonorable tactics.

One of the things we need to be alert to is the fact that boat owners tend to be rather wealthy people, and many of these people didn't become wealthy by being nice, charitable and honorable; some of them are rather ruthless businessmen. If we dare to cross swords with them, we'd best be prepared for the consequences. "Crossing swords" simply means doing anything that they would see as threatening their interest, such as merely investigating the cause of a loss in which they have an interest. When threatened by revelation of a truth they don't want revealed, the rich tends to start throwing their weight around.

When crossing paths with such people, we need to make sure that our client is fully behind us because in all probability the insured will try to pull an end-run by going above our client's head. An end-run means that the insured complains to a higher level company executive in an effort to get the investigator thrown off the case:

> One of my clients was a company that insured large yachts exclusively and the claims rep that hired me had never failed to support me. However, when really big issues came up, as I had been burned so many times in the past with other clients, I always felt a bit gun-shy, making it a point to let my client know that what I was doing would likely draw retaliation by the insured. "*So what will you do if the insured goes to your boss and claims that I'm an out-of-control madman?*" I would ask.

In such cases it's important to make sure that your contact person is aware of the possible consequences because we are not dealing with ordinary people here, but businessmen who got where they are by cunning and often devious tactics that they won't hesitate to use against us.

Such difficulties do not only exist when investigating insurance claims, but also can occur with any kind of investigation:

In one instance, an investigator was accused by a party to a dispute of having stolen things off his boat in an effort to poison the investigator's credibility.

The insurance agent who sold the rich man his policy is often one of the most dangerous adversaries because they may have tens of thousands (or more) in premiums to protect. Agents often won't hesitate to go to bat for the insured. Always be very circumspect about what you say to an agent. They will often call frequently asking the "status," using this as an entrée toward manipulating the investigator. We are not obligated to tell them anything about an investigation, and shouldn't. Never discuss investigations with anyone other than the client:

> In one case I'm familiar with, in order to get a good investigator thrown off a case, an insured called his agent and told him that the investigator had made sexual advances on his wife! In another, the boat owner in a third party case claimed that the investigator stole a camera off his boat.

Neither of these allegations were true, but desperate or unscrupulous people will often do desperate and unscrupulous things.

There are innumerable instances where the investigator exercised bad judgement by saying things that he shouldn't have said, seemingly harmless comments that were later used against him. Under no circumstances should the investigator engage anyone inside or near the investigation in discussion about the investigation, least of all the insured, to speculate on causation or anything else. Insureds will often press very hard to get the investigator to reveal his findings even before the investigation is complete. I've had instances where the insured was calling every day. If this suggests to you that something is wrong about the insured's behavior, you are right because this is not normal behavior. He's waving a red flag that says something is amiss.

As investigator, our job is to ask questions, not answer them. It is all too easy to end up becoming too friendly with someone associated with the case and end up saying something that is regretted later:

> In an instance, an investigator made an unfortunate statement to a boat yard manger who later became a witness at trial, and then testified as to what the investigator had said to him.

Lesson: never voice your opinions to anyone because you never know what side of the issue that person might turn up on.

> In another instance, two investigators were working inside a boat. Thinking they were alone they were making jokes and disparaging remarks about the boat and the owner. Turned out that they were not alone and the yacht's captain heard every word they said and testified to their words in court, thereby impeaching the credibility of their investigation.

Loose lips may not actually sink ships, but they sure can sink an investigation.

Sidestepping Questions

Investigators are usually bombarded with questions by the various interests involved in an investigation, particularly the insured or vessel owner. Investigators should take the same position that all cops do and avoid answering. The simple but effective answer to all such questions that avoids rudeness is:

I'm not in a position to discuss that now.

For an insured, the answer might be better stated:

We will be in a better position to discuss that after the investigation has been completed.

Of course, investigators never discuss their findings with the subjects of investigations. To do so is only to invite trouble. A technical but very important point is that an investigation is not complete until all the facts have been digested and the report is written. With insurance claims, it is never the investigator that informs the insured of the outcome of the investigation, always the claims adjuster, and then always in writing. Most states require this as a matter of law. If an insured is pestering us for an answer, in all cases we refer him to the adjuster whose job is to handle all claims discussions with the insured.

In non-insurance cases our response is essentially the same:

I'm not at liberty to discuss that.

Taking Statements

Upon reviewing the reports of others, a major fault that appears almost universally is the lack of taking formal statements, the recording of witness testimony. The taking of written or recorded statements is a major part of building a complete investigation.

Formal statements are an important form of evidence that most investigators seem to prefer to avoid. Perhaps one reason is that some states require an insurance investigator to obtain an insurance adjuster's license, and rather than go to the trouble, they simply avoid taking statements. The purpose of taking a statement is to get the witness on a written record.

A very common mistake by untrained investigators is to include undocumented statements by witnesses. "Bill Smith saw the boat still afloat at 10:00 AM," without having Bill Smith's statement in writing or on tape. Later, Bill Smith, at the most inconvenient time changes his story, or worse, says, "I never said that." An even worse mistake looks like this, "According to witnesses the boat was seen at 10:00 AM on Sunday to be . . . " The later quotation has no credibility whatsoever unless memorialized by a written or recorded statement. To put such a statement into an insurance investigation report is worse than useless. It plays into the hand of the plaintiff because it can be used to demonstrate that the investigator used false or unsupported allegations as a means of denying the claim. Such statements can be used to demonstrate bad faith. When it is necessary in a report to refer to witness statements, the report should read:

"Bill Smith stated, as per the attached statement, that . . . ."

The inclusion of the accounts of witnesses must always be backed up with formal statements and if not, they cannot be used as evidence in litigation unless that witness is willing to testify. Even then one can only hope that he maintains his original version, an iffy proposition at best. Even more importantly, getting witnesses to give deposition or testify years later can be difficult. He can avoid this inconvenience by simply saying that he doesn't remember. Fortunately, by obtaining his formal statement these problems can be avoided, for the testimony of witnesses can in many instances be introduced by means of affidavit without a personal appearance. An affidavit is a sworn statement of fact by a witness to the court — not the investigator, lawyer or anyone else, but the court. This saves the trouble of dragging the witness to deposition or trial. But in taking a formal statement, an investigator accomplishes an important result:

(1) No longer can the witness blithely change his story.

(2) By virtue of the statement he can be compelled to testify.

(3) And should he change his story, he will have to render a credible explanation of why his story is different today, something that is not easy to do.

Most surveyors don't like to take statements because they're unfamiliar with the process, or they hold illusions about it being difficult or uncomfortable process. Actually, it is very easy and the vast majority of subjects cooperate willingly and without reservation. See chapter Interrogation Techniques for a full discussion of this subject.

The Art of Listening

Studies have shown time and again that people are generally poor listeners when they are engaged in conversation with others. The simple reason for this is because people can't listen when they're thinking about what they are going to say while the other person is speaking; people simply do not listen.

It is vitally important for the investigator to become a good listener. The way to achieve this goal is to practice *not thinking* while the other person is talking. Concentrate on what the person is saying and not what your mind is trying to throw at you. Listen and observe body language. This can be done without staring by learning, at times, to use peripheral vision, looking up, down, or aside short of the degree to which vision of the person is lost; or by diverting attention away from the person frequently, but just as frequently returning to eye contact.

First Notice from Client

When testifying on an investigation you have conducted, count on the fact that opposing counsel will question you in detail about your first contacts with your client and what you were asked to do. This demonstrates the extent to which the opposition will go searching for your weaknesses.

It is the practice of claims surveyors to create an assignment form on which they record information as the assignment is called in. The importance of this form may not be apparent now but will become so in the future. This typically includes the following:

> Date assignment was received
>
> Name, address and contact numbers of client
>
> Name of person handling the case (report to)
>
> Name of person calling in the assignment
>
> Name, address and contact numbers of boat owner or insured
>
> Insurance policy and claim numbers
>
> Description of vessel (including all descriptive info possessed by insurer)
>
> Location of vessel
>
> Date of loss (as reported)
>
> Description of casualty as reported by insured or owner
>
> Current status of vessel
>
> Other relevant information
>
> Any special instructions

When claims persons call in assignments, there is a tendency to be very brief, hence the need of the form to prompt one to ask for all relevant information. If the client lacks information, as they often will, that's okay. Just make note that such information was not given. In deposition or on the witness stand, opposing counsel will be seeking to find out if you did all that you were instructed to do, or more than you were told to do. In most cases the client will assume that the surveyor knows what he should do, thereby leaving an opening to attack the surveyor. By use of the form we try to fill in these gaps. It also happens that the client doesn't really know what you do - perhaps a clerk or secretary was told to give you the assignment - in which case one should simply write down "investigate and report findings."

First Contacts with Insured

When dealing with an insurance case, the insured or boat owner should always be contacted first, for the insured may have information that could save the investigator a lot of time. It is a mistake to fail to contact the insured first because that lends to the perception of avoidance or secrecy. During an investigation we are not seeking to avoid contact with the subject, even though that may cause some uneasiness at times when we are bombarded with questions we can't or don't want to answer. To this end we should have a list of stock answers prepared in advance.

One of the most important stock answers is our opening introduction to the insured in insurance cases. It is necessary that it be spelled out in no uncertain terms who we are and how we relate to the insured's insurance claim, bearing in mind that he sees us as a representative providing service for which he has paid a lot of money. Here the import of this being a business transaction is again driven home. We're not agents of the government that can get away with being distant and demanding. Part of the bed side manner that we have to develop is how to be professionally courteous, to be pleasant without saying much, of knowing what to say as well as what not to say, without appearing evasive or insensitive.

It does not matter whether we are the claims adjuster or not, we are the one and only person that the insured sees and has personal contact with. Rightly or wrongly, he's going to look to us for answers that we don't have to give. We should assume that the claims adjuster did not pave the way for us by explaining our relationship in the matter and that we have to do that. And be prepared to do that effectively. My standard opening goes like this:

> Mr. Smith, my name is David Pascoe. I'm an independent marine surveyor and I have been assigned by ABC Insurance to investigate the cause of the fire on your boat (adding any other role we've been assigned). Here is my card with my contact numbers.

This simple intro is followed by a basic, preliminary interview of what happened, all the while taking notes of what the insured says. This is important in case he changes his story later on. Even more important is the situation when the facts begin to appear to be contrary to what we have been told. In this instance, the importance of having good notes becomes obvious because we don't want to be faced with not being able to recall exactly what was said. Many were the times I had rued the day when I failed to make notes of this initial conversation! Following this, it is explained, when necessary, how the investigation will proceed, and whether anything is required of the insured. In many instances we will want him to produce documents so that the sooner we ask the better. For example, if the boat is a total loss, we'll want to see the original title and registration ASAP. If a formal statement will be required, now is not the time to mention this point.

When requesting documents in person or over the phone, the importance of the request should be made firmly but tactfully. Don't give him the opportunity to forget. It should be stressed that without compliance, his claim will be delayed:

> Mr. Smith, it is important that you get these documents to me as soon as possible so that your claim won't be delayed.

Getting Started

At the beginning of the investigation we have very little information to go on and it can be confusing and difficult to discern where to begin, particularly in cases of fires and sinkings. This can be made much easier by following the practice of making sketches of the vessel and its physical systems such as electrical, plumbing, hull openings and so on before getting about the business of actually inspecting the various details. General sketches can be used to record locations and measurements quickly and easily.

It is critically important to consider all investigations from the standpoint of both inclusionary and exclusionary evidence. Inclusionary evidence is all that evidence that fits into and supports the conclusion of causation. Exclusionary evidence is everything that could have possibly caused the casualty, which we have examined and ruled out by virtue of not supporting the conclusion. Of course, there is always far more of the later than the former, and this is what makes it difficult and leads to confusion.

Exclusionary evidence must be accounted for since it is as vitally important to be able to say what caused the casualty as to what did not cause it. We need to be able to demonstrate that we have considered all reasonable possibilities so as to not leave our investigation open to attack. Whether that evidence is included in your report or not, it should be in your notes. Elimination of possibilities deals with the question asked by lawyers, *How do you know that it wasn't something else that caused the casualty? How can you be so certain?* The answer, of course, comes in the process of elimination of possibilities. Therefore, all other reasonable possibilities need to be dealt with in a manner which demonstrates that the investigator considered them and rule them out. There are a variety of ways that this can be accomplished, but whatever method is used it must be convincing.

Sketching out the systems or making lists at the outset will go a long way toward ensuring that all the bases are covered. Sketches are useful for visualizing systems that are partly or mostly hidden; completing the sketch helps to reveal points that would otherwise probably be missed. Equally important, sketches help generate lists from which the final report can be prepared more quickly and with a minimum of confusion and lost information.

Sketches or drawings don't have to be fancy or professionally rendered or have any artistic qualities, but it is important to try to get them to have as accurate rendering as possible, particularly with regard to spatial distances and detail. A ream of legal size copy or graph paper will usually suffice, and if necessary, tape several pieces of paper together. It won't do to have a lot of detail crammed into a small sketch. This is because distances are important and may become critical evidence, so that the sketch will need to be sufficiently large as to include room for dimension lines and other comments. Later on the original sketch can be redrawn if it is too sloppy, but if you don't have adequate paper space to start with, you won't be able to render an accurate spatial concept later because it isn't included on the original and it's unlikely that memory will be so good as to reproduce it later.

Keeping Logs

With small casualties it may not be necessary to do much beyond keeping a time sheet and general notes in a plain file folder, but for large losses that can be very complex, some way of keeping track of voluminous information and documents is necessary. With all cases it is necessary to keep a time sheet on which we not only record time expended but also a brief description of what was done, phone calls, miles driven, photos taken and so on. From this we prepare our billing.

Yet it is also frequently necessary to maintain a log of other things such as evidence obtained, comments of witnesses, names, dates and times. This is normally kept in the investigation book. When investigations become particularly large or complex, we may want to separate the daily log/time sheet from the book to avoid the problem of separating the two types of information at a later date.

With large cases one can maintain two legal pads on one of which is kept a running chronology of our actions along with time spent, from which the time sheet is later created. The other is the investigation notes that will be used to build the report. It includes notes on evidence, order of events, things to do, questions to ask, information needed, and so on. To it we may add a time line and a cast of characters along with contact numbers or other vital information. It's usually a pretty messy looking thing, but it's also something that will be worked with a lot. From time to time it can be reviewed in order to see where we stand or to refresh our memory.

Keeping phone numbers on scraps of paper inside the file wastes time looking for them, plus they tend to get lost. It is more convenient to write down all frequently called numbers on the outside of the file jacket that houses the working notes for quick access. That way not only is it not necessary to even touch a piece of paper but one doesn't even have to open the file.

Of course, we should always be aware that this document is discoverable and could end up in the opposition's hands, and so we'll have to decide if we want to keep it or destroy it before it gets subpoenaed. On those occasions where the opposition has gotten its hands on my notes, it invariably follows that I get questioned in detail about every word I wrote, even if this takes hours. That can produce unfortunate results, so be very careful of what you write in notes and leave in the file! Or be prepared to destroy them. Do you have a right to destroy your notes? Absolutely you do, but not *after* you've received a subpoena; this is why it's often necessary to maintain two logs.

Very often on large investigations I find it helpful to write out what I'm thinking. Most good investigators do this because it helps develop our thinking and to see new possibilities. This is speculative thinking and the very sort of thing that we do not want to have fall into the opposition's hands. Therefore, it is wise to make such notes on separate paper that can later be earmarked for destruction and destroyed without difficulty. I mark all such note sheets at the top with the word "DISCARD" so that I won't later overlook it.

Frequent File Review

It will happen to all of us, on almost every investigation, large or small — but particularly the large one — that we will overlook things, important things. All-too-often we discover the oversight after it's too late and we can no longer go back and obtain that information. This is something that we absolutely want to learn how to avoid because if the case goes to litigation the error is going to come back to haunt us.

While we can't completely avoid oversights, these problems can be minimized by periodically taking the time to review the file and making to-do lists. An active investigation file needs to be reviewed weekly when not worked on a daily basis. This is where keeping good notes on top of the investigation book pays off. A good practice is to keep a to-do list on top so that we don't have to plow through a large pile of documents unnecessarily.

There came a time when I realized that I was always doing a much better job when travelling than working at home, despite the additional problems that working on the road causes. The reason was rather obvious: spending nights in hotels left me with evenings with nothing to do except study my file. There is where I discovered that the more time one spends studying, analyzing and planning, the more fruitful and thorough an investigation will become. This illustrated the tremendous difference taking the time for very careful study can make. We comprehend and see things that would otherwise have been overlooked.

The Investigation Book

Rather than keeping a file, for large investigations we use a large three ring binder because files are clumsy and difficult to work with. Documents are kept in chronological order with each new document placed on top. Keeping them in a binder prevents them from getting out of order plus order is achieved automatically. When files become unusually large, we revert to the categorical filing method. And because documents are copied frequently, the binder facilitates this easily. It is also easy to maintain the time sheet, notes and to-do list on the top or inside pocket. At the time of reviewing the file, before writing the report, is the time when we cull the file for any notes that we don't want to be there in the event that the file is subpoenaed.

The investigator should have a standard format assignment sheet on which he records basic information and instructions at the time he receives the assignment from the client. A stack of such forms should be kept by whoever answers the phone or receives assignments. The form should be designed so that the person taking the call can quickly go down the list and write down the vital information. This may seem rather unimportant but one should be aware that in the event of litigation, the opposing lawyer will question the investigator closely on these details. The one question he will invariably ask is, *What were you asked to do?* The standard answer to that question is, *investigate and report.* Period, unless you were given special instructions.

So why would he be interested in such trivial details? Because a sharp lawyer would dearly love to be able to suggest that the investigator is some kind of wild, uncontrollable maniac that exceeded his bounds. He'll do everything possible to chip away at your credibility; your objective is to minimize the chips. This is the very same tactic that defense lawyers use against cops. The assignment form should have a simple blank for Assignment: Investigate and Report. Keep in mind that years later when you get that subpoena you won't remember a word of what your client first told you, so write it down.

The investigation book never leaves the office for very important reasons: (1) It wouldn't be good to have it fall into the hands of others; (2) if we lost it we'd be in really big trouble. Everything that need be taken from the office should be copied and only a copy taken into the field or anywhere else. Shall I tell you about the time I accidentally left my file in an opposing lawyer's office? Or when it fell off a boat into the drink? There's no end to the unfortunate things that can happen to a file out of the office.

Travel Jobs

Every investigator eventually has to make a decision as to whether he's going to accept out-of-town jobs as his business grows. In addition to the problems posed by working in strange places, travelling almost always takes up more time than we anticipate - and often more time that we will get paid for. This raises the question of whether travel jobs are worth it. The ultimate answer to this is a matter of whether one can command a high enough rate that all unaccounted for time doesn't matter much.

Another consideration is that if you're going to be travelling frequently, it will be a big help if you live close to an airport. What with the air travel difficulties posed by 9/11 it will be inefficient, to say the least, to have to spend a couple of hours getting to and from an airport.

The cost of travel jobs begins the moment one receives the assignment and begins making arrangements. Not only does it take quite a bit of time to make travel arrangements but we often have to rearrange schedules. We have to coordinate with people at the site, and when we return work has piled up in our absence and we have to work overtime to catch up. Airlines rarely provide convenient schedules at reasonable cost; business people always get socked with the highest air fares because we are always last-minute travelers. Sometimes we arrive home late at night, have to unpack and be ready for work the next day. Packing and unpacking also takes time, not mention taking care of those home issues before departure. Moreover, travel jobs always seem to come up suddenly, at the worst possible time.

Are you aware of how much time you will spend preparing to travel? Not only do you have to pack but to make arrangements for things that happen in your absence, both in business and personally. I find that on average it takes me a full day of preparation and at least several hours on return, so say ten hours! Unless I'm charging for this time, I'm losing money on the job because if I stay home, this time can be spent productively and I will be paid for it.

Make it a cardinal rule never to allow a client to purchase plane tickets for you. There are several reasons for this, the first being that you relinquish all control over your time. The client isn't likely to be concerned whether you have to sit in an airport for four hours waiting for a connecting flight, or arrive home at midnight. The price of a cheap ticket could be ten hours to travel a few hundred miles. Secondly, it is essential to have a transferable ticket because if you should happen to miss the flight, it is you who will be footing the bill for another ticket.

To summarize, the amount of time spent preparing to travel and return is usually a lot more than we think. In many cases we're exhausted when we return yet have to contemplate going back to work immediately.

At one time I had a foreign insurer that kept me hopping all over North America for five years. It all started with a phone call of inquiry from a company I'd never heard of and from one local job grew into a continent-wide territory. Of course, I had no idea of what the future would hold and was unprepared for it. These people were not reluctant to pay a premium price for top notch work, so that when their work began to conflict with my local work — not leaving me time for both — I was faced with a difficult decision. Travel work is tough, demanding and exhausting; one is always working on a rigid schedule. However, money-wise I was definitely doing much better with the travel work so I decided to stay with it.

The one big risk was that I had no way of knowing how long this client would continue to give me work. The work could dry up at anytime, and in the meantime I was losing many of my local clients because I wasn't around to serve them adequately. As it turned out, I made out very well financially, but when it came to an end five years later, I had few local clients and literally had to start my business over again. This proved more difficult than anticipated and if I take into account the loss of income that followed and average it out over all those years, my annual income would have been about the same as if I had stayed home. Following those years I came to the conclusion that it is best to pick and choose amongst the highest paying jobs because the costs associated with travel are so unpredictable.

Preparation for Travel

The first question to be answered about any inquiry for a travel job is whether the client is willing to pay the fee plus expenses which will always be higher than anyone anticipates. When it comes to business travel we have to travel on our time schedule, not that of the airlines. That means the cost of travel is going to be higher. Moreover, it is usually cost inefficient to spend a lot of time searching for the best prices.

Before accepting a job it is necessary to first research the travel situation, cost and availability. This includes airfare, hotel and car rental and anything else that is required. Once this is determined, our fee should be calculated to which the travel costs are added and then the final quote given to the client. If he's not in shock at the cost and is still interested, we then hit him with the requirement that we require the fee to be paid in advance. It is at this point that many potential clients go away.

Another important question to be answered before getting on a plane is whether conditions and circumstances will facilitate completion of the job. Check the weather to make sure that you don't get stranded in an airport or rained out of doing the work. It is imperative to find out the travel time from job site to airport so that we can correctly plan our day and avoid missing the return flight. It is essential to make sure that you can do what you expect with the subject vessel. Does the boat require special preparation or movement; do you require assistance in any way? Will the boat need to be hauled or launched? Will the people you need to talk to be available? All travel jobs require very careful forethought and preparation to avoid ending up not being able to do what you're being paid to do. Time is always of the essence, neither too much nor too little. These details should be worked out *before* agreeing to take the job.

Never underestimate the potential for things going wrong. It is very easy to miss flights so don't make the mistake of buying cheap, non refundable and heavily restricted tickets lest you end up paying twice. Clients will just have to accept the fact that we can't be expected to buy cheap tickets weeks in advance on the latest flash-in-the-pan airline.

When travelling, everything takes twice as long as it does at home due to unfamiliarity. It's bad practice to try to work on a very tight schedule; leave yourself more time than you think you'll need. If you're working late and flying red-eyes, if you don't need the extra time allotted, it can be used to rest up so that you don't arrive back home in a frazzle. There's a lot more to jet lag than mere changing of time zones. Travel work is stressful and tiring and things will go a lot more smoothly with less stress when scheduling is intelligently planned with adequate time for rest. Cutting corners on timing just makes it all that much more exhausting and error-prone.

Because this work is difficult and tiring, choosing a good hotel close to your work is important. Choosing a cheap hotel or motel to save the client money isn't a good idea because we end up paying a price. Over the years I've come to realize that good hotels are more than a matter of luxury, this is a matter of good working conditions and available services. Chances are we'll be doing work at night and we don't want to be doing it on a bed or tiny table crammed with hotel paraphernalia. Better hotels have better business facility such as desks in rooms, faxing and computer rental, plus more peace and quiet. If you need fast transportation to the airport, you won't find that at a low price hotel chain.

When booking hotels, try to avoid those with central booking agencies and call the hotel directly. Too many snafus occur when going through a booking agency or center. Ask if there is a convention booked there. If there is, go elsewhere if you want peace and quiet, because the hotel will be full of people drinking and partying at night. This kind of information can't be had from a central booking center.

Because marine work tends to take us to resort areas, let me caution about tourist hotels: they are noisy, crowded and typically have poor service. I avoid them like the plague and if I've chosen one accidentally, I get out of there fast. Stay away from beaches: there's nothing like a party going in the next room, or a hotel full of screaming kids roaming the hallways while you're trying to get some much needed sleep or do paperwork. Try to choose a business class facility. If it's only an overnighter I choose an ordinary, moderately priced hotel, but for a number of days I will choose one of those "suites" or apartment type or extended stay places. It is inappropriate to resign yourself to spending several nights in a concrete box with a worn out facilities. Resort areas can be tough in season so if I can't get a good hotel I look to those condo rentals that more or less act like hotels.

Suites that have full kitchens are very worthwhile since eating out is expensive and time consuming. It is efficient to stop by a grocery store and pick up some food so that I don't have to eat out every meal; cereal for breakfast and frozen dinners in the oven turn the trick for me. What isn't spent on food pays the extra cost of the better lodging. As of this writing, the average cost of eating out per day is about $60 not including beverages and will consume several hours unless eating at McDonalds.

When traveling to major metropolitan areas, rush hours can cause huge delays and problems, particularly with catching return flights. Pay close attention to rush hours and how this will effect your travel times, particularly in other time zones.

Fees

Most surveyors end up learning the hard way that fees for travel – except for insurance jobs, must be obtained in advance. The hard truth is that, if the client isn't willing to pay the travel expenses in advance, then chances are he isn't going to pay you later. Make it an inviolable rule to never travel without an advance payment, no matter how urgently the client exhorts you to do so. If there isn't time to get you the money, then you don't have time to go. End of story. Break this rule and you'll end up not only working for nothing, but spending your own money to boot.

However you set your fees it's important that the client understand the costs and agrees to them. It is bad practice that leads to payment problems to try to downplay what the overall cost will be if the client is more than mildly concerned about cost. I have found that while quoting by the hour is safest for myself, the client really doesn't have any way to anticipate how much time you'll spend. Thus, quoting an hourly-plus basis really isn't much of a quote at all and can lead to misunderstandings and difficulty in getting paid. Therefore, my policy has been to quote on the basis of day rates since the number of days required can be more accurately estimated.

Now, the drawback with day rates is that one never knows how many hours one puts in per day. If you charge $800/day that may sound reasonable if you're only working eight or ten hour days, but on travel trips such short days are rare, with twelve or more hours the norm. If your rate is $80/hour you should be billing near $1120/day. However, on a three day trip, most of your time is spent sitting on airplanes and waiting in airports, and not working 16 hour days, so you may want to figure that the short days balance out with the long days and settle for a reasonable average. But don't forget to account for all that preparation time.

There is no way of knowing how much time is needed for a travel job, nor the obstacles that stand in our way – and hence whether we profit or lose money on a job – without carefully questioning the client about logistics and availability of all the objects of our investigation, people, places and things. The following is an example of what can go wrong.

An investigator accepted a job involving a forty foot boat, requiring him to travel 600 miles by air, anticipating it to be essentially an overnight job of about 2 days. He arranged his fee accordingly. Failing to get a detailed description of the logistics, the boat location turned out to be a two hour drive from the airport through a congested urban area. As it turned out, the boat was essentially abandoned in a field. When he arrived, it was found that the hull had three feet of rain water in it with a layer of bright green pond scum on top. The interior of the boat was a veritable greenhouse with mushrooms and toad stools growing out the walls and furniture. All electrical and mechanical systems were badly damaged.

The owner hadn't looked at the boat in nine months. There was no electricity available to pump the boat out, so a gas powered pump had to be rented. By the time it was dewatered, it was the next day, but the investigator's situation became even worse when it was found that the evidence that the investigator had hoped to find was lost due to the condition of the boat. In terms of time spent, he had gone way over his customer quote, but then he ends up unable to perform an effective investigation. It thus comes as no surprise that his client doesn't want to pay him.

This example points to some of the questioning that is necessary of the client. Asking when was the last time the vessel was used, or serviced, is essential. We need to find out as much about the current circumstances surrounding the vessel as possible. Are lights and electricity available? Had the investigator located the boat on a map, he would have known that the distance was much greater than what he was told, and involved going through an urban area during rush hour.

Business Arrangements

The dilemma that an independent investigator always faces is one of working as a one-man band or start hiring others. I have had considerable experience running a firm of four or more surveyors, a situation in which there are numerous problems. If you hire others, they have to be *closely* supervised and you can't supervise employees and do investigations at the same time. Therefore, the employee(s) have to be more or less capable of supporting you with whatever income they can generate. Moving from a one-man-band to a firm of several investigators will require a significant transition period in which the proprietor's production will fall off greatly while he trains new investigators. But once the new guys are capable of standing on their own feet, then he faces the risk of their going out on their own after you've spent all that time and money training them. Your employees now know all the ropes, clients and how to get them. Even if you have a non-compete agreement, you have to be prepared to enforce it — and that is a serious problem. Now you've not only lost your productive employee but are faced with the prospect of hiring a lawyer to go after him for violating his agreement. Be advised that this happens much too often.

Most efforts to create firms of marine investigators don't work out, or last very long because of these problems, and explains why most investigators are sole proprietors despite the problems that working alone causes. Fortunately, there are a number of different options we can resort to. A more ideal situation is a two-man partnership that presents little or no burden of supervision and far less non-paying administration time.

Another way that the sole proprietor can ease the burden is to ally oneself with another independent wherein each can help ease the burden of the other by taking his excess work in slack times. An alliance is a situation where each investigator is working independently but sharing his excess or lack of work with another investigator. Every sole proprietor has to deal with the problems of boom and bust: it happens to everyone. Through no fault of your own, you may lose clients and find yourself with little or no work and income for short periods. One can only hope that the other guy's boom time does not occur during your boom time, or vice versa. I have done this on several occasions and it worked out fairly well. It is possible to share an office and secretary while still maintaining separate businesses. Should that not work out, the net loss will be quite small.

When allying with another investigator, it's best to reduce your verbal agreement to writing, not necessarily a formal contract but an informal written agreement. Put in writing what's expected of each of you during contingencies such as payment, obligations, what to do when you both have too much work. You'll need to work out what happens, say, if the client fails to pay. Does your ally have to pay you even though he hasn't been paid? That's a point where alliances are likely to come to an end if you don't have an agreement. My modus operandi was that my associate didn't have to pay me if he didn't get paid, however, I demanded full disclosure about the financial stability of the client so that I could make a decision as to whether I wanted to accept the risk. In another instance when I had too much work, I arranged to hire another independent investigator as an employee on an hourly basis when his work load was off.

Joint Investigations

Joint investigations may become necessary when more than one party takes an interest in seeing the cause of a casualty investigated. These may occur immediately following the casualty or sometime thereafter. Particularly with large losses, third party interests may announce their interest early on. The investigator can end up with clients on any side of the issue - his client could be the boat owner, or an injured third party. In some cases it might even be a lender concerned about his collateral.

Let us first be sure we understand all the objectives of a joint investigation, for there is more at stake than might first be apparent. Determination of the cause is the primary objective, but the fact that there is a joint investigation at all means that subrogation or litigation is in the offing. That participants other than insurer and insured are involved means that the other parties are considering issues of liability – against them or against us. These issues may be settled either through litigation or voluntary admission of liability. How we, as the lead investigators, handle the matter could well determine the outcome.

If we are working for an insurer, it is our client who will make the decision whether to throw the investigation open or keep it closed. Insurers lean toward open investigations, mainly with a view toward the idea that the issue may be settled without costly litigation. For the most part, insurers won't fight cases where their insured has clear liability for reasons that are deeply rooted in law. If there are representatives of other insurers present, their clients can be expected to hold the same attitude. In light of this, the benefit of an open investigation becomes apparent. Thus, we lean toward being more, rather than less, cooperative. Of course, when the other parties are not insurers, chances are that their motives will not be so charitable

It should be understood that non first party interests have no rights in the matter. Allowing them to participate is a courtesy based on legal consideration of appearances should suits be filed; we don't wish to be seen as hiding evidence. This position also stems from historical insurance company practices of cooperation amongst insurers. It is fitting and proper that the lead investigator should be the one for the vessel insurer by virtue of the fact an insurance contract takes precedence over all other interests. This is known as a first party interest, and may include the boat owner, insurer and possibly the lender, all of whom have an economic interest in the vessel, which is what makes them a first party.

When other interests present themselves and declare an interest in participating in the investigation, we have a pretty good idea that litigation is likely. Therefore, we cannot deny the other party the right to at least observe or even to participate to some degree. Having competing interests conducting separate investigations, or even attempting to work together at the same time obviously will result in contention and difficulties. Thus, in these circumstances, someone has to be the lead, which is rightly the investigator for the vessel owner or insurer.

The lead investigator essentially controls and conducts the investigation with the other participants looking on. Fire investigations are the one type where joint investigations are most common because fires usually cause damage to other property, followed by just about any kind of other big money casualties, or where fatalities or serious injuries result. I've participated in investigations where as many as thirty other persons showed up, all claiming a need to be there. Situations like this require careful planning and control measures.

When large casualties occur, the investigator needs to be prepared to handle such events because if he isn't, the situation will spin out of control very quickly and any semblance of conducting a reasonable investigation will probably be lost. What you thought would be a professional investigation now becomes a circus of the absurd as competing interests and their lawyers and investigators all insist on getting their way first. In Chapter Eight, I relate a how a fire investigation was improperly handled, which presents a good example of how not to handle a joint investigation.

Evidence

The first party interest should exercise his right to obtain and hold evidence; no other party has any rights until such time as a suit has been filed. The various interests should be allowed to inspect (but not necessarily handle) the evidence, and should be informed of who will retain it, where and what will happen to it, along with who will perform any lab work.

Avoiding the Circus

It's not difficult to anticipate when multiple other interests are likely to appear. Chances are you'll soon start getting phone calls as the insured or insurance company begins to refer these calls to you. A very typical example is when a sizeable new boat sinks or burns after multiple contractors have worked on it, and where the actions of each will be suspect as to possible cause. This is how we quickly end up with twenty people ringing your phone, so what do you do?

Obviously, if a cause is found that implicates one of the interests at hand, that interest will do everything possible to challenge your investigation, so you need likewise to do everything possible to eliminate the potential for criticism on the way the investigation was handled:

> Resist the temptation to start the investigation immediately. Take demonstrable steps to secure the vessel and all evidence.

> Take the names and phone numbers of everyone who calls. Require them to send you a letter stating who they are and what their interest is. Inform them that they will not be permitted to attend unless they do so.

Set a date for the investigation and mail a letter to each party that responded in writing announcing the date and place for the investigation.

The letter should spell out that (due to space and evidence preservation considerations) interested parties will only be allowed to observe the proceedings; that when evidence is found, they will be given the opportunity to inspect it personally.

When the time arrives do a roll call of all attendees and identify them.

Determine in advance what tools, equipment and support personnel will be needed to facilitate the investigation and have them readily available.

When Evidence is Perishable

There will be many situations, if not most, when it becomes apparent that evidence is perishable, such as evidence having been underwater. In these circumstances we have a demonstrable duty to begin an investigation immediately without the need to consider any other interests. Personally, I try to avoid joint investigations because they take too long to set up and evidence is prone to being degraded or lost.

Joint Procedure

How you carry out the actual investigation will depend entirely on how many people are present. In a burned out boat, for example, there shouldn't be more than one or two persons on board because it's bad enough that even four feet will be trampling evidence; we certainly can't have eight, ten or twenty feet doing that. There is always a problem of how to investigate without destroying evidence or simply having too many people in the way. The type of loss will basically dictate how to handle the situation.

When other parties have a clear and substantial interest in the investigation, it's best to cater to their interests within practical limits. Sometimes the lead investigator will be well-acquainted with an investigator for another party, and may choose that individual to work with him.

Before starting it's a good idea to address the assembled with a little speech outlining why we are here and what we hope to accomplish. It is important to stress that this is an unbiased investigation with the intention of letting the chips fall where they may, and that everyone will have the opportunity to see things for themselves. However, not everyone will be allowed to go traipsing through the wreck by himself.

In the cases of fires and sinkings, it is likely that the vessel will require some preparation to make ready for investigation. A sunk boat might be completely covered in diesel oil and full of deranged furniture, in which case a considerable amount of clean up work will be needed during which time you don't need to have many people standing around watching for endless hours. You'll need to use your own judgment as to whether this work should be done in advance and whether you need to consult with the other interests first and obtain their agreement.

Fire investigations pose special problems such as collapsed structures and the need for careful excavation of debris and debris removal. Yet in every case, the investigation should evaluate the wreck and determine in advance what will be necessary to facilitate the investigation with minimal delay because a lot of things can go wrong, such as:

> Rainfall unexpectedly filled the hull up with water and a half day is lost in arranging to have it pumped out.

> A burned, charred boat on a hot summer's day (it's 95 in the shade) all that black wreckage is so hot from sunlight absorption and no wind that the temperature inside the wreck is beyond human tolerance. I've measured temperatures within burned wrecks as high as 150F. This has happened to me on numerous occasions. One cannot conduct a good investigation under these conditions so something has to be done to make working conditions tolerable.

> Failure to anticipate the effects of weather.

With big money losses, consider engaging a service to erect a tent over the wreck. This is much cheaper and more practical than inside storage (no one wants a wreck inside their facility), that not only will serve to keep rain and snow off the wreck, but shelter it from hot sun.

If lawyers are present, as they often are, they are there with a view toward ensuring the investigation is properly conducted as well as building their case, so it's good idea to maintain a cooperative attitude, or at least don't ignore them. They are informed that they and their investigators will be given the opportunity to see things for themselves. I make it a point to periodically brief them as to what is going on. If conditions permit, I will bring them aboard and let them see things for themselves which usually does keep them happy. I also try to take note of who they are talking to and to eavesdrop if possible. This is now an adversarial situation and should be treated accordingly yet with adherence to the rules.

Far too many surveyors that I have encountered in joint surveys or investigations take a biased position and overtly work to protect their clients from adverse evidence. Sometimes they conceal evidence and at other times become obstructionist. These people are not searching for the truth, they are searching for a defense and their efforts are unethical at best; they are usually their own worst enemies. We need not be too concerned about them though it is useful to observe whatever it is that they are concentrating on because every investigator reveals his thinking by the area of his concentration.

In taking a break from the investigation and bringing others on board for a look-see, we are giving them an opportunity to voice objections or hear their opinions. They may raise questions that we need to answer. Also note that what they say is a clue to what they are thinking, whether they are there to gather facts or are simply there looking for ammunition with which to defeat you. This is useful to know.

As noted earlier, we want to deal with inclusive as well as exclusive evidence. It is all too easy to believe that we have found the cause and then stop looking. With all these other interests present, it becomes doubly important to be as thorough as possible. Furthermore, we want to be sure that the others are aware of the fact that we are going the extra mile, so a little public relations are in order here. At the conclusion of the investigation I like to bring all others on board and give them a little presentation on everything that was done by physically pointing out every area (or at least most of them) that was covered. Then I ask them if they have any questions or suggestions. I want them to leave being impressed by how thorough we were.

If the evidence is favorable to you, this is how you defeat serious challenges to your investigation. If the evidence goes against them, and they are convinced that you've done a very thorough job, they will be far more likely to advise their clients to settle the issue if they are liable.

When evidence is removed for analysis by other experts, this evidence should be shown to the others, properly packaged and labeled so that the chain of custody is established. They are then informed as to where it is going and what will be done with it, and asked whether they have any objections. If anyone does, take note of who and why, but as lead investigator you don't have to be influenced by those objections if you don't agree with them.

Legal Implications

Owing to the high risk of ensuing litigation, the surveyor/investigator should at all times think like a lawyer. What this means is to remain aware at all times that human beings are capable of behaving dishonorably, particularly when financial problems exist; that it is not prudent to conduct business as usual, for we are dealing with unusual events. We are therefore careful about what we say because people under severe financial distress can and do attempt to slander investigators. One should not underestimate the lengths that some people will go to protect their interests.

When litigation results, people routinely lie under oath; when a boat owner perceives that things aren't going his way, it is not at all unusual that the boat owner will advance slanderous statement about the investigator in an attempt to get him thrown off the case. Insurance agents, in an effort to retain their customers, will occasionally assist the insured in this effort. Thus, when conducting investigations, we are circumspect about everything we say, do not engage in casual conversations with those involved, and do our best to ensure that there is documentation or witnesses to what we say and do. An example will drive the point home:

I was once sued by a man who was at the time imprisoned on Federal charges of intentionally sinking a commercial vessel for the purposes of collecting insurance. The suit alleged that I had conversations with him and his wife that were a violation of his rights and constituted bad faith. The fact was that I had never spoken with either one of them. My time sheets and phone bills helped prove the point since I kept careful phone records. The only contact he had with anyone concerning the insurance claim was with the FBI and the Florida Department of Law Enforcement.

There is a good reason why police departments are viewed as insular and closed communities. It's because anything a cop says can and will be used against him; therefore they learn to say as little as possible to outsiders, an example we'd best take heed of.

When very large losses are involved, one should think through the situation before having discussions with the insured; don't go in blind but be prepared, anticipate potential stumbling blocks. Certainly we have to be pleasant and professional, but that also means maintaining a healthy skepticism about our dealings with others. This is a fine line to walk, but experience will ultimately prove the point, so it's better to learn this sooner rather than later.

Conducting marine investigations bears similarities to crime scene investigations with the main difference that we are seeking causes of casualties rather than solving crimes. The boat is our corpse, and its location our crime scene. In most cases the perpetrator is a failed part, bad design, a weather event or some other outside happening. Occasionally, it is the result of an act of an individual either accidental or intentional.

Attaching to the determination of cause is often the assignment of blame, as when the cause is the result of human error such as faulty design or manufacturing. We need to be constantly aware that our actions could well end up being judged by numerous other persons from other experts such as your peers, lawyers, judges and juries. Lacking any experience with litigation, it is difficult to appreciate all the pitfalls that face the novice investigator, so let's start with the realization that all those on the other side of an issue will go over our work with a fine tooth comb, searching for faults and weaknesses in our investigation and the way we handled it. The objective of the other side is to defeat us and our job is to not let that happen. This is why it is stressed that the investigator must constantly think like a lawyer and be alert to the probability of challenge.

Chapter 3

The Nature of Evidence

This chapter deals with the nature of evidence in depth, even though it is recognized that in the majority of routine cases, evidence is simple and clear cut. Yet there are always those cases where nothing is ever simple, and questions seem to revolve around everything. The investigator needs to be well prepared for these difficult cases and the myriad problems that arise from them. The inexperienced might wonder why I make such a big deal about evidence, but will come to a greater understanding when he reconsiders what an investigation involving a fatality, serious injuries, or major monetary damages is really like. Such cases become big money issues where the battles get intense and the rules of legal warfare are stretched to the limits.

Make no mistake, such cases are battles, and if we, the foot soldiers of these legal wars are insufficiently trained, we are very likely to become casualties ourselves. Evidence is the basis of our work product, so we need to be sure that we understand its nature thoroughly.

There are two primary types of evidence, physical and oral. Oral evidence is that which is observed and related by a witness, and among investigators of all sorts it is considered the least reliable owing to the vagaries of human nature. Observation and memory are rarely ever completely accurate. Two persons are unlikely to view the same event and then recount it exactly the same. This is due to the fact that all events and objects are not seen as they truly are, or even from the same physical position, but are filtered through the mind and edited by personal experience, beliefs and bias. Thus it is possible for a witness to view an event and then recount it very inaccurately to the point where the recounting is untrue, all the while honestly believing that he is telling the truth. The editing was done in the witness's subconscious without his awareness of it.

Evidence can further be broken down into subcategories, direct and circumstantial. Direct evidence is that which is not arguable because the fact speaks for itself: *the bullet found in the body matches the rifling of the gun owned by the accused.* This is not to say that direct evidence can't be limited in scope. The bullet found in the body does not prove that the accused shot the victim.

Circumstantial evidence relates to the circumstances surrounding the event. A single bit of circumstantial evidence does not, in and of itself, offer proof. But it is a common misunderstanding resulting from a well-worn cliché that circumstantial evidence is inherently weak. This is not true, for people are routinely convicted of murder based on circumstantial evidence. This not to say that either circumstantial or direct evidence can't be weak. Circumstantial evidence is defined as evidence that may be inferred from a set of circumstances. In other words, based upon logical reasoning. *The muddy boot prints on the floor suggested that the murder was committed during or after the rain.* That is an inference that may or may not be correct, but which may be further corroborated by yet other evidence. *The weather service records indicated that the rain ceased at about 9:35 PM and that it had not rained for a weak prior to this.* Therefore, it is a more than reasonable inference that the murder occurred after 9:35 PM based on two circumstantial facts. However, circumstantial evidence typically requires a greater preponderance of evidence than direct physical evidence.

Oral evidence, at least in criminal matters, tends to be less reliable than physical evidence for reasons stated above. It is considerably less of a problem in our work, owing mainly to the fact that non criminal matters produce considerably less motivation for witnesses to be biased by virtue of the less critical nature of the event. However, there is a natural tendency of witnesses to avoid reporting uncomplimentary information about other people to investigators. It is common for witnesses to hedge or edit that which they witness. The good investigator is one who can recognize when a witness is hedging and works to draw out the truth. He learns to listen carefully, recognize inconsistencies, and learns to formulate questions designed to draw out a more accurate retelling. This is a skill that is only born of experience and effort. The investigator who simply takes statements and accepts witness accounts at face value — in other words, just going through the motions — is doing a disservice in the same way that unmotivated police detectives not infrequently end up charging the wrong person with a crime simply because they did not care enough to work hard to get at the truth.

Obviously, oral evidence is much more difficult to work with and there is a natural tendency of investigators to avoid it and to concentrate on the physical evidence. But physical evidence has its own limitations in that the only story it can tell is that which is deduced or inferred by the investigator or technician. Once again, such inferences aren't always accurate since all physical evidence is subject to human interpretation. Here we will use common example that is often related in criminal courses because a common homicide is typically less complex than many marine investigations.

Improbable Possibilities

The following story illustrates the nature of evidence, both circumstantial and direct, pointing out why it is so important to keep an open mind to the range of possibilities. We all have a tendency to seize on the most obvious probability because that is the easy way. This example shows why that is wrong.

A man is laying on the ground who has been shot. The police arrive soon thereafter and find another man standing over him with a pistol in his hand. The instant assumption will be that the man holding the gun is the man who shot the man on the ground. Of course, a good police detective would make no such assumption for there could be many explanations for the man with the gun. Even if the gun were smoking, that would still not be proof of who shot the man, though the man holding the gun would surely top the suspect list of one.

In this case the truth was that the man was shot during a robbery. As improbable as this may seem, the man with the gun just happened to be taking his 38 caliber pistol to a shooting range for target practice when he came upon the robbery. He pulled out his pistol and fired a warning shot over the head of the robber, who's gun went off and shot the victim accidentally. Unfortunately for the good Samaritan, his gun and that of the robber are the same type and caliber. (Note here that the Samaritan's account is evidence whether it is true or not. Untruths can be just as evidentiary as truth, for every lie has a story to tell, other than that which was intended. The investigator's job is to discover why the lie was told.) It will require a ballistics test and analysis to determine whether the Samaritan's story is true or false. If the riffling of the bullet recovered from the victim do not match that of the Samaritan's gun, then the Samaritan is proven innocent. On the other hand, if the riflings match, would it be proper to assume that the Samaritan is the perpetrator? If not, why not?

The answer is that if the rifling matches the Samaritan's gun, the only thing that proves is the bullet came from the Samaritan's gun. It does not prove that the Samaritan intentionally murdered the victim. A good detective would then question the Samaritan about why and where he directed his warning shot. Did he fire it dangerously close and accidentally hit the Samaritan? Certainly that is a possibility.

However, and this is a very important point to take note of, in questioning the suspect, the detective will want to take care not to put ideas in the head of the suspect. It is okay to ask, *Did you shoot the victim?* It is not okay to ask, *Did you accidentally shoot the victim?* Because *accidentally* puts ideas in his head; it is an obvious "out". The detective will have to take his time and think through his questions and the order of questioning. The procedure will likely be a careful examination of the entire event, essentially focusing on a second-by-second accounting of every move. The detailed questioning proceeds slowly and deliberately, allowing the interrogator time to think through each answer and pose the next question. It could be that he will need to stop the interrogation at some point before it is concluded in order to obtain clarification of some particular point. Thus, the investigator should never be in a hurry and may have to carry out the interrogation in stages, which will appear to the suspect to be unnecessary repetitions of the same interview and covering much of the same ground, when in fact, it is a continuation of what amounts to one, long interview. See *Interrogation Techniques.*

This points up the reason why, on very important cases, one should never be in a hurry to take formal statements and why it is better to conduct informal interviews first. The insurance policy gives you one shot at a formal statement under oath and one shot at a formal statement not under oath. If statements are taken too early, the investigator will not have sufficient information from which to formulate the right questions. Therefore, the taking of formal statements is best reserved for a time when the investigator is well-armed with a basket of facts.

The Marine Corollary

In this case, a sunken boat is raised and it is found that the top is off a sea strainer. Since the top has to be unbolted to be removed, the removal of the top can be seen as an intentional act to sink the boat, but is it? Regardless of how improbable, we should ask whether other possibilities exist? One would be that someone was working on it and forgot to put it back on. Another might be that someone put the top on but failed to secure it and it later came off from vibration. Just because something seems improbable doesn't mean that it's impossible. Strange things can and do happen. As every police supervisor will attest, it is altogether too easy for investigators to succumb to taking the easy road by jumping on the first and most obvious conclusion. But when we do so, sooner or later this is going to come back to bite us, hard.

We can guard against establishing bad habits by developing the habit of always taking a moment to sketch out a list of possibilities, and then setting out to nail them down, true or false.

Physical evidence isn't necessarily more reliable than witnesses because physical evidence is always subject to misinterpretation. Whereas witnesses are almost always biased to some degree, as we, ourselves are, physical evidence is often subject to the bias of those who analyze it, but not always for some types of evidence that are beyond dispute. In civil matters, the nature of physical evidence is not subject to the strong review and challenges to its veracity as with criminal cases, yet because we never know when a civil case will turn into a criminal one, it is imperative to treat all investigations with the same degree of care.

In another case, a sunk boat is raised wherein it is found that two hoses below the water line are cut through. Examination shows that the cuts were made with a sharp knife and are fresh, not old. What could have caused those cuts? Is there anything in the immediate area that could have done it? The answer is no, they were intentionally created by a person. The question is, who. Who would have the means and motivation to go aboard the insured vessel and deliberately sink it? Since the owner is the most obvious suspect, we have to ask whether there are any other possibilities even though this looks like a cut and dried case. Despite the apparent obviousness, we need to resist the temptation to set about building a case to prove that the boat owner did it, but instead seek to eliminate any other possibilities first. This must be done if for no other reason than if litigation ensues, challenges will be raised as to the focus and scope of our investigation.

Taking Physical Evidence

Not infrequently does the issue of physical taking of evidence become an issue of contention. It must be remembered that evidence is almost always the property of the boat owner, or others, and in principle should not be taken without permission. In reality, because time is of the essence, we usually do take evidence without permission due mainly because of the insured's contractual obligation to cooperate. The need to take physical possession of evidence also stems from the need to protect the evidence and it's chain of custody, or to subject it to expert analysis.

Instances have occurred where the investigator removed evidence from the insured vessel and subjected it to testing without informing the insured. Later, the claim was denied and a suit was filed by the insured alleging that the investigator deprived the insured of his rights. This is the sort of thing we want to avoid.

The taking of evidence can occur under a wide range of situations, from the taking of a damaged part removed by a repairer that might otherwise be discarded, to the removal of evidence personally such as the cutting out of a piece of some material, removing a part. etc. Under most circumstances the evidence is damaged material which intrinsically has no valve other than evidence. In other cases it might be a major item of equipment of substantial value, thus there is a need to exercise good judgment with this issue.

If the insured or his agent is not present to ask, one may remove evidence in the form of damaged material, or objects of little intrinsic value, from the vessel without permission, but before doing so one should thoroughly photograph it prior to removal in its undisturbed position. One should also, if possible, have a reliable person present to witness its removal. The insured should be notified that such evidence is in our possession, particularly when the sample is the only possible sample.

If there is objection by the owner or his agent to the removal of evidence, the investigator should advise that person that the insurance contract requires the cooperation of the insured, cooperation that extends to the taking of evidence, analysis of same as well as the need to protect evidence from loss or inadvertent destruction.

When it is anticipated that evidence is to be removed for the purpose of analysis, the issue of whether that analysis is destructive, in whole or in part, need be addressed, particularly when the sample is the only possible sample. If it is one of many, then the matter raises no such issue. Destructive testing is only destructive of evidence if that testing renders the item such that no other forms of testing can be done.

Removing a piece or making a hole does not necessarily destroy the evidence. Many forms of forensic analysis are at least partly destructive so that if that is what the investigator contemplates, it is best to explain the situation to the boat owner and secure his permission. If he resists, it should be explained that he has a duty to cooperate. If he continues to resist, then attempt to get an agreement to remove the evidence to a place of safe keeping (as with a mutually agreeable third party) until such time as the dispute can be resolved. If he continues to resist, one might suggest that the evidence be deposited with a disinterested third party. Barring that one should immediately seek legal assistance through the client.

In a different type of case we have an apparent hit-and-run wherein our client's boat is docked in a marina and was struck by another boat. No one saw it happen, so the other boat wasn't identified. It happens that there is dark blue paint transferred onto our boat. Naturally, we go around the marina looking for a dark blue hull, and we find one. Low and behold, it has white paint transferred onto it. Here's a case where there is apparent evidence attached to a boat owned by an unidentified person. Do we take that evidence without permission, or seek to gain permission? Would permission be given if the other boat owner was the perpetrator? Not likely. More likely he'd try to get rid of the evidence rather than let you have it. Since the area in question is already damaged, the practical thing to do would be to go ahead and take a sample scraping for lab comparison. Can the perpetrator complain that the sample was illegally obtained? Not if it really is your client's paint on the other guy's boat!

In another, much more serious hit and run case, I located the other vessel which still had shards of my insured's boat embedded in it. In this case, rather than take the shards myself, I called the Marine Patrol and let them handle it as legally required. This was a significant crime, and I would be wrong to personally take that evidence.

In the first case cited, the amount of damage wasn't extensive and my judgement was that the police wouldn't be much interested in the matter. There was plenty of trace evidence, so taking a little of it wouldn't impair a police investigation in the unlikely event the overworked local department did one. I did, however, report the finding, which generated nothing more than another police report. The lab analysis of the transfer evidence resulted in a successful subrogation case.

Physical Handling

The removal and handling of evidence must be done in such a way as whatever portion of it is to be analyzed by a specialist is not in any way altered or damaged. For a broken part, this would mean protecting the fractured edge. If corrosion is involved, care must be taken that the relevant surface is not disturbed. Since we are rarely ever dealing with trace evidence, our methods of evidence handling are likely to be different than criminal methods. We don't place items in paper bags to prevent trace evidence from falling off or smudging finger prints.

Sometimes pieces of evidence can be very large, such as an entire steering system from a boat collision, or a propeller shaft. With large, unwieldy pieces, handling damage to exposed parts is easily incurred so care must be taken with such parts. Avoid placing evidence in plastic bags when evidence contains moisture. Condensation developing within the bag could end up damaging the evidence. Iron and steel parts must be protected from moisture and high humidity, being sure to store them in a location where this type of damage will not occur.

Trace evidence, such as scrapings of transfer paint from a collision should be handled very carefully to avoid contamination. Use a new white envelop rather than plastic containers.

Degrees of Proof

There are three standards of proof that are recognized in law. The first *is preponderance of evidence* which means that evidence is weighted in favor of a particular conclusion. It amounts to a simple majority of 51% and is the lowest standard and obviously embodies reasonable doubt. For civil cases, this degree is usually insufficient for a plaintiff to prevail. The second standard is *clear and convincing evidence* and while there is no precise definition of this term, the best we can say is that it constitutes more than a mere preponderance of evidence sufficient to convince, but is less than certain. This is the standard needed for plaintiffs to prevail in civil cases. The third standard is *beyond reasonable doubt,* which applies only in criminal cases and does not mean absolute certainty.

Many investigations produce evidence beyond reasonable doubt where only one possible cause is found that is completely convincing. The existence of reasonable doubt casts a cloud over evidence because it fails to close all other possibilities, while not illuminating them. The final standard is absolute certainty in which it is clear through the laws of physics that A caused B in the same way that two plus two is four; any doubts that are raised are not reasonably introduced.

The term *doubt* does not necessarily mean that disbelief is based on honestly held disbelief. Doubt can be, and often is, the result of self-interest, in which case it is inherently unreasonable. We see this frequently in criminal court cases where all sorts of irrational doubts are raised by defense lawyers. People often argue that we can have no way of knowing anything absolutely, as if this is a fanciful universe, and perhaps they are right. But the standard we are looking for is what we believe other reasonable, unbiased individuals would also believe or conclude.

Notice that when we attempt to analyze these definitions, we end up going in circles because none of these words in themselves have absolute definitions. What does "reasonable," "clear," "convincing" and "absolute" mean? So we come around again to that word *reasonable* which is very difficult to define. In a legal context it means the sound judgement of persons not motivated by bias and who are intellectually equipped to make such judgment.

If there is some doubt, then other reasonable possibilities must exist. If so, we need to identify and attempt to close them off. In some cases possibilities may exist that are beyond our means to prove for reasons such as cost, or perhaps they are merely flights of fancy. In this case, the degree of doubt is probably not reasonable.

In the end, it is up to the investigator to shed his bias and exercise his own best judgement as to the strength of his evidence.

Closing Loopholes of Doubt

During the course of investigations we should occasionally take time to consider the range of possibilities and the reasonableness thereof. Even if there is any reasonable possibility at all, in many cases we are unable, for a variety of reasons, to close them off completely. But we should do our best to accumulate evidence that *casts doubt on the reasonable doubts.* Should we have to testify, we would like to say, *I considered that possibility, but because of such and such, I did not consider that to be a reasonable possibility owing to a lack of evidence leading in that direction.* This leads to the often overlooked subject of exclusionary evidence.

Inclusionary/Exclusionary Evidence

Evidence can further be defined by these two categories that are two words that ought to be kept in mind while conducting investigations. Inclusionary evidence is all evidence that fits into and supports the conclusion of causation. Exclusionary evidence is all evidence that proves that other possibilities are not the cause. The purpose of collecting and recounting exclusionary evidence is to minimize the possibility of reasonable doubt. In the event of litigation, we must be aware that the opposition will do everything it possibly can to raise issues of doubt, so we want to take every opportunity to try to close those doors. Working with both types of evidence also helps to keep us from becoming fixated on the most obvious possibilities and expand our range of thinking.

To put it another way, exclusionary evidence is all those other areas (or possibilities) that were evaluated and found to be unrelated or not involved. With investigation reports it becomes necessary to describe, sometimes in general and sometimes in very specific detail, all those aspects that were examined and found not to be contributory. Example: *Both bilge pumps, wiring, switches and plumbing were examined and tested for proper operation with no faults being discovered.* Why? Because it is just as important to state what did not cause the casualty as what did. In doing so we are demonstrating to those who make use of our work that we were open minded and did not take the easy way out by seizing on the most obvious evidence; we did not jump to conclusions.

Exclusionary evidence is highly relevant with fire investigations in particular. It is as important to determine what did not cause the fire as it is to determine what did. This is because the failure to address obvious possibilities leaves the door open to our conclusion being challenged. With many types of casualties, there are always a handful of likely possibilities, and these are the ones that we need to be sure to address.

Obviously, the list of exclusionary evidence could be lengthy and we need to use some common sense about this. But notice how simple and telling the above example is; in one sentence the major component of a sinking loss is wrapped up, leaving no doubt about whether the investigator considered it without going into a lot of time consuming detail. The investigator can be questioned later about details, if necessary. Therefore it is fair to state that what is needed is to cover those aspects of evidence that would have the greatest potential for being involved. With a sinking loss, that would mean that every aspect for potential water ingress into the hull needs to be reviewed. It is not enough to say, *We looked at everything and found no other causes,* because that statement is far too broad and unconvincing. At the very least, what constitutes *everything* need be generally described: *When the vessel was refloated, nine through hull fittings and associated plumbing and hoses were inspected for leakage and none was found.*

The failure to deal with exclusionary evidence is probably the most common downfall of investigator's reports. They locate what is believed to be the one and only cause quickly, and promptly write a report saying that's it. Then when the investigator ends up on the witness stand, the opposing lawyer tears his report to shreds and impeaches it because there are numerous possibilities that he failed to evaluate, yet alone even mention. Take a moment and visualize a lawyer grilling a witness over numerous items that he did not report on. *Did you check this? Did you check that? Did you test ALL the bilge pumps, sir? Didn't you think that any of these other things could possibly be involved? Don't you think that it is important, if you want this jury to believe your conclusion, you should have checked on these things? How can you know that the cause wasn't this other thing if you didn't check it?*

Notice here that even if the witness says that he did check those things, he'll still be attacked. *But you didn't think any of this was important enough to include it in your report now, did you Mr. Jones. Is that because you didn't want anyone to know that any of these things were possibilities? How can your client evaluate whether they are going to pay the claim if you fail to give them the complete picture with all the facts? Tell us the truth, Mr. Jones, you really didn't do a very good job now, did you?*

Ouch! That hurts, but this is the sort of thing that happens to investigators frequently. From this, one can see how easy it is to attack an expert's credibility when he fails to address exclusionary evidence in his report. He will, unfortunately, have brought all this down on his own head since he could have prevented the impeachment by taking the time to do a little better job. Each casualty should suggest its own list of possibilities. If we make a list of these at the outset, we can then use the same list while writing the report to account for the exclusionary evidence.

Whenever possible, when dealing with physical evidence, unless it comes from an independent lab, it is best to get a second opinion. Second opinions can come from coworkers or colleagues, and with all large casualties, I always make it a point to run my evidence by a knowledgeable colleague. You may be surprised at how differently someone else may see what you thought was a certainty. We aren't always capable of doing a good job at second-guessing ourselves, so it's a good double check to use someone else.

In recent years the use of laboratory analysis has increased dramatically as new and more cost effective analytical machines and process have been developed. Less than a decade ago, the analysis of plastics was cost prohibitive. A new generation of chromatography machines has reduced the cost substantially, and since the vast majority of boats are made of plastic, this is tremendously beneficial to investigators.

Metallurgical analysis has long been used by marine investigators for machinery failure analysis as well as identification of corrosion issues. Virtually all material — with the possible exception of a few precious metals — are subject to various forms of deterioration. Almost all forms of natural degradation are referred to as corrosion. Corrosion consists of the common forms such as rust as well as numerous less common forms of electro-chemical activity. Corrosion also includes the strictly mechanical action of erosion, the abrasive effects of one material rubbing against another when suspended in a fluid. All of these forms are routinely dealt with in marine investigations and particularly insurance claims as casualties due to corrosion are widely excluded from insurance coverage.

Selective Evidence

There is nothing that gets investigators and prosecutors into more trouble than jumping to conclusions and selecting and manipulating evidence to fit into a theory. If evidence doesn't quite fit the theory, we massage it, shape it, whittle it down until the square peg fits the round hole. This starts with a bias, or laziness, reinforced by adherence to a preconceived theory, followed by selective use of facts to fit that theory. Such manipulations are usually very subtle and unconscious, but can be as crude as using an 8 pound hammer to drive that square peg into the round hole. When this happens, the investigator has so deceived himself that he is no longer aware of the utter dishonesty of what he is doing. He is, quite simply, self-deluded and his delusion will become obvious to everyone but himself. I use the simile of public prosecutors, particularly in high profile cases, who are very frequently politically motivated, because this happens so frequently and we are all familiar with the results of this behavior. These are lessons we should all learn from.

It is very easy for anyone to fall into this trap which, in our case, is motivated by nothing so evil as political power, but by mere inertia, the desire to do less work rather than more, work shorter hours rather than longer, to complete the job as soon as possible. Lest I appear to sound moralistic, or holier than thou, I'm willing to admit that I have made these mistakes. The only antidote for this laziness is to maintain awareness of the tendency and to guard against it until such time as doing the right thing becomes a force of habit.

What is a Fact?

We are all familiar with the parable that if ten people are asked to describe something as apparently simple as a tree, we likely get ten very different answers. From this we can come to two possible conclusions: either the perceptions of people aren't very good, or the subject is more complex than we thought. A tree is simple in appearance from a distance, but on careful analysis is not simple at all but a highly complex organism. So, the truth about "facts" is a combination of both possibilities: the tree isn't simple and people's perceptions can either be flawed or merely limited in focus, thus resulting in an incomplete description. If we ask ten people to describe that tree, differences will exist based on where they are standing in relation to it. Yet it is less a matter of their physical positioning than their mental conditioning that accounts for the differing viewpoints.

Police investigators are often frustrated by the witness who was in a position to observe an event but responds to questioning with "I didn't notice." They accuse bystanders of being unobservant or even uncooperative. While both counts may be true, it is also true that bystanders are caught by surprise by the event and were not focused on it in the way that the investigator is, yet the investigator expects that the witness should be. Bystanders are busy with their own affairs and not much interested in those of others, so while the event may have occurred within their vision, it doesn't make a deep impression. This is particularly true in our work that is a lot more mundane than crimes in progress. This will be discussed at greater length in the chapter on interrogation techniques.

The nature of facts as we deal with them daily is in the eye of the beholder. For our purposes truth is that which reasonable persons are likely to agree upon. That does not mean that which is ultimately true, but merely what most people believe is true whether it is true or not, that is the basis of the law. It goes without saying that we cannot define "reasonable person" either, so what we are really interested in is that which we believe we could convince a jury is true. You may believe it, your client may believe it, but will a jury believe it? There lies the ultimate question that interests us.

It is not enough to believe in our heart that we are right, we must be able to convince a jury in the event of a legal challenge. In our daily life, we get to use our powers of persuasion, but not in court. In court we can only answer questions that are asked of us, and we have no control over what those questions are. Our power of persuasion is limited to evidence in its various forms, so we'll need to be sure that our evidence is as convincing as we can possibly make it.

In and of itself, evidence won't mean much to the layman. It is within our powers to make that evidence meaningful. A witness may be the most knowledgeable person in the world but all that is for naught if the individual has poor abilities of expression. Unfortunately, this describes most scientists and technical people. If you watched the OJ Simpson trial you saw the prosecution repeatedly put bland and unconvincing experts on the stand, including DNA experts who were completely unable to make their science comprehensible to a jury of ordinary citizens. As a result, all their million dollar "facts" were not accepted as such because the witness failed to convince. An investigator who is a good witness is also a good teacher.

Therefore, one of the more important guiding principles that an investigator can be guided by is that of always thinking about evidence in terms of how he would present it to a jury, whether he could make them understand it, as well as believe it. If one does this in every instance, it's very unlikely that he will go wrong. This is a principle that should be applied in every case, regardless of whether litigation seems likely. I routinely advise my clients about how I feel about evidence and the prospects of successfully using it in court. There have been many cases where the evidence appeared very strong to me, as an expert, but for which I was completely aware that a jury would not see the evidence the same way. This is because it was too technical and too complicated to be conveyed convincingly to a layman. In the end, that is all that really counts so I advised my client accordingly.

Facts, Opinion and Hearsay

The investigator's job is to reveal the truth from a disorganized collection of facts, appearances, opinions and theories. Investigations turn up two kinds of information, physical evidence and verbal evidence, both of which are equally capable of being erroneous or true. Either we have a thing to *show* in court, or something to *tell*.

So what is a fact? The dictionary defines it as *an occurrence, quality or relation the quality of which is manifest in experience or may be inferred with certainty.*

If that definition sounds somewhat vague, consider that the term *forensic*, which is often used as a label for physical investigation work, including our own, has a similar definition; 1. [B]elonging to the courts of judicature or to public discussion and debate 2: used in legal proceeding or public discussions 3: the art and study of argumentative discourse; *broadly*: argumentative, rhetorical."

The key term here is *inferred with certainty.* As stated earlier, all human beings are biased to one degree or another, and for that reason what is fact to one, may be fiction to another. It is hard to get two people to agree on much of anything, yet it is the role of the courts to seek agreement through a jury. Thus, it is of some less importance to the investigator what he believes are the facts of a case, than his ability to convince others that his view of truth is the correct view. So what is the "correct view"? It is that which a majority of people (jurors) can be persuaded to believe.

Because evidence often consists of the statements of witnesses to a variety of related events, the investigator often finds himself in the position of having to pass judgement on the statements of witnesses. Police investigators often prefer to deal with physical over verbal evidence due to ease with which human observation is clouded by personal or physical perspective. Good homicide investigators become good precisely because they have learned to become good judges of character; they know how to discern whether a witnesses statements are accurate through the interrogation process that can reveal many clues about the witness himself. It is important to learn to develop these skills if for no other reason that being a good judge of character can save a lot of time and needless trouble when one comes to question whether a witnesses statements are accurate. In our line of work we do not often encounter lying witnesses, but do often encounter witnesses who's perspective is simply erroneous.

Opinion is not fact, but that does not necessarily preclude it from being evidence. Opinions of experts are admissible in court because, when coming from an expert, they are presumed to constitute a reasonable deduction based upon superior knowledge. There are two types of opinions, informed and uninformed. Anyone can have an opinion about anything without any knowledge whatsoever, which clearly renders the opinion next to worthless. Conversely, an opinion that is based on substantial understanding and knowledge of facts has demonstrable value, a reality that courts recognize.

In our work it is necessary to take great care to separate facts from opinions since the later are deduced from the former. Experienced investigators tell us that it is very easy to get carried away by our own opinions, especially when we allow a motivation to achieve a desired end to influence our work.

The way to avoid allowing opinions or bias from influencing our work is to recognize opinions for what they are, and then to keep them rigorously separated from fact. During the course of investigations we often develop hunches or theories, which are basically the same thing as opinions: informed judgments not yet supported by demonstrable facts. Hunches are useful tools so long as they are not so closely held as to overshadow facts as they unfold. It is a fairly easy thing to fall into a trap of developing a hunch, and then setting out to prove it. This is something that happens in homicide investigations, and with over-eager prosecutors fairly often and must be rigorously guarded against. The investigator avoids this by also seeking evidence that may disprove his hunch or theory. The difficult part is to hold in mind the idea of doing both; that is, both proving and disproving our theories by playing devil's advocate. There is a natural inclination to seize on the first ideas that come to mind (even when based on apparent evidence) and to attempt to prove that idea and get it over with quickly, without looking further for other possibilities. We will examine this in further detail later on.

Hearsay is second-hand information. As such, it is subject to misinterpretation and errors of all sorts, and is therefore not directly admissible as evidence in court. For example, it is hearsay when a witness informs the investigator of something that another person has told him, the witness. Hearsay is not worthless, for it may lead to a revelation of fact, but hearsay needs to be recognized for what it is and not misinterpreted as fact. Hearsay may be admissible as evidence in support of other facts. Example: when there are numerous witnesses who all report that a person said the same thing to him. Here, the veracity of hearsay is modified by the number of persons reporting the same thing, lending greater credibility to hearsay, to the point where it becomes nearly the same thing as a direct statement from the person who initiated the hearsay. Hearsay helped convict a member of the Kennedy clan accused of murder simply because the number of persons reporting the hearsay was large.

Many people have an unfavorable view of the legal system and especially jury trials. But as Churchill said about democracy, it's the best of a lot of bad choices. The functioning of the court system is deeply flawed, yet it is unlikely that anything better can be devised. One reason we have such a negative view stems from the fact that we hear about verdicts but are almost never given the full facts as to how that verdict was derived. Were we sitting on that jury, we might have a very different opinion indeed. The nature of our viewpoint of the legal system is rather like viewing it through a keyhole until such time as we have obtain a wider point of view.

Raw and Refined

Evidence eventually falls into one of two categories, good and bad, raw or refined. All investigations produce evidence, usually reams of it. But that evidence is never presented to a jury in its unrefined state. Before the case is presented to the prosecutor, it is reviewed by a supervisor and in many cases the prosecutor is consulted along the way, for it is ultimately the prosecutor who is the end user. Again, it should be pointed out that it is valuable to make the comparison to criminal cases because it is here where we get a glimpse of higher standards that could possibly be brought to bear in our work.

The marine investigator is usually his own supervisor and he does not have a prosecutor looking over his shoulder. Remember that the end user, our client, is likely to be far less knowledgeable than we are, so we need to take extra precautions that what we present as good evidence really is. I use the terms raw and refined to signify differences between evidence that has been analyzed and that which hasn't. As mentioned elsewhere, time has a tendency to put things in their proper perspective, and since analysis takes time, analysis serves a similar function.

Long periods of time will usually elapse between the time an investigation is completed and the case comes up in litigation — usually measured in years. Every seasoned investigator can relate how many times he has reviewed his own work years later and cringed at what he saw. Every mistake and error sticks out like a sore thumb with the passage of time. Why is that? Because the passage of time removes all emotional involvement in the issue and he is literally seeing the case with "new eyes." The sooner you understand this and come to grips with it, the sooner you'll cease being disappointed by your earlier work. Believe me, it happens to everyone, and it will happen you, if it hasn't already.

The cliché that "two minds are better than one," provides an alternative to time. If different witnesses seem to see things differently, so will investigators. All too often we lose sight of the forest for all the trees because we're too close to the facts, too deeply involved. Running the evidence by someone who is not involved is likely to either yield a different perspective or confirm our thinking. It's always a good idea to run difficult cases by a knowledgeable colleague.

As mentioned earlier, I always make it a point to analyze my own evidence for my client, its strength and weaknesses. I started doing this after a trial case in which it became apparent that I had unconsciously mislead my client into thinking evidence was stronger than it really was. Of course, analyzing the strength of evidence is not done in writing, but over the phone. Making a habit of this means that I have increasingly acquired the ability to critique my own work more objectively, reviewing how I believe my case would stand before a jury based on past experience.

Paper Trails

The vast majority of marine investigations focus mainly on the vessel, with occasional forays into the behavior of persons. However, there are certain types of casualties in which the behavior of persons is predominant. These include fraud, personal injury, collision and theft, where paper trials are a major source of evidence.

As we know all to well, it is impossible to go through daily life without leaving a major paper trail. Every time we buy something, a paper document or at least a computer entry, and probably both, is generated. People send and receive postal and email, purchase things with credit cards and so on. Then there are the innumerable government agencies that require licensing, registrations and whatnot. We can't make a simple phone call without leaving a record. Everywhere we turn there is paper, paper, paper and this paper becomes fertile ground for obtaining useful evidence.

Certainly many of these records are not obtainable by a private investigator (such as telephone, banking, credit card), but with a bit of enterprise you'd be surprised at how much of it is. Of course, the only evidence that is of value to us is that which is legally obtained, so what's legal, or rather not legal? Inadmissible evidence consists of that which is stolen, or taken without permission or obtained deceptively, bearing in mind that one has to be able to account for how one came in possession of it.

Is inadmissible evidence useless? Definitely not, because though not admissible, it is possible that it can lead us to other evidence that is admissible, or to obtain it by admissible means. However, some types of evidence aren't admissible under any circumstances.

What about buying evidence, which might also be called bribery? Technically, that will depend upon whether the information obtained is legally protected. There is certainly nothing wrong with paying someone for legal information. Giving money to a bank employee for financial records is obviously not legal. What about slipping $20 to a store employee for sales records? Is that bribery? Technically, if the employee is selling information that is not rightfully his to sell, that would be bribery, but that technical issue is between the employee and his employer and is probably not illegal, just unethical. There is no issue at all if the store is unopposed to giving out this information. The fact that so much information is available on the Internet about anyone has made the privacy issue almost irrelevant.

Here's one way to get around the bribery problem. In a fatality case in which the victim was a passenger in a boat found to be filled with beer cans, it was clear that the mere presence of beer cans is not proof that the operator drank all that beer. Part of a cash register receipt which detailed that a case of beer was purchased was found in a crumpled bag, but the top part was torn off where the name of the store and date should have been. Therefore, I began canvassing all the convenience stores in the vicinity. All but the one closest to the marina where the boat was kept was willing to search their records for me, without success. But the closest store, which was most likely, had a clerk who was reluctant, and whose owner was never around. I went back to that store four times, almost pleading with guy to check his register tapes for me. A money bribe finally turned the trick and I got a match. I did not ask for a paper copy, only the knowledge that the record existed. The fact that we now knew where the beer was sold was then used to issue a subpoena to obtain the record legally wherein it was proved that the beer was purchased only four hours prior to the accident.

So what about Internet information? Yes, there is a lot available if one knows how to obtain it, but the fact is that much of it is not easy to locate or to obtain, plus it's very time consuming to get it. There are however, outfits that specialize in obtaining such information which are easily located on the Internet. Be careful though, there are a lot of Charlatans out there. Credit histories can be obtained if you have the individual's social security number, but even without it credit histories can be had for a price from outfits that specialize in obtaining them with only a name and address. When contemplating working with this kind of information it's best to consult with an attorney. There's no point in wasting your time on something that can't be used. Remember, neither an insurer nor an attorney will not want to make a decision or take an action based in part or in whole on dubious evidence.

For example, I once suspected that a person was a con artist based solely on my perception that this person was much too knowledgeable about insurance claims process and coverages. I therefore initiated a personal history trace which provided information that this individual had used over a dozen different addresses in five years as his legal residence. This was way out of line for normal behavior and became the basis for performing a serious background investigation that turned up a substantial criminal record.

Many states now make auto and boat titles and registrations a matter of public record. Others like California, do not and only police officers have access to boat titling. In cases of total loss, particularly with non recovered theft or loss of vessel, the owners title and registration should be obtained and checked against the state records. My home state, Florida will, for a fee, provide a complete title history going as far back as when the vessel was first titled in the state. Proof of numerous fraudulent claims was obtained by this simple method. Be alert to titles and registrations that have been altered, examining them carefully for erasures and type-overs, color photocopying and so on. This is why we never accept copies in place of originals.

The U.S. Department of Transportation, Coast Guard runs the federal documentation program. The usefulness of this is that ownership and lien records are maintained for the life of the vessel and then some. This is available as a "document abstract" for a low fee. I use a documentation service to obtain these for me so as to avoid dealing with the bureaucracy myself.

File Records

When it comes to litigation, our files and everything in them, as well as any other thing in our possession that pertains to the case, is evidence. Note that there is no such thing as "potential" evidence. It either is or isn't. The word "potential" can only relate to whether the evidence is used or not. It probably wouldn't occur to most of us that our phone records, meaning the itemized case phone billing to the client, may be used as evidence in a case. This has happened several times when a subject of investigation alleged that I had phone conversations that I never had. Comparing his long distance phone bill with my phone bill proved the point that the call never happened.

In the event of local phone calls, the only thing to rely on is your time record. It is extremely important to record every single phone call, no matter how mundane it seems at the moment, for the chances of those calls becoming very important is high. Get in the habit of doing this with every job, not just those that appear at the moment to be troublesome. We never know when a case is going to erupt into something more volatile.

If a case may end up as a criminal case (the police become involved), or appears headed for litigation, it's a good idea to make a copy of your business phone bill and keep it in the file in case it is needed.

Receipts

There is almost no valid excuse for a well-to-do boat owner not being able to provide a proof of purchase or transaction. If they don't save receipts — which is unlikely — then they will surely have a credit card service that provides a detailed break down of all their credit card spending. Rare is the person who does not retain these records for tax reasons. For anyone to claim that they paid substantial amounts of cash with no saved receipt is simply implausible and this is probably a dead giveaway that something is not right.

Documenting Evidence

The most common failure of evidence handling is the failure to document the original location from which the evidence was obtained. This usually means photographing evidence before it is picked up or moved. While this is not always relevant, it is just good practice to get in the habit of always photographing a piece before it is moved. Be alert to those instances when it is necessary to photograph an object from more than one angle in order to reveal all the details of it.

It is very often the case that much of the analytical work of an investigation is later done from photos. This is due to the fact that we can only remain on the scene for a limited amount of time in comparison to the gross amount of analysis that we need to perform. It follows then, that the taking of a sufficient number of quality photos is indispensable, and to properly reveal the subject, we need to take photos from multiple angles.

Evidence Handling For Labs

The rules for evidence handling are simple and commonsensical. Small pieces should be placed in heavy plastic bags and marked with time, date and file or vessel name. It is not often that we deal with trace evidence, but if you do be sure that it does not become contaminated.

Before sending off to a lab you need to resolve the issue of whether the evidence will be destroyed, either partly or in whole, and how that will affect others. Partial destruction is usually not a problem, but complete destruction may cause problems if litigated. Therefore, one should secure agreement from the other parties whenever possible. If you cannot get agreement, you don't have to yield to objections if objections are unfounded. See to it that the piece is thoroughly and properly photographed. Where micro evidence is involved, the lab will be able to do this for you, but be sure to specify in your purchase order that you need before and after macro and micro photos.

Whenever evidence is collected and is to be sent to a lab, certain procedures should be followed. More evidence is lost that is in the custody of others than for any other reason, and that includes labs. The reason for this is usually because it was inadequately labeled and subsequently got misplaced or identified as junk and discarded since most evidence is junk in most people's eyes. Further, pieces of evidence can be difficult to affix labels to.

However it is labeled, we should make sure that the label does not in any way alter the evidence. You don't want to affix tape to something that will be subject to a gas chromatograph since the tape glue can alter the results. Whenever possible, try to use heavy tags with attachment wires, and also place it into heavy polyvinyl bags onto which identification is placed with permanent marker. Be sure not to use the erasable type!

Whenever possible personally deliver the evidence to the lab and make sure they log it in. If the lab knows their business they will log it in immediately; if they don't, you have reason to question the lab's competence. The log entry should contain the time, date, your name and a brief description of what the piece is.

The evidence should be accompanied by a purchase order on your letter head with the same information plus the description of analysis requested. Make your explanation as lengthy as possible. Your purchase order should also specify a completion date that you should have obtained agreement to in advance of delivery.

When the analysis is complete, do not leave it in the custody of the lab for it is too easy for it to become lost. As an investigator, you should make provision for safe storage of evidence on your own premises. Beware of the problem of others considering it to be junk and throwing it away; do not entrust others to safeguard it.

Evidence Handling and Storage

Whenever possible, the investigator is urged to take physical possession of evidence. To most people our evidence is just junk. This has proved to be a constant problem in this line of work that evidence is frequently discarded or lost by those in possession of it. Therefore, it is best to take possession of it and store it in a safe place after properly labeling it. Don't trust boat yards, engine repairers to retain and store evidence. Evidence may have to be retained for years, particularly in serious cases. The time of retention needs to take into consideration the statute of limitations for filing a law suit. Of course, if a suit is already filed, the evidence must be retained until the suit is resolved.

I used to keep evidence in my garage until it accumulated to such a large amount that I had to rent a small storage space since some of this evidence consisted of rather large parts like complete steering systems and engine parts. Be sure to tag the part in such a way that the identifier won't get lost or obliterated.

The investigator not only needs to know and follow proper rules of evidence, but also must be aware of insurance law when involved with claims work. He must understand the rights of the insurer as well as the insured. Evidentiary rules govern the collection, handling and storing of evidence. While it is true that in civil cases evidence handling is not as critical as in criminal cases, it is always wise to adhere to the basic rules of evidence as it applies to those who work with and handle it. When you deal with litigation, anything can happen.

- The loss scene should be treated with a degree of care similar to a crime scene so as to prevent alteration or loss of evidence.

- Evidence must be obtained legally. The property of others cannot be taken without permission. When in doubt about this, discuss it with an attorney.

- Evidence must be stored safely and not in any way altered. Do not clean evidence; it is dirty, it must remain that way.

- Destructive testing should not be conducted without the knowledge and participation of opposing parties.

- The chain of custody of evidence should be established in a provable manner. When turning evidence over to another person, always obtain a dated receipt, making sure to describe the items fully.

A fundamental rule of law establishes that one person does not have the right to deprive another person of his rights. This holds for evidence in civil cases as well. Both parties have the same right to evidence.

The alteration of evidence can occur in a variety of ways and sometimes with the best of intentions. A plaintiff lost his case against an insurer when his investigator "cleaned" the evidence which happened to be plumbing from the head system. Unfortunately for him, dirt or sludge on the parts was a critical aspect of the evidence, and it's removal destroyed his case.

What Is Not Evidence

That which does not constitute real evidence is anything that is of doubtful origin, from improperly handled or obtained physical evidence to documents to witness statements. Physical evidence taken from an owner without permission, when in fact it was obtained by theft, is not evidence that can be used. There is a fine line to this subject, so be sure to use common sense. Never just take anything that is obviously the property of others.

Photo copies are not suitable replacements for original documents unless such copies can be certified as true and correct. The best way to certify them is to check for yourself. When an insured submits copies, demand to see the originals and check the copies against them.

Hearsay is not normally evidence; second hand accounts should never be relied upon. Hearsay is second hand, indirect accounting of what another person has said, coming from a person who purports to have heard it firsthand. The only way hearsay can be used is as means of getting to the source of the original words, or when it can be corroborated.

Circumstantial evidence is only evidence when there is a preponderance of it. That is, more than one circumstance that points toward a reasonable conclusion. The magic number is three separate circumstances that all point in the same direction.

Documents received by fax. It is pathetically easy to alter documents and then fax them because fax quality is too poor to reveal poorly made alterations. Never accept faxes as substitutes for original copies as proof of anything.

Boat Owner Discovers Cause

Here's an instance where evidence may not be what it is purported to be. Typical case: A boat sinks, is refloated and then the loss is reported. In the meantime, the owner has discovered the cause and presents the investigator with the evidence of the cause. *Here Mr. Investigator, I've done your job for you.* The investigator has not had the opportunity to see the evidence in its original state. Note here that the source of evidence is the same as the person making the claim, thus the integrity of evidence is in question since the owner is not a disinterested party. In this case, the source of the evidence is of greater import than the so-called evidence. And, if he has witnesses for this evidence, these are likely to be friends or associates or service providers who also have cause to be biased. In such a case the evidence is said to be compromised and possibly tampered with or misrepresented.

This situation presents a chain of custody issue casting doubt on the reliability of such evidence. The investigator should keep this point in mind whenever he is on the defense side of a case.

Working the Defense Side

Working the defense side of a case requires somewhat different tactics than the plaintiff side. On the defense side we are usually a late comer to the case and following behind an original investigator, if not by weeks or months, then by a few days at least. We therefore do not know what evidence has been accumulated by the other party. To do our job effectively, we need to find out as soon as possible.

Although the other side must ultimately, at some point, disclose what evidence they have when litigation arises, they may be reluctant to do so before they are legally required, which puts us at an acute disadvantage. Here the best approach is probably not to make a direct request for their evidence, but to use the Columbo technique of frequent engagement and persistent questioning of more minor issues while hoping that they will divulge the big ones. In other words, go at them indirectly and obliquely. Contact them frequently about small things and look for opportunities to expand the conversation. In one case, I made eleven phone calls to an opposing investigator, each one with trumped up questions until I was satisfied that the man had told me far more than he had intended, even though he resisted telling me anything initially. I simply wore down his resolve by being persistent, friendly and appearing rather ignorant.

When doing a follow-on investigation, when the other side has physical evidence in their possession, one should always be searching for flaws in the way evidence was obtained, held and handled. Whenever dealing with other investigators, don't attempt to impress them with how smart you are. Again, use the Columbo technique and play dumb because dumbness causes defensive people to loosen their guard, while being smart causes them to be more reserved. Don't overdo the dumbness lest it become an obvious ruse. Perhaps a better word than "dumb" is unknowing; never reveal what you know or your experience. Act inexperienced.

Even if you've handled this type of case a dozen times before, see if you can't draw them out by asking questions you already know the answer to. Nearly everyone likes to demonstrate how smart they are and this vulnerability can be exploited. With a bit of planning and experience at this sort of thing one finds that it becomes quite easy to get people to discuss things that they know they shouldn't.

Other Investigation Reports

One of the best sources of impeachable evidence is the work of other investigators, whose work is so often of dubious quality that it can provide a wealth of ammunition for your side to impeach that investigator's work. The work of other experts bears long and careful study for clues that may reveal leads to other evidentiary sources. Often the most valuable evidence from other investigation reports is not what they say directly, but what they don't say. Look for obvious omissions of points that should be there. Read between the lines. Do the dates fit, are there obvious gaps and omissions?

In a recent case, repeated and careful review of an investigator's report gave rise to suspicion that the investigator did not do what his report suggested he did, at the time it suggests he did it. The tip-off was the odd use of language in which the investigator avoided specifically stating that he personally did something, even though he was the only one involved. The reporter strangely failed to state how evidence was obtained; dates of various events were lacking. It didn't take much more investigation to determine that this investigator did not attend the vessel at the times he said he did and, in fact, did not personally obtain any of the evidence in his possession. It turned out that his "evidence" was provided to him by his client.

It was further revealed that this investigator had a conflict in his schedule and was unable to attend at the time he should have, so he faked it. Thus, the investigator's report itself contained the tip-off that ended up discrediting both the investigation and the "evidence" which was not evidence at all. It's truly amazing what can be gleaned from the careful study of documents.

A good investigator is a cynic; he doubts everything until the veracity is proven.

Chapter 4

Marine Insurance and Issues of Law

While this chapter addresses issues involving marine investigators in the United States, investigators working in other Western nations will find that their national laws are, if not alike, then effectively similar, particularly those of English speaking nations. Insurance contracts are also more alike than different throughout the world. This is because marine insurance originated in England, spread to the U.S., and thence worldwide with only modifications rather than any major changes in principle taking place. In any event, readers from any nation will find that the U.S. legal rules outlined herein will provide a solid basis for ethical conduct just about anywhere. English, U.S., and Canadian law respecting Admiralty and insurance is remarkably similar.

The Federal courts have held, and repeatedly upheld, the precept that the intent of Article III, Section ii of the US Constitution was to establish a uniform set of rules and body of law governing conveyance over the navigable waters of the U.S. At the time the Constitution was created, there was no such thing as pleasure craft or non commercial activities significantly involving navigable waters, so despite the fact that maritime activity was almost exclusively commercial activity, it later came to be recognized that other activities could and would infringe upon navigation. It is for this reason that the courts have been willing to extend Admiralty jurisdiction over just about anything that touches on navigation.

The problem that we have in this work is that the nature of our work can fall under the jurisdiction of any court; our work can be the subject of either general common law or Admiralty, and this includes issues involving marine insurance contracts. And needless to say, the conclusions of a local or state court are apt to be quite different from those of a federal court functioning under Admiralty rules. However, where marine cases are initially filed is a matter of choice for the plaintiff, and one for the defendant as well since either has the right to claim maritime jurisdiction. If neither does, then the case will remain in the original lower court.

In this chapter we will consider the issues of marine insurance contracts and the laws that govern them, as well as the body of law that governs casualties and liability. These jurisdictions and bodies of law often overlap and come into conflict. Fortunately, that doesn't concern the investigator much since his role is not to sort it all out, but simply be conversant with how the various principles of law bear on our work.

The Role of the Marine Expert

Investigator, adjuster, surveyor, appraiser — these are four words that may denote four separate disciplines that may be all rolled up into one, so if the insured seems a bit confused about what your role is, don't be surprised. Moreover, it is reasonable to ask whether there isn't a conflict of interest here and is it fair that a person who investigates the cause of loss also appraises damage and adjusts the claim. The answer is yes to both due to the fact that were there a need to hire three or four separate individuals, the cost would drive the price of insurance up unnecessarily. If a news reporter can cover the news without bias while also being a political commentator, then an investigator or appraiser can adjust a claim or vice versa without bias.

This is tempered by the fact that, for a casualty investigator, a sound knowledge of basic insurance and legal principles is essential to conduct effective investigations. The emphasis here is on the word "effective" for there are two sides to the view that investigators should be knowledgeable of legal as well as insurance contract issues. The argument for the investigator being more rather than less knowledgeable of law is based on the conclusion that absent a basic knowledge of law, the investigator is unaware of the issues that may arise, and therefore will be unable to address them. If one is not aware of critical questions that need answering, the likelihood of obtaining those answers is lessened. In point of fact, surveyor and investigative societies routinely schedule lectures and seminars addressing legal and insurance issues. If my view is incorrect, then one has to wonder why so many admiralty lawyers are willing to give lectures to surveyors if they didn't think it was important for them to have this knowledge?

The argument against the surveyor/investigator being educated about law and insurance is that such knowledge will introduce bias into his findings. It would seem, however, that one who is prone to bias is going to be biased with or without a particular knowledge of insurance and law so this argument is not credible. The argument also stems from some old-line marine claims adjusters who don't particularly like the idea of any surveyor telling them what they view as their exclusive domain. We used to hear these comments decades ago from claimsmen, though I can't say I've heard it recently. Even so, there are surveyors who still advance this notion in lectures.

Most importantly, a marine investigator could not function effectively without this specialized knowledge, any more than a homicide detective could build an effective murder case without knowledge of law. But far and away the most important reason is to avoid inadvertently through ignorance bringing a lawsuit down the head of his client or himself. If one does not know how the law proscribes his actions, it's rather hard to comply.

Many insurance companies hire independent insurance adjusters to handle claims on their behalf simply because they do not have claims offices available everywhere. Independent adjusters, as with company employed adjusters, not only adjust claims, but also perform investigations in order to determine whether a loss is covered. The overall process of claims work involves, investigation, determination of cause of loss, assessing loss and damage, obtaining repair estimates and working out the final settlement.

An insurance policy is a contract to provide indemnification for certain casualties or losses of property insured, or for liabilities incurred by the insured. When an insurer hires an investigator, the basis of that investigation is to determine whether the casualty is covered by the contract. And because a contract cannot possibly detail every type of event that may occur, policies are written in general language. Obviously, then, this leaves much open to interpretation and judgement that ultimately hinge on the results of an investigation. It also provides the basis for much dispute between insurer and insured, a battle into the middle of which the investigator dares to enter.

The investigation of claims routinely necessitates the taking of a statement at least from the insured, and often other witnesses. It is in this area where the unlicensed investigator can run into trouble since the laws of some states require that anyone who investigates, takes statements, assesses damage and makes estimates be licensed as an insurance adjuster. The reader should also be aware that the insurance laws of the various states tend to change rather frequently, so one should keep up to date on whether or not an investigator currently requires a license. The problem of not being licensed is simple, dramatic and costly: it will invariably scuttle a defense case by virtue of the fact that illegally obtained evidence is not admissible, may result in fines, loss of face and usually the client.

It is necessary to explain all this to the reader because, unless a surveyor is also a licensed adjuster, he is likely to have little familiarity or understanding of these issues, and also because litigation often arises over insurance claims. If you are working outside the U.S. in another nation, or are a resident of another nation, you still need to check on the legal requirements of working wherever you are. The laws of the various states have substantial differences on the subject of investigations and licensing.

It is strongly recommended that investigators obtain a copy of and thoroughly review the insurance codes of the state(s) that he works in. Many states now have their statutes posted on the Internet so that they are easily obtained and we no longer have to pay a lot of money for statute books that quickly become obsolete.

Unfair Claims Practices Laws

Numerous states have Unfair Trade Practices laws generally or Unfair Claims Practices or "Bad Faith" statutes that specifically regulate the conduct of those involved with insurance claims. These statutes are generally applicable to anyone engaged by an insurer for just about any purpose involving a claim.

The surveyor should be aware that in some states the Unfair Claims Practices Act are applicable to both first and third party claims. First party, of course, means the insured; third parties are anyone who shares in the rights or benefits of the insured or the policy, or makes a claim against the insured, and are known as claimants. Common examples would be mortgage holders and any other to whom the insured may be liable. Claimants typically involve the liability portion of the marine insurance contract. What this means to the surveyor is that bad faith claims could arise from unexpected directions such as a non insured. Generally speaking, the surveyor should handle all communications and/or contacts from anyone claiming interest in the casualty in the same manner as an insured. Immediately report to the claims handler any such claim.

Bad faith statutes are the most common basis for suits against insurers, the preponderance of which are frivolous. But there is a lesson to be learned from this fact, which should be taken as a warning as to just how easy it is to end up facing a summons since more often than not the adjuster, surveyor and investigator *will be named as a codefendant*. Errors and mistakes in this regard can therefore become very costly.

This leads us to the question of who is an insured, for the answer is not always as obvious as it seems. It includes, of course, the individual, corporation or other entity named on the policy as such. But the policy will likely contain an additional definition of who constitutes an insured. These definitions vary with different types of insurance such as homeowners and auto. Marine or yacht policies are most often restricted to the named insured although laws may supercede the insurer's intent. Immediate family members may also be unnamed insureds. Another common example is mortgage holders who may actually hold title to the vessel or have collateral rights. Yacht policies typically have a *loss payee* clause which excludes the mortgagor as an assured[1]. A loss payee is not an insured and only has rights to claims payment if such is made. The loss payee does not have to be treated as an additional insured, but an insurer does have the obligation to issue claims checks in the name of both parties. Other policies may include the mortgagor as an additional insured, and it is in this later instance where the investigator/surveyor has to be very careful, for the additional insured has the same rights as the primary insured. In this case the lien holder must be treated as an additional insured. A reservation of rights letter issued to the insured must also be issued to the lien holder. The same applies to any investigation notices that may be issued to "parties of interest". Your assignment form should have a blank for the lien holder or loss payee. The investigator will need this information even if he isn't adjusting the loss for a variety of reasons.

While the surveyor may feel that none of this applies to him, since he has not been hired as the insurance company's claims representative, other persons may not see it that way. For example, when third party liability claimants are involved, the investigator will likely be in contract with such persons who will always view the investigator as the insurance company representative. When contacting non-insured claimants it is very important that the investigator specifically explain his limited role and provide the claimant with the proper contact information, usually the individual who assigned him the case.

Unfortunately, surveyors are often named in law suits as well as the insurance company in bad faith claims. While one cannot avoid being named in such suits, one can do much to ensure that the charges against him not be substantiated. Professional investigators will find it necessary to document all important communications by backing them up in writing. This means sending letters, lots of them. From confirming conversations, putting persons on notice, to documenting the chain of evidence, written communications are a part of the professional investigator's function.

When surveyors are enjoined, the chances for summary judgement and dismissal are small. The odds are that the trial judge will allow the suit to go forth regardless of apparent merit. Therefore, it's a good idea to address this issue with the client in advance as to whether or not they're willing to include you in their defense. Otherwise, the surveyor will be paying those costs himself. In actual practice, insurers will usually provide a defense (but not indemnification) so long as the investigator's interest does not conflict with their defense. An example would be when an insurer is accused of bad faith through the actions of the investigator and both are jointly named. But, if both are sued but for different reasons – say the insurer for bad faith, but the investigator for denial of rights, then the insurer would not provide a defense because they have an opposing interest. Moreover, it will not be the insurer who makes such decisions but his attorney. This is by far the most important reason why a surveyor needs to have a solid understanding of the law – his own self-protection.

It is sometimes the case that a claims manager assigning a case to a surveyor in another state is unaware of the laws of that state, as when one is working in a two or three state area. This is one of the more common reasons why bad faith claims arise, namely ignorance of the law. The surveyor may become implicated when the insured attempts to communicate with the company through him, whether verbally or in writing and that communication does not reach the company in whole or in part.

The following are pertinent provisions of many Unfair Claims Practices Statutes that could affect the investigator:

- Knowingly misrepresents to claimants and insured relevant facts of policy provisions.

- Failing to acknowledge with reasonable promptness pertinent communications with respect to claims arising under its policies.

- Failure to conduct a reasonable investigation.

- Failure to conduct a timely investigation.

- Taking any action that could be construed to damage the insured's rights.

Knowingly misrepresents to claimants and insured relevant facts of policy provisions.

It is a common rule amongst experienced surveyors and investigators that he or she never makes comments to an insured or claimant concerning the insurance coverage. Whenever asked, the question is referred back to the claims adjuster. The reason for this is that anything said by the investigator can be held as binding on the insurer under the doctrine of estoppel. See page 95. Therefore, the wise investigator defers all questions concerning the insurance coverage to the appropriate claims representative.

Failing to acknowledge with reasonable promptness pertinent communications with respect to claims arising under its policies.

Because of the risk of being construed as an agent of the company, all communications received from an insured or claimant must be promptly forwarded to the claims representative and to follow up to ensure that such was received.

Failure to conduct a reasonable investigation.

Statutes that mandate reasonable investigations benefit both insurer and insured. When it is anticipated that a claim may not be covered, it becomes increasingly important to consider whether the investigation has been thoroughly and objectively carried out. Bear in mind that in the event a claim is declined, litigation becomes very likely. In that case, the investigator will have at least one lawyer and perhaps several other experts evaluating his work, asking the question of whether the investigation was reasonably conducted. "Reasonable" means that which most professional investigators would consider as necessary and appropriate. But it can also mean a reference to common sense, as when some line of inquiry obviously needs to be done in order to answer an obvious question. In other words, all loose ends need to be tied up. If the investigator falls short, he personally runs the risk of being accused of having caused the insured or claimant monetary harm. Note here that the standard is predominately set by your peers, a standard that one should be completely aware of and always strive to attain or exceed.

A "reasonable investigation" may run hard up against the issue of cost. Costly laboratory analysis of evidence is often necessary but claims representatives may be reluctant to foot the bill. In such cases, the investigator is the one who should make the decision whether such analysis is reasonable and prudent; is this the sort of thing that is commonly done? If so, he should try to convince the claims representative of that necessity and always make such recommendation in reports.

At the opposite end of the stick lies the problem of excessive investigation, wherein it appears that the insurer is on a fishing expedition searching for any excuse to deny the claim. Once again, taking care that the scope of the investigation falls within what can be described as the professional standard will keep us out of trouble. This is where "reasonable investigation" statutes have a bearing.

Failure to conduct a timely investigation.

Conducting a timely investigation has several implications. The first is that the investigation should be started promptly, and then be completed within the time period that is often mandated by state law. Typically, the insurer is required to answer a claim within sixty or ninety days. It is the investigator's responsibility to know if and when such statutes apply in his state, or any state in which he is working.

Investigations often end up taking longer than expected. When that is the case, the insured should then be advised of this fact in writing, giving the reason why it is taking longer. While the investigator is not the one to write such letters, it is best to bring up the issue with the insurer to be certain that it gets done, and that the insurer understands the reason why. Note that failure to advise the insured occasionally ends up with the investigator being enjoined in a suit against the insurer, so the point here is to avoid this problem by making sure that all bases are covered.

Taking any action that could be construed to damage the insured's rights.

We should recognize that when people get into financial trouble, there is a tendency to lash out at anyone within striking range. Denial of the insured's rights are most often construed from allegations of libelous statements, estoppel issues or withholding evidence, such as removing evidence from the scene without the insured's knowledge, destructive testing of evidence and so on. Not only must the insured be informed of such actions, but when there are other announced parties of interest, these parties must also be informed. An announced party is any party that informs either the insured or insurer in writing of their prospective interest.

Independent Adjuster

While the surveyor may not have been assigned the role of company representative, unfortunately the insured is very likely to see him as just that, because most often the surveyor is the only person he sees and is sometimes his only direct contact, or at least the person with whom he has the most contact. If neither the surveyor nor the actual claims representative takes the time to explain this relationship to the insured, then one can bet that the insured will see the surveyor as the claims rep. In this case, it's easy to understand how trouble could arise if the surveyor does not understand his responsibilities under the law, which are many:

> Florida Code 626.855:"Independent adjuster" defined.—An "independent adjuster" is any person who is self-employed or is associated with or employed by an independent adjusting firm or other independent adjuster, and who undertakes on behalf of an insurer to ascertain and determine the amount of any claim, loss, or damage payable under an insurance contract or undertakes to effect settlement of such claim, loss,

or damage.

California, for example, under Section 14020-140445.k (2/03) permits:

> Any building contractor, engineer, technical expert, or other person who is engaged
> by an insurer or licensed adjuster to provide an expert or professional evaluation
> of the extent, cause or origin of damage to the insured property, but who does not
> otherwise participate in the process of adjusting claims. [Emphasis added]

While the California provision permits the marine surveyor to investigate the cause and
damage to physical property, it does not permit him to investigate persons or activity
of persons, or organizations or records of same. He is confined exclusively to providing
technical advice about the property itself as it pertains to cause of loss. The Florida
statute, however, defines as independent adjuster as *"any person who is self-employed . .
. and who undertakes on behalf of an insurer to ascertain and determine the amount of any
claim, loss or damage payable under an insurance contract . . . "* Clearly by this definition,
anyone assessing damages is defined as an adjuster. The issue of investigating cause or
origin is not directly addressed, yet determination of cause could well be considered
as instrumental to determining coverage. The Florida Department of Insurance has
been inconsistent with its definition of this issue, but surveyors in the past have been
prosecuted for adjusting without a license.

This is in contrast to the State of New York which specifically exempts the marine
investigator under paragraph (E) of the New York Insurance Code (2/03), reprinted
below:

> 1) The term "independent adjuster" means any person, firm, association or cor-
> poration who, or which, for money, commission or any other thing of value, acts in
> this state on behalf of an insurer in the work of investigating and adjusting claims
> arising under insurance contracts issued by such insurer and who performs such
> duties required by such insurer as are incidental to such claims and also includes
> any person who for compensation or anything of value investigates and adjusts
> claims on behalf of any independent adjuster, except that such term shall not
> include: [Emphasis added]
>
> > (A) any officer, director or regular salaried employee of an authorized insurer,
> > or any manager thereof, individual or corporate, or he manager, agent or general
> > agent of any department thereof, individual or corporate, or attorney in fact
> > of any reciprocal insurer or Lloyds underwriter, or marine underwriting
> > office, unless acting as an auto body repair estimator as defined in section (j) of
> > this section;
> >
> > (B) any adjustment bureau or association owned and maintained by insurers
> > to adjust or investigate losses, or any regular salaried employee or manager
> > thereof who devotes substantially all of his time to the business of such bureau
> > or association, unless acting as an auto body repair estimator as defined in
> > subsection (j) of this section;
> >
> > (C) any licensed agent of an authorized insurer who adjusts losses for such in
> > surer solely under policies issued through his or its agency, provided the agent

receives no compensation for such services in excess of fifty dollars per loss adjusted;

(D) any licensed attorney at law of this state;

(E) any average adjuster or adjuster of maritime losses;

(F) any agent or other representative of an insurer authorized to issue life and annuity contracts, provided he receives no compensation for such services.

Paragraph (E) would appear to exclude the investigator, but does it really? The definition of maritime is "of and relating to the sea, especially with respect to ships" a definition that does not necessarily include pleasure craft. Be sure to check with the insurance department of the state in which you propose to operate. Insurance codes are often written in a legalese that is difficult to comprehend. A call or letter to the insurance commissioners office may yield a quick answer.

It often happens that a surveyor is given jobs in other states, in which case it is wise to check with the insurance office of that state. The author has found that the licensed adjusters from one state are often given verbal permission to operate in that state with just a phone call.

Obtaining an Adjuster's License

For the surveyor who develops a good business in investigating marine losses, it is wise to obtain an independent adjuster's license. Such a license empowers the investigator with broad authority to perform extensive investigations, including background checks, obtaining financial reports, documents and records, as well as the taking of statements, both sworn under oath and otherwise. This is highly useful for big money losses where a lot is at stake, and where the best type of statement is taken with a court reporter. The author frequently uses court reporters for the reason that one avoids having to transcribe long statements, as well as permitting statements to be taken in much greater detail.

The easiest way to obtain an adjuster's license is through one of the courses offered by private tutors who roam around from city to city, state to state giving license exam preparation courses. These courses are designed to get you to pass the state exam whether you know anything about insurance or not. Most states require 240 hours of instruction which is accomplished in 6-8 week evening classes that somehow manage to cut the actual time considerably. Check with the claimsmen association office in large city for a referral.

Advice to the Client

In an ideal world the investigator would present his report to the claims supervisor and at that point his role would be terminated. Indeed, some marine surveyors advocate that surveyors should not provide the client with any advice about coverage but I do not agree with that view. In reality, many people who adjust marine claims do not posses adequate knowledge or experience in this specialized field. I've run across many instances where my client (the person who gave me my assignment and was supervising me) was a person who had been recently transferred from automobile or other property claims and was essentially unqualified to be doing what he or she was assigned to do. With marine claims this is something that occurs rather frequently.

In situations like this, if the investigator possesses knowledge superior to his client, then he ought to provide his client with the benefit of that knowledge. After all, it is the investigator that possesses the most direct, firsthand knowledge and his opinion is of value. For instance, there are always those cases where evidence is manifold but otherwise generally weak and may not be sustainable. We shouldn't assume that the client is capable of making this judgment. It is appropriate for the surveyor to offer this advice.

Then there will be many instances when the client is looking to the investigator for advice, even if they don't ask; the client may be embarrassed to say that they don't understand what the investigator is telling them. When it comes to court cases, complexity and highly technical situations are difficult for laymen to comprehend. Machinery damage claims are prime examples. Juries by nature are laymen and it has to be assumed that they will not understand esoteric complexity. If the investigator has trouble getting his client to understand his findings, think how much more difficult it will be selling that to a jury. Therefore, when dealing with weak or troublesome evidence, I always make it a point to tell the client how I feel about it. That does not mean that one should make comments about claim coverage, only how one feels about the strength of the evidence. If you feel that it is weak the client should know that, as it will surely influence his or her decision. The reality is that claims adjusters rely very heavily on their surveyor's advice.

Furthermore, many cases which were rightly denied were lost on court challenge simply because the evidence was complex and difficult for laymen to understand. Highly technical evidence is always a difficult sell to juries on insurance cases, but my experience is that when combined with complexity, that is, numerous mitigating circumstances, it's a killer. It has been rare in my experience for insurers to win court cases like these. If you have that kind of experience, it's wise to advise your client of your opinion. If you don't yet have that kind of experience, best to keep quiet.

The standard that I use for this is one of trying to visualize whether I could make a jury understand. Can I reduce my findings to simple enough terms that a non expert could readily understand? If not, then I feel that I've got a problem with my evidence if only an expert can understand it. This problem frequently crops up with machinery damage investigations.

Reasonable Doubt

A general principle of insurance is that reasonable doubt accrues to the benefit of the insured. That means that if there is reasonable doubt about the cause of loss, the claim should be covered unless the insurance contract is so worded as to preclude this. Conversely, the burden of proof is on the insured to (1) prove that the loss actually occurred, and (2) the monetary value of that loss.

The laws of many states include the provision that issues of doubt are to be decided in favor of the insured where the cause of loss is concerned. This does not apply to the issue of whether a loss has actually occurred. Named Peril policies, which are a more limited type of coverage, are designed to cover only very specific types of losses so that what constitutes reasonable doubt is much narrower. Because casualties often involve confusing or conflicting evidence, it is fairly common that causation cannot be stated with certainty. When that uncertainty involves a preponderance of evidence that is within bounds of the coverage provided, reasonable doubt accrues to the benefit of the insured.

Conversely, it is possible that reasonable doubt involves factors all of which fall outside the bounds of coverage; that is, say there are three possible causes, none of which would be covered were they established in fact as the cause. In this case, reasonable doubt does not accrue to the insured, and the claim can be rightly denied. This points up yet another reason why all investigations should be performed as completely as possible, namely that unproven potential causes can end up becoming a major bone of contention.

Insurance Policies and Concepts

Principles of Insurance

The fundamental principle of insurance is to indemnify the insured for the dollar value of his loss. The policy will state whether that is Replacement Cost or Actual Cash Value. Other principles are:

- The insured shall not profit by the insurance afforded.

- Pleasure craft policies are very different from commercial marine policies which are always *named peril* policies.

- Insurance covers stupidity and accidents caused by the insured. It does not cover recklessness or gross negligence which is legally construed as being willful or with knowledge of consequences.

- Insurance does not cover willful acts causing loss or damage or injury such as arson.

- Insurance does not indemnify an insured for the legal liabilities of others. An example is defective products and product liability of the insured property.

- Insurance does not cover inevitable events such as age, deterioration, breakage or mechanical breakdown. Whether the results of such events are covered is a matter of individual policies.

- Insurance polices establish the right of the insurer to investigate losses and demand all relevant documents in the possession of the insured.

- The insured is contractually required to cooperate with the insurer.

- The cost of salvage, wreck removal and disposal is normally covered unless contractually excluded.

- Resultant pollution from a casualty may or may not be covered. Insurers have been increasingly limiting this coverage as government levied penalties and costs have escalated.

Marine policies are divided into two major coverage sections, though nowadays many "plain language" policies are organized more like automobile policies. The first is the Hull coverage which means the boat and whatever is on it. Next is the P&I or Protection and Indemnity section which covers liabilities that the vessel or insured may encounter. This may include things such as gratuitous medical payments to passengers.

Hull coverage covers the vessel and its appurtenances, that equipment which is necessary for the operation of the vessel. It may also include stores and provisions but normally excludes the owners or passengers personal items. Sports equipment is not normally covered by the hull coverage, but only by special endorsement.

All Risk Yacht Policy

The purpose of the following discussion is to recognize how insurance coverage can and should direct the course of investigations so that the client may be able to correctly answer difficult questions. It is not for the purpose of determining coverage ourselves. If one is working for a boat owner with a claim against an insurance company, one will also need to be familiar with coverage issues.

"All risks" does not mean that the policy covers virtually everything. Instead, it covers everything *except* that which is specifically excluded. However, it is vastly broader than the Named Peril policy discussed further on. In the U.S. there is no standard, nor any requirement to have a standard contract and therefore from company to company, policies vary considerably. In reality, few companies actually write their own contracts from beginning to end, but rather modify existing contracts to suit their purposes which, in effect, renders most policies as being quite similar in scope but different in details. These are often literal "cut and paste jobs" that may be so ill-considered as to produce unfortunate results.

One of the most important distinctions is whether the insurer intends to cover loss and damage *resulting from* wear and tear and gradual deterioration. Some do and some don't, while for others the language is unclear or imprecise or just plain awkward. Consider this one:

> "We will not pay for loss and damage due and confined to wear and tear, gradual deterioration . . . "

"Due and confined to . . ." would mean that so long as the wear and tear results in larger damage such as sinking, the larger loss would be covered. In other words, if a corroded valve sinks the boat, the larger loss is covered, but if not, there is no coverage for a corroded valve:

> "We will pay for direct and accidental physical damage unless otherwise excluded."

Both the above clauses appear in the same policy. Deterioration is certainly not accidental and is traditionally defined as inherent vice. In this case deterioration is doubly excluded for a sinking loss. However, many policies use similar phrases differently which produce different results. For example, one policy provides coverage for "accidental physical loss" with the same deterioration clause quoted above. In this case, coverage should apply to a boat sunk by a corroded sea cock, but would not pay the replacement cost of the sea cock.

Note how the term "accidental" is imprecise. Is a sinking due to a deteriorated condition accidental when the owner isn't aware of the condition? Some courts would rule yes, while others would recognize the duty to maintain a sea worthy vessel.

Another policy uses a similar but modified clause:

> "We will pay for direct and accidental physical damage resulting from any external cause . . . "

This clause is much more precise in that it is excluding *internal causes* specifically. In no way would deterioration give rise to a covered loss. Okay, so what if the vessel is at sea and a corroded battery retaining device results in a battery going adrift that in turn starts a fire? In this case, fire is not the cause of loss but rather corrosion that resulted in a fire. Under the later coverage phrase, the loss is absolutely excluded because the cause is internal in nature.

Yet other policies - and there are quite a few of these - will cover loss resulting from deterioration but will not pay for the deteriorated component. Such policies are actually insuring the failure to maintain the vessel, a situation that runs contrary to the principle of insurance.

Agreed Valuation

All Risk policies preset the value of the vessel "as agreed" at the time of insuring. This raises the question about what happens when it appears that the insured value is far greater than what it is actually worth? When an insurance company agrees to the valuation, it is their responsibility to know what the vessel is worth, or to find out, which is one reason why underwriting surveys are requested. Unless that value or the nature of the vessel is fraudulently misrepresented by the insured, then the insurer is obligated to pay that amount.

ACV Policies

ACV means Actual Cash value, the liquid value at the time of loss, the same as with auto policies. This type of policy is almost always used for outboard motor powered boats and trailers. The essential feature of the ACV policy is that it is not an agreed valuation policy and is only insured to the current market value of the vessel and engines. The coverage is typically a bit narrower - particularly regarding engine damage - than all risk policies.

Seaworthiness Warranty

It is important that marine investigators understand the seaworthiness warranty and how it is applied in various cases so that they don't go chasing rats down black holes. This means conducting investigations and wasting time and money on useless issues. When we understand the elements of law combined with the specifics of policy coverage, then we have the opportunity to avoid making mistakes and wasting time.

It is a principle of marine insurance that the vessel owner warrants that the vessel will be maintained in seaworthy condition. This is undeniable because for the insurer to insure an unseaworthy vessel not only makes a loss inevitable, but jeopardizes the rights of all other insureds. It would be a denial of the moral hazard. This does not apply under virtually all circumstances.

Vessels by themselves, unaided, will not remain afloat by themselves indefinitely; it requires human intervention to keep them afloat and hence the necessity of the Seaworthiness Warranty. A vessel that is not seaworthy is inherently dangerous and poses a hazard not only to itself and owner, but to passengers and navigation generally. This is also known in insurance parlance as the moral hazard which insurance does not, or should not, insure against, such as someone deliberately allowing their boat to sink just to collect the insurance money. Note that the moral hazard involves active behavior as well as passive behavior.

However, unlike Jones Act and general liability issues, seaworthiness is mainly a contractual issue for pleasure craft. In Jones Act liability there is an absolute duty to maintain a seaworthy vessel. But insurance companies, by their contract language, may ignore the general doctrine, as we will see in a later discussion of coverage issues.

To get a better understanding of the purpose of the seaworthiness warranty, consider for a moment the insurer's position. While it has been argued that the insurer should know what he is insuring, it is not reasonable to suggest that the insurer can maintain his knowledge of seaworthiness indefinitely; that is the owner's job since he has a basic responsibility in law to maintain a seaworthy vessel. He is responsible and absolutely liable for any damage or injury that his vessel may cause to others under almost all circumstances except "Acts of God." Because he has this general duty at large, it is reasonable to extend this duty to the insurer, even if the insurer takes it upon himself to determine the condition of the vessel.

Conversely, if we take away the seaworthiness warranty, then what we have is the insurer indemnifying the vessel owner for negligent (as in neglectful) behavior; the motivation for owners to maintain their boats in seaworthy condition is thereby removed, or at least reduced, since anything that goes wrong can be simply dumped onto the insurance company which, ultimately, all purchasers of insurance will have to pay for.

In maritime law the seaworthiness warranty is implied and does not need to be stated; this is known as an *implied warranty*. The lower courts have not been consistent on this issue in application to pleasure craft issues where they tend to rely entirely on the insurance contract language.

Most marine insurance policies have an explicit seaworthiness warranty, that is, the warranty is written into the contract. However, contracts can void that implicitness by covering losses *resulting* from wear, tear and gradual deterioration, but *excluding* the deteriorated or worn part.

Unless someone has made a mistake, commercial vessels such as pleasure craft involved in business operations such as tour boats, diving boats, charter boats, and so on, are always insured under a named peril policy. Think of the named peril policy as being the commercial vessel policy whereas the all risk policy is for pleasure craft operated as pleasure craft. The named peril policy almost always has an explicitly stated seaworthiness warranty. The investigator should assume that the courts will uphold this warranty.

Seaworthiness is a constant issue in the marine investigator's work since sinking is a common casualty that we encounter, and sinking always raises the issue of whether the vessel was seaworthy. The following quotation from an appellate court ruling generally illustrates the doctrine:

> A claim based on unseaworthiness enforces the shipowner's "absolute duty to provide to every member of his crew" a vessel and appurtenances reasonably fit for their intended use.'" Hubbard v. Faros Fisheries, Inc., 626 F.2d 196, 199 (1st Cir. 1980) (quoting Mitchell, 362 U.S. at 550); McAleer v. Smith, 57 F.3d 109, 112 (1st Cir. 1995). The duty includes maintaining the ship and her equipment in a proper operating condition, and can be breached either by transitory or by permanent defects in the equipment. Hubbard, 626 F.2d at 199. A "temporary and unforeseeable malfunction or failure of a piece of equipment under proper and expected use is sufficient to establish a claim of damages for unseaworthiness." Id. (citing Usner, 400 U.S. at 499). Finally, the injured seaman must prove that the unseaworthy condition was the sole or proximate cause of the injury sustained. Id. Although the duty is absolute, "[t]he standard is not perfection, but reasonable fitness; not a ship that will weather every imaginable peril of the sea, but a vessel reasonably suitable for her intended service." Mitchell, 362 U.S. at 550.

Most important to this discussion is that a claim of unseaworthiness is not dependent upon a finding of negligence. "The reason, of course, is that unseaworthiness is a condition, and how that condition came into being — whether by negligence or otherwise — is quite irrelevant to the owner's liability for personal injuries resulting from it." Usner, 400 U.S. at 498 (emphasis in original).

(Ferrara v. A & V Fishing, Inc. First Circuit 1996).

The above citing involves a seaman's injury in a Jones Act commercial marine case. Note that this ruling is exceptionally harsh for a civil case and would be unlikely to be applied to a pleasure craft case unless involving paid crew or shipside services. The significance of this stems from the fact that the courts have consistently ruled that it is the intent of Admiralty law to be applied consistently across the board to virtually all issues involving vessels or navigation, even aircraft crashing into waterways and jet skiers running over swimmers. The number of first party cases that have been litigated at Admiralty has been limited, i.e., insurance coverage issues, owing mainly to the issue of cost; however, there are numerous court rulings on third party cases involving injury and property damage, wherein the vessel owner is always held to the high standard of seaworthiness.

How, then, can the courts apply this doctrine in thousands of cases of passenger or crew injury, and yet apply a different standard to insurance companies? The answer is that the courts generally do apply the same seaworthiness standard, unless the contract voids it. How juries judge the matter is another issue altogether.

While this places a tremendous liability on the vessel owner, it also presents an issue with respect to the seaworthiness warranty. There is a big caveat to the above: Some companies selling All Risk policies today do not include a written warranty, and only rarely will try to invoke the implied warranty of seaworthiness. Instead, they prefer to rely upon the "wear, tear and gradual deterioration" and other exclusions. In policies where the warranty is explicit, a defense will often invoke both issues. Exceptions to the rule are policies issued by foreign insurers (referred to as "surplus lines") who typically provide coverage for vessels that first line U.S. companies will not insure. This provides one of the rare instances where named peril policies are issue for pleasure craft.

Perils of the Sea

Surplus lines or high risk vessels are likely insured under the more limited Named Perils policy which insures against *perils of the sea*. The laymen is apt to equate sea perils with anything that happens to the vessel. The nature of the perils insured against has substantial precedence in the courts which can appear to be very confusing.

It is often difficult to assess whether perils of the sea or unseaworthiness caused a loss. A simple test is to determine whether the loss was caused by injury or violence from without as opposed to weakness from within. If an otherwise unseaworthy vessel sinks during a storm, the test would be a question of whether a seaworthy vessel would likely also have been sunk by the storm. Or, to put it another way, would the unseaworthy vessel likely have sunk absent the violent weather; did the inherent weakness add to the vessel's vulnerability to the point that, absent that weakness, the vessel likely would have survived?

Thus weather is an obvious peril of the sea, but only to the extent that the violence of the weather threatens a seaworthy vessel, not an unseaworthy one. Grounding, collision, pirates fouling of propellers and rudders and many, many other unanticipated happenings that are not generated internally within the vessel, including the actions of its crew:

> The "Miss Jay Jay" case, occurring and litigated in England[2] in 1985 illustrates the perils of litigation. The "Miss Jay Jay" was a production model 50 foot motor yacht of cored hull construction that on crossing the English Channel in moderate sea conditions (adjudged as non exceptional) the hull delaminated. As would be expected, the insurer denied the claim based on the hull damage not being a peril of the sea but rather a construction defect. On litigation, the trial judge came to the strange conclusion that while the vessel's hull was clearly faulty and "wholly unfit for its purpose." But in searching for a proximate cause, he comes up with two: both the sea conditions and the faulty hull were equally contributory. In other words, one would not have occurred without the other.

The judgement, which was also upheld on appeal, is patently absurd because, if usual sea conditions are a cause of loss, then the vessel is patently unseaworthy. The judge comes to this conclusion, not because he is an unreasonable man, but by way of inappropriate application of precedent and legal tests. In other words, for sea conditions to be a proximate cause, they would have to be so severe that any fit vessel would likely be imperiled. Yet, it is irrational to imply that seaworthy vessels are threatened by moderate conditions. This case stands the whole issue of seaworthiness on its head, yet this case still stands as precedent:

> In another English case, the judge comes to a correct decision in Glowrange v. CGU Insurance, 2001, wherein the yacht "Moana" was anchored in an open harbor when strong sea swells suddenly occurred. Conditions were such that other vessels were having difficulty, pulled up anchor and left that anchorage, as did the "Moana" which headed out to sea. About 30 minutes later the skipper noted that the yacht was behaving sluggishly, and upon investigation the hull was found filling with water. Shortly thereafter the vessel was wallowing and in danger of sinking when the crew abandoned her. The yacht sank in deep water and was not recovered.

During the trial, neither her owners nor crew could offer any explanation as to why the yacht was taking on water, but advanced the notion that it could be any of a number of possible causes which are perils. After underwriters denied the claim because the claimants failed to establish that the loss was caused by a peril of the sea, the trial judge upheld the denial: "an assured who puts forward a claim under the policy must establish that it is more probable than not that the cause of loss was a peril within the scope of cover[age]".

Cases can occur where an unfit vessel is proximately caused by conditions of weather, such as a vessel lost in a hurricane when other vessels were also lost. In this instance, the vessel would likely have been lost regardless of its condition. Granted, the unfit condition may have aggravated the cause, but the test is whether the loss would have occurred anyway. If not, then it is not a peril of the sea:

> Such a case occurred in the early 1990's in which a 200 foot, one hundred year old sailing ship used for Caribbean cruises was lost in a hurricane with dozens of casualties. No surveyor in his right mind would certify such a vessel as seaworthy due to its aged and deteriorating timbers and fasteners, but the fact was that it was lost in a storm that probably would have destroyed her even if she were built yesterday. Thus, the probable cause was not its age but the storm, since few ships of its type ever survived such storms.

In these brief examples we see how the issues of seaworthiness come to the fore in myriad ways, even should no express warranty exist. It should be noted here that it is not necessary that the insured provide absolute proof beyond reasonable doubt. All that is required is a "reasonable preponderance of evidence." The investigator's burden will therefore be greater than the insured's if he is to refute the insured's allegation. This confirms the doctrine that the benefit of reasonable doubt accrues to the insured.

Weather

When weather is the cause of casualties, the law considers this an "Act of God," and no person is responsible or liable for related happenings. There are, however, as with everything in law, exceptions to this rule. There have been rulings wherein a vessel owner was held liable for damages caused to other vessels or property when his vessel broke loose as a result of his not taking proper action to secure his vessel for the approach of a tropical storm that was several days in approaching. A vessel owner that abandons his vessel (through failure to protect it) in the face of a storm may be said to be negligent when the risk of not doing obviously threatens other vessels or property:

> In the Bunge v. Freeport Marine Repair (2001) the 11th circuit held that not only did the vessel owner have a duty to secure his vessel in the face of an approaching hurricane, but that those efforts must be reasonable and prudent, which in this case were shown to be less than prudent.

The criteria applied is one of whether additional measures are likely to prevent a vessel from breaking its moorings, and the threshold to be applied would be whether the additional measures of other vessel owners were successful. For example, if all boats in a harbor are wiped out regardless of how extensive the preparations, then there would be no basis for an argument of negligence. The issue of negligence in mooring pleasure craft and resulting damage during storms is fertile ground for litigation and subrogation because so many boat owners do not know how to moor a boat properly and because so many simply abandon their boats in the face of approaching storms.

Moreover, as we saw in an earlier section, ignorance is not a component of reasonable and prudent behavior. To be prudent, one must have appropriate knowledge of the effects of one's behavior. Thus, a vessel owner who attempts to plead ignorance as an excuse for failure to take prudent action will not prevail.

Negligence -vs- Gross Negligence

Black's Law Dictionary defines negligence as:

> The omission to do something which a reasonable man, guided by those ordinary considerations which ordinarily regulate human affairs, would do, or the doing of something that a reasonable and prudent man would not do.

In US but not necessarily English law, there are distinctions between negligence and gross negligence and one should be familiar with these distinctions since they are relevant to insurance coverage as well as civil and criminal issues. Gross negligence is a higher degree of negligence.

Willful and wanton misconduct, reckless disregard, and reckless misconduct are all terms that are used as synonyms and often interchangeably for gross negligence although a closer examination will reveal that willful misconduct is not negligence but an intentional act.

The following quotation is taken from the Michigan Law Review Commission of 1996 that argues some inconsistencies in Michigan Law that I find illuminating:

> Second, in all other cases, conduct shall be deemed to be "so reckless as to demonstrate a substantial lack of concern for whether an injury results" when the mental attitude accompanying the conduct amounts to conscious indifference to the rights, welfare, and safety of others. Such a mental attitude can be inferred from an intentional failure to perform a manifest duty imposed to protect others from serious injury (i.e., from a showing that the actor knew about a serious peril to another, but his acts or omissions demonstrate that he did not care.

The commission review argues whether gross negligence can include intentional acts that, on the face of it, one would be inclined to say not, for an intentional act is a definition of its own. On more careful consideration however, it is pointed out that willful intention can lead to negligent acts without those same acts being intentional as in the cause-effect relationship where the intentional cause creates an unintentional or uncaring result.

Thus, gross negligence can reasonably be said to mean *conduct so reckless as to demonstrate a substantial lack of concern for whether damage or injury results.*

Most accidents are caused by what we might refer to as "honest" mistakes. Human beings are far from perfect, and so we all fail to act responsibly from time to time.

Insurance does not exclude coverage for the results of these mistakes because that is the way most casualties occur. Honest mistakes are not part of the moral hazard, but intentional acts and abnormal behavior are excluded. Normal mistakes are classified as negligence, whereas gross negligence is *abnormal* behavior. An example would be a vessel owner not taking action after having been notified that his boat appears to be taking on water.

Common negligence is distinguished from gross negligence by the legal phrase "reasonable and prudent" behavior, which is simply defined as the actions that responsible people would take. However, reasonable and prudent is contingent on knowledge; if a boat owner knows nothing about boats and maintenance, it is not possible for him to act prudently or reasonably because he lacks the proper foundation to make such judgments. The lack of prudent knowledge cannot be an excuse because *that* is imprudent. Thus, a boat owner who fails to take appropriate actions is likely to be held grossly negligent based on a lack of reasonable behavior.

When it comes to sinking losses and machinery damage cases, the evaluation of reasonable and prudent behavior is a common factor since it is almost always necessary to determine whether the owner's action or lack of action was the proximate cause. Another example:

> A boat owner turned the main battery power switch off in order to replace a bilge pump, but he forgot to turn it back on. It then rained and the boat sank.

That is negligence but insurable negligence that does not fall outside the reasonable and prudent definition because it is recognized that people make mistakes. Oversight or forgetting does not constitute imprudence but does fit the definition of negligence.

A vessel which has an ignorant owner as captain and crew is technically unseaworthy since the safe operation of the vessel is dependent upon a competent crew. The situation is no different than an unqualified person flying an aircraft. Unfortunately, what with the courts becoming increasingly "individual rights" oriented and the decline of personal responsibility, the seaworthiness clause of marine policies is increasingly being ignored. That does not mean that the investigator should ignore it, too. It's a well-known fact that insurance companies often pay claims that they shouldn't simply because they believe that they would not prevail in court if challenged. That is a decision that flies in the face of the insurance contract, but even anticipating such a result, the investigator should maintain his integrity and call the cause as he sees it.

Why should an investigator point out a cause of negligence when he knows in advance that his client is going to extend coverage anyway? Because an investigator can never anticipate whose hands his report will end up in, and how that report will be used. In the chapter on report writing I discuss this point in detail and the reader should pay careful attention to it. Anytime an investigator overlooks, ignores or downplays evidence he creates a situation that could come back to haunt him. If the client wants to ignore evidence, fine, that is his prerogative, but it is never the investigator's prerogative to do so.

Sue and Labor Clause

All marine insurance policies contain this clause in one form or another. Sometimes it is captioned "Duties of the Insured" and lays out what is contractually required of him. Sue and labor is an old term that currently means to take all reasonable and necessary steps to protect the stricken vessel from further damage following the loss. This principle applies in all property insurance policies.

Subrogation

Nearly all property and certainly all marine insurance contracts of any type will contain what is known as a subrogation clause. This simply means that in the event the company pays a claim for damage which it believes was caused by another person or entity that is legally responsible, then the policy holder assigns his right to seek recovery to the company. The rights of the insured are subrogated to the insurer when the insurer pays a claim. The insured forfeits his right to recovery should he concede his rights to another.

Estoppel

In this section we will consider the issue of estoppel in the context of sinking casualties where the issue of salvage arises before the investigation has even started and coverage is determined. The doctrine of estoppel means that one cannot deny (legally) that which he has already admitted, or vice versa.

Because the marine surveyor is usually the first person from the insurance company that the insured has contact with, he will be expecting the surveyor to provide answers to his questions. We understand that we shouldn't discuss coverage issues, but novices – or even old pros, may get into trouble by being sympathetic to the insured's plight and then making some unfortunate comment or action that could lead the insured to believe that the loss is covered and it turns out that the loss is denied. The courts have been so clear on this issue that there is a name for it, estoppel. Any action taken, or comments made by the surveyor that leads the insured to believe that coverage exists would be an admission of coverage.

In sinking investigations in particular, the need to have the vessel raised and refloated, presents a problem of salvage costs and who pays those costs before the issue of coverage is resolved. Any actions undertaken by a surveyor on his own initiative may construed by courts as behavior by the insurer that suggests that coverage will be extended, unless one does something to make the situation otherwise clear.

An estoppel situation can also be created by the making or obtaining estimates before a coverage determination is made. It happens when a surveyor, trying to help the insured expedite the claim as quick as possible by calling for a contractor to make an estimate at the same time he's investigating. The making of damage estimates can be construed to mean that the insurance company intends to pay the claim. If the insured asks about this, of course, he is free to do that on his own, but the surveyor should never give instructions or do this himself until coverage has been determined.

The typical case is that of a sunken vessel requiring refloating or salvage where the need to control loss and damage as well as costs is offset by our lack of authority. This point is driven home by the realization that coverage for the loss and all associated costs does not apply until a determination of causation has been made, a decision that may be days or weeks in the future. For this reason, it is the insured who must sign the salvage contract, even though the insurer has the right to approve the contract by virtue of the fact that it may become obligated to pay. It is customary that the surveyor reviews the salvage contract with the insured and to render his blessing as to whether he believes it is fair and reasonable. However, this point must be made clear to the insured; it does not mean that the insurance company agrees to pay the cost. To this end the surveyor/investigator should never call a salvor on the insured's behalf.

At this point the insured is bound to be shaken up a bit because he was probably expecting an immediate pronouncement of coverage; he may even have expected the insurance company to take over and handle the salvage operation. Now he's going to be disappointed that they aren't. Even worse, he's facing the prospect, no matter how remote, that his loss may not be covered and he may even turn hostile.

Rare is the instance when an insured gets a surveyor to represent his interest, but it does happen. It is at this point that I often advise the insured that he has the right to engage his own expert, particularly when I have reason to suspect that the loss may not be covered. An example would be when I see that the partly submerged boat has barnacles growing on the superstructure, tipping me off that it had lain sunk for a long time. Much like the way cops are required to read a suspect his Miranda rights when arrested, it's a good idea to advise the insured that he has a right to his own expert. In most cases, this will make our job easier while at the same time making the surveyor look less like the bad guy in the insured's eyes.

The Prudent Uninsured

Instances frequently arise when the insured asks the surveyor for advice about refloating his vessel or salvage. The cause of a sinking cannot be investigated with the boat sitting on the bottom. Whether you are the investigator, claims surveyor, or both, the odds are almost certain that you will be dealing with a boat owner who does not understand your role and may be uncertain, as to how to proceed. It is equally certain that he will turn to the surveyor for advice, and while it may appear to be merely a matter of human kindness to give that advice, beware that to do so is fraught with pitfalls. This is not unlike the situation where the Good Samaritan stops to give first aid assistance to an accident victim, only to be sued for some imagined grievance later on. The investigator should have a firm understanding with his client on all aspects of this subject in order to avoid problems with estoppel.

Experienced surveyors approach this thorny problem by thoroughly explaining the situation to the insured who certainly doesn't want to hear this. At this point, the only thing the insured wants to hear is that his loss is covered, that insurance company is paying *all costs*, and that his boat is going to be a total loss. He is certainly thinking in his own mind that he paid for this insurance and now the company seems to be backing off its commitments. It is necessary to explain to him that both the law (if that is the case in your state) and the insurance contract require the company to perform a thorough investigation to discover the cause. We have to utter those hated words that the insured does not want to hear, that he has to act as a *prudent uninsured.*

The doctrine of prudent uninsured is well established in law and is simply defined as meaning that the boat owner is required to behave as if he did not have insurance on the vessel, and that all costs and damages will be born by him, until such time as the coverage question is resolved. This does not mean that the insurance investigator and the insurer will take a hands-off approach until the vessel is refloated and the investigation completed. Nor do all insurers approach this issue of refloating and salvage in the same manner.

The surveyor is presumed to be an expert, and the insurer to have superior knowledge on the matter, and therefore *may have a duty to assist the insured with that expertise.*[3] Therefore, it's not a good idea to simply leave the insured to his own devices, but to render prudent advice with the appropriate caveats. Both parties have a motive to keep the costs down and limit the damages, though in many instances the insured wants to ensure that the boat is a total loss and will show little interest in limiting damages. But the law is clear on this point (and on your side) that he must act as a prudent uninsured with the implied threat that failure to act could result in a diminution of recoverable damages.

The experienced surveyor will therefore inform the insured of the doctrine of prudent uninsured, explaining to him his duties, as well as those of the insurer and himself, for as of the moment we now have three parties involved: the owner, insurer and surveyor who is not a de facto agent of the insurance company. The surveyor then proceeds to explain that he has been hired by the insurer as an impartial investigator. Understandably, the insured is not going to believe that he is impartial, but there being no governmental agency that does such investigations, this is the way things work in the world of marine insurance claims.

It takes quite a bit of experience before we become comfortable dealing with these difficult situations and in the meantime it is wise to consult with our client frequently. Experience shows that our clients will have varying degrees of marine experience from none to a lot. The highly experienced marine claimsman will almost always take the bull by the horns, so to speak, and handle these issues directly with his insured. The inexperienced or overworked frequently leave all initial communications to the surveyor, and that is why, though we are not supposed to do claims adjuster's work, we are often thrust into some of those functions anyway. We'll be a lot more successful and have happier clients by being well prepared for such problems when they inevitably arise.

The Non Waiver Agreement

All of the above problems can more or less be eliminated by obtaining a signed non waiver agreement. This is a standard form agreement that has been in use by insurance adjusters for over a half century. This agreement simply puts in writing what the investigator should say to the insured verbally, that he is investigating the loss as to its cause or extent of loss and damage for the purpose of determining whether said loss is covered and, if so, the dollar value of said loss; that no efforts of investigation shall waive any rights of the insurer or insured. In other words, the agreement states that the insured is aware of the reason that the investigation is being conducted.

Many companies are adverse to the use of legal documents, particularly early on. It hardly need be explained what anyone's reaction is to being presented with something to sign. However, the usefulness of the non waiver in difficult circumstances should not be underestimated. It is simply a reaffirmation of both party's respective rights and duties. But its net affect is to provide proof that the insured acknowledges these. This removes both estoppel issues as well as limiting the potential for bad faith and unfair trade practices actions. When asking an insured to sign a non waiver, the surveyor should always explain the document in detail by reading it to the insured line-by-line as this helps remove the fear and reluctance.

Cooperation

All policies require the insured to cooperate in the investigation of losses or accidents, as well as agreeing to provide documents and/or financial records relative to a loss. Since most marine policies are obligated to provide a legal defense in the event a covered casualty generates litigation, the insured is also required to cooperate in all claim-related litigation.

When it comes to documents, while the insurer has a right to related documents, it does not have the right to go rummaging around in the insured's general finances. It should be noted that failure to cooperate can be a basis for denial of a claim, and this could include the production of relevant documents as well. The investigator needs to proceed with caution when requesting documents to be sure that the request is reasonable, relevant and necessary. You don't want to end up creating a situation in which the insured blames you for invading his privacy. If you are not a licensed adjuster, the need for documents should be relayed to the claims adjuster who should make the request.

Insurance policies usually have a requirement that the insured provide a sworn statement under oath. This is rarely done except in cases where a legal challenge to a claim denial is anticipated. Most often, less formal recorded statements are taken. Even if the insured has an attorney, he is still required to cooperate so the investigator should not permit a lawyer to attempt to scare him off taking a statement. If an insured should refuse to cooperate with any reasonable request which the investigator feels is mandated by the requirement to cooperate, he should advise his claims supervisor before taking any action.

The Insured's Rights, Insurer's Rights

The rights and duties of the insured are spelled out in the insurance contract and any state laws that may supercede the contract. This is yet another reason why it is imperative that the investigator should be familiar with insurance policies and the law.

As previously mentioned, when the vessel owner hires his own expert, we may now find ourselves in the position of conducting a joint investigation, for the insured has a right to be present, or have his own expert present, but not to interfere in any way. He may conduct his own investigation, but that must not interfere with the insurer's investigation, whose right to investigate is primary. The insurance contract gives the insurer that right; that does not mean *after* someone else has investigated. If a joint investigation is to take place, the insurance investigator is always the lead investigator who has the right to direct the course of the investigation.

It happens occasionally that the insured hires a non-maritime attorney who demands that all investigation work stop. Time is of the essence with investigations and the attorney has no right to demand that the investigation cease or be delayed in any way. To do so is to fail to comply with the provisions of the insurance contract. If an attorney attempts to stop the investigator with legal threats, the client should be immediately advised of this and the insurer should send the lawyer a reservation of rights letter pointing out that his actions violate contract provisions and may void coverage.

The Time Element

The laws of most states include a provision that the insurer must inform the insured whether he is covered or not within a certain period of time, usually 60 or 90 days, or notify him in writing of any extenuating circumstances. There are, of course, situations when that will be an insufficient amount of time to complete a complicated investigation.

It should also be noted that investigators not infrequently find themselves working for clients that are out of state or international who are not knowledgeable about specific state laws. This is yet another reason why it is important for marine surveyors to be conversant with state insurance laws. This is one state requirement that the investigator should definitely be aware of, and also that state laws frequently change, so there is a need to keep one's knowledge current.

When investigations for an insurer threaten to go beyond the proscribed time, the investigator should advise his client that it's time to send a reservation of rights letter. It is not in our best interest to assume that the insurer knows this or will do the right thing. Most insurers have a standard format for this letter, or they may need to craft a special one to meet unique circumstances. A reservation of rights letter, as its name suggests, reserves the right of the insurer to extend the time needed to complete the investigation based on extenuating circumstances. The failure to send such a letter can have very serious consequences for the insurer, and possibly the investigator, so it's a good idea to make sure that a reservation of rights gets sent.

Latent Defects

Most yacht policies have a latent defect clause which provides specific coverage for latent defects, while others specifically exclude latent defects from coverage. The term latent defect in maritime use is widely misunderstood, for it is not the same thing as with common law usage. A latent defect is an *unknown defect not discoverable by such inspection or test as the law reasonably requires under the circumstances,* i.e. reasonable and prudent inspection.

Why does this definition use the phrase *inspection or test as the law reasonably requires?* The answer is that different circumstances mandate different requirements in terms of what the law reasonably requires. That is, the requirements for a cruise ship are going to be considerably different than for a yacht because the cruise ship is a public conveyance.

It is a principle of insurance that insurance does not cover property that is in any way defective because, to do so, would be providing a warranty for the defective product. That, of course, is the responsibility of the manufacturer and would be providing free insurance for the manufacturer. However, marine insurance policies have long provided coverage for loss and damage caused to the vessel as a *result* of a latent defect. Say, for example, an error in the lamination of a vessel hull results in the hull breaking open, causing it to sink. In this case, if the policy had a latent defect clause, under that clause the insurance would cover the resultant damage, but not the defect itself. Typical coverage wordings are:

Latent defects, excluding the cost of repairing or replacing the defective part.

The real problem with latent defect is in defining this term that is remarkably broad in scope: Latent means not discoverable by such inspection or test as the law reasonably requires under the circumstances. It can also mean a defect that has not become manifest yet; that is, a fault may exist within a material or component which, short of destructive testing, cannot be discovered, but which as time goes on will eventually become apparent as the part begins to fail or fails. The latent defect thus becomes a patent defect.

The kind of inspection necessary would be that which any reasonable and prudent person or entity would be expected to carry out in order to ensure that the thing in question would not harm the vessel's seaworthiness. What the courts have determined does not constitute a latent defect is any kind of wear, normal stress or deterioration. In other words, the natural tendency of nearly every material to age, deteriorate and wear out.

Latent defect includes faulty material and faulty workmanship, but does it include faulty design? The answer is yes, but . . . . but only if damage results from faulty design; it does not cover correction of the faulty design.

Historical Perspectives

At this point is it necessary that we should back up a moment and consider where this "latent defect" business comes from. The term first appeared in 1888 in the English Institute Hull Clauses, which refers to ocean marine hull insurance for ships. Heretofore, there was no reference to the term in common law; it was exclusively maritime. The concept quickly crossed the Atlantic to be incorporated into the American Institute hull clauses and thence into yacht policies and finally into common law.

Today, civil lawyers throw the term latent defect around like snowballs after a heavy wet snow, and has little to do with the maritime definitions. Latent defects have a substantial legal background and precedent upon which to draw, not only in the U.S. but particularly Europe where it originated. Even so, there remains today a great deal of controversy within the U.S. courts about the myriad ramifications of what constitutes an insurable latent defect. What with the tremendous advancements in materials these days, there are apparently no limits to the meaning of the word "defective." Because the term has a strictly maritime ancestry, the maritime context of the term should apply, along with all Admiralty case law, both English and domestic.

Error in Design

Design errors or faulty design means that the specifications concerning how the vessel is to be built – or repaired. These specifications concern the form and functioning of the vessel, the *choice* of material and the *process* of manufacture. Say, for example, your boat has a balsa cored bottom that subsequently became saturated with water. Is that an error in design? Most likely, because one of two things had to happen: either the lamination design was faulty or balsa was an improper choice of material for the application. By definition, error in design is something that happens before construction or manufacture even begins. We'll consider this subject in more detail in a moment.

Faulty Material

In the above case of the balsa core, was the balsa itself a faulty material? No, balsa may have been an improper selection of material for that application, or possibly the design of the laminate was faulty. There was nothing wrong with the balsa material itself, for balsa has been used for decking and other structural cores successfully for at least 50 years. Faulty material means that the material itself was faulty before it was incorporated into construction or manufacture. Examples of faulty materials are hard to find, but flawed castings, extrusions or forgings are rare examples.

Materials may be said to exist in three states, raw, processed and finished. The meaning of the word "material" implies that it is to be used to fabricate something else. A log from a cut tree is a raw material; after it is cut into planks it becomes a processed material. Made into pre finished plywood panels it becomes a finish material. This point is relevant because we may confront the question of what is a fiberglass laminate. Plastic resin is a process material because it is made from a number of raw materials that are processed into the resin. In the building of a boat, plastic resin is further combined with fiberglass fabrics and other materials into a hull or other components. At each step of the manufacturing process, errors may occur. Added to our laminated hull is a finish called gel coat. Thus, the question arises, for the purpose of dealing with insurance issues, of how do we define what is the excluded "part" that contains the latent defect because recovery cannot be made for the defective part.

In the case of plank or plate on frame construction, if a frame is faulty and fails, resulting in damage to the hull skin, we have little difficulty discerning the independent parts of a hull; the frame is clearly a part distinct from the plating. But in the case of a molded hull, this is a bit more difficult.

With a wood hull, the distinct parts are joined together with screws or bolts; with aluminum, the parts are welded together; with FRP, distinctly separate materials are joined together by means of chemical bonding. The common point amongst all three is that once distinct elements have been joined in some manner and where they were once separate, now appear as a single whole, yet those elements remain distinguishable.

Therefore, it would appear to be a reasonable and correct argument that a composite hull consists of separate parts and that a fault in one could cause damage to the others. The significance of this as it relates to latent defects will surely not be missed.

Premature Failure

A material may be said to fail prematurely when it fails to achieve the normally expected service life as a result of unexpected conditions. An error in design or materials could possibly result in advanced wear or corrosion that occurs at a rate far faster than normal. In a case where a yacht had sunk because a sea strainer, which was held together by a single bronze rod, came apart due to what appeared to be corrosion or electrolysis. But metallurgical analysis revealed that the rod was worn completely through as the result of bits of oyster shell swirling around within the strainer (the shell was not present because the strainer had been cleaned earlier but the captain failed to notice the damage to the rod). In this instance, we were dealing with *erosion*, not corrosion, which is a matter of wear. Furthermore, the strainer had failed within three years, which was shown to be far less than a normal service life. However, the vessel owner claimed that the cause of the failure was faulty strainer design because there was no material that could reasonably be expected to resist erosion by oyster shell. Indeed, other brands of strainers have the securing rods on the outside where they are not subject to erosion.

As to the discovery issue, it was shown that the yacht captain routinely inspected and cleaned the strainer on a monthly basis, but never observed the eroded shaft because of the awkward position of the unit that would require the thing to be completely removed and dismantled to see it. Thus, the vessel owner prevailed by virtue of claiming a latent defect in design.

What is Damage?

If insurance covers the resultant damage caused by a defect, then we need to ask what is damage? Here the issue gets a bit murky because we can inquire whether damage to a hull caused by a defect in design falls within the context of "damage"? While it is doubtful that this is what underwriters intended, a bad design that results in a hull splitting open, or a core becoming filled with water could certainly be construed as damage. It has often been asserted that the design error is the selection of balsa as a core material for hull bottoms, the damage is a core full of water renders a vessel at risk of hull failure due to hydraulic erosion of the core.

To carry it a step further, what about blistered hulls? If a policy does not specifically exclude blistering (many do) could the blisters be construed as damage? Blistering is caused by an improper selection of materials, namely general purpose polyester resin, because we know that better quality resins do not blister; therefore, a hull that is blistered is by definition built of inferior materials, a design fault. If a policy does not specifically exclude blistering – or some words to that effect – then blistering itself is not a latent defect because blistering is the *result* of improper selection of materials, i.e., blistering is the resultant damage, the casualty.

But yacht policies are worded differently than ship hull policies for the former usually contain the phrase *excluding the cost of repairing or replacing the defective part.* That would appear to mean that if the part itself is damaged by the defect, it still is not covered. So where does our soggy balsa cored bottom leave us?

Here's where it gets interesting. The latent defect must develop in a way that results in a casualty. If the fault is in what we call the bottom (a part) and that fault causes the plies to separate, the balsa to turn to mush due to hydraulic erosion, then clearly a casualty has occurred to the bottom; the essential structure has sustained severe damage as a result of improper design. In other words, the part (bottom) is not defective, but some aspect of the design of it. The casualty is damage not to all aspects of the entire bottom, but to the core, which constitutes another "part" as discussed earlier. Therefore, if water migration into a balsa core results in ply separation, or degradation of the core by means of hydraulic erosion, then *that* is the resultant damage, the casualty and should be covered.

Look at it this way: the balsa itself is not defective, the fiberglass laminates are not defective, but the defect that caused water to somehow get into the core has resulted in damage to both. The latent defect is therefore the means by which water got into the core.

In the case of the balsa cored bottom, at issue will be the question of what constitutes the defective part that will not be covered. The bottom consists of balsa wood sandwiched between two skins of fiberglass laminate. The core is either full of water or has already begun to separate from the skins and possibly degrade. It would appear, then, that neither the core nor the laminates are defective materials so we have to look elsewhere for the latent defect.

The casualty is the damage that occurred as a result of water intrusion whatever the outcome of that may be. In the case of Sea Ray Boats, that company built several hundred boats with balsa cored bottoms, yet we know that not all of them have failed. My extensive searches have produced only 43 verified cases, though surely the number is far greater. And of those 43 cases there were at least four differing means of water intrusion, so there are at least four different perils that produced the same casualty or type of damage.

The phrase *excluding the cost of repairing or replacing the defective part* is intended to exclude coverage for the manufacturer's error, yet it is intended to cover the insured for his fortuitous loss that was not his fault for want of due diligence to maintain his vessel. The reality is that many of the Sea Ray core saturations were caused by faulty design wherein the core was extended completely around the keel, thereby creating a weak spot on the apex of the bottom or keel. When the vessels were blocked after hauling, the laminate fractured in way of the keel blocks. Thus, there was indeed a major design error that resulted in water intrusion into the core, but the use of balsa as a core was not the de facto error; the error was in the manner in which balsa was used, i.e. on the point of the keel.

In several instances, holes had been inadvertently drilled through the inner hull skin that allowed water into the core. No one knew why, but there they were. And in other cases the builder failed to seal the core in way of port holes, the deck joint, and other hull penetrations. Again, none of this was the fault of the balsa but the failure to employ proper construction practices, be it workmanship or design.

We can look at the issue from one final angle, that of the question of whether it is possible to build a hull using balsa core that will not inevitably fail. My answer to that is yes and the fact that not all balsa cored hulls fail proves the point.

Were the above cited instances involved in insurance claims – which some were – the "defective part(s)" that would not be covered range from repair of the drill holes to redesigning the keel laminating schedule, but in every case, repairing the damage, the saturated or separated core, should have been covered.

In the case of the cracked keel area mentioned above, the defect not covered would be the correction of the use of balsa in the keel area; the rest of the wet core damage would be covered. This illustrates the point that ferreting out the correct interpretation of latent defect issues is often not easy, and frequently leads to wrong conclusions.

Similarly, if an under sized I beam used to construct a building collapses because it is under dimensioned, it is not the *I beam* that is defective by being undersized. No, there was nothing wrong with that particular I beam. What was wrong was the architect's specified use of that size I beam. Here we clearly see that the engineering is defective. What should not be covered would only be the difference in cost of the larger beam over the smaller beam. Seemingly nitpicking distinctions of semantics can produce very different results so far as insurance coverage is concerned.

As to hull blistering, the blisters are the damage resulting from a defect not discoverable by reasonable inspection and therefore latent. Many all risks policies specifically exclude blistering, a clause that will override the latent defect clause. Named peril policies typically do not contain blistering exclusions and so blistering will fall under the latent defect cover. However, there may be some difficulties. The latent defect is the selection of improper material, polyester resin. If the cover excludes repairing or replacing the defective part, what is the defective part and what is the damage?

Here, again, we have to consider the issue carefully: the defective part is the selection of plastic that is used to construct the entire hull. Obviously, that can't be undone. But the damage is not primarily to the plastic that binds the glass fibers together – though certainly some plastic damage does occur — but a blister that has formed *between* the gel coat and the laminate. The damage is an accumulation of fluid and a distortion of the gel coat which is *not* the defective part and thus repair of the gel coat should be covered even though that will not resolve the problem. However, those looking to their insurance for relief of blistering problems will be faced with the tough issue of proving that the blistering originated within the insurance policy period.

Machinery

Latent defects in machinery were the original basis for creation of the latent defect clause. In the Institute named peril policy (ships) the cover is:

> This insurance covers loss of or damage to the subject matter insured caused by
>
> > Bursting of boilers or breakage of shafts but does not cover any of the costs of repairing or replacing the boiler which bursts or shaft which breaks
> >
> > Any latent defect in the machinery or hull but does not cover the cost of correcting the latent defect

Yachts, of course, don't have boilers, but the essential purpose of the 1888 English clause concerning latent defects remains. To wit, damage resulting from latent defects is covered.

Wear, tear and gradual deterioration cannot give rise to a latent defect which is confined to a manufacturing defect in materials, design and workmanship, but as we noted earlier distinctions can be made between normal and abnormal wear and tear.

The latent defects clause of yacht policies is one of the most under utilized areas of yacht insurance because it is so poorly understood, and because latent defects can be difficult and costly to prove. In most cases when machinery fails, the exact cause is never determined but ascribed to a generic cause such as piston failure without ever determining why the piston failed.

Instances of latent defects in basic engine components (crankshaft, rods, pistons, bearings, etc.,) are very rare, yet design errors in fuel and induction and cooling systems are quite common. Latent defects occur in exhaust system designs, engine mounting systems and generator installations. A builder who installs a generator under a non watertight hatch commits a design error.

Limitations on Claims

The only limitation for making a latent defect damage claim is that the claimant must be able to demonstrate that the damage – not the latent defect – occurred during the period that the policy was in force. It does not matter whether one is the first owner or the fifth owner of the boat.

Admiralty Law

A surveyor's need for a foundational knowledge of Maritime law is based on the fact that legal jurisdiction and law will not only govern his behavior, but also shape the direction of his investigations. This is most critically important in the area of marine salvage where he will encounter these issues frequently. The reason for the existence of Admiralty was discussed in the opening of this chapter.

Before we get into the subject of salvage, we first need to have a basic understanding of the concept of Admiralty Law, which is synonymous with the term maritime law. A knowledge of maritime law is important from the standpoint of the special rules that govern maritime activity, including recreational boating. Another important reason that we need to be familiar with Admiralty stems from the fact that our clients, more often than not, are not themselves sufficiently familiar with it, so that we can lend great assistance by being able to steer them in the right direction. This is not to say that we advise on legal matters, but that we can know when to advise the client to get legal advice. More importantly, ignorance of the law is no excuse for anything.

It was not very long ago that Admiralty law and jurisdiction was considered to be a body of law designed strictly to deal with issues of commercial shipping. However, several landmark Supreme Court decisions have very broadly extended the scope of admiralty jurisdiction to cover just about any tort that occurs on navigable waterways anywhere in the U.S.

Admiralty is widely regarded as the most complex area of law in U.S. jurisprudence. Even so, it behooves the marine investigator to have more than a passing familiarity with its main tenets as respects sunken vessels and vessels in distress, for the investigator will inevitably become involved in litigation. One can never be certain in which jurisdiction litigation will end up. More importantly, the investigator needs this knowledge so that his actions can be properly guided by a basic understanding of maritime law.

Embodied in Admiralty law is the concept of legal action *in rem* as opposed to *in personam*. The *in rem* proceeding is virtually unknown outside of Admiralty law and is based upon the idea that certain events or unfulfillment of obligations arising out of a contract or situation gives a claimant party a property interest in the vessel known as a maritime lien. But there is a difference between ordinary liens and maritime liens in that it is independent of possession and does not cease upon sale of the vessel. The lien is against the vessel, not the owner. Such actions can only be brought in federal court.

The basis for this is simply predicated on the fact that vessels can move from state to state or nation to nation. Thus, maritime law makes it possible to arrest a vessel as if it were a person when certain legal conditions are met. This can occur not only in the U.S. but in many other nations as well, thereby making it difficult for vessels to escape their financial obligations by fleeing the locality in which the obligations were incurred. Of course, there are many nations that do not reciprocate, so this only works in theory. Fortunately, all U.S. neighbors do reciprocate, albeit sometimes grudgingly.

Admiralty jurisdiction is conferred by Article III, section 2 of the United States Constitution and is the exclusive domain of the federal courts. Its reason for being has been argued and restated by the Supreme Court almost since its inception and remains a contentious issue to this day, but is essentially this: Admiralty law provides special considerations for uniquely maritime issues such as maritime liens, general average, capture & prizes, limitations of liability, cargo damage and last but not least, claims for salvage.

The primary focus of admiralty jurisdiction ". . . is unquestionably the protection of maritime commerce . . . . " and the need for "uniform rules of conduct" that are unlike those found on land[4].

Litigation under Admiralty trumps state and local laws only to the extent of Admiralty strictures so that Admiralty and state laws often apply to a case simultaneously. While a trial in Admiralty will not try cases of other jurisdictions, Admiralty courts take cognizance of other applicable laws and will render decisions about which is supreme, Admiralty or local.

Admiralty is founded on ancient and historical maritime tradition and evolution of the difficult conditions in which vessels can find themselves. It is therefore just as uniquely qualified to preside in a case of two ships colliding as it is for two yachts.

While it may not be directly germane to our work, the reader should be aware of the reasons for this contentiousness over jurisdiction. There are three primary reasons why plaintiffs or defendants would seek admiralty jurisdiction: (1) federal courts under admiralty rules are far more conservative than state courts that often have notoriously liberal judges, and (2) the provision for limitation of liability to the value of vessels and cargo, (3) it is advantageous for defendants from the standpoint that awards for pain and suffering or punitive damages are not available in Admiralty. Thus, concerning the later, liabilities under admiralty are not open-ended as they may be under common law, causing many defendants with potentially large liabilities to seek admiralty jurisdiction. Under certain conditions liability may be limited to the value of the vessel:

28 U.S.C. Sec. 1333. - Admiralty, maritime and prize cases

The district courts shall have original jurisdiction, exclusive of the courts of the States, of:

(1)   Any civil case of admiralty or maritime jurisdiction, saving to suitors in all cases all other remedies to which they are otherwise entitled.

(2)   Any prize brought into the United States and all proceedings for the condemnation of property taken as prize [Obsolete except for treasure salvage].

As of this writing, there are two basic tests for admiralty jurisdiction:

The first is the strict locality rule:

Every species of tort, however occurring, and whether onboard a vessel or not, if upon the high seas or navigable waters, is of admiralty cognizance. – The Plymouth U.S.S.C. 1866.

And the maritime activity rule:

"[Any claim that]…. bears a substantial relationship to traditional maritime activity." – Sisson v. Ruby, U.S.S.C. 1990.

In actual practice, both of these tests have been stretched to the point of absurdity as when any kind of accident occurring on waters navigable or not, and not involving any kind of maritime relationship such as a swimmer being run over by a jet ski, plane crashes and large objects falling into waterways, have found their way into admiralty courts.[5] The basis for this is in "maintaining a uniform body of law," that, unfortunately, produces some unintended consequences. However, there are two main areas where admiralty law frequently comes to directly bear on the work of the surveyor/investigator, salvage and seaworthiness.

Salvage

Salvage has long been a contentious issue in maritime shipping as well as for pleasure craft. The marine investigator constantly runs up against the numerous issues concerning salvage since salvage and salvors are almost always involved when vessels sink. We will therefore consider these issues in some depth. The surveyor is the insurer's man on the scene so he is the one who must deal with myriad issues and problems that arise with respect to salvage.

In theory a salvor is supposed to be helping a vessel owner, but in reality it is usually an adversarial relationship in which the salvor seeks to squeeze as much money from vessel owner and insurer as possible. Moreover, salvors are often also found to be working hand-in-hand with lawyers to maximize their legal leverage over the situation. To say that many salvors engage in predatory practices is putting it mildly, and into this fray steps the marine surveyor.

Salvage can be defined as the act of saving or rescuing a vessel or cargo from perils of the sea, but salvage is also "the *compensation* paid for saving a ship and its cargo from perils of the sea, or for the lives and property rescued from the wreck." The issue of salvage and pleasure craft has become contentious and complicated in recent years, owing largely to the application of the Admiralty law to pleasure boating issues. Lawyers representing salvors have been very aggressive at expanding the definition of salvage.

Jurisdictional issues are important to us because it is helpful to know whether or not the special Admiralty law applies to the issue of salvage since a salvor's involvement will likely give him the maritime lien against the vessel. That means that after raising the vessel, he can take possession of it and tow it away. This is one very important reason why the surveyor does not want to become directly involved in hiring a salvor for he could end up bringing on himself liabilities for very large sums indeed should things not go according to plan.

Since the definition of salvage involves the word "peril" we need consider the meaning of that. The definition of peril is endangerment, risk of damage, injury, loss or destruction. Thus, there can be no salvage of a vessel that is not endangered in some way. This is what leaves the door to contention wide open.

Refusal of Salvage Assistance

As mentioned earlier, the marine surveyor will inevitably encounter many unscrupulous salvors, including those that insist on performing salvage efforts where none is wanted. It often happens when a boat in a marina sinks; a salvor comes along believing he has the right to raise it without permission. *This is not true*, for while the law of salvage is intended to encourage rescue, a salvor cannot force salvage assistance without the owner's consent. The exception is when the vessel is in distress and there is no crew or owner present to proffer a refusal, as in a vessel disabled at sea or about to go upon a reef where destruction of the vessel is imminent.

In this situation, the *prudent owner rule* comes into play, i.e., a prudent owner could be expected to accept the assistance absent the owner or masters presence. There is substantial case law in support of the notion that salvage cannot be forced on a resisting party. "Therefore, when a ship is in distress and has been deserted by its crew, anyone can attempt salvage without the prior assent of the ship's owner or master." In International Aircraft Recovery v. United States 11th Cir., 2000, the appellate court said, "We . . . . . interpret the law of salvage to permit the owner of a vessel in marine peril to decline the assistance of others so long as only the owner's property interests are at stake." Ibid at 664. "Salvage cannot be exacted for assistance [that is] forced upon a ship."[6]

A situation could arise where the sinking of a vessel causes a hazard to other vessels nearby, as in a case the author was involved in many years ago. In this instance a marina was threatened by an unusual tropical storm that came from a direction that such storms do not normally come from, and thus the marina was exposed to waves and surge from a direction that did not happen previously. This caused a number of boats to sink that subsequently threatened nearby boats. It was fortuitous that a marine construction company was performing dock repair at the time and had a crane barge within the marina, that was rapidly moved into position and plucked the sunken boats from the water before they were totally destroyed, or caused damage to others. This was all done without notification or permission of the owners.

Needless to say, the marine construction company claimed for and was given a salvage award by a court, not only from the sunken boat owners, but also those nearby that were threatened by the sunken boats, under the *prudent owner rule*. The dock company did not have permission or a contract with any of the parties but still prevailed at obtaining an award from all parties. The principle here being that time was of the essence and that a prudent owner would have approved of the action. This was a case where the salvor's benefit to others was very clear, yet in other cases the issue can be very murky.

Hazards to navigation do not automatically give rise to the right to affect salvage when the option to provide a means of warning of the risk exists. Should a vessel sink to a depth in a navigable waterway that constitutes a hazard to navigation, that vessel owner has an immediate obligation to either eliminate the hazard or post warning. Absent that warning, a salvor may assert a right to salvage the wreck.

Abandonment

From time to time the investigator will encounter the issue of abandonment, as when a salvor claims a vessel is abandoned. This is a very complex issue that will not be discussed at length here beyond stating that abandonment legally occurs only under very precise and limited circumstances. The U.S. Navy and insurance companies have long fought the notion of sunken and lost vessels as being abandoned, even after decades of sitting on the bottom. A lost vessel cannot be declared abandoned by virtue of not being able to find it, any more than a lost child is abandoned by its parents. Neither does not making continuing efforts to locate it constitute abandonment. Salvors will often claim abandonment when no visible effort to recover a distressed vessel has been made.

Moreover, abandonment does not merely mean that there is no one aboard the vessel. In one case where a small boat washed ashore and the owner walked off in search of help, a "salvor" came along and snatched the boat off the beach and held it for ransom, the ransom being a payment for 175% of its precasualty value (award plus fee). In this case the court held that the salvor had no right to salvage the vessel because it was neither abandoned nor in peril since the boat was fully ashore; what damage it had sustained was already done, plus was being guarded by a family member to prevent looting, whose objections the salvors ignored. The owner was on his way to place a call to a friend who owned a vehicle towing company that could easily have removed the boat from the beach at a cost far lower than what the pirate salvor sought.

Therefore, we see in this instance that the boat owner had the situation under control, there was no peril, and the salvor had no right to do what he did. Unfortunately, situations like this are common, even when boats merely sink at the dock. When such situations occur, the best course of action is to have the insurer contact their own attorney for immediate legal advice. Salvage issues can involve considerable sums of money and these are issues best handled by a legal expert. When we run into such sticky problems, it's best to advise our client to call their lawyer. This will remove the responsibility from both the surveyor and boat owner and place everyone on more solid footing.

Salvage Fees -vs- Salvage Awards

A legal concept exists that a marine salvor is entitled to an award for his efforts from the vessel owner when he, the salvor, has successfully saved a vessel from peril. The misunderstanding of this concept has inspired a rogue's gallery of salvors who have sought to capitalize on the potential for what they perceive as easy money. Among the more common misconception is that of "salvage rights" wherein the concept is taken to mean *finders - keepers*, that is, the one who finds a distressed vessel has the right to keep it as a reward for his efforts at salvage. The courts have well established that a salvor has no such rights unless a vessel has been abandoned which, as mentioned above cannot occur within a matter of days, weeks or months and is hard to establish in any case.

The only right a salvor has is to an award for the successful effort at saving the vessel from peril at sea, and undertaken with the consent of the vessel owner. Whether a vessel having sunk at her dock is "at sea" or "in peril" is questionable; if the vessel crew or owners have the situation under control, there is no valid peril, for it can be argued that the damage is already done. For example, I have encountered cases where a salvor comes along a boat that is sunk at its dock in quiet waters and asserts a right to salvage, claiming that the vessel was in peril. Being sunk does not necessarily constitute a peril if the major part of the damage has already occurred with little likelihood of additional damages. In any case, the owner still retains the right to refuse assistance. The prudent owner rule does not supercede an instance where a vessel owner appears to have made an imprudent decision.

The occasion of refloating a sunken vessel that is not at risk is properly called refloating and not salvage.

There are numerous issues surrounding when a salvor can engage in salvage efforts without the vessel owner's permission. Despite the fact that a vessel owner has the right to refuse services of a salvor, there have been numerous instances where boat owners have had to fend off would-be salvors, sometimes placing the "salvor" more in the category of pirate than salvor. For this reason salvors are not always held in high esteem by surveyors.

The situation with salvage has become so abusive, what with just about anyone with a boat and a pump could call themselves "salvors", that at least one insurance intermediary (Boat US) created its own towing and salvage company, TowBoatUS. Boat US also created its own salvage contract form which can be found in appendix B. The student surveyor should read and study this contract closely for it covers many of the difficulties encountered with the salvage business such as liens, possession, interest, storage charges, and etcetera.

Notice that this contract does not mention anything about salvage awards, but rather approaches salvage as a contract fee-for-services rendered with methods of pricing and payment included. On the face of it, it would seem to preclude the salvor from making a claim for an award; however, it remains subject to Federal maritime law and the 1989 International Convention on Salvage. The controlling factor will remain the issue of imminent peril and whether the salvor has "saved" the vessel from destruction. Whenever large sums of money are potentially involved, it is always best to have the client bring in their own legal counsel as soon as possible.

Towing versus Salvage

One of the more common contentions with salvors is the issue of towing versus salvage. Towing services are normally charged for on an hourly fee basis, wherein a vessel is not in a position of immanent peril, as when a vessel simply loses power. On the other hand, a powerless vessel that is at risk of soon going up on a reef or beach and dashed to pieces is a different issue altogether. In the later instance towing becomes salvage to the extent of risk involved and the degree of impending damages that would result had no assistance been promptly rendered.

As if the salvage weren't difficult enough, environmental issues have crept into the mix to tip the balance in favor of salvors. Originally intended to deal with environmental situations such as the EXON VALDIZ oil spill, the 1989 International Convention on Salvage (U.N.) has been interpreted to apply to environmental damage caused by grounding, thereby extending the right of salvors to infringe on vessel owner rights. This has even been extended to include damage to sea bed grass as a result of ground in Federal Parks such as the Biscayne National Monument in the northern part of the Florida Keys.

Example

Issues involving salvage that the surveyor faces are rarely simple. A yacht sinks at her dock. As a result of the sinking myriad components of the yacht go adrift, such as large seat cushions, seating modules and other loose and semi loose items that float and go adrift. Such items can cause a major hazard to navigation. In addition, the fuel in the tanks and engine crankcase oil also floats out and causes oil pollution. This occurs on a weekend in a busy marina and the local marine patrol or U.S.C.G. personnel are on hand to observe the situation. The owner of the vessel is directed to contain the pollution as well as eliminate these hazards to navigation. The owner is under a lot of pressure and hasn't a clue what to do and will direct all his questions to the surveyor whom he sees as the agent of the insurer.

Meanwhile, a salvor has shown up who is pressing a salvage contract on the insured. At this point the surveyor must take the opportunity to carefully explain the reason for his presence and the extent of his responsibilities at this time. Again, the doctrine of the prudent uninsured must be conveyed to him, and it's best that the surveyor have a witness present at the time he does so. He should also have a blank copy of the Standard Form Yacht Salvage Contract on hand that he presents to the insured and urges him to read. After reading it, the surveyor can explain that he will assist him, but such assistance is *without prejudice* to either his rights, or the rights of the insurer; in other words that his assistance does not bind the insurer into coverage of the casualty, nor payment for the salvage contract costs. What the surveyor can do is to advise the insured, on behalf of the insurer, whether he considers the salvage contract amount to be fair and reasonable, this by virtue of the fact that he has been hired by the insurer based on his expertise on this issue.

Note that at this point if the surveyor engages in negotiations of salvage costs or other details with the salvor, he could become liable in some unanticipated way. Therefore, it's prudent that the surveyor keep his distance from the salvor and confine all his comments to the vessel owner alone and let him handle all negotiations with the salvor. Of course, the situation can work out differently if the surveyor knows and trusts the salvor, but escaping oil from sunken vessels is an inevitable result of sinking and must be dealt with immediately and effectively. As to pollution and hazards to navigation, the vessel owner is required to take reasonable and prudent actions to minimize these hazards. Experienced salvors will know how to handle these problems, and will have oil pollution booms available, though one should never make that assumption.

Oil pollution damage liability claims often occur in crowded marinas, particularly when black crankcase oil floats out of diesel engines. This can cause quite a mess on the hulls of other boats. If this has happened, the surveyor should take extensive photographs of the affected vessels and document the damage as best possible. It's a good idea to keep a low profile while doing so as not to encourage claims. Here is where a good telephoto lens becomes indispensable. Also watch out for floating docks that use Styrofoam as floatation as diesel oil will damage the Styrofoam and may give rise to a very large damage claim, so be sure to try to document the precasualty condition of the dock as well.

Hazards to Navigation

Should a casualty result in a hazard to navigation, very prompt action is required to minimize that hazard. In a 1989 case, a yacht collided with an Intracoastal Waterway marker, a 10" steel "H" beam, laying it over almost parallel to the water. Although the insured was advised that he had to take action to notify the Coast Guard and have the damaged marker "marked", he was slow to act. In the meantime another vessel skewered itself on that marker giving rise to a huge claim not only for physical damages to the vessel but also passenger injuries. Of all things to hit that downed marker, it had to be a small tour boat carrying passengers. In such cases it is wise for the insurer to take direct action himself through the surveyor who should know how to accomplish the task. That was a lesson I learned the hard way; I could have saved my client over a million dollars had I just picked up the phone and made a call to the U.S.C.G. station nearby who could have promptly marked it.

In such an instance, the surveyor would not be acting on behalf of the vessel owner, but on behalf of the insurer's liability interest. In a later and similar case, within hours of an accident, I engaged a marine contractor on behalf of the insurer to erect a temporary warning in place of a damaged water way marker. Here again, the issue is one of reasonable and prudent action. Never mind any issue of authority, prompt action to prevent further accidents is what counts.

Recommending Salvors

Salvage contracts can range from a verbal agreement to raise a small boat sunk at its dock that can easily be accomplished by a couple come-alongs and a pump, to more complex problems involving large sunken yachts in difficult conditions. What separates the experienced from inexperienced surveyors is their knowledge of skilled and trustworthy salvors as well as the unscrupulous and the bumblers just out to make a buck, as well as what kind of equipment is needed and how it is to be used.

Should the salvor decide that he wants to make a claim for a salvage award, he may tow the vessel away and hold it as collateral until the claimed award is paid or litigated, a sort of legalized ransom. Above all, this one thing we want to avoid, and the reason why surveyors will want to try to influence who is chosen to refloat the vessel. The risk of this happening should be explained to the boat owner so that he is fully aware of the potential seriousness of the situation.

The question inevitably arises, should the surveyor recommend a particular salvor. The answer depends on the individual case and whether the loss is known to be covered. If coverage is questionable making recommendations could incur some liability for the surveyor should things go wrong, so it is prudent to avoid direct recommendations. There is a better way to handle this. Instead of making a recommendation, he should explain to the owner that he cannot make recommendations, but he can inform the owner of those salvors whom he has dealt with and, who in his opinion are qualified and honest. It should be made clear that this is not a recommendation.

In events such as collisions where the insurer clearly has coverage, surveyors will usually take direct control even to the extent of directly hiring the salvor, since at this point they are operating on behalf of the insurer and not necessarily the insured that, in all events, must always be consulted because it is his property. The same applies to catastrophes where issues of experience, logistics, price, efficiency and the best equipment are important criteria as who gets hired.

Types of Salvage Contracts

There are two types of salvage contracts. One is the agreement *in extremis* entered into by the master of a vessel in danger under the stress of circumstances. The second type can be entered into by the owner and a professional salvage team after the immediate peril has ceased. The *in extremis* agreement will be enforced only if the court finds that it has been fairly negotiated and not entered into under duress with the result of an extortionate bargain for the salvor. If the court finds that a form of extortion was attempted, it may reduce the award or forfeit it entirely.

Until recently, the Lloyds Open Form Salvage Contract, a contract designed for issues of ships, has been used for boats. It universally opens up the vessel owner to liability for salvage awards in virtually any situation. Such a contract may be fine for ships and the corporations that own them, but they're not so fine for boats owned by private individuals with limited budgets and little ability to pay substantial awards.

The BoatUS Yacht Salvage Contract goes a long way toward addressing many of the problems presented by the Lloyds form, in that it provides for three price options (1) The International Salvage Convention of 1989, (2) A fixed price agreement, and (3) hour or day rate fees. All are based on a No Cure, No Pay basis. There are instances where the amount of time and effort to refloat a vessel can be estimated with a degree of accuracy, while the opposite is equally true, so it's good to have both options available.

The surveyor may feel free to make changes to the salvage contract as he sees fit so long as he doesn't mind putting himself in the position as negotiator. As for myself, I often find it advantageous to forego the no-cure-no-pay clause and go with an hourly or day rate on a not-to-exceed basis. I have a very simple reasoning for this. I want to establish a good relationship with my salvors by creating a win-win situation; I don't want them to fail and lose money. Why not? Because I know very well that they will try to make up for it on the next job that they will most surely quote higher. Thus I don't really win by not paying anything if the salvor fails, or the wreck breaks apart, because he'll hit me up the next time around. Then I do whatever I can to make sure that he doesn't fail.

If I don't like something the salvor is doing, I don't hesitate to call a halt and discuss the issue with him. A good example was the lifting of a large yacht where one strap out of four was considerably frayed. The salvor protested, complaining that to get another one would take too long. This was on a no-cure-no-pay job that hadn't gone well. I insisted and the job was delayed one day with rental equipment costs escalating. The yacht was lifted and no straps broke. I had already seen what happens when a strap does break and wasn't about to let it happen again.

Truly professional salvors must necessarily charge more than Billy Bob with a boat and a pump. They have much higher equipment and personnel costs. If we want to keep the professionals around, and not let the business be taken over by hacks, then "reasonable cost" must be considered in light of the cost of professional equipment. When comparing bids, we need to keep in mind who's bidding.

Incompetent Salvors – Surveyor as Salvage Master

It is not the least bit unusual to run across incompetent salvors; dealing with them is a very thorny issue indeed. The problems that ensue from incompetent salvors are either failure to salvage or severe damage caused by salvage operations. This damage may ensue not only to the distressed vessel but other property. Here are some examples of salvage gone seriously wrong:

> During an attempt to remove a vessel gone ashore, a salvage crane collapsed and landed on a condominium.

> During a salvage operation to remove a vessel from a condominium property, a crane was brought over soft ground near a swimming pool causing damage to the pool, side walks and parking lot.

> An aged, frayed lifting strap broke while attempting to move a large yacht from a reef. The yacht rolled over the edge of the reef and was lost in 200 feet of water.

> A salvor attempted to lift a 40 foot boat that was full of water; the hull collapsed and fell out of the lifting slings and destroyed a concrete dock.

Each of the cases cited above resulted in law suits being brought against both the salvor and boat owner. This is not something that the surveyor would want to happen to any salvage operation that he had any involvement in. In each of these cases the accident was predictable and would have been avoided by using common sense, but the salvor had none. This is why insurance companies hire experienced surveyors, and therefore it stands to reason that the surveyor should review the salvor's equipment, capability and plans.

As we can see by the above cases, the insurance company has a much greater risk exposure than merely the value of the vessel, as does the insured. If the client is not aware of these requirements, be sure to explain to him the possible consequences that can attach to the lowest bid.

In case of the damaged condominium grounds, the surveyor reviewed the salvage plan and anticipated the damages that a 125 ton truck crane lifting a 50,000 lb. boat would cause to the grounds. The vessel owner was a high ranking military officer who felt confidant of what he was doing and the signed the salvage contract over the surveyor's objections. The surveyor insisted that the insurer bring in their attorney and three days of negotiation ensued wherein a hold harmless agreement for the insurer was inserted in the salvage contract. Whereafter the salvor proceeded to ignore the surveyor's warnings and drove his 75 ton crane across 150 feet of concrete parking lot, over the swimming pool deck, badly breaking up both and causing $140,000 in damages to the property. Although the salvor, boat owner and insurer were jointly sued, the hold harmless agreement ensured that the suit against boat owner and insurer was dismissed on summary judgement.

Another example will illustrate why the low bid isn't always the best bid. A sixty foot Hatteras was sunk and was laying on its side with the bottom against a sea wall 2/3rds submerged. Because of this, it could not be righted. With all those glass windows under water, the only way to get it up was by means of a 150 ton barge crane and only one was available. The barge owner proffered a contract at $48,000, an amount that I thought was quite reasonable, but the insurer did not. At the insistence of the insurer, who thought the amount excessive, the salvage was put up for bids and the job went to the low bidder of $25,000, an unusually low amount.

The salvor bolted plywood to all the large windows except those on the bottom side that could not be reached since they were deeply embedded in mud, and then proceeded to try to pump it out, oblivious to what would happen to the exposed windows on the bottom side once the hull was freed from the bottom mud. Oddly enough, as the water level inside the boat went down, the pressure on the outside collapsed the plywood and the boat filled with water again. After a week of fooling around with other methods, the salvor finally gave up and the barge crane was called in. It took several days with a water jet to tunnel under the hull to get straps around it, but ultimately it was lifted and pumped until refloated without damage.

While what we were dealing with here was clearly a constructive total loss, our main interest was in minimizing damage so as to maximize salvage sale value, thus minimizing the loss.

To minimize these thorny problems, experienced surveyors seek to establish a relationship with a salvor they can trust. Unfortunately, this, in itself, can cause problems with a perception of collusion between surveyor and salvor. To avoid this, it is useful to explain one's actions and preferences toward a particular salvor to the client and the reasons for doing so. Unfortunately, in the event of litigation, even that will not protect the surveyor from a possible charge of collusion by the insured.

There is nothing wrong with having a preference for one salvor over another, but it is dangerous to create the appearance of collusion. This can be avoided by being open and up front about what you are doing. Take the time to advise both the insured and the client as to why you repeatedly use or recommend the same salvor. In instances where there is time to solicit bids from competent salvors, one should do that. Note that if we fail to do that, our actions may become indefensible. We do have the right to discriminate between who is competent and trustworthy and who is not. There is no obligation to solicit bids from companies that do not have adequate equipment or a demonstrable expertise.

Salvage Bidding

Particularly in cases of yachts sunk at the dock, as well as some other situations, there may be time to solicit salvage bids. This, of course, is regulated by the potential for additional damage, such as that posed by wind and waves, including vessel wakes. Over time, the surveyor becomes familiar with many salvors so that a few timely phone calls can bring a number of salvors in to bid on the job, which is the preferable method for casualties where salvage contracts are likely to exceed $5,000. For amounts below that, there isn't likely to be sufficient savings to justify the additional time and work of obtaining bids, making it economically impractical.

All of the above is applicable to those working in major boating centers, but for those working less populated areas, one has to make do with what he has available.

(Footnotes)

1. The terms insured and assured are synonymous, as are the terms insurer and underwriter.

2. Since English law is very similar to U.S. law, it is appropriate to consider English cases.

3. There have been a number of court rulings to this effect.

4. Foremost v. Richardson, USSC 1982

5. In Executive Jet Aviation, Inc. v. City of Cleveland, 409 U.S. 249, 260 (1972) a private jet crashed on take off from Cleveland's Lakefront Airport and went into Cleveland Harbor. Executive Jet claimed and won Admiralty jurisdiction which limited the company's liability to the value of the jet based solely on the fact that the aircraft ended up in the water.

6. Merritt & Chapman v. United States 1927

Chapter 5

Bilge Pumps & Batteries

Of all marine investigation types, sinking investigations are the most commonly encountered. Therefore, this and the two following chapters cover the various elements involved as completely as reasonably possible within the confines of a single book. All three chapters are inter-related, but are kept separate to avoid confusion and maintain clarity.

Bilge Pumps

Bilge pumps are a critical element to any pleasure craft remaining afloat. All boats either have leaks or will develop leaks in the future. Moreover, many boats are not intended by design to keep all water out. In time, any boat without a bilge pumps will accumulate water and eventually sink. This is the essential argument that boats cannot be seaworthy without such pumps. Indeed, the vast majority of pleasure craft sinkings occur while the vessel is unattended, and as a result of pumping system failure.

For this reason, complete evaluation of the pumping system must go hand-in-hand with determination of the source of water ingress. In all cases of sinking or flooding of a hull, the bilge pumps need to be tested for proper operation. From an evidentiary standpoint, it is important to be able to prove or disprove whether any and all pumps were or were not functioning at the time of sinking. When investigating bilge pump issues, the system must be viewed as a whole, for these are systems that can be either simple or complex.

The central question in all boat sinkings is why the bilge pump(s) didn't keep the vessel afloat since that is the purpose of their existence: in most cases the bilge pumps should have kept the boat afloat, so the initial assumption will be that the pumping system has failed. Therefore, the state of the pumping system *at the time of sinking* becomes a primary focus. The investigator will also need to establish the condition of the electrical system that powers the pumps, including the batteries and battery charger which runs off the shore power system, if there is one.

Correct assessment of the cause of the loss depends on determining whether the sinking was the result of a system failure, or the result of the pumping system being overwhelmed. Failure of the pumping system will be the proper assessment unless it can be demonstrated that the pumps could not be reasonably expected to discharge the amount of water entering the hull. Pumping systems must necessarily be divided into two classes, those with charging systems and those without. Absent electrical system failure, pumps in vessels with battery charging systems can more or less be expected to run indefinitely[1] so that the issue of whether the water ingress was a long-term or short-term event is less important than it is for a boat with no charging system. Pumps in vessels without charging systems will run only until the battery is depleted.

The significance of the distinction between the two as it may affect insurance coverage is that pumping system failure may be classified as an internal defect, whereas absent any system failure may be strictly the result of an external event. Then there will be those cases where both circumstances were involved, so that we have a primary and a contributing cause. With insurance cases, the investigator will need to give very careful consideration to these factors in order to draw the correct conclusion, since the boat owner's insurance coverage will depend upon it.

Key Components

Bilge pumping systems can get rather complicated, for a system is made up of numerous components each of which is dependent upon all other components. Were the pumps overwhelmed by the amount of water entering the hull? Did the pumps ultimately discharge the batteries and stop pumping? Did the battery charging system fail? Or were the pumps or some other aspect of the system faulty from the start? These are the basic questions we are charged with answering. There are twelve key components of a typical medium size pleasure craft pumping system, starting with the pumps and working back to the shore power system, itemized as follows:

Bilge pumps

Float switches

Helm panel switches

Pump circuit breakers

Fig. 5-1. One of the first tasks of an investigation is to secure the electric panel and photograph it so as to memorialize the position of all switches.

Main panel DC circuit breaker

Battery switch

Battery

Battery charger

Main panel AC circuit breaker

Shore power inlet breaker

Boat side shore power connector

Dockside shore power connector

Dockside, main and sub circuit breakers

This list covers the key electrical components in addition to which is the plumbing and wiring. A fault in any one component could be a potential or contributory cause and thus all key points need to be inspected and evaluated. To conduct a thorough investigation, each needs to be examined and eliminated as a potential cause, and should also be specifically covered in the report. This list should be used as a standard checklist to be covered on every investigation. To fail to do so is to leave an unanswered question, which is the downfall of many investigators' reports.

In determining the role that bilge pumps play in the sinking of the vessel, it is first necessary to observe and record the general environment in which they are functioning. Is the bilge area clean or dirty, does it contain sand or other abrasives that could damage the pump? Are there larger pieces of debris that could have caused it to become jammed? Many boats have substantial amounts of debris in the bilge including quantities of nuts, bolts, screws, wire connectors and bits of wire and so on. Such things can momentarily or permanently jam pumps.

Fig. 5-2. The Rule 1500 pump viewed from the bottom side.

One should note the general location and position of the pumps, and then the lowest point of the bilge. Most boats do not float perfectly level, and therefore water will likely run forward or aft. Only occasionally is the keel perfectly level to the water line. Some few boats, usually trawler types and larger motor yachts, may have a bilge section that is deepest amidships.

The area or compartment in which the pumps are located must also be evaluated, noting such things as size of compartment, relationship of position and height of pump, number of pumps, possible restrictions or obstructions to proper pump operation. Note the location and positioning of the float switch; could it have been damaged by water rushing through the bilge as the boat gets up on plane and water in the forward section rushes aft?

In most cases it will be necessary to also determine whether there is free communication of water between compartments. That will include limber holes between stringers and bulkheads, as well as any cut outs. It will generally be necessary to establish an overview of how water entering the vessel will spread through the hull. Whether a bulkhead is water tight or nearly so, or has large openings in it at various levels may be highly relevant to the investigation. There are many smaller express cruisers in which the forward engine room or cabin bulkhead does not have a limber hole at the bottom, and therefore the forward and aft sections of the hull are separated. Some of the smaller boats will not have bilge pumps in the forward section simply because the cabin sole is only a couple inches off the bottom of the hull, leaving no room for a pump. Obviously, a boat designed in this way poses serious questions of seaworthiness, since there is no way to remove water that accumulates in the forward section.

Where water entering the hull will go to first is particularly important, for in part this gives an indication of the subsequent sequence of events. With rear engine boats (stern drives and vee drive) water always accumulates aft and for that reason the aft bilge pump is the most important pump in the vessel. If that has failed, we naturally want to

Fig. 5-3. Jabsco diaphragm pump. This type of pump must have a filter on the intake side to prevent debris from damaging the diaphragms, such as seen at left.

know whether any other pump could pick up the slack, or whether an aft pump failure played a primary role in sinking. Some builders recognize this point and install two pumps aft. This leads to the question of; why don't all builders do the same? Can we say that a stern-heavy boat with only one aft bilge pump is seaworthy?

Moreover, when a hull has a sealed bulkhead, this causes the boat to sink by one end only, with the opposite end remaining buoyant. This causes the hull, as respects sinking, to behave in unexpected ways. The point here is that it is helpful to try to evaluate what role the compartmentalization of the hull played with the functioning of the bilge pumps. This, combined with any water lines that may be present, will help to reveal the how and why the sinking occurred.

Types and Brands

Rule Industries has been making the same basic style centrifugal pumps for over 30 years, pumps that have proved so reliable that this brand dominates the industry by a margin of about 20:1 over any other brand. Thus it will be the Rule pumps that we'll be dealing with most of the time so we need to know a thing or two about them. Many boat owners complain about the unreliability of bilge pumps but they are mistaken. It's not the pumps that are unreliable but the supporting system, most particularly the float switches and wiring. Anytime we have electrical/mechanical apparatus in an environment like a bilge, such systems will have a high requirement for maintenance. Corroded wire connections are undoubtedly the number one cause of pump failure. And, of course, if a motor is run on wiring with corrosion and high resistance, there is the risk of damage to that motor.

Rule pumps have even improved over the years. In decades past, if the float switch stuck in the up position and the pump ran dry for many days, it was likely to overheat. Today, we don't see this happening. I still find old Rule pumps in boats that are over

Fig. 5-4. In some cases, the only way to open up sealed pumps is to cut them open. In this case the manufacturer failed to glue the top on and the pump housing filled with water.

25 years old, testifying as to the quality of these pumps.

Other brands such as Jabsco manufacture both centrifugal and diaphragm pumps, the later of which are rarely found anymore, or only used for special applications such as completely dewatering a bilge where a centrifugal pump can't do that. These pumps have capacity ratings ranging from 6-12 GPM and are subject to the diaphragms wearing out and rupturing, in which case the pump doesn't pump at all.

The Rule pumps can be dismantled to inspect the motor (See **Fig. 5-4.** above). Press the two snap release tabs to release the red impeller cage plate, then remove the six screws from the inner plate which seals against a rubber o-ring. To remove the motor completely, cut away the sealing grommet around the wires at the top of the pump. This will allow the motor to slip out completely and the determination of whether water has leaked into the motor can be made.

Testing

The tools needed for testing pumping systems consist of a multimeter with an audible continuity tester, four fifteen foot jumper wires with alligator clips and a spare 12 V battery. We have to make up our own jumpers because such long ones are not commercially available. Tip: try to find some very fine stranded, highly flexible wire as stiff wire is hard to manage. Why four jumpers? Because we may need up to three and it's always a good idea to have a spare as they easily become damaged. If you intend to do much of this work, you'll find that a good 12V battery is needed for testing in those cases where the boat battery is dead. I use a gel cell battery since this type does not lose power at the same rate automotive batteries do, and requires charging only twice per year.

I maintain a fishing tackle box that contains electrical tools, test lights, wire connectors, terminals, fuses, lengths of wire and anything else I might need to test a boat's pumping system. When I get to an investigation site, I have everything I might need on hand, including a set of jumper cables. There are also now some very good and versatile portable chargers on the market that can be used in place of batteries to test pumps.

Before disturbing the pumping system in any way, the pumps should be tested in place with the existing electrical system. This may require replacing the vessel's batteries to conduct the test, or one can connect up the portable charger. It will be clear whether the DC system was hot when the boat went down by the condition of the wiring. If the batteries were at a high state of charge, the main cables and lugs should have been destroyed by electrolysis. If the cables and lugs are less than completely wasted away, then the batteries were probably at a lesser state of charge.

Note whether the wiring to the pump, as well as the supply bus, are wasted and to what degree. When a boat sinks in sea water, the degree of electrolysis will be substantially greater than in fresh water. With experience an investigator gets a feel for the state of the batteries at the time of sinking just by looking at them. One can, of course, measure the remaining charge, but more often than not they will be dead. Much will depend on how long the vessel was submerged. Most 12V pumps stop pumping altogether at 7 volts. By examining the state of the electrical system, one can decide whether to test it by connecting up a new battery to the boat's system.

What we most want to know is whether the wiring from the pump's bus to the pump remains operational. Possibly the bus or terminal bar has completely corroded away. If not, then it should be tested because if the wiring system does still operate the pump, then you will have eliminated any fault in the wiring as being the cause. In this way, segment by segment, we test and prove the system, searching for a fault if any exists.

The Battery Switch and Wiring

As the DC wiring diagram (**Fig. 5-5.**) presented on the next page attests, electrical systems on even a thirty footer can be complex. Attempting to figure out the scheme by tracing wires on the vessel may be a hopeless or at least very time consuming task. Therefore, it's wise to seek to obtain the vessel's wiring diagrams which are often contained, at least in rudimentary form, in the owner's manual. Pumps can be wired in numerous ways and activated or turned off from more than one position. Dual control station vessels might have as many as three switches for each pump.

One of the first things we need to do is to test whether the pumps have been properly wired, that is, whether the main battery switches when turned off will cut off power to the pumps. The bilge pumps should be wired to a power source independent of the switches. One of the first things we will have done is to check the positions of the battery switches. If they are in the OFF position, we next need to trace the bilge pump wiring to its source and determine whether it is before or after the switch. There should be a supply wire to a separate bus that is independent of the battery switch, i.e. taken off

DC Electrical Diagram

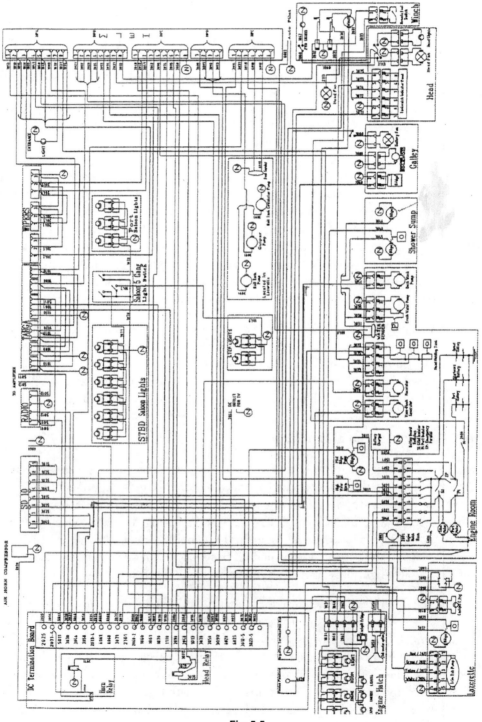

Fig. 5-5.

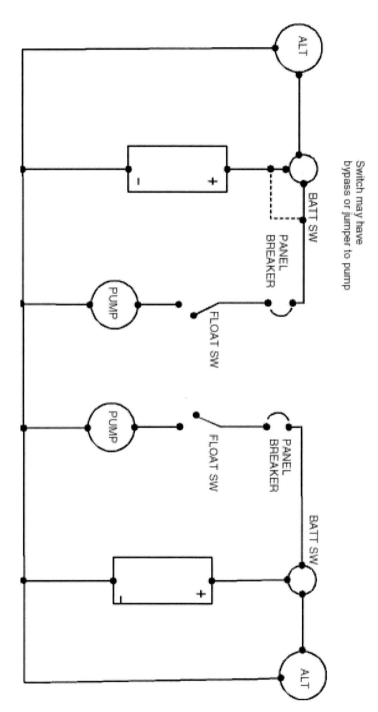

Fig. 5-6. Typical DC bilge pump wiring scheme

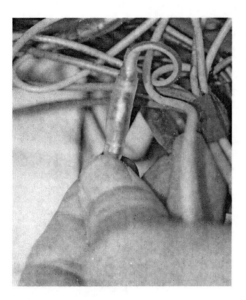

Fig. 5-7. The Ray-Chem wire connector is supposedly water tight. We see here that it clearly is not, and neither is shrink wrap. Open butt connectors usually fare better than any type that attempts to seal, but only succeeds in holding the water in. It's better, if the connector gets wet, that the water should be able to drain out.

the battery before the switch so that in turning the switch OFF it cannot disable the pump. Most often the pump power feed is off in feed side of the battery switch. Most later model boats will have a small circuit breaker panel (usually push-button type) for this purpose somewhere near the batteries or in the engine compartment. One way or another it must be proved that the switch does not de-energize the pumps.

If the pump does not function through the original wiring, then move on to inspecting all the splices and connections. Test each connection to find out where the fault is, and once found try to determine it was the result of the sinking or pre existed. One of the most common causes of pump failure is an improperly made wire splice that either comes apart or gets wet and corrodes. If the pump does not function on the internal wiring, or the pump bus is wasted away, one method of testing the remaining wiring is to scrape some insulation off the wiring and connect the test battery to pump wires to test the whole circuit. Alternatively one can use a continuity tester to determine if current flows across the various connectors, including those of the float switch. Each of the connections should be tested and proved. I use a Dremmel tool with an abrasive cutter to open up butt connectors to examine the metal-to-metal contact when corrosion is involved.

If a wire connection is an open circuit (broken connection) now, it doesn't necessarily follow that it was an open circuit prior to sinking. An attempt should be made to determine if this connection was damaged before or after it went under water. Conversely, if it works now, it surely was working pre casualty.

Once the pump wiring scheme has been determined, make a detailed sketch of it.

Determine and note the location and height of the bilge pump wiring connections. The significance of this is to determine whether any of the connections were being submerged

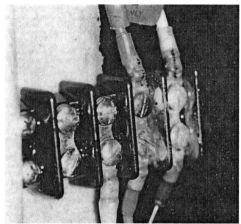

Fig. 5-8. Corroded terminals and splices are the most common cause of pump failure.

by rising water, or could be submerged by normal levels of bilge water. Especially note the location of the connections for the aft bilge pump, keeping in mind that for all but displacement speed vessels, bilge water will run aft when up on plane. Because of this, virtually all water in the aft bilge accumulates in a much smaller space up against the transom, and in a bouncing boat, the wire connections often get wet.

Electrolysis corrosion is distinguishable from normal oxidation corrosion by the brightness and general lack of much oxide present. Corrosion of metals with a heavy build up of oxides usually indicates nothing more than repeated, long-term water exposure or possibly galvanic corrosion, whereas current flowing through an exposed conductor will carry away most of the corrosion by-products and leave the surface bright. Or a copper conductor may show dezincification caused by electrolysis, in which case the metal appears dull orange instead of green. Whether the copper is orange or bright is a matter of the amount of current passing through it. Low voltage dezincifies whereas high voltage carries all metals away, including oxides.

Note: Electrolysis cannot occur in water unless there is a ground source. As an example, electrolysis cannot occur to an electrified piece of metal that is immersed in a plastic bucket of water as the bucket is insulated from any grounding.

Check the polarity of pump wiring; on Rule bilge pumps the brown wire is positive. If wired backwards, the pump will run at less than half the capacity according to the manufacturer.

Turn the pump over and check that the impeller is not loose on the shaft, and that the shaft turns freely. Is the pump securely attached or did the pump fall over on its side?

If the impeller does not turn freely, examine the pump housing; distortions in the plastic, particularly at the top, are an indication of overheating caused by running dry for long periods. Pumps that run on low voltage are likely to overheat and seize up. However, if

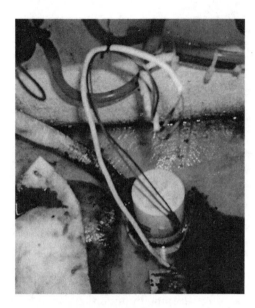

Fig. 5-9. This photo underscores the importance of careful observation and testing. This pump still ran after the sinking, but note that water is shooting out of the side of it, and not out the discharge hose which was blocked with debris.

the pump is submerged, water will keep the outside cool so that the burning will only be evident internally, and therefore the pump should be opened up and dismantled.

Test that the pump float switch turns the pump on and that the switch is free of any restrictions. It is often the case that the float is restricted from operating fully by wires, hoses or other objects. It is always possible that some object held the flapper down, and then later floated away or was otherwise moved. Is the switch secured or is it free to move or float around?

Improper wiring installations and/or repairs are a very common occurrence. As mentioned earlier, the pump wire connections to the power source are a weak point prone to getting wet and damaged simply because the bilge is a wet environment, particularly the aft bilge and bilges that are under open cockpit decks where hatches are prone to leak. Obviously, then, if wire connections aren't protected from water, they will corrode and either break the circuit or cause very high resistance that is likely to damage the pump motor. Twisted, taped wire connections should never be used, and neither should wire nuts. The later because they can easily come off, and also because these cup-shaped devices can trap and hold water.

Butt connectors are better, but by no means trouble free. Within these the wires and crimped connection can corrode, although it will take longer to eventually break the connection. Shrink wrap and most other supposedly water resistant types usually fail to keep water out and in many cases only exacerbate the problem by holding water in. It is insufficient to simply continuity test connections; it is necessary that the resistance of all connections should be metered to ensure that there isn't excessive resistance.

More and more pumps these days are the so-called electronic variety, meaning that they have unintelligible computer stuff inside a sealed compartment. The housing should be checked for water intrusion into the circuitry.

Float Switches

The vast majority of bilge pumps are controlled by float switches, of which the Rule "flapper" switch is the most common, though there are many other types including those that are contained within a housing of some sort, as well as the "electronic" type pumps. These switches can be a real monkey wrench in the gears of an investigation by reason of it being difficult to prove whether the switch was functional or not. A common example is a switch located in an area where any number of hoses or wires or possibly even debris such as rags could have prevented it from working, but as a result of the sinking, those items are no longer in their original position, or perhaps are now completely out of the picture for one reason or another. The only point to be made here is to try to be aware of and account for such possibilities. Example: In a report it's useful to state: *No conditions were found that would indicate that the float switch was impaired in any way* — if that is the case.

Aft bilge pump float switches can be torn off their foundations as a result of a heavy surge of bilge water at the time the boat rises up on plane. This happens when the Rule flapper is facing forward instead of aft, like it should. If the flapper is torn off its hinges, this is the most likely reason.

Caged float switches prevent large objects and water surge from interfering with switch operation, but they remain vulnerable to becoming bound up with sludge.

Bilge Pump Capacity Ratings

Almost all bilge pumps come with a capacity rating emblazoned in large numbers on the pump. That is not necessarily how much water the pump will discharge because those are perfect world numbers. That rating is achieved at the unlikely high battery charge rate of 13.6 volts and with a static head of zero. At 45" of static head and 12.5 volts, the Rule 1500 pump was tested and found to pump only 512 GPH, roughly one third of rated capacity[2]. My own tests of both Rule and Attwood pumps uniformly failed to perform up to their published GPH ratings under any conditions. Other testers such as Powerboat Reports and other surveyors have produced results similar to mine.

The principle of the DC electric motor is that the more voltage that is put to it, the faster it will spin, and the reverse is also true. Thus, as the battery declines, a pump will progressively pump less and less until it stops altogether at somewhere very near 7 volts, depending on head pressure. Note that with no load on the pump, it will turn at very low voltages so that testing under no load conditions is not proper.

It should be also be noted, however, that there are a wide range of variables that can affect pumping capacity, including the length, routing and type of discharge hose used. My tests are intended only for demonstration purposes. Whenever possible, the system in question should be put to the test to determine its actual pumping rate as installed.

Water Leakage Rates

Five hundred gallons per hour bilge pump discharge rate is nothing to sneeze at so long as the rate of leakage into the boat isn't heavy, so let's try put these rates into perspective. A leak that is a steady stream about 1/8" in diameter translates to one quart per minute, or 15 gallons per hour, 360 gallons per day and 2520 gallons per week. In a large boat this is no problem, but in a 24' outboard that rate of leakage could put it on the bottom in a short time if the pump doesn't work properly.

In this scenario the pump would probably activate at least once per hour for about fifteen seconds. 500 GPH is 8.4 gallons per minute so that to move 15 gallons would take roughly two minutes. Our rate of leakage says that the pump would cycle about 24 times per day for a total of 48 minutes per day. That's not much, but when we multiply this number times the number of days since the battery was last charged, it becomes very substantial. Since outboard boats rarely have charging systems other than alternators, if one week elapsed since last charging then this amounts to 5.6 hours of pump running time, enough to deplete older batteries. A five amp pump running for 5.6 hours equals 28 ampere/hours. The fly in the ointment here is that as the battery declines and the voltage goes down, so does the pumping rate; the pump will therefore have to run even longer to pump the same amount of water out, so our calculated 5.6 hours in reality could be longer.

If we use Rule's data showing a decline of 200 GPH or 16.66% in the pumping rate at 3.35' of head when voltage declines from 13.6 to 12.0 volts, we can project this across the time the pump would run until it quits being effective at around 10.0 volts. This works out to an uncompounded 33.3% rate of decrease in flow rate across 3.2 volts of battery discharge. This reduces our pumping rate to a mere 333.5 GPH. While this is not totally correct reasoning behind my math because the actual rate will vary across the range of voltage available, it does give a general idea of how much the rate could be reduced by a weak and declining battery.

Of course what we're dealing with after the fact is theory with these calculations because we will never know the exact status of the battery before the boat sank. But this is not our purpose, which is to support or disprove a theory of causation by means of calculation.

Pump Placement

With vessels with multiple pumps, take note of where the pumps are placed relative to the communication of water throughout the bilge spaces and what will happen if one pump fails, or water accumulates in one compartment only. Let's consider the case of a rear engine 30' boat that two bilge pumps, one in the engine compartment and one up forward in the cabin area. Chapter Seven discusses at length the problems associated with unbalanced boats and the fact that with stern-heavy boats, water will always run

Fig. 5-10. At first glance, this would appear to be a very high riser on this pump discharge line. However, the outlet is actually only two inches above the waterline. It actually discharges through a seacock seen at upper right.

and accumulate aft, causing it to sink with much less water than a mid engine boat. Here we anticipate that it probably won't matter how many pumps a boat has if they are not placed where water will normally accumulate. This is why we are increasingly seeing larger stern drive boats with two pumps placed in the stern.

An inexperienced boat owner probably isn't going to be aware of this situation, but feels confident that because his boat has two pumps everything is fine. Of course, he does not know that if the stern pump fails, the forward pump won't do any good; the boat goes down by the stern and sinks long before water ever reaches that pump. In my view such a situation constitutes a defective design. At the least, the boat builder has a duty to warn the owner of the danger posed by this situation. The fact that some builders have recognised the risk and have added two pumps is proof of the point.

The Bilge Pump Discharge

Problems with the pump discharge hose or piping arrangement are often traced as the cause of sinking, mainly resulting from back flow of water from outside the hull due to improper installation. There are two means by which water can enter through a discharge plumbing, siphoning and ordinary back flow. If the pump outlet is only an inch or so above the water line (and this is why it is so important to record any and all water lines that show up on the hull) then it is inevitable that under certain conditions

Fig. 5-11. Above: heavy bronze check valves severely restrict flow rates of bilge pumps and can become clogged with debris.

Fig. 5-12. Left: a bilge pump discharge installed only an inch or so above the water poses an obvious hazard.

water will back flow through that outlet. The usual method to prevent this is by means of a riser that brings the pump outlet to a safe level above the water line.

After all these decades of boat building, bilge pump discharge lines still get installed in such a way that reverse siphoning can occur. The potential for this exists when a discharge is installed very near the water line — say an inch or two. The way this happens is that when the pump shuts off there is still water in the discharge line. Gravity will then pull that water back down toward the pump. If the discharge outlet for any reason happens to be under water, this condition will then start the reverse siphoning process. This can even occur when there is a substantial riser loop. Under "normal" conditions the outlet won't be underwater, but abnormal conditions, such as the boat listing to one side for any reason (a common one is an engine having been removed), or possibly wave action, getting caught under a dock and so on, can create the abnormal condition.

When this happens it can set up a repetitive cycle. Water siphons in until the bilge water rises and activates the float switch and the pump then discharges the water. When the pump stops, the siphoning continues. This repeats until either the battery is discharged or, if there is a battery charger, the pump finally fails or shore power is interrupted leaving no evidence as to what happened. The key to discovery is the positioning of the discharge outlet.

We know from experience that siphoning requires ideal conditions to be set in motion. Riser loops serve the purpose of inhibiting the ability of gravity to pull water back through the discharge hose by means of elevating the height and therefore the gravitational pull required to overcome the additional height. Riser loops *do not* add to the amount of static head to be overcome by the pump because the increase in height is offset by the additional force of the water falling on the other side of the loop, thus

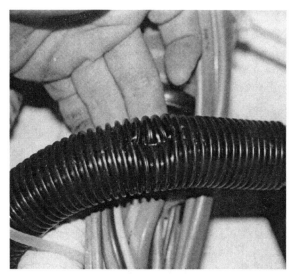

Fig. 5-13. This molded plastic bilge pump hose is very thin and once was in widespread use. It damages very easily as can be seen here where I've practically cut through it with my fingernail. Because it is corrugated, it also causes turbulence and reduces flow rate.

canceling it out.

Note that there is a difference between siphoning and simple back flow. Figure 5-12 shows an improper installation with no riser loop where the discharge outlet simply went underwater and water back-flowed through the system. Water can back-flow through all centrifugal pumps, but not positive displacement impeller types.

Check valves are sometimes used as a back-flow prevention, but if the check valve should get clogged up with debris or stick for other reasons, the prevention fails. Moreover, some pump manufacturers recommend against using check valves because they cause restriction in the line and reduce capacity. If there is a check valve in the system, then it needs to be checked for these problems. The use of heavy bronze check valves can reduce flow rates easily by 50% or more.

Another occasional problem that is encountered results from excessive static head in the discharge line. A pump's capacity is greatly reduced by the height which it has to push water upward against gravity. Most pump manufacturers publish a table of static head heights showing how much each additional foot reduces capacity. Such information may be available on the manufacturer's web site.

If a pump discharge is installed in the forward half of the hull, it is possible that the bow wave will push water back through the discharge line, so be alert to this situation.

Discharge hoses may become crimped as a result of improper routing or by means of the hanger or method of securement used.

Molded plastic hoses are subject to cracking or being easily cut or holed. This can result in a situation where the hose is putting the discharge water right back in the hull. This is yet another reason why it is important to test the system in the boat as is, so be sure to examine the discharge plumbing for leaks.

Corrugated plastic hose was at one time supplied by pump manufacturers. This type of hose has been found to cause such severe water turbulence within the hose as to reduce flow capacity by up to 50%. The material is no longer widely sold, though I recently saw some in a local marine store. If you find corrugated hose, its flow rate capacity will need to be tested and proved as to the actual flow rate. The amount of resistance is proportional to the hose length.

Another common problem is broken plastic through hull fittings to which the discharge hose is attached to. These may be located in an area that cannot be seen from the inside so that if the fitting fractures, the discharge may be putting the water right back into the boat. If the boat has plastic through hulls, be sure to check all the fittings from the exterior.

Boats that have been stored ashore for a long time have been known to have insects such as mud dauber wasps build nests within the discharge outlet. Discharge lines can get clogged for other reasons as well, so be sure to check for restrictions.

On occasion it may be necessary to restore the existing pumping system in place so as to test the system as it was built whenever the pumping capacity is in question. Whenever the investigator suspects that there will be a counter claim against a manufacturer or other third party, particularly one with considerable expertise, it is best that these systems be tested in place so as to closely replicate the original conditions as possible, and to have a reliable witness present when such tests are set up and conducted.

When conducting such tests, be sure to analyze all aspects of the test to be sure that there are no conditions that could render the test subject to challenge. Rest assured that if the case goes to litigation, the manner in which the test was conducted will be challenged.

Conditions to Be Alert To

In summary, the following is a list of the most common causes of pump discharge related causes that can occur either singly or in combination:

> No riser loop
>
> Restricted or clogged check valve
>
> Discharge line crimped
>
> Discharge line holed
>
> Discharge line clogged
>
> Excessive riser height
>
> The use of corrugated hose
>
> Vessel caught under dock on rising tide

Engine or other heavy object removed from vessel

Wave action

Permanent change in vessel trim by means of alterations or additions to vessel

Testing Bilge Pump Capacity

In most cases the investigator will want to test the actual bilge pump capacity, which needs to be established for three reasons: (1) to determine if the pump meets the advertised capacity, (2) to determine the actual pumping rate as it existed in the boat and, (3) to build a case with definitive proof of any defects and the net result of those defects.

Testing of the bilge pumps can be conducted as it exists in the boat with the existing plumbing so that all the previously existing conditions are the same, or it can be removed and set up for testing outside of the boat. If done with care, either method is acceptable. With larger yachts the later method is usually employed due to greater distances and difficulties involved. With any type of testing for forensic purposes it is, of course, imperative to replicate the actual pre casualty conditions as closely as possible. Close attention need be given to dimensions such as riser heights, hose lengths, wire size and lengths and any other factor that could render an inaccurate result.

This raises the difficult question about the condition of the batteries. There's no perfect solution to the problem of how to replicate the condition that the boat's batteries were in before the sinking occurred. All we can do is to attempt to extrapolate the past condition from the current condition. Much will depend on the type of battery, whether it has been totally discharged, and whether there was sea water intrusion. If the battery has not been completely discharged, and has no sea water intrusion, then it can be recharged with the expectation that the amount of charge that it accepts will be reasonably close to what it was previously. But the investigator will also have to take into consideration such issues as whether there was an operating charging system.

Another method would be to cut the battery open and examine the plates. This is most useful where the battery will not accept any charge and there was no charging system and there was no pass-through current to run the pump. Battery condition can be reasonably approximated from the condition of the plates; if the plates are badly deteriorated then it's clear that there was little or no battery power.

Tests can be carried out using discarded five gallon paint buckets available in dumpsters at construction sites everywhere. Place the pump in the bucket with a garden hose in it flowing at the same rate that the pump is emptying it. Set up the discharge hose at the appropriate height along with the other bucket. Time how long it takes to fill a five gallon bucket and convert to an hourly rate. Next, run the pump with the original battery and time it until the pump completely discharges the battery.

A table of discharge and pumping rates based on battery state can then be created to show what the timing would be at various charge states, if this would be helpful.

Batteries

The first thing to be said on the subject of batteries is that this is a very complicated subject owing to the wide variety of types — that is construction, materials and intended application of batteries. Moreover, the issue is further complicated by questions of actual circumstances of use and recharging. This is made even more difficult by an industry that manipulates specifications for marketing purposes, resulting in a lack of standardization for ratings. For the marine investigator there is no escape from having to understand the subject of batteries because these are what power the bilge pumps and expert knowledge is critical to every investigation. Therefore we will examine this subject in depth.

The determination of the condition of the boat's batteries prior to the onset of the event is the most difficult part of any investigation. This is due to the fact that the rated capacity of the battery is only available at the time the battery is new. From the moment it is put into service, battery power and capacity begins to decline and recharging cannot completely restore it. It therefore becomes very important to understand how the different types of batteries perform. The two basic types are *automotive* and *storage* batteries.

The controlling factor of battery life - besides design and quality - is the discharge/recharge cycle. Virtually all batteries are damaged to some degree when they undergo significant discharging. Each time they are recharged, the amount of recharge possible is somewhat less than it was originally. For a storage battery the amount of service life lost with each recharge cycle is far less than that of an automotive battery.

Automotive Batteries

Also known as cranking batteries, these batteries are basically designed for use in road vehicles where the primary need is for engine starting, a function that requires very high initial bursts of energy. These are batteries which, once the engine is started, are recharged by means of alternators that, in road vehicles, are typically used frequently. Of course, pleasure craft are used far less frequently so that charge state is often a problem. These batteries also provide secondary power needs for such things as lighting and other low demand accessories, however, these secondary power demands are usually met by the alternator passing power through the battery without discharging it because the power is going straight from the alternator to the electrical equipment.

The important feature of automotive batteries is that they provide high initial cranking power but have very little *reserve power*. These batteries are good at providing high bursts of power, but far less able to provide a sustained rate of power over time. That's

Fig. 5-14. High quality automotive battery cut in half. Each plate consists of lead powder packed on a plastic screen. Each plate is packed in a separate plastic pouch. This battery is completely wasted and the sulfated debris can be seen accumulating on the bottom. A battery in this condition does not hold any charge.

why, if the headlights of a car are left on without the engine running, this will deplete the car's battery rather quickly. Automotive batteries typically have about 20% reserve power, which is not very much, and certainly not adequate for powering bilge pumps for any length of time. When discharged beyond 20%, the plates begin to suffer permanent damage. Every time an automotive battery is significantly discharged beyond its 20% maximum, the battery sheds material from its lead plates until little material is left.

Automotive, sealed and RV batteries are also severely affected by vibration so that application in high speed boats substantially reduces service life due to slamming. Automotive battery plates are made of a more loosely compacted lead powder that can disintegrate when subjected to shocks. This is one reason why so often we see batteries that barely last a year. Therefore, just because a battery is only a year old it doesn't automatically mean that it's in good condition. The life of a car battery can end in as little as a dozen discharge cycles.

Boats have much higher power demands for such things as pumps, DC refrigeration, lighting, and so on, making the automotive battery a poor choice for use in boats. Unfortunately, because cranking batteries are much cheaper, they predominate in small to mid size boats.

Battery state can be reasonably determined by measuring its voltage. The charge state of a battery with a CCA or CA rating (automotive type) can be approximated by voltage as follows:

Voltage	Charge State
12.65+	100%
12.45	75%
12.24	50%

| 12.06 | 25% |
| 11.89 | Discharge |

Discharge in this case means that the battery will not crank an engine.

The above scale was published by a battery manufacturer. Notice that the range between full charge and discharge is less than one volt. This reveals that most of the battery's power in terms of amperage is at the high end of the voltage range. The discharge rate of 11.89 volts is the point where it will no longer crank an engine.

The use of automotive batteries in small boats has proved to be a problem, not only because of the low reserve power that these batteries provide, but because bilge pumps need to be able to operate over long periods of time without recharging, and few outboard boats have battery chargers and shore power systems.

Storage or Deep Cycle Batteries

This type of battery is designed to meet power demands over much longer periods of time. Deep cycle means that it can be discharged up to around 80% of total power without suffering serious damage, and when recharged will come back to very close to its original power rating, the exact opposite of an automotive battery. These batteries both charge and discharge much more slowly and are problematical when used in "stop and go" applications. These batteries are largely unaffected by vibration or slamming of boats. This type of battery is rated in ampere/hours and carries physical size designations such as 2D, 4D and 8D of 60, 125 and 250 amps respectively.

Deep cycle batteries can be and are used for engine starting purposes, but because they are not capable of providing the same initial bursts of energy, this type of battery needs to be larger in physical size in order to make up the difference in initial capacity. This is because the plates in storage batteries are substantially thicker, and therefore take up more space. Virtually all larger yachts use storage or deep cycle batteries for starting big diesel engines, as well as running high demand house systems, so this is clearly not a problem.

Marine

True marine batteries are designed for dual use of engine starting and house service and are therefore hybrids. These will have spongy, porous plates that are significantly thicker than automotive batteries. A true marine battery will tolerate up to around 50% discharge, whereas a deep-cycle also tolerates up to 50% and industrials up to 80%. Numerous batteries found in small boats will be labeled "auto/marine" and the only way to tell the type is by cutting it open and examining the plates unless one is looking at a reputable brand. *There are also very many brand names of this type, and also many of low quality.*

Deep-Cycle

This class of battery is distinguished by having much thicker plates (1/4" for Surette[3]), up to seven times thicker than an automotive battery, but higher quality batteries will have solid lead plates versus others made of a lead powder composite. Deep cycle batteries withstand greater abuse and thousands of charging cycles and have much greater service life than the other two types. They do not, however, have as great cranking or burst power, being designed to provide power over longer periods of time. Best for use with inverter systems. They are identifiable by their cost of 2-3 times that of other types and 20 hour AH ratings. True deep cycle batteries are usually only found in larger, higher end boats and yachts due to their greater cost, as well as the huge power demands of larger boats. *The number of brand names of this type is relatively small since the cost is higher. Good quality ones are usually not found in discount stores or mass retail outlets.*

Golf Cart

These batteries are generally a quasi-deep cycle similar to marine, and though not as good as batteries with solid plates, they are better than the auto/marine types. This type is usually set up in banks of six volt batteries, yielding high amperage from a much larger number of plates to provide longer periods of use under a constant power demand and deep discharging. T-105, US2200 and GC-4 are common identifiers. These batteries can discharge up to 80% without being damaged. They are not better for use with inverters than true deep cycle batteries.

RV Batteries

This name has recently begun appearing on batteries found in boats. Within the industry, there is no common battery type known as "RV" but it can be assumed that, like the "auto/marine" designation, it is probably a hybrid somewhere between a cranking and deep-cycle battery but may be little more than a marketing gimmick.

Industrial Batteries

"Industrial" or "commercial" has long been used as a designation for deep cycle batteries used in fork lifts, sweepers, floor cleaners and similar battery powered machinery. Similar to golf cart but usually true deep cycle types with much heavier and pure lead plates up to around 0.270" thick. These batteries can discharge up to 80% without being damaged. Unlikely to be found in boats.

Obviously, the deep-cycle is the preferred battery type for marine use but for its one drawback of being less able to provide high cranking power. This is overcome simply by increasing battery size.

Across the market there is considerable overlap in the hybrid class of batteries as between one designation and another, as well as quality. Actual battery performance, as well as

Fig. 5-15. Sealed AGM battery. Plates are completely wasted and will not hold any charge.

construction, often doesn't live up to marketing claims. Discount price batteries are typically discounted quality as well. One should be more skeptical of store brand than well know name brand batteries.

Gel Cells

The primary difference between gel cells and flooded acid batteries is that the electrolyte in gel cells has been gelled by the addition of silica gel, turning the liquid into a thickened mush the same way napalm is gelled gasoline. Once hailed as the messiah of marine batteries, gel cells have since revealed their weakness of being damaged by heat and overcharging as these batteries cannot be fast charged by ordinary fast chargers and require much slower charging rates. Gel batteries sustain a far lower number of charging cycles than wet cell batteries, 2,000 versus 500 cycles for gel cells. This makes them less than ideal for marine applications. Additionally, they do not hold up well in hot engine rooms where, unlike lead-acid batteries that actually benefit from heat, gel batteries lose power with higher temperatures. The added cost of gel cells has not proved worth the meager benefit of not spilling acid. Despite the common misperception, the gel cell electrolyte does evaporate over time.

AGM Batteries

AGM stands for Absorbed Glass Mat, a relatively new design which contains the electrolyte absorbed in a mesh of Boron-Silicate glass fibers. Thus there is no fluid electrolyte to leak or spill nor will they suffer from freeze damage. There are two big advantages of this type. First, it can be charged with conventional chargers without fear of damage from modest overcharging. Second, water loss is reportedly reduced by 99% because hydrogen and oxygen are recombined within the battery. Further, this type has a modestly lower self discharge rate of 1-3% versus up to 15% with standard lead-acid batteries. The AGM is a true no maintenance battery. It otherwise has similar characteristics as the standard lead-acid battery. They have yet to see much use in boats, probably due to the higher cost. Widely used in battery back up power systems and solar systems.

The down side is the cost of around 2-3 times comparable standard batteries. Thus their greatest benefit is for installations where it is hard or impossible to ventilate charging fumes such as the interiors of sail boats. AGM batteries are likely to become increasingly popular with boat owners as this type does what the gel cell was expected to do but failed. Both gel cells and AGM batteries are the storage type and are rated in ampere/hours.

Battery Ratings

A thorough understanding of battery ratings is very important to the investigator, for it is through the use of these ratings that he is able to estimate how much water the bilge pumps are capable of pumping since the pump capacity is only part of the equation.

Some common battery ratings are:

Ampere-Hour Rating

Ah is a common battery rating of storage and deep cycle batteries, and is the most useful and versatile rating of all. Amp-hour rating of battery capacity is calculated by multiplying the current (in amperes) by time (in hours) the current is drawn, making it possible to easily calculate the adequacy of batteries. Variations of the amp-hour battery rating is the most used rating outside of automotive applications. It most commonly signifies a deep cycle, marine or industrial battery.

Ah ratings can be configured in a variety of ways. Example: A battery which delivers 2 amperes for 20 hours would have a 40 Ah battery rating (2 x 20 = 40). This is known as the 20-hour rating versus other ratings based on times such as 5, 10 and 100 hours, but also at different amperage rates. This could also be expressed as 5 amps for eight hours or 10 amps for four hours. Such ratings are given based on what is considered most useful for the intended application. A battery intended to supply low amperage for long periods, for example, would use the 100 hour method, whereas a 5 hour rating would likely be for a high amperage rate, but in any case the total Ah rating of the battery is the same.

Notice that unlike the RC rating (described below), the Ah rating does not have a cut-off point. Ah is the total number of amps deliverable until the battery is dead. In the test results shown on page 20, the pump ran until the battery declined to 7.4 volts, after which the pump stopped. But the remaining 7 volts would still light a flashlight bulb. Thus a battery can produce volts without there being any real power in those volts.

In discussing bilge pumps, it is easy to see why the ampere hour rating is so important, for if we have this information a simple calculation renders a reasonable estimate of how long the pump could run.

Cold Cranking Amperage

CCA is the discharge load in amps which a battery can sustain for 30 seconds at 0 degrees F. and not fall below 1.2 volts per cell (7.2V on 12V battery). This battery rating measures a burst of energy that a car needs to start on a cold morning. This rating is used mainly for rating batteries for engine starting and tells you that you are looking at a starting battery. Example: the battery in my car is rated at 580 CCA. What does that mean to you and me? Well, probably nothing for its meaning is relative to starting the engine only.

The inevitable question to be asked is whether a CCA rating can be converted to another rating such as Ah or RC? The answer is no, it cannot be because CCA is derived from the design of a particular type of battery and therefore is not convertible to other ratings. This is because A CCA rated battery is designed for sudden burst energy, which is not convertible to long term amps.

Reserve Capacity Rating

RC is the number of *minutes* a new, fully charged battery at 80°F will sustain a discharge load of 25 amps to a cut-off voltage of 1.75 volts per cell (10.5V on 12V battery). This battery rating accounts for a continuous load on the battery and is a much better indicator than a CCA rating of how it will operate bilge pumps. An RC number given in the specification indicates that it is more than just a cranking battery and probably a hybrid starting battery.

Reserve capacity is directly, though not completely, related to battery plate size and quality. As a general rule, cranking batteries have little reserve capacity after a cranking operation unless they have thicker plates. If they have thicker plates, it will have a lower CCA rating. RC can be converted to AH by multiplying RC by 0.6.

MCA, Marine Cranking Amps is a proprietary rating that is the same as CCA. It's an indicator that the battery is most likely an ordinary automotive cranking battery sold as suitable for boats. Not to be confused with "marine battery."

Group Size In recent years batteries are being sold by group size, as in "Group 27." This description comes from the car industry and refers to the physical size of the battery, which is only very loosely related to power and is in no way an actual power rating. This specification is all about fitting a battery in a particular size space and has nothing to do battery performance. Since power output is a function of plate size, Group Size is only loosely related to power.

Ratings By Month Increasingly consumer batteries are being sold with month/life ratings, such as 24, 48, or 60 month, etc. As with all advertising, the words are better than the reality, particularly when you don't read the fine print. The bold print giveth and the fine print taketh away. Virtually all of the batteries that I have investigated that use month/life advertising, *do not* make any warranty that the battery will last that long. Instead, if the battery dies in 18 months instead of the proclaimed 24 months, they will refund on a pro rata basis and you get 25% of the purchase price credited toward a new battery, but only if you buy it. In other words month ratings are just a marketing gimmick and may only be loosely related to life span.

"Maintenance Free" or Sealed Batteries

Contrary to popular misconception, the so-called "maintenance-free" battery is anything but. The only difference between this type and those not so designated is that one can't top off the electrolyte (add water) when it evaporates, but batteries still need to be maintained in other ways as they will not function properly when ignored.

The vast majority of all boat batteries are the common wet cell, lead-acid battery, usually the sealed type. Sealed batteries are not really sealed because all wet cell batteries have to be vented in order to discharge the build up of pressure during charging. Thus, even maintenance-free batteries can lose fluid, especially as a result of over charging. The primary difference is that one cannot add water to a "sealed" battery. This type will also leak if laid over.

All lead-acid batteries will naturally discharge themselves over time at a rate of anywhere from 1% to 15% per month, depending on type. These batteries should not be left uncharged month after month, but should be maintenance charged on a regular basis. Notice that if a battery loses 15% per month for three months, the net loss is 45%, enough to ruin most automotive batteries. Therefore, in conducting sinking investigations, it will be important to interview the boat owner and determine when the boat was last operated for a sufficiently long period of time to adequately charge the batteries.

Typical Service Life by Battery Type[4*]

Cranking battery	12-18 months
Marine	1-4 years
Gel Cell	2-5 years (excluding hot climates)
Golf Cart	2-6 years
Deep Cycle	4-6 years
Surette Deep Cycle	6+ years[5]

The wide ranges given above are indicative of the widely differing conditions and treatment batteries receive and serves to illustrate why the optimal ratings provided by the manufacturer are unlikely to be obtained. Since boats typically are used infrequently, when investigating marine losses the lower end of the range should be used when estimating battery life.

Dates and Codes

Most of us are familiar with the punch-circle stickers on batteries that no one ever bothers with. That sticker is put there for use by the purchaser. Some more conscientious manufacturers either stamp the date or use a date code, while others do not.

A date code may appear as 3CN1 (Delco, stamped on side of case). The number 3 is the year and C is the month expressed alphabetically. This date would be March, '03.

Exide and some Sears will have a code like RO8BOB where the fourth or fifth character is the month and the next is the year, in this example, Feb. 2000.

Others may have a more simple letter/number code such as C3.

Battery Charging

For boats that have shore power systems and battery chargers, theoretically the batteries should be able to power the pumps up to the point of pump failure. Bilge pumps are not designed to operate continuously for indefinite periods and eventually they will wear out and fail when run continuously under load at some point. Marine battery chargers are usually rated at 20 amps or more so that any of them will power at least two moderate size pumps continuously, i.e. two 8.5 amp pumps for a total of 19 amps.

Battery chargers exist in two types, ferroresonant and electronic, with the former being the older type which has some shortcomings. Ferro chargers have long suffered the problem of difficulty in sensing whether a battery had taken as much charge as it could, and then failing to shut off at the proper time. This resulted in overcharging or "cooking" the batteries, an event that can vastly reduce battery life. More recent ferro chargers are likely to have electronic sensors that do a much better job of not only shutting off in time, but in regulating the charge rate.

An excessively high charge rate also damages batteries, thereby reducing life span. During the charging cycle, as batteries gain charge, the amount of charging amps they can take declines, so that beginning rate should be much more than the ending charge rate. Electronic chargers have the advantage of being able to more closely sense and adjust the charge rate, and are often known as multi-stage chargers. This has the effect of extending, or at least allowing a battery to achieve, its normal life span.

With sinking investigations it is necessary to attempt to determine if the battery charger was (a) operational, and (b) functioning at the time of the sinking. The only way that this can be ascertained is through examination to determine whether any electrolysis occurred during submersion. This will not prove that the charger was charging, but only that the unit was energized at the time of submersion.

Can it be proven that a charger was functioning at the time of sinking? The answer here is not directly and probably only in the negative; that is, by demonstrating that there is nothing to prove that it wasn't operating. On the positive side, extreme electrolysis damage to both the AC and DC systems is a strong indicator, but not actual proof, that the charger was functioning.

Battery Banks

A "bank" is a reference to when two or more batteries are joined in parallel. Two 12 volt, 60Ah batteries when joined yield 12 volts at 120Ah whereas two 12 volt batteries in series yields 24 volts at 60 Ah. Think of battery banks like two fuel tanks that are connected by a pipe at the bottom - add 30 gallons of fuel to one and they both gain 15 gallons equally, and it's the same on the discharge side. A 30 amp draw will pull 15 amps from each assuming everything else is equal.

But what would happen if one tank is 100 gallons and the other 200 gallons? Because the pressure in the larger tank is greater, the same fuel added at the same pressure is not going to split the additional fuel equally. The smaller tank would get more and the larger tank less. A similar situation happens with batteries that are not of equal capacity.

Multi battery systems can end up with serious problems when they are not set up properly. When connected in parallel, multiple batteries of equal size and capacity will charge and discharge at equal rates. But with batteries of differing type and capacity, the charge and discharge rates will not be equal. If the plates in all are not the same type, then the rates of charge and discharge will also be unequal. As with our connected fuel tanks, the power draw is from both but when they are of different capacity, one will discharge faster than the other. Therefore, battery banks should always utilize identical batteries.

Batteries set up in banks must always be replaced in banks for the reason that the older battery will drag down the newer battery to the older level because the two will equalize. The most common battery bank problem we have with boaters is that when one battery goes bad, they replace them one at a time instead of replacing both. Not only does the older battery drag down the newer, but the older one will fail that much sooner.

When inspecting battery banks, always attempt to find the dates, which if they do exist are likely to be in code. The codes vary widely and tend to change frequently, so the best thing to do is write down the code and contact a retailer for translation.

Yet another problem is mixing batteries of different sizes or capacities unless they are connected with a diode isolator. Typically, a boat owner will just go out and buy any old battery as long as it looks about the same size, without ever bothering to check on its specifications. A diode isolator will allow both batteries to charge to the proper level.

But the worst problem for mismatched batteries is what happens when mismatched batteries are charged; the two batteries will receive an identical rate of charge, meaning that one will be overcharged while the other may not be fully charged. This leads to very rapid battery failure.

Multiple battery banks are usually fitted with a battery bank integrator (BBI) or isolator. This diode controlled device controls the connection between two banks in both the charge and discharging modes. Its primary function is to maintain the banks at equal levels; with the use of this device, it is not necessary that both banks have identical batteries which must be the same within a bank.

From this explanation it can be seen that there are numerous possibilities for engineering errors that can lead to battery failure and thus boats sinking, so that when litigation is anticipated there will be a need to prove, or at least evaluate the efficacy of the entire DC electrical system. This is the reason why, increasingly, investigators are turning to marine electrical experts to assist them with investigations. Therefore, should we encounter mismatched battery banks, there is a high probability that this situation is a causative factor and needs further investigation.

After Refloating

Immediately after refloating, the boat's batteries should be disconnected from the system by removing all connectors after photographing them first. One should not assume that because of submersion that the batteries are completely discharged as often they are not. With the batteries disconnected, put a meter on them and check the voltage, for this will be very revealing. However, before doing so, be sure to make a preliminary check of the switching for the pumping system. If the pumps were shut off, inadvertently or otherwise, activate the system and check whether the pumps will now run. Failure to do this may result in a critical loss of evidence.

When dealing with a major loss, it may desirable to remove the batteries to an independent company that has expertise with batteries. This may be a retailer, distributor or electrical service company. If litigation appears likely, it is far better to utilize an independent expert with demonstrable electrical credentials, and the sooner this is done the better. In addition to more complete testing of the condition, ask the expert whether he is capable of opening up the battery and examining and evaluating the condition of the plates, something that may yield irrefutable proof of battery condition. If not, information on how to evaluate a battery will be found on below.

Critical Questions

The inevitable question that surrounds nearly all sinking investigations is how long did the battery(s) power the pumps. This is a question that is fairly easy to answer if we're dealing with storage batteries, but a bit more difficult with other types. Say, for example, we have a pair of batteries designated by group size and a CCA rating. Since a CCA rating cannot be directly converted to ampere hours, the only way to determine how long such a battery will run a pump is by means of testing it.

Inspecting the Batteries

A visual inspection of the battery will tell a lot about its condition. As battery plates deteriorate, they undergo a process called sulfating, that is, they build up layers of lead sulfate, which expands the size of the plates. Auto batteries shed lead material at rapid rates. Plates can also warp due to overcharging. The net physical changes of the later may be apparent by visible distortions of the battery case. If the case is ballooned outward, it's a sure sign of a battery that is damaged and has reached or is near the end of its service life.

A less agreeable, but far more revealing method of determining condition is to cut the case open and expose all the plates. This should be done whenever litigation is considered likely. To open a battery case, obtain a large plastic pan, a box of baking soda and a disposable, fine tooth hand saw, and protective gloves. Place the battery in the pan. Drill several holes in the bottom and drain all the acid. Neutralize the battery acid with the baking soda so that it can be safely disposed. Next, cut the top off at a distance of about 1/2" below the top. The top should then lift off the casing with all the plates attached. With some batteries you may have to cut the whole casing apart.

With cranking batteries, a lead powder is compacted onto a plastic screen (See **Fig. 5-14**). The amount of material still left attached to the screen, along with the amount of residue that has gone adrift and remains at the bottom, will give an idea of the condition. If any part of the screen is showing, the battery is pretty well wasted and cannot be considered serviceable. If no part of the screen is showing, the battery is in good condition.

Higher quality, more expensive batteries will have a different construction, such as composite lead plates set in a plastic pouch, or even solid lead. The degree of deterioration will be revealed in the amount of lead sulfate accumulated at the bottom of the pouch, on the plate itself, or as sludge at the bottom of the case. Lead sulfate will be a whitish color, but other composites may turn black. In any case, a battery in good condition will have little or no detritus at the bottom and the plates will be smooth and not eroded or powdery.

A gel cell or AGM battery typically has a packed powder plate set in a soft paste electrolyte. When the battery is depleted, these plates will be white and crumble readily (**Fig. 5-15**). All of the above described conditions prove that the battery was in poor condition and at or very near the end of it's service life.

Battery Testing

There are three methods by which to test battery condition, with a voltmeter, hygrometer and load tester. Only the last method will yield a highly reliable result of true battery condition. The others are approximations.

There is nothing theoretical about load testing a battery, so this is the most definitive method of determining actual battery performance. Load testing is best accomplished with a dedicated load testing device that functions using resistors. Short of that an improvised load test can be conducted by connecting it to any high draw device. Trying to start an engine with a marginal battery will likely result in the starter not engaging and thus not be a good indication of residual power. Instead, after connecting to an electrical system and a voltmeter, turn on a high draw accessory such as head lights, power windows, seats, etc. and record the amount of voltage drop. The residual voltage at this point is indicative of condition. Anything below 10.5 volts should be considered discharged.

What we are looking to determine is the ability of a battery to hold a charge. Weak batteries, despite the fact that they may show 11 or 12 volts, will drop rapidly (detectable on the meter), whereas a strong battery will show a lesser and slower voltage drop.

Testing specific gravity is a theoretic indicator of battery condition. We know what the electrolyte in the battery should be, and we can determine what it actually is. Yet there are factors that can cause these readings to be inaccurate such as the introduction of water inside due to submersion. Batteries that have not been charged recently will result in heavier particles sinking to the bottom, thereby giving false low readings. Therefore, when testing using a hygrometer, shake the battery or roll it over several times to mix the electrolyte.

Testing the specific gravity of a battery with a hygrometer may only serve to show that water got into the battery. The specific gravity of pure water is, of course, 1.000; for sea water in the western Atlantic around 1.025, though it should be noted that sea water can vary due to the influx of fresh water from rivers and heavy rain. The specific gravity of sulfuric acid electrolyte varies by battery state or rate of charge that is also affected by temperature. At 60F the electrolyte of a fully charged battery should have a reading of 1.273; at 50% charge, 1.198. Refer to the scale on the instrument.

Voltmeter testing provides a good initial indicator, but one that is dependent on determination of other factors. The problem with using voltage as an indicator of battery condition is that voltage does not tell us how long that voltage can be sustained, something only load testing can do. Voltage is likely to be low due to either immersion or discharging and is to be expected. However, high readings on a submerged battery, say above ten volts, are very revealing and indicate that the battery was capable of running the pump, albeit at greatly reduced capacity The charge state of a battery with a CCA or CA rating is as follows:

Voltage	Charge State
12.65+	100%
12.45	75%
12.24	50%

12.06	25%
11.89	Discharge

Notice that the discharge state only relates directly to engine cranking ability because at 11.89 volts a battery will likely continue to run a pump for several hours. Based on my own testing, I'd place the discharge voltage at 10.5 volts. See my discharge/time rates in table in next page.

Unsealed lead/acid batteries when new and fully charged will have a voltage of around 13.00 - 13.5 volts, while sealed batteries 12.6 to 12.8 volts by reason of a different type of plate material (antimony, calcium or silver alloys). It is interesting to note how rapidly under load the high and low end voltages fall off whereas the mid-range voltages remain much more stable over time.

The bottom line is that if one is going to be doing this kind of work frequently, purchasing a load tester is the best way to go as these are available for as little as $150.

Common DC System Faults

Mismatched batteries

Undersize cables & wiring

Corroded battery cables & terminals

Faulty or no battery isolation

Battery isolator gets wet

Inadequate cooling for isolator (bad mount location)

Under/oversize alternator

Corrosion damage to charger

Battery Performance With Bilge Pumps

In order to determine how long a bilge pump would operate, a new battery and a two year old battery were subjected to a pumping test with a new Rule 1500 pump drawing 4.3 amps. The actual test performance proved to be very close to calculated running time rates based on specifications, that is, time multiplied by amps equals ampere-hours.

Minutes	Voltage	Minutes	Voltage
Start	13.56	170	12.24
10	12.72	210	12.15
20	12.66	230	12.15

30	12.44	270	12.08
50	12.38	330	11.92
70	12.35	370	11.69
90	12.33	400	11.50
110	12.29	430	10.90
130	12.27	480	7.40 - Pump Stopped

Net Yield: 34.4 Ah

The table above shows the performance of a new, never used low cost ($40), store brand battery (Wal-Mart) rated at 550 CCA with an RC of 65 which would be the same as a 39 Ah rating. The battery started with a charge rate of 13.56 volts and ran for 8.0 hours until the pump stopped. In the sixth hour the voltage dropped below 12 volts and by the seventh it was at 11.5 volts and the pump had slowed by over half. At 10.5 volts the pumping rate was down 63% and stopped altogether at 7.4 volts.

In this test a 4.3 amp pump was used and therefore if we multiply time (8.0 hours) by amps (4.3) we get 34.40 ampere/hours, very close to our conversion rate of 40 Ah. To convert RC to Ah we multiply RC x 0.6 = 39 Ah and so we have proved the rating to be reasonably accurate.

Now notice in the test below utilizing a used battery how the net yielded ampere-hours dropped to only 18.49 Ah, demonstrating the effects of age reducing available power by almost half.

Start Voltage = 12.90

Minutes	Voltage
10	12.36
30	12.19
80	11.89
140	11.57
200	9.84
260	7.31 pump stopped

Net Yield: 18.49 Ah

In this second test we used a two year old higher cost "marine" battery priced at $65, also rated at 550 CCA but had no RC rating. This battery had been in service at the time and is typical of boat batteries that have been in service for around a year. It was not charged up before testing but was taken directly from a boat that was last operated the previous day. The starting voltage of 12.90 volts dropped off by a half volt in the first ten minutes of running the pump; in the next twenty minutes another third volt (0.36) to 11.99 volts, and it died completely after four hours, sinking to 7.31 volts when the pump finally stopped.

These limited tests demonstrate a remarkable difference between the performance of new and older batteries, wherein the old battery was only capable of running the pump for 260 minutes or 4.3 hours, roughly half that of a new battery. However, in the later case the pumping rate began to slow down significantly after three hours compared to nearly six for the new battery. Note that in both cases the pump stopped at about 7 volts.

Rough Estimates

There will be times when it is necessary to make a rough estimate of how long batteries will run a pump. This is easily accomplished by taking into consideration several factors. In addition to the battery rating, consider its age and the fact that boat batteries without chargers don't get regular charging. Based on testing of thousands of boat batteries (during surveys), the voltage found in the vast majority of them is in the range of 12.1 to 12.5 volts, a rather narrow range. This is a state of charge rate of approximately 50 - 75% as defined by manufacturers. This can be further adjusted for an age factor to yield a very approximate time period that a pump would operate. For example, as the above testing shows, a "two year" battery that is one year old should only be expected to operate a pump half as long as a new battery, and our testing confirms that.

Also noteworthy is the fact that while the rate of discharge was not consistent from one time period to another, it is certainly close enough that from these times and voltages we can easily draw an average rate of discharge. For example, the battery discharged a total of 5.32 volts over a period of 8.5 hours (throwing out the drop of 0.8 volts in the first ten minutes as being unrepresentative) we get an average drop of about 0.625 volts every hour. This average holds down to about 11 volts after which the discharge rate plummets.

Note that neither of these tests reflect the performance of a boat battery that had been sitting, unused for a week or more as will be the case with the vast majority of boats that we are involved with. We shouldn't forget that batteries will naturally deplete at rates up to 15% per month, and that boats that have not been used for a long time are likely to have fully depleted or even dead batteries.

Natural Depletion Rates

Battery manufacturers tell us that normal depletion rates for a battery that is just sitting, unused and not connected to anything, is between 1% and 15% per month. That is a useless number as far as we are concerned because it is a range that is far too broad to be of value. This is more relevant when we know that cranking batteries have a higher rate of discharge than storage batteries owing to the nature of the plates. But, in addition to native depletion rates, with boats there is also the matter of system leakage rates which can be much higher than natural power loss. Thus, boat batteries tend to deplete much faster than vehicular batteries.

Batteries in boats are unlike automotive batteries in that boat batteries are grounded while vehicles are not because they sit on rubber tires. Due to water and corrosion, the only boats that don't have a substantial degree of stray current in the DC system would be a new boat. All others tend to leak power to a significant degree[6]. Fifteen percent per month would be a better estimate of native power loss. We know this to be a fact because most boats without battery chargers can't sit for very long without the batteries going dead, typically a period of several weeks to around a month. That coincides with a rate of around 15% per week.

In the end, use of the above data can only be used to confirm a probable cause because most often there are too many variables and unknowns to use such calculations with certainty unless all the variables can be accounted for. When a boat that doesn't have an operating charging system sinks, I inquire of the owner when was the last time he ran the boat sufficient to charge the batteries. If he tells me two weeks, it's fair to assume that the batteries were at least half depleted. Of course one should also ask about the history of the batteries, whether the batteries have gone dead before and so on.

(Footnotes)

1. Most pumps manufactured within the last 10 years will run for at least 48 hours without failure.

2. Rule sets a rating of 1000 GPH @12.0 volts and 3.35 ft. head. With those factors I barely got 400 GPH.

3. Surette is widely regarded as one of several premier battery manufacturers.

4. Assumes proper installation and maintenance, and a properly calibrated charger. Based in part on personal observation from surveys as well as views of other experts.

5. Surette batteries are often found in large yachts where short battery life is rarely a problem, in part due to high grade chargers and frequent maintenance.

6. The reference to stray current is in terms of milliamperes.

Chapter 6

Finding the Leak

In many cases finding the source of water ingress into the vessel will come quickly and easily, but for many others it will turn out to be a long, dirty and arduous task. There are huge differences between investigating a sinking of a twenty foot outboard boat and a larger yacht where the greater size presents more difficulties. In some instances the investigator will find it necessary to take measurements and perform calculations in order to establish flow rates, volumes of water and periods of time. How to perform such calculations will be discussed in this chapter as well as Chapter Seven, Sinking Due to Rain.

Sinking investigations that end up in litigation of prove to be problems for the investigator who is asserting a cause. This is because there are always numerous possibilities for every case that aren't easy to disprove. Since the investigator never gets any advance indication that litigation will result, his best approach is to assume that it will. Therefore, in this chapter we will consider some of the more technical aspects of proving a cause, even though more often than not such measures will not be required.

Once the investigator finds what he believes is the cause, he may get an indication at this point whether litigation will be forthcoming. If so, he should proceed to cover every possibility. Conclusively proving a cause can be time consuming and, as usual, the investigator is likely to find himself up against time and cost constraints. The novice needs to be reminded that covering what is not the cause can be just as important as what is. As always, he will need to impress upon his client that solid proof will be needed to win a case.

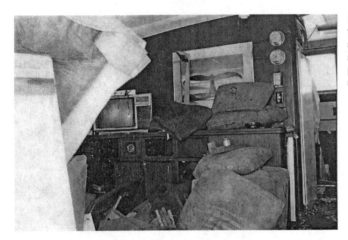

Fig. 6-1. It's usually a topsy-turvey world after a larger vessel sinks and is raised. An ordinary set cushion can weigh 50 to 100 pounds. A soggy sofa can weigh nearly a half ton.

A key question the investigator will frequently have to ask is whether the evidence is so obvious that it speaks for itself and will stand independently as proof, or does the evidence require concise demonstration that it is proof. This is a question that will present itself in many ways but is frequently difficult to answer. The safe solution is to always seek to gain whatever additional demonstrative proof as may be available. This will include such measures as calculation and empirical testing.

Clean Up

When boats such as cruisers and motor yachts sink, the interior usually ends up a shambles with furniture, upholstery, carpets, fabrics and a host of other items all looking like the boat was turned upside-down and shaken. Moreover, some items such as mattresses, furniture and carpet are capable of absorbing hundreds of pounds of water, making them extraordinarily hard to move. In some cases the vessel will be filled with sand, silt, seaweed or other aquatic debris.

In a recent case of an eight foot yacht sinking, the investigation process took six days, two of which were devoted to clean up; the larger and more complex the vessel, the longer the investigation is likely to take.

In most cases it will be necessary to move the vessel from the place where it sank to a boat yard or marina, a task usually handled by the salvor. Influencing the decisions that will have to be made is whether we believe that the boat is repairable or will be a total loss, the storage cost and, if a total loss, the method of disposal. But determination of the cause of sinking is the top priority.

Small boats such as outboards won't require any significant clean up other than perhaps moving a few things around. But with larger boats it is a different story. The first task we have to attend to is clearing out the mess so that we can work safely and effectively. We shouldn't be surprised when faced with unpleasant things such as a bait freezer full of rotting bait, refrigerators and galleys containing rotting food, and worst of all, a damaged or leaking sewage holding system. Deranged and water-soaked furniture and other items need to be removed from the boat as these will just get in the way. Below decks, particularly the engine room, there is also likely to be a jumble of displaced things, including water soaked paper, clothing and so on.

It is best that all these hindrances to conducting a good investigation be cleared out, and to do this will require considerable labor, a job that is usually tasked to a boat yard crew, and not undertaken by the surveyor. The cost of this is not to be born by the assured if we are dealing with an insurance claim as this is rightly part of the cost of conducting the investigation. This is a point that should be cleared with the client in advance so that he knows he will be paying the cost, and because the people doing the work will expect quick payment, so we'll want the client to be ready to issue a check.

Diesel fuel contamination usually isn't much of a problem because it disperses and evaporates fairly quickly. Lube oil escaped from the engines is an entirely different matter as it can coat everything and pose a considerable danger to the investigator or anyone else trying to move about the vessel. If the boat is covered with oil, degreasing the boat is a must since slips and falls can result in serious injuries and liability issues.

It is necessary to accomplish all of this without disturbing any evidence, a difficult proposition at best. The investigator needs to try to get into the vessel and locate the leak before heavy clean up work is started because clean up often damages evidence. However, be alert to the fact that a boat coated with oil is extremely dangerous, he should not risk injury to himself but wait until cleaning has been accomplished.

Degreasing can be done either with a steam cleaner or using a spray of oil emulsifying detergent, but this method may compromise evidence. Water and rust trails, corrosion deposits and other evidence may get washed away. That's why it's best that the investigator be present to supervise the clean up. It may be possible to limit the cleaning that will not disturb evidence yet still make the boat reasonably safe to work on.

We also have to be wary of moving heavy objects around, like displaced hatch covers and other things that may get lodged in the bilge. Therefore, it will be necessary that the investigator be present while this work is ongoing to supervise the work crew to prevent destruction of evidence.

An illustration of what can happen is demonstrated in a recent case in which a clean up crew apparently stepped on a plastic elbow that was part of a saltwater intake system for a generator and broke it into pieces. This same elbow was later determined to be the cause of sinking as microscopic analysis of the broken plastic revealed that dirt on one of the fractures was old, but the fact that it had been stepped on made the job considerably more difficult and costly. The saving factor was that the investigator was present and saw the fitting being stepped on, otherwise the cause might never have been identified correctly.

Examine the Exterior Hull First

If, after the boat is refloated, the source of the leak does not soon become apparent, the best way to avoid an arduous and time-wasting search is to examine the bottom. By examining the exterior it is possible to catalogue every possible source of water entry. In theory, were there no openings, no plumbing and no penetrations through the hull, then the leak could not occur through it. It is therefore expedient to catalogue all possibilities and complete the process of elimination. Moreover, should litigation occur, this would be the most thorough method of building a case because every possibility will have been considered.

With the boat hauled almost every possibility for water ingress can be catalogued, including many that would be very hard, or perhaps impossible, to observe from within. In one case a boat owner installed clam shell strainer/scoops over his engine intakes using #6-32 machine screws. He made the mistake of using steel nuts. One by one, the nuts corroded and let go until water pressure eventually pulled scoop off. A #6 screw needs only a 3/32" hole that was impossible to see in a sludge filled bilge, even though there were four of them – under the engine. After an entire day of searching, I gave up and ordered the boat hauled, whereon the bottom the pattern of the missing scoop was very obvious and the four tiny holes located within minutes.

Essential Calculations

There are times when it becomes necessary in a sinking investigation to resort to calculations to determine things such as flow rates and the amount of time it took for the vessel to sink. While it is difficult to anticipate what those circumstances may be, they can include situations such as being uncertain about a particular source or cause, unable to locate the source, and most especially in anticipation of litigation when a cause requires very definite proof.

The methods described herein are only applicable to hard chine power boats as the shape of most sail boat and round bilge hulls is too difficult and time consuming to measure.

A common example of when calculations prove necessary is when we have a boat which we believe sank due to a propeller shaft leak. Because the rate of leakage is slow, and the issue of functioning bilge pumps arises, along with considerations of whether neglect is a factor, the matter of time becomes important. If it took a week or more for the boat to sink, the issue of negligence comes into play. This, we can often establish by means of calculation.

There are three primary things we may wish to know about how a boat sank:

- Volume of water required to sink the boat
- Size of opening or rate of flow
- Time period

Given any two knowns, the third can always be derived by calculation. The size of the boat gives us an idea of how much water is required to sink it, along with a guess at the size of the opening. There will also be instances when we want to establish a time line, as when knowing when the last time the boat was seen afloat. In some cases this can be critical while in others only vaguely helpful.

Usually, what we want to know is how much water it took to sink the boat, but there are a number of factors that influence this. Among these is whether any bilge pumps were working at any time during the event, along with the size of the boat. A one inch opening will sink a small boat much faster than a large one, so size figures into our consideration.

Another factor is the threshold point. Nearly every boat has a point at which, when it starts sinking, water will begin entering in through other openings such as heads, showers, scuppers and fish wells. At this point, the original source is aided by the secondary sources which are not the cause. These secondary sources usually greatly increase the rate of flooding, and are therefore not considered in our calculations. For our purposes, the amount of water required to sink the boat consists of the internal volume up to the threshold point. This volume can be expressed as either gallons or pounds of water.

Before we can proceed, we first have to determine the threshold point, which is the first point water would enter through another source. The threshold point establishes the upper limit of the internal volume of the hull that we will use to calculate the amount of water required.

Note: Whether we ignore or include secondary openings in our calculations is a matter of their size because size determines the time factor (if that is what we wish to know). If a secondary opening is very small, say ¾", the amount of water flowing through that opening will be relatively small, and so we may wish to include this opening by raising the threshold point to some higher level. Consider the relevancy of this first small opening and how it may have affected the situation. Then note the distance between the first and next higher opening, if any. What if there are three secondary sources all within a few inches of height? Obviously, then, they all should be ignored. Conversely, if it is a pair of 2" x 5" scuppers, we would certainly want to consider the scuppers as the threshold point.

Also note here that as water enters the hull, the rate at which the boat settles deeper in the water is not constant due to factors such as changing hull shape and internal volume that is displaced by things like engines and tanks. This is not something that we can account for because it becomes way too complicated. Suffice it to say that with most boats the rate of sinking tends to slow since the internal volume to be filled with water increases the farther down it settles. However, this consideration does not materially affect the end result since it is total time that we are considering.

The reader will find that there will be a natural tendency to complicate these issues when, in fact, they are very simple. Contrary to what one might think, objects placed low in the hull such as engines and tanks have no bearing on these calculations and need not be considered.

To take measurements and create the necessary drawings, the following instruments are needed:

- Plumb bob or large level

- Tape measure or carpenters rule

- Two large 45 degree drafting triangles

- Architects scale

- Thin batten or spline

Calculating Internal Volume

Displacement or weight of a vessel is the amount of water that the hull displaces that, for our purposes, we express in pounds. If a boat weights 16,500 lbs. on dry land, the amount of water it displaces will be exactly the same.

Calculating hull displacement from scratch is time consuming, but fortunately there are simpler methods to derive the data we are seeking. If we take a hull and slice it like a loaf of bread horizontally and lengthwise, it really quite easy to calculate the volume of each slice. If each slice is one inch thick, then the volume is defined by LxWxH. Of course, the area shape contains some curves which increases difficulty of measurement. The way we get around that is to simply straighten out the curved lines in such a manner that our new shape contains the same volume as the original. See **Fig. 6-2A.**

By way of example we'll use an older 30' Bertram sport fisher weighing 16,500 lbs

*For our examples, we will use salt water.

Displacement: The weight or the volume of fluid displaced by a floating or submerged body.

	Gallon/Cubic Ft.	Pounds/Cubic Ft.	Pounds/Gallon
Salt Water	7.48	64.1	8.56
Fresh Water	7.48	62.4	8.34

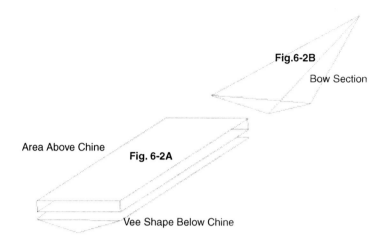

Fig. 6-2. Polygons for displacement. Any conventional power boat hull shape can be converted to regular polygons for easy calculation of internal volumes or displacement as shown here.

with dimensions of 26.6 LWL x 10.33 B x 2.5' D. Make sure your draft measurement doesn't include depth of propeller or a fin keel. It has big cockpit scuppers about 6-8" above the water line so that once the boat sinks to this depth, it will go down fast.

The Short Method

There are two ways we can approach the problem. If we know the original dry weight when new, we may be able to work from this number as long as we have reason to believe that the boat remains close to this weight years later. An experienced surveyor should be able to quickly size this up. The weight of liquids, fuel and water, is not included in the original weight, so this will have to be added.

Most boats will have a scum line on the hull that will tell us exactly where the water line is. This scum line will often have a range of an inch or so which reflects the changing fuel status over time. The best way to determine the fuel status before sinking is to simply ask the owner, then pick the water line accordingly. The volume of the hull below the water line defines the 16,500 displacement which is equal to 1928 gallons of water, derived by dividing 16,500 by 8.56 lbs. per gallon.

Notice here that we can avoid more complex calculations by simply dividing displacement by the weight of a gallon of water. This defines how much water will fill up the inside of the hull to the normal water line. All that remains to be determined by actual measurement is that additional volume up to the threshold point.

In most cases the threshold point will be one foot or less above the normal water line, which is the additional volume we need to determine. Next, we will need to determine the beam, not at the deck but at the hull section we are considering. Find the widest part of the hull at the deck, then hang a weighted string down from the deck and measure inward to the hull (**Fig. 6-2A**). Subtract this amount times two (for each side) from the maximum beam, which yields the beam at the point we are seeking. Next, we will divide this hull section into a rectangle and a triangle where the rectangle represents the aft section and the triangle the bow area (**Fig. 6-2B**). Find the point at which the hull side begins to curve forward and mark it. Measure this distance from this point to both bow and stern; this yields the length of our rectangle and the height of our triangle. Also measure the beam across the transom.

All the above measurements should be taken at the vertical mid point between threshold and water line so as to obtain an average. Using an architect's scale, choose an appropriate scale and lay out the triangle and rectangle on paper. At this point you may have noticed that we have ignored some hull curves that might render our work inaccurate. The accuracy will vary depending on the shape of the hull and it is your task to determine whether more adjustments need be made.

If there are heavy curves, if the beam at transom is much less than beam at amidships, adjustments need to be made. If our section profile is too heavily curved or too irregular in shape, we must resort to another method described below.

Area of the Water Plane

Returning to our sliced bread analogy, the area of the water plane represents the area of any bread slice. Note here that each slice is referred to as a water line. The area of water plane is useful for other purposes including determination of Pounds per Inch Immersion.

Determination of the area of water plane involves taking six half-beam measurements. Take the water line length at the desired point and divide this length into six segments as shown in **Fig. 6-2B**. Using a level or plumb bob, measure outward from the keel or centerline to the level (a short level can be extended by attaching a long straight-edge to it). Then measure from the level inward to the hull side and subtract the difference. This will yield the half beams at each of the six points.

To create a scaled drawing, use a large piece of paper and draw a baseline on it at the bottom of the paper. Use a triangle set to the base line to ensure squareness. This is an easy substitute method for using a T-square. Use a moderate scale such as 3/8" or ½" = 1 foot as paper permits.

Again, using the appropriate scale, draw a line equal to the length of the hull centerline or length of water plane being used. Plot the six segment distances and the half beams on paper, being sure to maintain squareness. Note that five lines will create six sections, as the last will be the transom line. Using a spline or batten, draw a curved line connecting each of the half beams. The end result is a scaled one-half section of the water plane which is then doubled to give the complete water plane area.

Using straight lines, convert the half section into a rectangle and a triangle, the later representing the bow section. To straighten a curved line, draw a line through it so that it cuts off equal parts inside and outside the line, a process of averaging what lies inside the squared shape with what lies outside the shape. This is done entirely by eye and estimation. The end result will easily be within 10% accuracy, which is good enough.

The Long Method

In the preceding method we worked from the advertised weight of the vessel which experience shows is usually quite accurate. But if that weight is not available, or we have reason to suspect that the weight has changed, then it is possible to make our own displacement calculation. The good news here is that in performing the area of water plane calculation, the job is now half complete.

In making a rough calculation of displacement we use the same method as with area of water plane except that we are adding a second triangular polygon, the area representing he vee section of the bottom as shown in **Fig. 6-2A**. For the immersed section, divide the hull between areas above and below the chine. That is, separate the vee section from the more rectangular shaped upper section. The upper limit is defined by the normal water line. The bow section is defined by a triangular polygon. The volume of all three sections are calculated and added together to yield the immersed whole. This volume in cubic feet is then converted to the weight of water.

If you have already done the area of water plane, then you can just add the triangular vee bottom section. Reverse this, and the area of water plane is easily extracted from your displacement work.

The Block Coefficient

Naval architects use an even faster method for *estimating* displacement. This method can be used when one needs a really quick estimate of displacement, and is accurate enough for creating a rough estimate of who much water it takes to sink a boat. However, it may not stand up to scrutiny in litigation. The block coefficient represents that proportion or percentage that a hull shape bears to a rectangular block defined by the principle dimensions of a hull. Say our thirty footer has a water line length of 26'6" by 10'4" x 2'6" which defines the size of our block, in this case 684.4 ft^3. Since the hull is not rectangular, we have to estimate what percentage our hull is of that solid block.

For most power boats the number ranges from 30-50%, depending on how shallow or deep it is. Our Bertram is moderately deep so I'll use 40% which yields 342.2 cubic feet. Multiply this times 64 pounds per cubic foot and we get 17,520 lbs. Compared with the advertised weight of 16,500 lbs., this is an error of only 1,020 lbs., only 6%. Of course, the degree of accuracy here is only as good as one's ability to estimate.

Pounds Per Inch Immersion

This term is defined as the number of pounds required to sink a hull one inch deeper than a previous level. It is very useful for all sorts of estimating.

Notice that the water plane does not remain constant, but rather increases with each additional inch of immersion because most hulls flare outward toward the gunwale. But on an inch by inch basis, this increase is usually very little, so that over a six inch height, the difference is only a small amount (typically 5%) that can be estimated and adjusted rather than going through time consuming measurements. The formula for PPII is:

$$\frac{\text{PPII} + \text{Area of Water Plane X 64}}{12}$$

This handy formula by-passes any need to calculate cubic volumes and associated conversions. All that is needed is to obtain the area of water plane. The only measurements needed are:

    Length waterline

    Beam (maximum) waterline

    Beam at transom

Using our earlier 30' Bertram example with large scuppers six inches above the water line, we do not need to calculate any displacements. Since we know that it only takes another six inches of immersion, the PPII formula can easily be applied here multiplied by six. The area of water plane for the Bertram is 191.6 square feet:

$$\frac{191.6 \text{ X } 64}{12} = 1021.8 \text{ lbs.}$$

Thus, it takes 1021.8 lbs. of water to immerse the hull an additional one inch, which translates to only 119.4 gallons (1021.8 divided by 8.56). Multiply that times six and we now know that it takes approximately 716 gallons of water to immerse the hull to the threshold point where it would sink in a matter of minutes.

Knowing this tells us a lot about the size of the initial leak we're looking for and how long it would take to sink the boat based on flow rates. A one gallon per hour leak translates to nearly 30 days to sink the boat, whereas a gallon per minute leak would put the boat on the bottom in less than 15 hours.

Summary

While it takes some time to complete these measurements and drawings – typically it takes me a day – calculating internal hull volumes, and consequently the amount of water it hold, is very useful in difficult cases, as well as when litigation may be involved and additional elements of proof are needed. This is particularly important where the cause may be attributed to deterioration that results in no insurance coverage. In such instances these calculations should be considered mandatory.

Flow Rates in Gallons Per Hour

Pipe	Distance Below Surface		
Size	**6"**	**12"**	**18"**
1/8"	10.2	18.0	21.9
1/4"	52.8	72.0	91.8
1/2"	207.6	294.0	360.0
3/4"	466.2	660.0	810.0
1"	837.6	1176.0	1452.0
2"	3329.5	4716.0	766.0

Table 6-1.

The same applies to heavy rainfall cases where one needs to demonstrate that the amount of rainfall was actually capable of sinking the boat, rather than merely accepting an assumption.

Water Flow Rates

The calculation of water flow rates is not quite so easy because it involves fluid dynamics, a subject that is very complicated and involves math well beyond the means of everyone but engineers. Uppermost in the investigator's mind will be the question of what will be the flow rate through a given opening. This depends not only on size of opening but pressure and resistance, the later two of which can be very hard to determine, and depends on the following:

Water Pressure – The amount of water that can flow through any opening in a hull is related to the pressure behind the outside water. At the surface the water pressure is 1G, one gravity or atmosphere. The deeper the opening, the greater the water pressure will be. Thus, the flow of water through an opening two feet below the surface is going to be greater than two inches below the surface.

Atmospheric Pressure – The amount of absolute water pressure depends on the existing atmospheric pressure which is variable. For our purposes, this is insignificant.

Resistance – When water flows through a pipe or hose, resistance occurs at the point where water meets that which is conducting it. Moreover, water flow rates are affected by changes in direction, as at elbows, through valves and so on. Further, water flowing through a pipe that is twice the diameter of another, doesn't necessarily mean that the flow rate is doubled. Flow rates through smaller pipes are proportionately less than through larger pipes. This is because the surface area of the pipe is proportionately greater for a small pipe than for a large one. In other words, proportionately more water flows through a larger opening than a smaller one. In the table **6-1**, note that the flow rate through a ¼" is five times that of an 1/8" opening.

In situations where the calculation of water flow rate is complicated, my procedure is to obtain the necessary data and have an experienced engineer perform the calculation for me.

An example will illustrate how difficult it is to determine water flow rates. Using a five gallon bucket, an ordinary paint or oil bucket filled with water as an example, we know that water flowing through a ¼" hole in the bottom will flow much faster than the same size hole near the top of the bucket. The reason for this is that there is more weight of water at the bottom than at the top. Thus, the essential issue when dealing with openings in boat hulls is the depth of the opening since a matter of just a few inches can translate to huge differences in water flow rates through those openings.

A simple hole in a hull is the most straight-forward water flow rate problem to deal with. Unfortunately, we often have to deal with water flowing through a complex array of plumbing before it actually enters the hull. Or, perhaps an irregular or ragged-edged opening. Compounding the problem is that as the boat sinks, the level of the opening or hole changes as the boat takes on water and settles deeper. In theory, the water pressure should increase because the depth increases. However, this will only be true so long as the opening inside the boat has water flowing into air; if the hole is on the bottom of the boat, we then have water flowing into water and the amount of resistance changes.

How much will it change? That is impossible to estimate by means of calculation because there will be far too many additional factors to account for. Therefore, the best we can reasonably do is to assume that the flow rate will average out a net percentage deduction from the initial calculated uninterrupted flow rate. The table **6-1** on previous page presents tested flow rates from standard size round openings located one foot below surface that can be used as a basis for estimation.

In summary, when it becomes necessary to calculate water flow rates through complex openings, it is prudent to engage an engineer that is proficient in fluid dynamics.

Our example boat:

> If the boat was last seen afloat at 7:00 PM on Monday, and was discovered sunk at 7:30 AM on Tuesday, we can then establish that the boat sunk during a period of 11-1/2 hours and, in conjunction with the known internal volume, we can then calculate an approximate rate of water flow required to sink the boat. This method works best for mid engine boats and sail boats wherein the center of gravity is located near the mid point of the vessel. Obviously, it works less well for rear engine boats that are likely to settle stern first, but even that situation can be measured and calculated.

Therefore, if we have a 16,500 lb. boat that sank in 11.5 hours, we can establish the minimum water flow rate required to sink it. Since the dry weight is very close to displacement weight, absent any other factors it probably took at least 16,500 lbs. of water to sink the boat or 1928 gallons. The rate of water ingress would have to be 168 gallons per hour. Of course, nothing is ever that simple, because in this case we have cockpit scuppers 6" above the waterline as our nearest point of water entry, meaning that it will take something more than 168 gallons per hour because the actual sinking volume, based on threshold point, is the volume up to the scuppers.

As shown in previous section, our volume figure will have to be adjusted to reflect that additional 6" of water. To obtain that we calculate the average area of water plane and multiply by 6" for the additional volume of water. Let's say that works out to another 7800 lbs. which we add to the original 16,500 lbs. This raises our total to 3249 gallons.

However, it is a fair assumption that the boat with all that water in it is not going to float level but change its trim at least somewhat. Perhaps waterlines will provide that answer. If not, then we can assume that the rolling or pitching forward or aft will alter our base estimate.

In this case it is less important to try to guess at what that might be, than it is to be aware that our final amount of water and rate of flow could be something less than the basic calculation, so once again, what we are really trying to do is bracket a probable numerical range, both in terms of time and volume.

This number then becomes useful for including or rejecting a variety of possibilities. If, for example, it is determined that point (A) allowed X amount of water ingress, our calculation will either confirm that source or give cause to suspect the source or the calculation. Either way, we are forced to go back and reprove the point, and in this way the investigator is far less prone to making an error or false conclusions. Moreover, if challenged, his conclusion stands a far better chance of holding up.

At this point it must be recognized that the number of possible variables is nearly endless, but our objective here is, first and foremost, to narrow down those possibilities. That is purpose of these calculations, but if they also serve to back up our findings, so much the better.

Obviously, in larger, more complex vessels the number of possibilities for water ingress, increases dramatically, many of them obscure and/or difficult to locate and access. There will be many instances where the leak has occurred in a location that is completely inaccessible, such as between a shallow section of hull and cabin sole where there are no hatches, and where it will later be necessary to cut part of the deck out to get at it.

Thus, we seek to establish a method of working backwards by calculation for the purpose of trying to isolate the source of water ingress while not wasting time and effort.

For example, if we have determined that it will take an initial flow rate of 100 gallons per hour to sink the boat in the time allotted, then we can, for the time being by-pass all potential sources that would yield significantly less than 100 gallons per hour, sources such as leaking shaft packing glands.

Adjusting for Error

In the method described above, it will not be possible to be 100% accurate as the flow rate will change somewhat as the boat is being lifted and the water pressure changes. Here is a method that can be universally applied to adjust out the error when the test cannot be rigidly controlled. Let's say we leave the boat in the water for 5 minutes to measure the leakage rate; the Travel Lift will take about 60 seconds to lift the boat out of the water, during which time the rate of flow slows to zero and our period now increases to six minutes. But that last minute is at a diminished flow rate. Once we determine the flow rate per minute based on the 5 minute rate, we can take that last minute and average it by dividing in half (since the range diminishes from X to zero) and adding that amount to the five minute rate so that it now becomes a 5.5 minute rate that we then recalculate to get the more accurate hourly rate:

> During our test 2.75 gallons flows into our container in five minutes. This is a 2.2 quart per minute rate. However, it took the Travel Lift one minute to lift the hull from the water so that during that last minute the flow rate went from 2.2 to zero. Averaging that last minute we get 1.1 qt. We can either adjust our rate to a six minute rate, or subtract that last 1.1 qt. and use a five minute rate of 9.9 quarts for a total hourly 118.8 qt/hr or 27.7 gal/hr.

Empirical Testing Methods

By far the easiest way to assess such problems and determine water flow rates with reasonable accuracy is by duplicating the conditions under which it occurred. This can be accomplished either by creating a mock up, or many times by actually measuring the rate of flow within the vessel from the actual source whenever that is possible. This is by far the preferred way since – all things being equal – the result is more accurate so long as the exact conditions are replicated. With things like cracks in hulls, this is the only way that any kind of measurement can be done without spending a lot of money.

Flow rates from ruptured hoses, broken pipes and the like are easily measured with accurate results. One consideration has to do with the depth of the opening combined with the amount of additional water the vessel has absorbed as a result of sinking. This may be thousands of pounds of water that would obviously skew the result of empirical testing. A boat that is heavier with absorbed water would result in the offending opening being somewhat deeper and therefore with a slightly increased pressure which would skew the results. The simple way to avoid this error is to examine the scum line on the hull which should indicate how the boat was floating pre-casualty. Then retrim the vessel by removing or adding weights as needed to correct to the original trim.

Overlooking this step could lead to impeachment of one's testimony and the negation of all the investigator's hard work.

In cases with problems of plumbing, if the item can be removed from the boat, then it is usually a simple matter to rig up a test platform to replicate the conditions and measure the flow rate. When the thing to be tested cannot be removed, when the vessel is hauled, there is yet another method for testing that can be used. This involves placing a container of water at the desired height and connecting it to the hull opening to be tested so that the necessary water pressure is maintained. As in the previous example, a pump and valve are used to maintain the test reservoir at a constant water level.

An alternative method, when it's not practical to launch the vessel to actually test flow rates and the size opening is known, is to obtain a piece of large diameter PVC pipe, say about 10 inches, and place a sealed cap over the bottom. Drill a hole at the bottom the size diameter that you want to test. Measure the distance on the side up from the bottom to the depth that you want to test. Calculate the volume from the diameter of the pipe and the mark you made. Drill a small hole in the side of the pipe at the water line mark, then insert the wire or nail as a stop gauge mark that you'll be able to see on the inside. Using a stop watch, shove the pipe down in water to the marked depth and then note the time it takes to fill up to your mark. This will be the flow rate for that particular size hole at that depth. This will simulate a hole that is at or near the very bottom of the hull.

This method cannot be reversed, that is, fill the pipe with water and let it run out through a hole. The reason is that water running out of a container into air does not encounter any resistance as it does when running into a partly filled container, so the timing rates of the two methods will not be the same.

However, if the hole is somewhere above the bottom of the hull, say just above the chine, a different method is needed. In this case, measure the distance between the leak point and hull bottom. Using that distance, mark the point on the *side* of the pipe. Mark the overall hull draft on the pipe as before, and carry out the test as before.

Causes of Leaks

Gauging Shaft & Rudder Seal Leakage

The point at which a propeller or rudder shaft exits a hull is always a potential source for heavy leakage. In recent years the old flax packing stuffing box has been replaced with the so-called "dripless" seals, though many of the old type still exit. It is generally true that dripless seals don't drip, but like all mechanical devices they do wear out, and when they do the end result is the same. These seals can also leak and become damaged due to engine misalignment and bent shafts.

Fig. 6-3. One wouldn't expect a boat builder to run a control cable through the hull below the waterline, but there it is. The heavywater trail clearly reveals a serious leak.

Leaking shaft seals, as with the flax packing before, are a common cause of sinking. We measure the rate of leakage by placing a suitable container, or, if no container will fit under it, a diverter device into a container, so that the rate of water flow can be measured. Note that bent or misaligned shafts can fool us. The rate of leakage may depend on the position of the shaft, a position that may have changed after the sinking. Therefore, it is necessary, with the vessel afloat, to turn the shaft a full 360 degrees to check the rate of leakage at all positions.

This kind of testing can also be done by holding the vessel in Travel Lift slings and measuring the water flow rate per minute from the source in question. Then, multiply the per minute rate by 60 to get the hourly rate. To use this method for tough problems like cracks in hulls or other things that are difficult to measure, simply allow the water to flow into the hull, then stop the flow by lifting the boat out, then pump or drain the water from the hull into containers of known volume (such as 55 gallon drums or 5 gallon buckets) to determine the amount. Most boat yards will have portable high capacity electric pumps on hand that one can borrow for this purpose.

Testing leakage rates for rudder seals and hull cracks needs to be done by drying out the hull, launching it for a predetermined time, then hauling it and measuring the amount of water accumulated in the hull. With the Travel Lift the bow can be lifted so that all the water can drain out a transom drain or easily be pumped out.

Hidden Leaks

It will happen from time to time that the source of the leak is not found, even after extensive searching. The boat is refloated but no water comes in. There are a number of reasons why this happens. First, we have to consider whether the source of water ingress was due to an abnormal condition of the weather, tides, location of the vessel or any other condition that was present then, but is not present now. Secondly, conditions may change that cause the leak to close up. I've seen this happen with anything from damaged hoses to hull cracks and there are no easy answers as to how to find the leak short of determined investigation with the vessel afloat. In most cases, however, the leak doesn't close up completely, but merely slows down a lot.

Fortunately, most such leaks occur over time and will leave a water trail as shown in **Fig. 6-3.** that is very obvious. Unfortunately, newly originated leaks are less likely to leave a visible water trail and are harder to locate. In these instances, the best short cut method is to dry out the bilges completely so that even very small leaks can be traced. In one case a very small hull fracture occurred on the very bottom of the keel that was not found when the bottom was inspected. This leaked water into a hollow keel area that was apparently sealed off from the bilges with a glassed-over plywood false bottom. A large battery had been removed from its holder and set onto the false bottom that effectively sealed the leak. Only by drying out the bilge completely by hand using sponges and rags was it noticed that a small trickle of water was emanating from under this battery. When the battery was moved, the water then flowed at a much higher rate. Unfortunately, days of frustrated searching led up to this point.

Alterations and Additions to Yachts

High value yachts frequently undergo major alterations and additions in which substantial additional weight is added to the vessel without consideration for how this will change the trim. At the time the yacht was built, plumbing and drainage systems were installed in accordance with the original design trim. The addition of additional weight, such as hydraulic transom platforms designed to hold tenders are a prominent example of how such ill-considered changes can cause serious trouble from deck drainage to water entering the hull and water backing up through exhaust systems.

There's really no end to the number of things that can go wrong when excessive additional weight is added to a vessel that wasn't designed to carry it. The investigator should always be alert for major additions and changes to vessels, and the fact that for older boats, these changes can be cumulative over a period of many years. Look for changes in the height of the boot top or bottom paint as this is a good clue that the boat has become heavier.

Improper Ventilator Design

Many mysterious sinkings have been ultimately traced to bad designs involving hull or engine room ventilators. Foundering at sea can occur when vent design brings in excessive amounts of spray, something that is not often thought of until it is too late. Vents can easily be designed in such a way that no matter how much spray goes into them, no water enters the hull. This is called the *dorade box* design and is the way that all hull ventilators should be designed.

Another event that might not be considered is that rain water going into vents has also been known to cause sinking. In one case, a flashy "Euro style" boat had tear drop

Fig. 6-4. We can identify at least three different water or scum lines on the transom of this boat. A hydraulic lift platform and RIB boat tender weighing over 2,000 lbs. were added. This changed the trim of this 50 footer by at least six inches, causing the bilge pump discharge to reverse siphon, almost sinking it. The trim change was so drastic all the water stayed aft, and when the aft pump failed, the hull flooded and the engines filled with water.

shaped vents placed in such a way that most of the water coming off the foredeck ran straight into the vents on each side of the hull. Five of the first dozen boats of this model went down in less than a year.

Small Boats

Far more small boats sink than larger ones, and there are several reasons why this is so. First, it takes a lot less water to put a small boat on the bottom. Second is the matter of scale: being small means that the freeboard is lower and that positioning of openings in the hull are going to be closer to the water line. Third, and equally important, is that most small boats are open, a factor that invites the weather to play a role in sinking them.

Heavy rainfall plays a major role in the vast majority of small boat sinkings that usually occur at a dock. Fortunately, it is usually possible to determine how much rain has fallen in a given area, as well as to determine by means of calculation just how much water a boat can accumulate during any given weather event.

Over the years, uncountable numbers of small boats were built and sold that had design faults both large and small. Most of these boats are still with us and are in use, regardless of age. Therefore this section examines the evolution of small boat design and the many faults they may have because the investigator will be dealing with boats built over a span of twenty to thirty years or more.

Rear Engine Boats

Boats that have the engines mounted in the after section are much more prone to sinking by virtue of the fact that these boats are off-balance. These include outboards, stern drive and vee drive boats that constitute a majority of boats in existence. Most rear engine boats have a natural attitude of being trimmed down by the stern or, we might say, they are stern heavy. The significance of this is that when water enters the hull, that water will run and accumulate aft. This type of boat will sink much faster than mid engine boats because, with all the water running aft, it takes a lot less water to put it on the bottom.

When we analyze how boats ultimately end up on the bottom, we discover that hulls have a lot of holes or openings in them, both above and below the water line. Boats don't sink because the hull completely fills up with water to the gunwale; no, boats, start to sink long before the hull completely fills. Initially, some source of water ingress into the hull starts the ball rolling. Water comes in and depresses the hull down in the water until, at some point, water begins to come in from other sources, the most common of which are cockpit drain scuppers.

Most small boats have what are called self-bailing cockpits. That is, any water that goes onto the deck, whether from rain or splash, is intended to run overboard through deck scuppers that, due to the smallness of the boat, are almost always dangerously close to the waterline. Thus, when a certain amount of water enters the hull, that self-bailing feature is turned into a self-sinking feature since the water that is intended to run out can also be reversed and run into the boat and cause it to sink. This is termed the threshold point, that point at which water will enter the hull through other openings.

Normally we think of the hull freeboard as the height to which a hull must settle into the water before it sinks. That is, that water must come over the sides or transom to sink it. That would be true if hulls weren't full of all sorts of holes and openings, some of which may unintentionally allow water into the hull. The threshold point, in a addition to cockpit scuppers, can include things like heads, bait wells, shower sumps and even bilge pumps. It could be one of these or virtually all of these sources combined. This is why conducting a sinking investigation is rarely quick or easy, for each of these has to be identified and determined how it relates to the whole.

Outboard Boats

Traditionally, outboard boats have made up the bulk of the marine surveyors sinking investigations by virtue of the fact that in the past, so many were so poorly designed. Numerous outboard boat builders have been put out of business because they built boats that were almost guaranteed to sink sooner or later. The typical 24 foot outboard

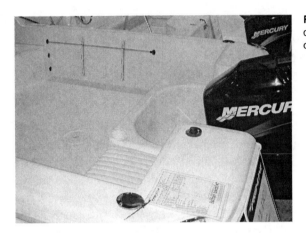

Fig. 6-5. The old-fashioned motor well design does a good job of keeping water out as long as there are no holes in the well.

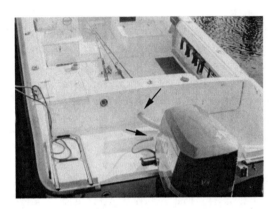

Fig. 6-6. This properly designed platform extension has the cable pass-through up high enough that it is not leakage problem, plus the cables are in a sealed conduit. Along with a gasketed transom door, this boat will withstand rigorous sea conditions.

Fig. 6-7. Circa 1985 no well design leaves the cockpit wide open to the seas. Note the removable deck section on which the cauling has gone bad, letting large amounts of water into the bilge.

boat with twin 200 hp outboard motors weighs 3,000 - 4,000 lbs. without the motors which will weigh another 600 lbs. each. Unlike a cabin cruiser, our outboard boat has very little in the way of weight up forward; the major weights are the engines that are hanging off the stern of the vessel.

Outboard boat designers have tried various means for making their boats seaworthy. The essential problem with the outboard boat stems from the cut-down transom which necessarily has to be lower than the gunwales of the hull. Here we had the transom being the lowest part of the hull combining with the weight of the engines all at one end, a set of factors that tends to defeat the boat's ability to remain afloat. Beginning around the 1950's we saw the motor well design which consisted of a molded fiberglass well that was integral with the transom. Water could slosh freely over the cut down transom and into the well that was self-bailing, thus keeping water out of the hull proper.

The Motor Well Design

The motor well design worked just fine but for one thing: people's tendency to cut holes in it to route the steering and motor control cables. Some builders would supply the boat to the dealers without any holes in the motor well, leaving it for the dealers to mount and rig the engines. In order to make the installation appear nice and neat, the dealers would then cut holes low down, at the same level the controls came out of the engine cowling. Putting the cable pass-throughs low down in the well, of course, completely defeated the purpose of the well since there was virtually no way to seal up the opening. Steering and engine control cables move and exert a lot of force, so no matter how hard anyone tried to seal it up, water would always enter the hull through the cable pass-through.

Some few builders were smart enough to place the cable pass-through above the level of the transom cut out. Yet other builders go even farther afield and place access hatches or ports at the bottom of the wells. This was usually done in order to be able to service an aft bilge pump. These hatches or access ports are the plastic variety that has proved to be anything but water tight. In test after test, it has been demonstrated that these plastic ports invariably leak, leaks from small amounts to large amounts, and almost always enough to sink a boat over time.

For a motor well to be effective, it must have no holes in it below the level of the lowest part of the transom.

The No Well Design

Beginning in the 1980's we began to see outboard boats that did not have motor wells. Instead, the cut down transom was open to the cockpit deck, a factor that allowed water that sloshed over the low transom to go right into the cockpit area. Ostensibly, this would not be a problem so long as the cockpit deck was water tight. There being the need to service such things as bilge pumps and batteries and the like installed below the deck, which meant that builders would install hatches in the deck, thereby negating the deck's water tight integrity. In most cases, a simple pie port — so long as it was not installed too close to the transom — would not sink a boat as long as the cockpit deck was designed in such a way that it facilitated fast drainage. An example would be a deck with a crown in it that caused water to run off to the sides into a gutter that led to the drain scuppers. With a pie port being on the high side of the crown, water would not stay there long enough to permit much leakage into the hull, and whatever leakage it did cause, the bilge pump could easily handle.

Unfortunately, the vast majority of decks in no motor well design boats did not have a crown, but were flat. Even worse, pie ports or even large plastic hatches were installed close to the transom. Typically, the deck is very close to the normal static water line. Thus, with a bilge pump or battery failure, it only would take a very small amount of water in the bilge to depress the hull down to the point where water is either back flowing in through the scuppers or sloshing over the transom, ultimately leading to the sinking of the boat.

The no motor well design is a patently foolish design that most naval architects would argue is demonstrably unseaworthy while the vessel is at rest, and we haven't even mentioned the risks associated with this design while at sea.

Bolt-On Brackets

A transom bracket is a device that was first conceived to facilitate the conversion of an inboard powered boat to an outboard powered boat. Transom brackets have been fashioned from steel, aluminum or fiberglass and are attached to the transom usually by means of bolts. Originally, brackets were simple weldments of pipe but eventually evolved into box-like structures. In part this was due to the huge trim problems that brackets caused by placing the engines so far aft that often resulted in the boat sinking. Thus, it came to be realized that it was necessary to increase buoyancy in the stern, something that could be accomplished by building buoyancy into the bracket.

Today, motor brackets are sold only as after-market products and are most often used by boat owners in converting stern drive boats to outboard power. And because such conversions are done by amateurs who are incapable of calculating the change of trim effects, such conversions often end creating unseaworthy boats. Therefore, anytime boats with motor brackets are encountered on a sinking investigation, it becomes necessary to determine whether the vessel is hydrostatically seaworthy since it will often be found that it isn't.

The Integral Platform Design

This design, which first appeared in the early 1990's, is an outgrowth of the bolt-on transom bracket. The integral platform design is an innovation that solved most of the unseaworthiness problems of the outboard boat. It gets its name by being a combination integral swim platform and motor bracket. But it did so at the expense of making outboard boats considerably more costly, for the integral platform makes a boat longer by means of making a mounting bracket integral with the hull. Instead of being bolted on, it's now included in the boat's hull and even deck mold. Outboard boat owners like the idea of bracket mounting engines because it gets the engines out of the cockpit area. The problem with the motor well design is that the well takes up a good two feet or more of cockpit space.

To create a boat with an integral platform the transom is moved (which is actually a false transom) farther forward, creating a platform-like area on which the motors can be mounted. This, of course, shortens up the cockpit considerably, so to avoid that the hull is made a couple feet longer. The main difference between the bolt-on bracket and the integral platform design is that later includes an actual lengthening of the hull proper. Thus, hull buoyancy in the stern section is increased and the boat is easily designed to maintain proper trim.

Of course, the engines are still hanging off the stern and the boat is stern heavy, yet with this design we no longer have any dire need to put holes in the hull that risk sinking the boat. A well-designed integral platform boat completely eliminates all the fundamental inadequacies previously inherent in outboard boats. By the year 2000, nearly all new center console boats being sold had integral platforms. This should have put an end to the huge number of sinkings that occurred every year with outboards, but it did not. And the reason why is that many boat builders continue to take a lackadaisical attitude toward sea worthiness. Good news for investigators, bad news for owners, builders and insurers.

While a good integral platform design is capable of producing a seaworthy boat, the design can easily be defeated by the same means as the old motor well, namely by putting holes in places where they shouldn't be. Once again it is still necessary to run engine controls from outside the boat to inside the boat, and if this is not done at a height well above the water line, we're right back to the same old problem of putting holes in the hull too close to the water line. Photo below **(Fig. 6-8)** clearly demonstrates the essence of the problem with a typical boat at rest while at sea in favorable conditions.

With the integral platform design the transom — actually a false transom — is moved forward. In order to make use of the platform for things like swimming, diving or water skiing, instead of having to climb over it, the designer puts a door or two in it. That is no problem either so long as the cockpit deck immediately ahead of

Fig. 6-8.

the false transom isn't full of holes or leaky hatches, for that then defeats the seaworthy design. The door certainly isn't water proof, but moreover while at rest when using the platform for its intended purpose, that door or doors is going to be open. Most builders use a door with a rather high sill that prevents at least large amounts of water from rushing forward, but some don't, so be alert for this possibility

Stern Drive Boats

Stern drive boats suffer the same unequal weight distribution problems that outboards and, indeed, all rear engine boats do, plus one more. The extra problem is created by the method used to seal the submerged and moving stern drive parts. Both the engine drive shaft and the exhaust pass through the transom below the water line, thereby creating a means by which water can enter the boat. And because most of the weight is in the stern, once again relatively small amounts of water are capable of sinking stern drive boats.

Sailboats

Sailboat sinkings in my experience are infrequent and most often due to improperly installed and back siphoning heads, sinks, engine and generator raw water systems. Heads in sailboats are usually located below the waterline so that the raw water line to the pump can readily backflow if precautions aren't taken to prevent this. The usual method is with a siphon break valve which, unfortunately can fail. The discharge lines also have siphon breaks, but these large diameter lines are not prone to siphoning if the riser loop travels substantially above the water line. The danger is for backflow when heeled over, not siphoning.

Engine and generator water pumps can also backflow since these too are usually below the water line. The anti siphon vacuum break valve is also needed for this purpose. After refloating a sunken sail boat, check the engine for water flowing out of the engine heat exchanger tank overflow tube.

Sinks are another problem area. Most sailboats have sinks that use common household plumbing fittings and will be of zinc or plastic. Zinc fittings will disintegrate fast in salt water and result in the pipes and/or hoses going adrift. Plastic fittings are sometimes stressed and broken.

A more common casualty for sailboats is hull flooding due to bilge pump system failure. Sailboats often have inadequate bilge pumping. It is not at all unusual to find forty footers with only one pump, and only a moderate capacity pump at that. Because the pumps are very deep in the bilge, the static head that the pumps have to overcome is usually very high, severely reducing the capacity of the pump, sometimes as much as 75%. Typically it will take about three times as much water to sink a sail as a powerboat owing to high sidedness and a more limited number of through hull openings. Therefore, sailboats don't often sink all the way, and when they do, it's usually a really big leak if the boat went down fast rather than by being neglected for weeks.

When sailboats do go down fast, look for contributing causes such as heads and sinks backflowing once the vessel settles down a few inches.

External Factors

There are a number of external factors other than rainfall that lead to small boats sinking that are much less likely to contribute to a large boat sinking.

The Effects of Tides

One very common cause of small boat sinkings results from getting caught under a dock during a rising tide. Typically, this comes about through ignorance in knowing how to tie up a boat properly, or a dock that is improperly designed for small boats. Usually it is the transom corner that gets caught and the force of boat buoyancy is more than sufficient to leave plenty of evidence of what happened. Normally the evidence will be plain in the form of gouges and splintered wood on the under side of the dock, or gel coat embedded in the concrete if it is a concrete pier. The first sign that getting caught under the dock usually appears in the form of minor damage to the gunwale.

There have been occasions when there was very little evidence of getting caught under the dock, as when it occurred in an area of very calm waters where no significant boat movement took place to cause obvious damage, but this is rather rare. Or there are occasions when it is an aft mooring cleat that contacts the underside of the dock, leaving no marks on the boat. In this case, the underside of the dock (often a hard place to access) needs to be examined closely. This is particularly difficult when the investigator doesn't know exactly where the boat was positioned, so that there may be a large area that has to be examined at low tide from a dinghy.

Just because a boat sank in a place that doesn't have tides doesn't mean that fluctuating water levels can't have the same result. Water levels can change for a wide variety of reasons including strong winds, so when working inland areas we still have to be on the lookout for this possibility.

Wave Action

One of the first things we need to do in any investigation is to determine the position of the boat at the sinking site. Assuming it was a dock, the effects of wave action must always be considered even if it is a protected or no wake zone. While wind generated waves are always a possibility, a more remote chance exists that a large wake from a single passing boat could have contributed. Unfortunately, the only evidence that the wake from a passing vessel leaves is the sunk boat itself, and hopefully a witness or two.

A common danger to outboard boats is a dockage location that is exposed to wave action, particularly when the stern of the boat is docked toward the direction of wave action. One of the more common dangers is a location on a canal or tributary off a larger body of water that on first impression appears to be protected but is exposed to high amounts of surge. Often, these are canals directly off the Intra Coastal Waterway where large wakes of passing vessels are never-ending.

In this situation, small amounts of water sloshing over the transom and entering the hull from any one of dozens of possibilities causes long term and frequent operation of bilge pumps. This can lead to wearing down of batteries, ultimate bilge pump failure and finally sinking. But, when the claims investigator arrives on the scene, he could end up being fooled because the cause does not become apparent (perhaps there are no boats passing at that time) and all he is faced with as evidence is a dead battery. How the water got into the boat remains a mystery. Therefore, be alert to the potential for wave action, and do not be fooled by present conditions. The two key things to look for are fetch and boat wakes. Absent those things, a strong clue may be that slime or moss is found on the hull sides far above the water line. This indicates that wave action is near constant.

While it doesn't happen often, another thing to be alert to is the unusual effects of wakes of very large commercial vessels on narrow waterways, particularly tugs pushing or pulling barges. When moving in narrow waterways, these large vessels displace huge amounts of water. As they approach a given location, a barge will push a large amount of water in front of it, causing the water level in the waterway to rise significantly, and then as it passes, the water then falls suddenly, only to rise back up again as the vessel passes. This can cause problems with pleasure craft that aren't moored properly, particularly outboard boats. When a boat sinks due to this phenomenon, more often than not the cause appears to be a mystery as the large vessel is long gone, and such may not pass very often to tip off the investigator to this possibility. Broken dock lines, displaced or damaged cleats and unexplained damage may offer clues.

The Right Circumstances

This leads to a question that is commonly asked by boat owners about why, if their boat has a particular defect, it sank at this particular time, and not earlier. Say we have a boat that is five years old that has some sort of design defect that we believe caused the sinking, and that defect had been in existence from the day the owner purchased it. Why, the owner asks, didn't the boat sink sooner. This question may also baffle the investigator for a time, but if he continues his investigation he will usually discover the answer. This is a question that sinking investigators will face frequently, and the answer is that the boat sank only because exactly the right set of circumstances had to combine to cause the sinking, circumstances that were not present until this point.

A typical example would be an owner that normally keeps his boat in dry storage, but on this occasion had left it in the water for a week. Another example is a boat that normally is docked in a marina with the bow facing the direction of any on-coming wave action, but in this instance the boat was turned around with the stern facing wave action. In other words, at the time the boat sank, something had changed from the normal circumstances. It has been my experience that boat owner usually is not aware of the change, or is unable to make the connection between the change and why the boat sank.

The two examples cited here are easy and obvious ones, but more often than not the changed circumstances are much more subtle, such as a case where some dock repairs were found to be the cause. In this case, the property owner, who was not the boat owner, had a section of deteriorated dock repaired. The repair work was rather shoddily done and the repairman had left a large, bent spike sticking out of a piling. The boat's stern line had caught on this nail with the effect of shortening the line so that when the tide came up the stern line was now too short. This pulled the stern under on a rising tide by perhaps three inches, just enough for water to enter the scuppers and flood the deck. While the damage to the boat was only about $8,000, it took a bit of effort to discover the mysterious cause that ultimately led to a recovery from the repair contractor. Proof of the nail being the cause was determined by matching up a point on the dock line where the nail caused fraying of the line.

In this line of work, the abnormal happenings are normal, the bizarre is an every day occurrence, and the impossible is always possible. Keep you eyes open for the unexpected.

Peculiar Circumstances

Last but not least, investigators should keep an open mind to the possibility of very unlikely circumstances. On an August afternoon I was performing a survey on a nearly new forty foot "open" sport fisherman that had been recently repossessed by a lender. The boat had a tuna tower with full enclosures so that when an afternoon thunderstorm hit, I was able to keep working. I was crawling around the engine room when I heard what sounded like a large amount of water falling. Searching further, outboard and aft of the starboard engine a large amount of water was cascading down the inside of the hull – actually between a fuel tank and the hull. Both bilge pumps were running non stop, but the water in the bilge was rising. Going back up on deck, it was noticed that the entire foredeck area – which was very large — was channeling water down the side deck and dumping it into the cockpit. The stream of water was fully four inches wide by one inch deep.

But that water never made it into the cockpit because there was a fold-out boarding step built into the cockpit side liner right below that little water fall. This fold-out step created a hole roughly 14" x 16" so that that waterfall was going straight into the bilge. Over the years I've witnessed this sort of thing repeated in a variety of ways. When the cause of a sinking appears illusive, consider the watershed of large deck areas and how they drain. Does the water go overboard or does it somehow find its way into the hull?

Even more illusive as a cause may be the watershed of some other structure; many boats have been sunk by being docked under the edge of a roof. In one case, drainage from a parking lot was channeled over a bulkhead into a small boat docked parallel to that bulkhead. The tip-off in this case was that the subject vessel had a lot of small gravel and sand in it. Otherwise, I might never have found the cause.

In another case, the engines had been removed for rebuilding when the boat sank. Naturally, the disconnection of exhaust pipes and plumbing was immediately suspected, but proved not to be the cause which took days to find. Of course, the removal of the engines drastically changed the vessel trim, but the relationship was not discovered until the flying bridge area was examined where it was noted that the engine control cable chase, as it passed through the bridge deck, did not have a cofferdam around it. Thus, the vessel now trimmed up by the stern, caused a failure of the bridge deck drainage. Instead, the deck area collected water and channeled it down the cable chase. Combined with the fact that the batteries were disconnected, the pumps didn't work and this fifty-footer sank.

Sketches & Drawings

When it comes to court testimony, it is not sufficient that the investigator merely locates the cause of sinking and documents it. Similar to criminal investigations, it is necessary to examine all possible causes and eliminate them. In other words, the investigator needs to be able to demonstrate that he was *thorough*. Perhaps most importantly, the creation of sketches assists the investigator toward making sure he has covered all possibilities and helps keep complicated issues in perspective; sketches help us visualize what we can't see. Sketches need not be fancy or particularly artistic; the important point is that they should contain all relevant items.

One very good way to do this is to create a sketch of the vessel and then identify all possible sources of water entry. The author does this by making separate sketches for (1) vessel plan view, (2) port and starboard side profiles and, (3) a stern profile. On the plan view all through hull openings are shown, along with bilge pump placement, relevant plumbing, along with all other relevant items. On the profile and stern views the through hull openings are shown in their proper positions and elevations. For vessels where cockpit height above water line may be an issue, cut away views are usually helpful. Sketches should be large enough so that there is room to add in dimensions and other notations.

Don't worry about your drawing ability; sketches don't have to be fancy or artistic, only illustrate the situation. A crude sketch is still better than no sketch. If your drawing ability is like that of Grandma Mosses, that's fine, even for a courtroom presentation.

Reports

While it may seem premature to consider reports, we will do so at this point since it is important to know what a well-written report should and should not contain, as this will help keep the investigation on track. The ability to write clear, concise reports that do not cause problems for attorneys – for example by containing speculation, ambiguities, contradictions, unsupported statements, irrelevant information or are excessively wordy – is a skill that is sadly lacking in most marine investigation reports the author has seen. Indeed, unless one has had formal training, good report writing skills are not easy to come by.

It is equally important to cover what is not the cause as well as what is. To that end, detailed notes should be kept about every possibility that was checked out. Here is where the sketch becomes invaluable, for instead of pouring over a lot of hand written notes, one can quickly obtain an overview of all aspects involved from looking at the sketches. Here is where we see that the more detailed our sketches are, the better job we will do in covering all bases.

In many cases the investigator will want to incorporate his sketches as exhibits attached to his report. Hand drawn sketches made on the scene will naturally be rather crude, and at some point he will need to decide whether these sketches will need to be refined for a more professional presentation. For typical claims work wherein it is only necessary to provide clarification to the client, hand made sketches are usually adequate. But at some point it may become evident that the loss may not be covered, or one may already know that a case is destined for litigation, in which case sketches should be prepared with advance knowledge that they will need to be refined.

It may turn out that the investigator discovers what he believes is the source of the water ingress early on. This does not mean that he can terminate his investigation at this point because he still needs to cover all possibilities. Thus, the body of the report can follow the process of investigation, highlighting each of the items considered, and the reason for elimination as contributory. Note here that sinkings often have many contributory causes, yet another reason why all possible causes need be investigated.

It is not sufficient, as many investigators do, to merely state that all other possibilities were considered and eliminated. Each potential should be identified and the reason for elimination spelled out. This information can be included as an addendum or appendix so as to not clutter up the main body of the report.

Typically, investigations involve direct physical investigation of the vessel, forensic investigation possibly by other experts, interviews and research. All of this may take many days to accomplish, resulting in the accumulation of a great deal of information. The amount of information is often overwhelming and very hard to manage. Coming to grips with it all can be difficult. The way professional investigators keep a handle on it is by keeping a "book," usually a loose-leaf binder in which every note, document and relevant scrap of paper is placed. It is a poor practice to just throw all documents into a file folder for this is hard to organize and handle, plus it is easy for documents to get lost if one has to take the file out in the field. Later the report is constructed from this book.

Many investigations are rendered incomplete or inconclusive by the inability to resolve all questions, particularly when mitigating circumstances and contributory causes are present. Complex issues like this tend to lead the investigator around in circles when writing his report. A common situation is the chicken-or-the-egg syndrome wherein one cannot determine which event occurred first, thereby rendering the investigation inconclusive. Many investigators get blind-sided by this problem after discovering the mitigating factor exists after the physical investigation is completed and the door has been closed on the opportunity for further investigation for any number of reasons. These problems are best avoided by forward thinking and being aware during the course of the investigation on the vessel that such problems are likely to arise.

For example, a common situation is where a bilge pump is found with the fuse blown or circuit breaker tripped, the batteries are dead, but the surveyor failed to document the position of all circuit breakers or fuses. Thus, he does not know whether a bilge pump circuit fault tripped the breaker before or during the sinking process. A number of days or weeks goes by before he discovers that he failed to cover this point. In the meantime, someone may have altered the position of circuit breakers on the panel. Now he's stuck with trying to deal with this issue in his report, thereby introducing the element of uncertainty into the report. If he does not deal with the issue, surely the other side will take note of this and attack his investigation for this deficiency. In this way we can see that a seemingly minor oversight could end up sinking an entire investigation.

The structure of the report should be laid out categorically, with distinct major areas such as plumbing, electrical, weather factors, interviews and so on covered as separate sections similar to the pattern of the investigation. Then, at the end of the report in a conclusion, these diverse elements are pulled together and summarized.

Chapter 7

Sinking Due To Rain

Rain is the single largest cause of small boat sinkings, sinking not only small boats but occasionally larger ones, too. This type of casualty is therefore one of the most frequent types of losses investigated by marine surveyors. Smaller boats sink more frequently due to several factors: First by virtue of being smaller, second by being more open, and third because most do not have shore power operated battery charging systems. There is a host of contributory factors, such as outboards and stern drive boats being unbalanced and stern heavy, as discussed in previous chapter.

Heavy rainfall also results in partial sinking, or hull flooding, including hull flooding of hauled vessels. Of course it is never expected that rainfall will sink a boat because almost everyone expects boats to be designed in such a way as that they will withstand the effects of what we consider to be normal weather. That statement raises an interesting question: How much rainfall should a boat be expected to withstand?

Design Issues

Rain is usually not the only factor, but its combination with design issues, maintenance and system failures that causes a boat to sink. It is the rare case in which heavy rain, alone, is the sole cause. This presents the investigator with the interesting challenge of having to assess the adequacy of both structural and systems design. For this reason this chapter will explore the wider variety of design issues that also cause boats to sink.

No matter where you live, unless perhaps, it is in the desert, all regions from time to time will receive extreme amounts of rainfall, amounts that are well above normal. How we define extreme will be dependent on what is defined as "normal" for a given area. In this regard we should be cognizant of the fact that many, if not all, boat builders market their boats nationwide and even internationally. With that being the case, the builder has an obligation to design his product to withstand the normal range of weather of the region with the highest rates of rainfall where he markets his products.

The issue of proper design is often raised, as it was in a recent case involving a new $250,000 thirty-four footer that sank because the cockpit drainage system was improperly designed. The boat suffered a bilge pump failure in addition to the fact that the aft deck was designed in such a way as it shed all rain water directly into the bilge. After paying the loss, the insurer sued the builder over the faulty design and recovered based upon an investigation that left no doubt as to the cause of the sinking.

The faulty deck design was the primary cause because the boat should have been able to withstand a four inch rainfall even without bilge pumps. But the pumps did not work because the builder had improperly wired them. Turning off the main battery switches cut power to the pumps when it is standard procedure to wire the pumps independent of this switch. This new boat owner made a habit of always turning the switches off when leaving the boat, not knowing that he was turning his bilge pumps off.

Negligence

We address the subject of negligence in this chapter because it often figures into the cause of boat sinkings. There are two levels of negligence that the investigator needs to be aware of here. The results of ordinary negligence is normally covered by insurance. Second degree negligence is the result of human error, such as making a mistake in judgement or forgetting to do something, which is how most casualties occur.

Gross negligence involves conscious awareness that the taking of an action, or not taking an action will result in negative consequences, a willful act in the face of a known hazard. It must be assumed that a boat owner knows that his bilge pumping system must be kept in operating condition in order to keep his boat afloat, in the same way that one cannot drive a car on a flat tire. It's common knowledge that boats will not remain afloat indefinitely without a pump. Therefore, the failure to maintain a pumping system implies the knowledge of the end result of that failure. The failure to act in the face of a known hazard constitutes gross negligence and is not covered by insurance because it is classified as a willful act. In this sense, gross negligence is nearly the same thing as intentionally sinking a boat. The only difference is the means by which the sinking is accomplished.

The investigator will often be called upon to make judgements about whether a casualty involves simple or gross negligence by virtue of the fact that he, alone, is collecting and analyzing evidence. By way of example, let's say that bilge pump doesn't work due to a single corroded wire connection, and that connection is located in a position that is very hard to see. Would this constitute gross negligence? Not likely because it can be argued that the fault was an oversight since it did not present a clear hazard. On the other hand, what if that connection was on a badly corroded terminal block that is readily visible to anyone with just a cursory glance? Thus these issues come down to a matter of reasonable and prudent behavior, and honest oversight versus willful neglect.

Levels of Causation

Proximate Cause

The term *proximate cause* is not normally used by investigators but, rather by lawyers since this is a legal term and does not normally figure into issues of insurance coverage. However, it is important in all cases that contributory causes be identified and so categorized as mitigating factors that may indeed affect the determination of coverage.

In law, there are a number of names for different levels of causation. These are Primary, Root, Proximate and Contributory. Root cause is not, and should not, be used for this type of casualty. Proximate cause is term that is often used without correct knowledge as to its meaning and even in litigation there is a great deal of controversy over its meaning.

Proximate Cause is a term that appears frequently in civil litigation. Most often it is used in connection with legal liability issues in reference to whether an individual's actions either caused directly or precipitated an effect. The standard dictionary definition is *a cause that directly or with no mediate agency produces an effect.* This is in conflict with most legal definitions. The legal definition, as defined by a number of law dictionaries produces a mish-mash of confusing definitions, and legal interpretations by the courts are no better.

Here's one: *A proximate cause is the first event in a chain of events that gives rise to a claim,*

And another: *In law, a proximate cause is an event sufficiently related to a legally recognizable injury to be held the cause of that injury. Two elements are needed to determine proximate cause: the activity must produce a foreseeable risk, and the injury must be caused directly by the defendant's negligence.*

The word "proximate" means close to, very near, immediately following or preceding — again as defined by the dictionary (Webster's Third New International). Notice that this seems to conflict with the word "direct." Here's an example of proximate cause:

> While Jim was preparing to clean his gun, it accidentally fired. John, who was standing at the head of the stairs, was so startled by the blast that he tripped and fell down the stairs.

In this instance, the proximate cause of John falling down the stairs is not tripping, but the gun firing. Had the gun not fired, John wouldn't have been startled, wouldn't have tripped and fallen down the stairs.

Therefore, proximate cause is essentially a legal definition that engenders a great deal of contention and ought not be used by the investigator for routine first-party property losses because it involves legal opinion. Instead, the investigator should use the terms "primary", "direct" and "contributory" since these terms are clear-cut in their meaning. Let the lawyers wrangle over the meaning of proximate if they so desire, while we stick to less argumentative terms.

Primary Cause

A *primary cause* is one which can directly lead to a sinking without any contributing factors, though contributing factors may exist. The very term itself implies this possibility. We wouldn't signify that something is the main cause unless there exists other possibilities. For a cause to be primary, it would have to initiate the casualty absent contributory factors, though possibly not in exactly the same way.

Contributory Cause

A *contributory cause* is contributory by virtue of not being able to cause the casualty by itself.

When a cause is an only cause, there is no need to qualify it, for it is *the* cause, period. If any kind of qualifier is to be used, it should be the word "direct." So what happens when it appears that two causes appear to have acted equally?

Cases will inevitably occur in which it is impossible or at least very difficult to assess the degree to which each of multiple factors contributed. There will be cases in which it is difficult to say whether cause A is more significant than cause B, or whether the loss could or would have happened absent either one of them. When these doubtful situations arise the investigator should so state his conclusions in his report. I will state it here and in other places in this book that one should not ever feel pressured to draw a definite conclusion when evidence is weak or inconclusive. It is okay for investigations to fail to determine the cause; that conclusive evidence does not exist is not the fault of the investigator, and he should not feel compelled to find evidence that does not exist.

Examples

The following examples build on a central issue and illustrate how mitigating factors can come into play and complicate things:

Example #1

A boat owner removes a hose from a through hull opening that is a few inches above the water line and fails to cap off the opening. The boat does not have a battery charger but does have adequate pumping capacity. A few days later, a very heavy rainstorm drops eight inches of rain that sinks the boat. Which of these two conditions is the cause of the sinking? To answer, we ask: would the rainfall or the open through hull in and of itself have caused the casualty? The boat should have been able to withstand the heavy rains, whereas with the open hull fitting, it is likely that sooner or later wave action would keep putting water in the hull sufficient to wear down the batteries and result in sinking. Thus, the proximate cause is the uncapped fitting, not the rain.

Example #2

The same boat, same uncapped fitting, only this time it is found that both batteries were totally dead at the time of sinking. A complete lack of electrolytic corrosion on battery terminals proves the point. It is also found that a bilge pump wire is corroded and broken. There are no dates on the batteries, but on checking the battery plates these are found to be wasted. In this case, the proximate cause is gross negligence based on a failure to exercise reasonable and prudent maintenance. The uncapped fitting might be construed as ordinary negligence and accidental, but the failure to maintain not only breaches the seaworthiness warranty, but is grossly negligent since the sinking then becomes entirely inevitable and predictable.

Example #3

In this case we have the same circumstances only this time one of the batteries is dead and uncorroded while the other is heavily corroded (electrolysis from immersion). The pumps otherwise work fine. In addition, heavy rains also occurred in the week's period leading up to the sinking dates. On checking with the National Weather Service database, we find that rainfall for the entire month was ten inches above normal. The owner states that he intended to cap off the opening, but had forgotten about it. This is an instance where ordinary negligence combines with an abnormal weather event to cause the casualty. Either one of these factors alone might have caused the sinking and would largely depend on how rain water got into the hull. As far as the policy coverage is concerned, it would likely cover in either case.

Notice that in each of these cases the behavior of the boat owner is relevant to the issue of negligence and could have an effect determining whether insurance coverage applies. Thus, in each case the investigation will have to go beyond investigation of the physical facts and the owner will need to be interviewed.

Example #4

A 35' cruiser sinks wherein it is found that: (1) there is a cracked plastic through-hull near the water line, (2) a shower sump pump installation is improperly designed and allows water to back flow into the hull from the through hull opening. (3) the battery

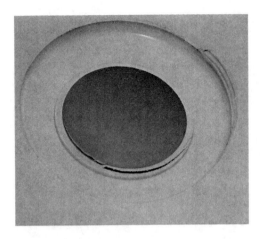

Fig. 7-1. Broken plastic through hull fittings are one of the top causes of sinking. This one is badly cracked, but hasn't yet separated.

switches were turned off and it is found that this also cuts off power to the bilge pumps, (4) the shore power was found to be unplugged from the dock connection, apparently accidentally; (5) a loose bolt on a swim platform bracket is found to be leaking.

In a case with this many relevant conditions, one might conclude that there are too many possibilities to be able to sort it all out, but that is not necessarily true. It is necessary to work through each relevant condition to determine the individual effect and how it relates to the whole. For items one and five, it is necessary to determine the rate of water flow through these openings as both appear to be contributory causes. That the shore power cord was disconnected is only marginally relevant since the power was completely cut off to the pumps in any case. If the rate of water ingress into the hull was such that the pumps could have handled it, then the primary cause of sinking was the pumps being inactivated because, absent this fault, the boat probably would not have sunk; sinking becomes even less likely had the battery charger been working.

However, if the pumps would have handled the water until the batteries were eventually depleted that would be matter of hours or a few days at best. But the fact remains that the pumps were turned off and the shore power unplugged, so that absent one or the other, the sinking would have still occurred. Thus the primary cause of the sinking was the pumps being turned off. The two points of leakage were contributory causes.

At first this might appear to be an illogical conclusion until we consider that boats commonly have leaks and this is the purpose for having bilge pumps. A boat that leaks a small amount cannot be said to be unseaworthy; it would only be unseaworthy if there were no operating pumps. Had the pumps been on, they may have been able to dewater the boat until such time as the condition was discovered and repaired, but it's going to depend on a calculation of the rate of water ingress.

Now let us say that the batteries are old and determined to be dead at time of sinking due to age, not depletion by the pumps. Would that make the batteries the proximate cause? No, not if the battery charger would have been able to provide sufficient amperage to power the pumps to keep up with the water flow. The charger would be expected to provide a pass-through rate through even a "dead" battery equal to the rating of the charger (a 20 amp charger would easily power three 5 amp pumps despite the battery's inability to hold a charge). In this case, the unplugged shore power cord would be the primary cause with all the other things being contributory because, had the charger been working, the sinking would not have occurred.

The above examples illustrate how determination of the correct cause can often come down to nearly splitting hairs, establishing a very fine line based on a "what if" analysis. When there are multiple possibilities or contributing causes, each has to be evaluated based on its effect absent all the others, and in isolated combination with each of the others. This illustrates how sinking events can become rather complicated. In fairness to all parties involved, it is important to get it right.

Rain

Heavy Rain

The Florida peninsula records some of the highest rainfall rates in the continental U.S. and since I am a long-time resident of that state, I will use this state as a benchmark for this discussion. Florida sees annual rainfall rates running as high as 80 inches annually, the vast majority of which occurs during the six month rainy season. Since there is a very large number of boats in this region, the area serves as a good example of how boats perform in the extremes of rainfall. Although no agency keeps track of how many boats sink, my experience in marine claims over thirty years suggests that the number of boats that sink every year in this state due to heavy rain runs in the many hundreds. One can see that this is no small issue when we consider that nationwide, this number would be in the thousands of boats sinking due to combinations of heavy rain, bad design and other faults.

Heavy rainfall is a normal and predictable event that the design of boats and their systems are expected to withstand if they are to be considered seaworthy. To say that a boat sank as a result of heavy rain is to tell only part of the story due to the fact that rain is only one of several factors involved. However, abnormally heavy rainfalls do occur infrequently at rates that exceed what some types of boats should be reasonably expected to withstand. One such event occurred in South Florida in 1980 when 22 inches of rain fell in 24 hours. In February, 1976 seventeen inches fell on one day. By any definition, those were extraordinary events. Did that cause all boats to sink? Did it even cause most small boats to sink, boats without battery chargers? No, it didn't, though certainly a few did. This makes the point about survivability of even catastrophic rainfall; if most boats can be designed to withstand it, all boats can.

The difficulty we run into here is a matter of coming to agreement of where is the dividing line between normal, abnormal and extraordinary. The later such events may be classified by the insurance industry as "catastrophes", events such as hurricanes or slow moving tropical storms that drop prodigious amounts of rain that cause widespread damage. The investigator should be aware that when a catastrophe is declared, it would be very difficult to make the case that seaworthiness alone is at issue. Not once during my long career as an insurance investigator has an insurer ever been willing to contest the cause of a sinking that occurred during a storm, even when there was clear evidence that the storm was not the sole cause.

When investigating sinking losses that occur during non catastrophe events, it is important to keep in mind that sinkings may or may not be wholly the result of the weather event. For example, the condition of the vessel may be such that it would not have withstood even a normal heavy rainfall (i.e. the pumping system failed or suffered some other fault of design) so that the heavy weather event was merely coincidental to the sinking which would have occurred sooner or later anyway. When it comes to insurance claims, these are always difficult calls by the claims adjuster in terms of extending or denying coverage. However, the investigator should not be influenced by coverage issues when writing his report, but report the facts as he sees them.

Catastrophes

A catastrophe is an event of disastrous proportions that causes heavy property losses. These are not necessarily natural events since 9/11 was declared a catastrophe. The American Insurance Association makes these declarations and assigns numbers to them. They are, however, predominately natural disasters such as earthquakes, hurricanes, floods and tornadoes and frequently involve heavy rainfall events and therefore result in marine losses caused by rain.

Unfortunately, such events are exploited by people attempting to take advantage of the situation for personal gain. Equally unfortunate is the fact that dealing with false claims following a catastrophe becomes exceptionally difficult due to the sympathy factor that arises. At such times the preponderance of evidence needed to successfully deny a claim therefore increases due to this sympathy factor since any jury will be even more predisposed to give the benefit of doubt to the insured. During catastrophes, insurers noticeably relax their coverage standards and the investigator should be aware of this. For a successful claim denial, the evidence had best be very strong.

Timing

Most sinkings that result from heavy rain do not occur during the rainfall event but sometime after, usually, but not always, within a matter of a few hours. The reason is that rain is rarely sufficient to fill a boat up to the sinking point, but often is the catalyst that sets in motion a chain of events, i.e., contributory causes. The hull accumulates water to the point that other sources of water ingress are brought into play, sources such as scuppers, wave action and so on. Exceptionally heavy rains can be either short or longer term events, and this is what will typically determine when the sinking occurs. Six inches of rain may occur in three hours with the pumps discharging all the water but wearing down the battery. A subsequent lesser rainfall occurs that sinks the boat because the battery is now dead and the pump not functioning at all. In some cases the boat may continue to float long after the initiating event that ran the battery down but then a slow leak is the final coup de gras.

The point made here is that the time span over which the loss was initiated may be longer than is readily apparent, illustrating the need to have access to historical weather data. If a boat sinks a week after a major rain event, the investigator may not make the connection and be misled by the timing. With sinking losses the investigator should always check on rainfall data for the period preceding the loss.

Parameters and Profiling

For the investigator, it is useful to establish categories or parameters to define and limit the range of possibilities. This works similar to the way criminal profiling works to direct an investigation. The types of profiles we would use for this type of investigation might be:

> Long term rainfall
>
> Short term rainfall

And,

> Boats with dockside power and battery chargers
>
> Boats without dockside power and battery chargers

The reasons for the later categories are obvious but for the former less so. For the former, we have two issues to deal with; total rainfall amounts over time and daily rainfall rates. Extreme rainfall amounts can occur over a period of time, say several days or weeks, or we may be faced with an extreme rainfall rate that occurs all in one day, or even a few hours. The maximum rainfall rate that can occur (other than catastrophic events) is about 4" per hour, but that is very rare, though 3" per hour is more common. Such rainfall rates can easily overwhelm an open boat even with a working bilge pump.

Short term rainfall is a sudden and fortuitous event, whereas long term rainfall is likely to involve negligence, neglect or intentional act. That is, if it has been raining heavily for a long time, a reasonable and prudent owner of a small, open boat would be moved to check on his boat.

Whether a sinking event is the result of a short or long term process can usually be established from weather data. It is important to try to narrow the event down in terms of time since there are important differences between longer and short term events. A single heavy rain event tends to rule out factors such as negligence whereas rain fall over longer periods tend to signify neglect. A boat without working pumps may survive one or two normal rain events but not multiple events over time. In cases like this, the cause is not the rain but failure to take reasonable and prudent action to protect one's property since prudent action would have prevented the loss.

Therefore, the investigator can probably save himself a lot of time by checking the historical data before ever leaving the office because in doing so he will have armed himself with information that will narrow the investigation. Consulting the rainfall data produces the amounts shown below. The record shows that the 4.3" of rain fell on June 7; the sinking is said to have occurred on June 8, today's date is June 10 and the record shows that only 1/2" of rain fell in the period prior to June 7. In that case it's a pretty good bet that 1/2" of rain didn't sink the boat, so the possibility of a cumulative loss is eliminated.

6/3	0.00"
6/4	0.15"
6/5	0.00"
6/6	0.46"
6/7	4.43"
6/8	No rain, boat sank

Conversely, had the data shown substantial rainfall in the days prior to the sinking, the prospect of a cumulative rainfall raises the prospect of neglect or systems failure.

With boats that have shore power systems and battery chargers, the range of possibilities increases dramatically, for it would be expected that a battery charger would provide power to the bilge pumps more or less indefinitely, absent any system failures. It is the prospect of system failures that gives rise to the much greater number of possibilities.

It therefore falls to the investigator to analyze, test and prove the charging and shore power systems to determine whether that system did or did not provide endless power to run the pumps. The first thing to do is total up the amperage draw of all the bilge pumps and compare that to the maximum output of the charger. If the charger provided adequate power, then the state of the batteries becomes irrelevant because the charger would provide sufficient pass-through voltage to keep the pumps running. The charger will pass power through even a nominally dead battery, although possibly at a diminished rate so we may need to test for this. However, even a small 15 amp charger would be sufficient to run two bilge pumps.

Next, it needs to be determined if power was being supplied to the charger. This is something that can usually be established through the condition of the wiring in the charger circuit, or the battery charger itself, When those circuits went under water, electrolysis damage should have occurred. Of course, if the battery terminals themselves are completely destroyed, then nothing further need be done since it becomes clear that the batteries had a high rate of charge.

The batteries should be tested by attempting to recharge them. It is surprising how many instances there are when submerged batteries — even the unsealed type – that do not take on salt water. Note that automotive batteries usually become permanently damaged due to extreme rate of discharge whereas deep cycle or storage batteries do not. If the batteries accept anywhere near a full charge, say even 50%, then that is good enough to rule out a battery or charging system failure.

Calculations

As discussed in previous chapter, when rainfall is suspected as the probable cause, one of the factors necessary to prove the theory is the determination of how much water could have entered the hull. In every case, there are two primary issues to consider: the amount of water coming into the boat, versus the amount of water the pumping system is capable of evacuating from the hull. Both can be determined by means of calculation.

With the vast majority of cases we will be dealing with boats where the decks are at least intended to be water tight, whether they actually are or not. the fact that the boat sank after heavy rain suggests that decks are not water tight and that water did not drain overboard and somehow water entered the hull. Discovering the water entry point is usually simple enough, but the determination of just how much water could enter is a bit more difficult. We will need to determine how much rain *could* enter the hull versus how much actually did.

In the following case we will use an example of a 24' center console outboard boat with a self-bailing cockpit that has scuppers only 3" above the normal trim waterline as established by a scum line. There is a tree nearby that could have put leaves into the cockpit and plugged the scuppers up, but because the boat sunk, the leaves are no longer there. The deck has hatches in it and we have already determined that none of them are watertight.

Calculating Surface Areas

To determine the amount of rainfall that an open boat (or open areas of any boat) can collect, it is necessary to determine the surface area. Contrast a typical center console outboard boat wherein the entire cockpit area is capable of putting water into the hull, to an express cruiser where the foredeck will shed most of the water overboard. Thus, we start by including only that surface area that could possibly channel water into the hull. In most, but not all, cases this will be the cockpit only. In the case of a cruiser, we will need to determine whether the foredeck channels water aft, into the cockpit, or whether a bridge deck also puts water into a cockpit.

Outboard boat cockpits are not regular shapes but usually involve curves. We can come to reasonably accurate calculations by means of dividing the area up into regular shapes. A typical outboard runabout cockpit is likely rectangular shaped in the aft section, but rounded or triangular in the forward section. Thus, we can divide the area up into a rectangle and a triangle to make calculation easier. When an area contains curved

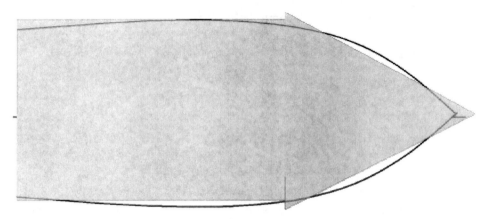

Fig. 7-2. To measure the area of odd shapes, convert them into regular shapes with straight lines, cutting off equal amounts inside and outside the curved shape.

boundaries, as shown in illustration (**Fig. 7-2**) on next page, draw a line through the curved segment in such a way that it cuts off equal parts of the curve at each end. This averages out the amount within and without the line of our triangle so that the final result will be sufficiently accurate. Then apply the formula 1/2(BxH). Or, if the area is heavily rounded, one can use a half circle and use the formula 1/2 pi times diameter.

Our example of a typical 24' center console outboard boat has no decks or tops to shed water and all rainfall goes directly into the cockpit. In addition to how much rain can potentially go into the hull, we will also need to know the weight of that water and what the effect on trim will be, so two sets of measurements and calculations are necessary, the deck area and the area of water plane of the hull.

To calculate the area of the water plane, it will be necessary to take a number of beam measurements from which we approximate the square footage of the areas we are seeking. If the hull has a scum line showing the normal floatation then measurements can be taken with the boat on a trailer. If not, the normal trim water line will have to be marked with the boat afloat.

Lay a two by four across the breadth of the boat and measure the beam at regular two or three foot intervals. Hang a plumb bob or other weight over the side at the edge of the deck and measure inward to the hull and subtract the overhang. I use a lead weight and heavy spring clamp, measuring the inset on one side only, then multiply by two and then subtract this amount from the total beam measurement at the deck, which yields the beam at water line. Use this same method to measure the cockpit area. Don't forget to measure the length water line. Next, plot these measurements on standard graph paper and we will now have the shape of the water plane and the cockpit area.

Note: to measure a larger boat with a superstructure, with the boat hauled, hang a plumb bob from the edge of the deck on each side, after using a tape to mark the increments at which the beam measurements will be taken on each side on the deck.

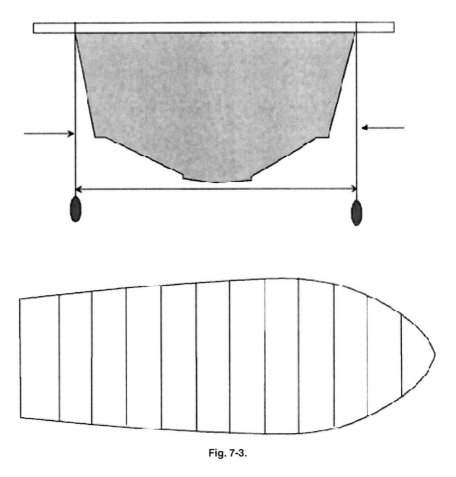

Fig. 7-3.

Then clamp a plumb bob on each side and take the measurements from beneath the boat, subtracting the over hangs. This job takes two people to accomplish.

With a little practice, most boats can be measured up in about and hour or so. Once the measurements are obtained and plotted on graph paper, we can now calculate the areas. Here again, we usually divide the hull into a rectangle and triangle. In either case one will need to have an existing water line showing, or find a way to determine where the normal water line is located.

Calculating Amount of Rainfall

Now we know our open deck area and can determine the amount of rain water that fell into the boat. Note that it is necessary to deduct any raised deck areas that will shed water overboard. It will also be necessary to evaluate whether tops or any covers could either put water in the boat or direct it overboard. A T-top, for example, is unlikely to shed water overboard, but Bimini tops might; each case has to be evaluated separately. In this example we arrive at a cockpit area of 105 ft^2. With 7.5 inches of rain falling on the deck this calculates to be 65.63 cubic feet of water in total. With a cubic foot of fresh water weighing 62.5 lbs. this comes to 4101 lbs. of water or 546.8 gallons.

This is the total amount of water falling in the cockpit; we do not yet know how much actually went into hull. This will be determined later after the leak is found and the amount of water determined by actual testing.

PPII

Next we calculate the pounds per inch immersion by determining the water plane area of the hull. PPII is the number of pounds required to sink the hull one inch deeper than its normal load water line (LWL) *on an even keel trim*. We determine the water plane to be 132.8 square feet with measurements described above. From this one can easily calculate the area accurately enough (typically a +/-5% error).

PPII = Area of waterplane x 64/12 = 708.3 lbs. per inch immersion

The result here is that it would take 708.3 lbs. of weight placed in the center of the boat (center of buoyancy, to be precise) to immerse the entire hull one inch. Of course, the shape of the hull and the fact that this is an outboard tells us that the water will not go to the center, but will all accumulate aft due to the weight of engines and hull configuration. So this calculation doesn't give us exactly what we want, which is the moment to change trim one inch or MTI. This is not one inch at each end but, rather, one-half inch at each end for a total of one inch. In other words, adding a weight at one end results in equal changes of trim at both ends, but in opposite directions.

Determining how 4100 lbs. of water (total rain fall) all running to one end of the boat would affect its trim requires a much more complex calculation, which you'd need a naval architect to accomplish. Fortunately, there is an easier and cheaper way, which is to actually measure the amount of weight needed to depress the stern one inch. This we can do with buckets of water, concrete blocks or whatever known weights we have at hand to use including people, placing the weight in the center at the stern. Before doing so, tape a six inch plastic rule to the existing waterline, then begin adding weight at the stern of the boat until the one inch mark is reached. Then record the amount of weight added to reach that one inch mark.

Threshold

Once we know how much weight is needed to depress the stern one inch, we can then figure how much weight (in water) will be needed to depress the stern until water begins flooding in an opening such as a deck scupper. Since a gallon of water weighs 8.5 lbs. most likely a few old five gallon paint or oil buckets will be enough to serve the purpose.

In this example we have determined that 4100 lbs. of water was many times over what would be needed to sink the boat. In some cases as little as 100 gallons or less of water is all that is needed, what with 100 gallons weighing 850 lbs. From this example it is evident that establishing *exact* data and rates is not always possible, so that what we are seeking to determine is a close approximation and a reasonable probability. It again has to be emphasized that this sort of evidence needs to be viewed from the standpoint of whether the investigator believes it would be possible to convince a jury before he decides to draw his conclusions in writing.

Another Approach

There is yet another way to approach this question. If we know that the rainfall rate was 3" per hour for at least one hour, then 196.35 gallons fell in the cockpit during that hour and at 8.5 pounds per gallon then the boat took on 1668.98 lbs. of water. By our weight to change trim 1" we have determined that it takes 300 lbs. in the stern to depress it one inch. We also know our cockpit scuppers and deck hatches are only 3" above the water line and thus it would only take 900 lbs. or 105 gallons to depress the hull enough that water would come in through the scuppers, flood the deck and sink the boat.

After these measurements and calculations are made, it is necessary to establish how much water could actually enter the hull, and under what conditions. In this case, we already know that the hatches are not sealed, so that if the scuppers got plugged up, most of that water is going to go into the hull. There being no other cause of water entry into the hull found, we can state that the preponderance of evidence is that the boat most likely sank because the scuppers got plugged up with leaves and most of 546 gallons of rain went into the bilge. Even though there are no leaves as absolute proof, the lack of any other evidence is sufficient to draw this conclusion. Or, if we're lucky, the leaves left tannin stains on the white gel coat, thereby proving their presence. In any case, we now know that the insurer can't advance a subrogation claim for improper design, even though the scupper design does not meet the ABYC standard since the cause of loss is mainly an accidental event with mitigating circumstances.

Rainfall Rates

The National Weather Service keeps daily rainfall data for every metropolitan area large and small, as well as from many rural points. These are all available on Internet databases but these web sites are constantly changing so I do not provide the addresses here as they will soon become obsolete. Rainfall amounts over short distances can vary substantially, so data from even a nearby recording station may or may not reflect conditions at the subject location; this will need to be backed up by other information. One of these can be the Doppler radar graphics which give very good data on rainfall coverage - that is, rainfall based on a color coded graphical display over a continuous area. By comparison of the graphic with numerical data, the actual rainfall amount can be confirmed with reasonable accuracy. This data is not directly available on their web site but is archived and you will need to contact NWS for the method to obtain these graphs. This data is also available from the NWS on a subscription basis. If you plan to do a lot of this type of investigation, you'll probably find these services worth the relatively low cost.

Rainfall rates can vary drastically even over very short distances so that rainfall amounts at the local recording station are not representative of what fell on the boat in question. The investigator should have some knowledge of weather and local conditions. Was the rainfall the result of a general weather system, in which case the rain amounts would be more uniform, or was it a localized condition like summer thunderstorms? In the later case, rain rates can be radically different over short distances. Fortunately, there's a way to minimize errors.

First, one might canvass neighbors to see if any has a rain gauge. Failing that, if, in the immediate area of the boat you can find any type of container that collects water, the amount of actual rainfall can be closely approximated. The container will have to be out in the open so that it is not shielded by any trees or structures. Buckets, cans, bottles or anything that collects water and can be determined to have been empty before the rainfall can be used. This works best for containers that were recently placed such as cups, glasses, bottles and so on. Such objects are rarely ever uniformly straight sided, so the amount of water in them can't yield an accurate amount (unless they are straight-sided with a mouth opening the same diameter) without making calculated adjustments for the diameter of the mouth versus diameter of the container. By way of illustration, let's say we have a jar with a 3" inside diameter and a mouth opening of only one inch. Since the jar has one inch of water in it, how much rain had to fall on it? Since the opening is $1/3^{rd}$ the diameter, the answer would be three times one inch.

But what if the container is tapered? One can draw an average based on the top and bottom diameters of the level of water in it. Then calculate the adjustment from there. If the bottom of a bucket has a 12" diameter and has 3" of water in it; if the diameter at the 3" level is 13", then the average diameter is 12.5 inches. Now divide this average into the diameter at the mouth, say 15". This ratio of 1.2 is then multiplied by 3" yielding 3.6" of rain. It well worth the effort to look around for this type of evidence for it becomes very hard to dispute in the event of litigation.

To the extent that reasonable and prudent behavior is such an important part of the law, what constitutes normal and abnormal rainfall becomes an important factor in determining what is reasonable and prudent behavior. Obviously, prudent behavior in southern California is not the same thing as in Florida where torrential rainfalls are common. Obtaining the historical data goes a long way toward properly making these definitions.

Small Boats

Cockpit Decks

The design of the cockpit deck can be a primary cause or a contributing factor. Cockpits in fishing and center console boats are almost invariably "self-bailing," which means that any water going onto the deck is intended to drain overboard. But reality doesn't always measure up to design intentions, particularly when the deck is very close to the water line. Decks will have hatches or ports that will allow some amount of water to enter the hull and it will be the investigator's job to find out how much.

As with the case of a common, hinged deck hatch, the amount of leakage possible will be nearly unlimited since these hatches are normally unsealed and have no securing devices known as "dogs." It is a simple enough matter to measure the height of the deck and cockpit scuppers above the waterline to determine the probability of water entry. Small boats with deck openings that are only a few inches above the water line are patently unseaworthy unless the deck is absolutely water tight, so the first thing to be done is to determine if the boat is seaworthy.

To accomplish this we can refer to the ABYC standards H-3 and H-4. H-3.3.5.2 is a standard for determining watertightness. It reads as follows:

> The test for watertight devices or structures shall be:
>
> Subject the device or structure to a solid stream of water,
>
> a.   from a one inch nozzle,
>
> b.   at a pressure of 15 psi,
>
> c.   with the nozzle 10 feet away,
>
> d.   water temp approx. 50 degrees,
>
> e.   for a period of five minutes,
>
> f.   without leakage.

The problem with this test specification is that a one inch hose at 15 psi will not shoot a stream of water the specified ten foot distance. If you take an ordinary 3/4" I.D garden hose at full city water pressure (usually around 50-60 psi) the stream of water will only travel about four feet, thereby rendering the test requirement impossible unless the reference is for a ten foot vertical distance, which it clearly does not. Secondly, it is unreasonable to have a water temperature requirement of fifty degrees when water at that temperature would not be available in some places without going to great expense of having to cool a nearly unlimited supply if the local water temperature is 75 degrees. On further consideration, the test is flawed in other ways; note that it does not state

Fig. 7-4. The transfer of the black o-ring rubber mark to the hatch frame - (or lack of transfer), clearly indicates that the o-ring is not sealing in places.

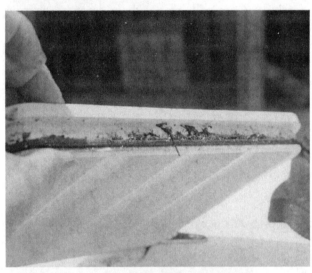

Fig. 7-5. The tendency of dirt to accumulate is yet another reason for failure of plastic hatches to seal.

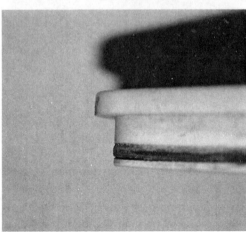

Fig. 7-6. The reason these hatches don't seal well becomes apparent when examining the profile of the o-ring. This one stands proud by only a few thousandths of an inch and doesn't bridge the gap between cover and frame.

in what proximity the water source is to be to the test item. If it were to be above then the force of water on the test item will be vastly greater than if on the same plane.

The author finds many such ABYC standards to be unreasonable and poorly conceived. Moreover, to the extent that ABYC is now largely boating industry supported, and the standards have been demonstrably weakened in recent years, their standards, which they no longer call standards but refer to as "Recommended Practices", are wide open to challenge.

A proper and easily conducted test for deck hatches is to subject it to similar conditions that it would normally be exposed to. This can be done simply test it by covering it with water as follows:

a. Vessel can be either hauled or afloat,

b. Trim vessel so that water will remain over hatch or opening to be tested.

c. Close off cockpit scuppers,

d. Place water catchment trays under hatch(s) to be tested,

e. Flood the deck with water to a level of one inch for ten minutes,

f. Drain deck and determine volume of water in container,

g. Convert amount and time to an hourly rate.

Caution: Before trying this test, be sure that hull, deck and whatever the vessel is resting on, if not afloat, can withstand the weight of water added. In most cases it will not be excessive except when a vessel is poorly shored up or on a trailer.

However, if the hull has a drain plug in the transom, there is an easier method. Instead of placing containers under the leaking hatches, we measure the amount of water that comes through the drain hole. First, add water to the bilge until the water runs out the drain and stops. With this method, make sure that the leaking water isn't being trapped somewhere in the hull. Flood the deck with an amount of water to approximate actual conditions, or alternatively one inch. Using catchment containers is best when amounts of leakage is small such as testing a plastic port.

Obviously, variations of this method can be used to fit the circumstances. In all cases one should examine the hatch or port, along with the deck for mitigating factors and take those into account. If a test needs to be adjusted to fit the circumstances, then do so. Just be sure that the test can stand up to a challenge by an expert.

In conjunction with actual testing, take note of whether the surrounding deck is flexible and deflects when walked on or a load is placed on it. This is particularly important with plastic hatches and ports that are highly flexible and usually lack adequate rigidity. As shown in photos (**Fig. 7-4, 7-5 & 7-6**) on opposite page, there may be direct physical evidence that indicates whether the hatch was leaking. Plastic hatches typically have

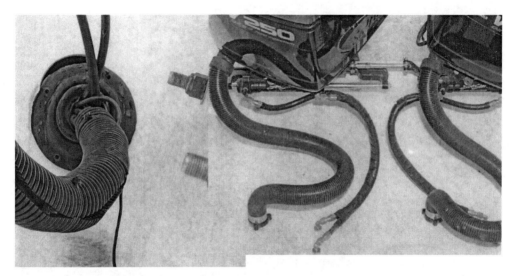

Fig. 7-7. Left: This cable pass-through deep within an outboard motor well is rather typical of what happens to these rubber boots. A situation like this is an imminent risk of sinking. Imagine this boat in the conditions shown on the next page.
Fig. 7-8. Right: A good solution to the problem, these fittings are water tight. This hardware has only recently appeared on the market.

an o-ring type gasket that is intended to seal it. However, being highly flexible, both the hatch or port frame can easily be distorted by the screws holding it in place, thus causing it not to seal due to the distortion.

Very often this o-ring leaves a dark mark where it was in contact with the plastic, and where it did not make contact there is no mark, demonstrating that no seal was taking place. Additionally, long term leakage is likely to leave water trails of dirt, slime or mineral deposits that are very obvious.

The design changes that took place with outboard boats in the 1990's replacing the cut down transom mounted engines with an integral transom platform should have eliminated the problems we had with outboard boats sinking. The new designs helped, but many builders subverted the added safety of the design by installing plastic ports and hatches in the platform. Many of these are actually recessed into a shallow well that almost guarantees that the hatch is going to leak copious amounts of water into the hull.

Cockpit Integrity

Cockpits would have no problem with water tight integrity were it not for the fact that holes get made in them for all sorts of reasons such as routing wires, control cables, fuel lines an innumerable other reasons. Very large numbers of sinkings occur because of this. Most often these holes are made by builders and dealers, but also sometimes by the boat owner. If the later case, the loss will be covered since that is an owner error. If the former, we have an unseaworthy boat in which the loss is likely to be paid and

Fig. 7-9. Stopping at sea can lead to a perilous situation in many outboard boats. This photo was taken in the Gulf Stream with a light swell. The motors go partly submerged and if there are any unsealed openings in the platform area, the boat will be taking on significant amounts of water.

Note: This is the same photo as Fig. 6-8 in Chapter 6. Placed here for reader's convenience.

the insurer will attempt to recover from the builder. Thus, litigation will ensue and so a careful investigation must be done with a view that it should be able to withstand legal challenge.

ABYC standard H-4 in my view is more reasonably conceived and the investigator should become intimately familiar with it. While it is not my intent to write a critique on ABYC, the investigator and litigants have to deal with these standards wherein ABYC has left itself wide open to challenge by issuing revisions that in many cases greatly weaken the safety values. Note that the 1999 version has been dramatically changed over the 1994 version wherein the minimum height of the cockpit deck above water line for boats with watertight cockpits was set at a flat four inches. The 1999 version inserts a complex calculation and a "whichever is greater" criteria of 76 mm which is only three inches.

Oddly enough, if cockpits really were watertight, none of the above would matter, but since they almost never are, it does matter. Inexpensive plastic hatches are the primary source of trouble.

Cockpit Openings

In addition to hatches of all descriptions, there are numerous types of openings that can allow water to enter a hull. Foremost among these is the opening for the motor control cables as shown in photos (**Fig. 7-7 & 7-8**). Typically, a builder or dealer rigger will add a bellows type soft boot to the opening through which the controls pass, which is either soft plastic or rubber. Ostensibly, the boot is supposed to keep water out, but a careful consideration will clearly show that it cannot; at best it can only reduce the size of the opening somewhat. When placed near the transom and close to the water line, the risk should be obvious to anyone. Unfortunately, the attitude prevails that, if the builder made it that way, it must be okay.

Placement of the hole for the pass through for controls from inside the hull to outside is a difficult proposition to be sure, and it's one that needs to be addressed during

Fig. 7-10 & 7-11. The removable deck section at left obscures the fact that the cockpit is awash as water backs up through the scuppers. This is rather typical of boats designed for inboard power but were converted to outboard power with brackets. Also sold as an inboard version, this 26' Pursuit was powered with outboards that shifted the center of gravity too far aft. It sank twice before the reason was discovered. The assumption that a gasket would seal the deck proved wrong. The illustration (**Fig. 7-12**) reveals why it had to happen. In this case rain was not involved but, had the scuppers become plugged with debris during a rainstorm, the result probably would have been the same.

the boat's design stage. But when it becomes an after thought, that's where builders run into trouble. For control cables to function properly, they cannot be bent beyond a certain minimum radius, so that it is this criteria that often leads to conflict with seaworthiness. If the opening is situated up high enough, then it's not going to be a problem, but the point where controls enter the engine housing is always down low, creating an interesting design challenge, but difficulty does not relieve the builder from the obligation of selling a seaworthy boat. Photo (**Fig.7-7**) on page 204 illustrates a control pass-through situated at the very bottom of a motor well.

Other common sources for water entry are holes made for fuel and hydraulic steering lines. Many builders are now using machined metal couplers that allow pass-through of fluids without any leakage, yet some builders do not use these. The ones that do set the standard.

Most outboard boats have removable deck sections to facilitate access to the fuel tank. These are usually sealed with caulking, but don't always stay sealed. The caulking may age and shrink, or the deck or cover may flex or shift, thus opening up a seam that leaks.

When Cockpits Are Very Low

As previously mentioned, a boat that has an otherwise water tight cockpit, may be rendered not watertight by actions of owners, repairers and dealers who rig the boat. A typical example was a dealer that installed a piece of hardware that had only two screws when it should have been attached with four bolts. The piece of hardware pulled loose and allowed water to enter through two small holes unnoticed. In this case, the platform area was frequently awash due to wakes of passing vessels and the

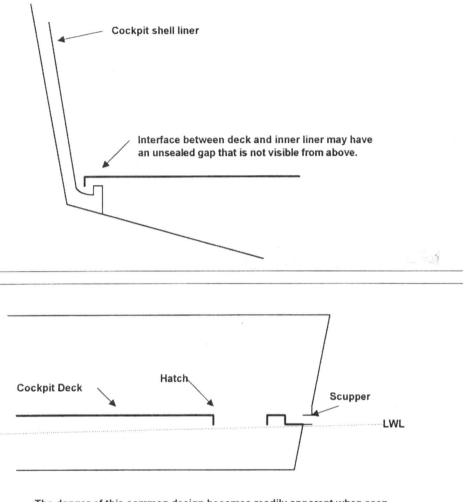

The danger of this common design becomes readily apparent when seen
from profile plan view.

Fig. 7-12.

boat was unattended for some time. The steady but slow leakage eventually ran down
the batteries and the boat sank.

The above illustrations (**Fig. 7-12**) show two views of a low cockpit deck that has a
large removable section. In the cross section profile view, the proximity of the scuppers
and hatches is shown relative to the waterline. Deck sections are not always sealed as
in this case it has a gasket that does not seal well. The water went under the gasket
and sank the boat because the deck was simply too low.

Further investigation determined that the builder sold this model boat in both a mid
engine inboard version and a bracketed outboard version. The reason for the low

Fig. 7-13. A dangerous situation: the deck of this boat is barely two inches above the unloaded waterline which is at the top of the black stripe.

cockpit therefore became clear: the boat was originally designed as an inboard and was converted to an outboard without consideration for the resultant changes in trim.

Older Outboards with or without Motor Wells

There remains in service a fairly large numbers of older outboard boats that have either motor wells or no motor wells, the later of which are probably unseaworthy not only because they do not meet any minimum standard, but simply because they violate common sense, in addition to the fact that cockpits are nowhere near water tight. Such boats are not infrequently involved in tragedies at sea, a number of which captured national attention. Such cases usually result in vigorous litigation against multiple defendants wherein the expert investigator will need to demonstrate in no uncertain terms the reasons why the vessel was unseaworthy. In such cases the procedure is to conduct actual performance testing while videotaping the test.

Motor well boats may have been built seaworthy but are later rendered unseaworthy as a result of holes or other non water tight conditions having been created post purchase.

Old Style Motor Brackets

Boats are built and sold using brand name mounting brackets for outboard motors, a type usually constructed of welded aluminum. Additionally, there are a substantial number of inboard and stern drive boats that have been converted to outboard engine power by means of adding these brackets. Regardless of who installed the bracket, these things can severely change the trim of a boat that was not originally designed for engines mounted this way.

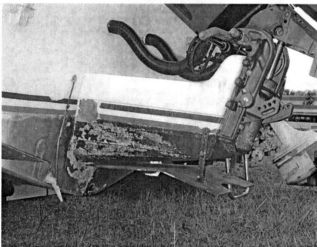

Fig. 7-14 & 7-15. Both of the above boats were formerly stern drive powered inboards later converted to outboards on brackets by the owners. This shifted the center of gravity so far aft that they could no longer remain afloat due to the decks going awash.

Because these brackets usually change the center of gravity by several feet, they can easily render a boat unseaworthy. Photos (**Fig. 7-14 & 15**) reveal why. The effect of shifting engines further aft is the distance in feet times the weight of the engines. If the engines weight 500 lbs. and are shifted aft 2.5 feet, the net effect is that of adding 2,500 lbs. to the stern of the boat — (2) x 500 x 2.5 = 2500 ft/lbs. This usually leads to a situation where the cockpit scuppers are constantly awash with resultant leakage through deck hatches, ports and so on.

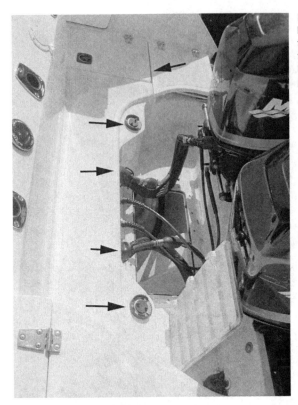

Fig. 7-16.   Not only is there a large plastic hatch at the bottom of this motor well, but all the cable pass-throughs and the engine oil filler caps. At upper left is one of two unsealed hatches. In the author's opinion, this vessel is patently unseaworthy.

Bad Platform Design

The modern outboard platform design is a combination swim platform and motor mounting bracket. While the integral platform was originally intended to remedy the seaworthiness problem of outboards, some builders seem to have forgotten that and have created boats that are almost guaranteed to sink. Photo (**Fig. 7-16**) is a very expensive Boston Whaler that has a large plastic hatch at the bottom of a deep well with a transom cut down to within six inches of the waterline. The plastic hatch cover leaked at a rate of 1.2 gallons per minute. And, while there are two 1" drain holes in the transom, these drains can easily be plugged up with debris. As if that weren't bad enough, notice the two hatches on each side, both of which are unsealed. This boat nearly sank while at sea because of this amazingly near-sighted design.

In photo (**Fig. 7-9**) on page 205 I test an outboard boat at sea by stopping with the stern to the waves. Notice that the platform area is completely submerged in wave conditions of about 12" on top of light swells. This should leave no doubt about just how much water and stress this area is subjected to and the potential for disaster.

Mid Size Boats

Since larger boats are inboard powered, and therefore better balanced, sinking due to rainfall is fairly rare when it comes to mid engine boats. But it's an altogether different story with stern or vee drive arrangements where the major weight of engines is situated far aft. Whenever these boats sink, the predominant cause results from poor design of the deck hatch guttering. To preclude water from going through hatch openings, a hatch must have a properly designed guttering system. Difficulties come about in creating large hatches that are not adequately supported, that is, they bend and flex when walked on. Further, these gutters have to be structurally strong and adequately drained so that the gutters don't overflow.

Hatch Cross-Beams or Supports

Whenever two hatches are immediately adjacent and intersect with a common seam, there must be some means of support at these points. This usually comes in the form of an aluminum channel that also forms a gutter. A constant problem with this method occurs at the point where the aluminum channel attaches to the perimeter gutter with metal fasteners. The method is usually to caulk and screw, which may yield a water tight seam for a short period of time, but over time that channel will receive a lot of stress and eventually the fasteners, which are screwed into fiberglass, will come loose and the whole thing starts leaking. In most cases this sort of leakage will not sink the boat directly, but the resultant water damage to an electrical system or a battery charger will.

This design fault is a very common cause of generator damage, main engine damage, short circuiting and fires. When inboard engine boats sink, the guttering system should be evaluated to determine if (1) water ingress from leaks was involved, and (2) if water damage to the electrical system prevented the bilge pumps from operating.

Hatch Gutters

In past years hatch gutters were typically poorly designed and poorly drained. The drainage system was usually made up of drain holes and hoses attached to nipples glued into a hole. If the drains didn't get plugged up with debris — which they most always did — then the nipple came loose when someone bumped it, thus resulting in sinkings despite the gutters. This could occur directly from leakage, or indirectly from water damage occurring to electrical apparatus that caused the pumping system to fail.

In all probability it has been numerous law suits that motivated many builders to giving a bit more thought to hatch guttering in recent years, but not so much that guttering problems are now uncommon, for sinkings still occur by this cause. Some builders have excellent designs while others don't. Drainage for water that enters around the

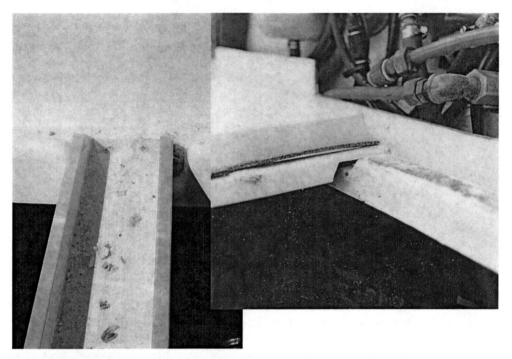

Fig. 7-17 & 7-18. There isn't much point in a designer creating a hatch gutter if he's going to make a hole in it. Here are two examples where the designer defeated his own design. The end result was severe damage to engines and generators.

gaps in hatch covers essentially involves a complete system in the same way that house guttering is a system. There are the gutters themselves to consider, plus the means of safely draining them.

Drainage System Integral with Deck

Beginning in the late 1990's, a number of builders or designers began designing a complete system that is integral with the deck. That is, the drainage system is incorporated into channels built into the deck mold. The gutters discharge the water into a side channel that in turn empties into a deck perimeter gutter which leads directly to the cockpit scuppers. Some such designs are better than others while some few are found to be completely ineffective. The vast majority of these are a great improvement over the old ways. That all builders don't do a good job of it results from the fact that designing and creating a more complex system involves substantial additional cost.

Boat sinkings are caused by a wide array of bizarre happenings, things one would never think of until running across them. It is a very strange thing but I often find molded guttering systems that have been completely defeated by some other aspect of the gutter design directly in the mold. One such case was a large anchor rope locker hatch that had a molded-in notch for the anchor rode to pass through from under the hatch. Instead of bringing it up through a hawse pipe as any experienced designer

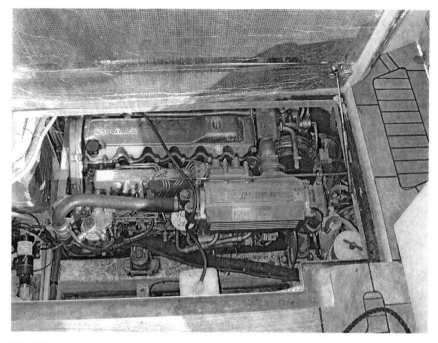

Fig. 7-19. A clear-cut case of design error, this hatch has welded aluminum gutters of straight channel; the deck, however, is crowned and the gutters follow the angle of the crown. The gutter system thus has a high side and a low side, with one 1/2" drain on each side, making only one drain effective. When it plugged up with debris, the gutter overflowed directly onto the engine.

would, this one defeated the gutter with this notch that allowed very large amounts of water from the foredeck to go into the anchor locker. It was calculated that the locker could hold 412 gallons of water that weighed 3300 lbs. which ultimately sank the boat by causing a head to go under water. This boat had almost six feet of bow overhang, which created a lever arm of 3300 pounds twenty-seven feet from the CB for a grand total of 89,100 ft./lbs. forward of the center of buoyancy! Water lines at the top of the rope locker proved that this is what happened, but it took days of searching before evidence of this bizarre event were discovered.

Scuppers and Channels

Less infrequently do problems with cockpit scuppers and drain channels lead to sinking, but it does happen. The more frequent instance is due to the cockpit deck simply being too low and water comes back in through the scuppers. Another is that debris plugs up the scuppers and heavy rain causes the water to flood the deck, ending up in the bilge. Still another is that there is a gap inside the scupper opening between the hull and deck molding. It is very difficult to seal this joint permanently due to movement of both parts. This is frequently a major source of leakage.

There have been many cases where boats have sunk, or extensive machinery damage was sustained because the gutter drain was too small. In a recent case, a hatch that

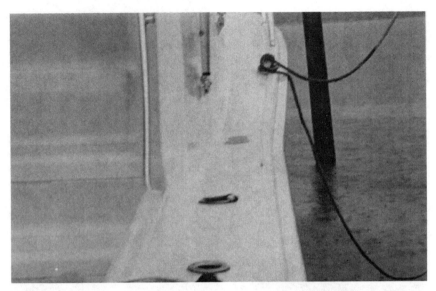

Fig. 7-20. Two serious but unusual design errors combined to almost sink this 36' Luhrs. Due to a structural weakness, the side decks are sagging inwards, causing ALL the water from the foredeck to be channeled aft into the cockpit, where otherwise at least some of it would have gone overboard. The second error is that there are no coffer dams to channel the water overboard. A third is that the bond between cockpit deck and transom broke loose, allowing all this water into the bilge. This photo was taken by the author during a lull in a tropical storm during which 12" of rain fell. At right the water is seen cascading onto the shorepower connection which shorted and tripped the breaker, cutting off the battery charger.

measured 3' x 4.5' with a 2" wide x 2" deep gutter had only a single 1/2" drain on the outboard side. Thus, if the boat were listing at all with the drain on the high side, the gutter would overflow. In another instance the drains were at the forward end of the gutters, again on the high side causing the gutters to overflow.

Watersheds

From time to time problems with drainage areas of large deck areas such as fore decks and cabin or other tops cause sinking or other damage. Sport fishermen typically have fore decks that are very large and much higher than cockpit decks, and may be so designed that the entire expanse of foredeck drains aft into the cockpit. This can happen because the side deck, for whatever reason, cants inboard, a raised toe rail creates a waterway, or the designer failed to incorporate a diverter to direct the water overboard. In more than one instance the foredeck water drained directly onto a shore power connection and caused a fire.

Poor drainage of flying bridge decks was often a problem a long time ago, but no longer is on U.S. built boats. But for some foreign built boats this remains a problem. Recently a foreign built catamaran with a huge bridge deck area was found to slope forward even with level trim of the vessel. Unfortunately, the bridge deck drains were

Fig. 7-21. A casualty in the making. Water running off the foredeck, along the side deck and dropping into the cockpit where a fold-out step channels it into the hull. At the peak of the rainfall, ten times the amount of water you see here was cascading into this hole.

at the aft end. The small 3/4" drain holes became plugged up. This allowed 10" of water to accumulate that was calculated to weigh approximately four tons. Not only did all that weight nearly collapse the deck, but when the vessel inevitably rolled under the weight of this water up so high, this caused the boat to sink. It took a while before I noticed the water lines on the inside of the flying bridge and figured out what happened. Again, bizarre events due to ignorance of untrained designers and builders. A trained naval architect knows that drainage of decks is a top priority for vessels, just as it is for designers of buildings.

Photo (**Fig. 7-21**) depicts yet another casualty in the making due to improper drainage of a watershed on a forty footer. Photographed shortly after a torrential rainfall let up, it captures water running down a side deck and into a fold-out cockpit step which leaves a void space directly into the bilge. Shortly before this photo was taken, I estimated the rate of water going into this hole at 5 gallons per minute and it put 18" of water in the bilge with three pumps running while the author was onboard. The rainfall rate was probably over 3" per hour and lasted for nearly two.

I was in the engine room when I heard the water falling and notice bilge water rising fast. Following the sound, I located the area but could not actually see where it was coming in because it was behind a fuel tank.

If this boat had sunk it is unlikely that anyone would make the connection between that step and a heavy rainfall unless he is aware that such unusual things can happen.

Waterlines

Boat Load

For the purposes of testing and deriving the load water line where no scum line exists, the boat should be loaded to the maximum full fuel and any other fluids capacity. Of course it will also be necessary to replicate the actual conditions at the time it sank, if possible. When refloating a boat be cognizant that a sunken boat can absorb huge amounts of water, particularly large boats on which there is substantial carpet and upholstery. I once discovered a 34 footer that floated two inches deeper after the sinking than before, something that could have lead to a completely wrong conclusion as to the cause. Be sure to check how the boat now floats with the old water line. Conditions like this will need to taken into account and possibly adjustments made.

Telltale Evidence

The process of sinking invariably leaves telltale evidence in the form of waterlines which are caused by either dirt in or on the water, or inside the hull. These water lines are likely to be present both inside and outside the hull. Only if a boat is brand new and sinks in very clean water, it is likely that there will not be any water lines showing. This, of course, would be a rare event, since water is rarely ever very clean and boat bilges most always contain dirt and sludge so that water lines inside the hull are almost inevitable.

As a hull sinks in the water, dirt, particularly dirt that is floating on the surface, is deposited on dry surfaces so that as a hull sinks, there is very likely to be a progression of water lines up the sides of the hull, inside and out. Water lines are not created as easily when the hull side is wet, as when it is raining, so that boats that sink in rainstorms may not show any water lines, or only water lines that are very faint on the exterior.

An exception to this is soot created by engine exhaust which commonly exists in crowded marinas or anywhere a large number of boats are docked. When there is carbon soot floating on the surface, it will cling tenaciously to a sinking hull leaving a clear history of the time-span of the sinking event but, of course, not the time of the event.

The significance of water lines is that they are valuable clues from which we can learn many things, such as where in the hull water accumulated, the trim of the vessel before it sank, as well as during the sinking process. Water lines can even indicate how rapidly the boat sank. For example, in cases of neglect the succession of water lines often coincides with rain events showing that the boat sank deeper each time it rained over a period of days, weeks or even months. In some cases with small boats it is even possible to calculate how much it rained from the water lines.

Fig. 7-22. Waterlines often tell the story of what happened and how. The normal waterline is at the lower arrow while a series of additional waterlines appears at and above the boot top. This indicated that the boat sank in distinct stages which corresponded to dates of heavy rainfall. The boat does not have a self-bailing cockpit. It filled up with water and sank due to battery failure.

In seawater, water lines may be even more revealing about the time frame by the amount of marine growth that occurs on surfaces not covered with anti fouling paint. There have been numerous cases in which, with the help of a marine biologist, the time frame of sinking was established by the size of barnacle growth on unpainted hull sides. This proves particularly useful if there is a university marine biology department nearby that is likely to have extensive data on regional marine growth that could be admissible in court as evidence since marine biologists are often called on as expert witnesses.

Old Versus New Water Lines

It is sometimes the case that a boat has sunk, or more likely has taken on water, more than once by virtue of a previous problem that was not corrected so we have to be careful not to become misled by prior events, and with older boats this is fairly common. Instances where a boat has sunk twice recently are not unknown, such as when the first time it sank, it was uninsured but the second time occurred after the owner purchased insurance on a already damaged boat.

Water lines existing on the inside of the hull may not have been removed so that one has to be careful not to mistake these with those of the current event. In some cases it may be difficult to determine whether they are old or new, a determination that can usually be made due to the old water lines having been at least partially removed or otherwise disturbed.

Boats that have chronic leakage problems often have an abundance of confusing water lines both inside and out. These can often indicate a boat that was leaking badly and has been repeatedly pumped out without the source of the leakage having been eliminated, so that while the waterlines may not provide specific evidence of the latest sinking event, they may provide evidence of a long-term problem that was not corrected. In such a circumstance, these water lines may provide the critical evidence of neglect.

As mentioned earlier, sometimes boats sink under circumstances without leaving much in the way of waterlines. This becomes particularly problematic when a loss is reported late, or for whatever reason the surveyor does not see the vessel in its submerged state, but only after it is raised. This can lead to doubt and contention about how far the vessel sunk, and by extension, how much damage it sustained. Even if the boat sank months earlier, a careful examination will usually turn up evidence to indicate how far it did sink.

Typically, this sort of evidence is found in very difficult to reach places, such as the back side of plywood panels. Since plywood is used extensively, and because the wood is usually only surfaced on one side, the raw, untreated wood on the back side stains easily and will usually reveal at least a faint but distinguishable water line.

If there is doubt about how far a boat sank, start at the lower portion and work upward. Plywood bulkheads are the obvious place to look, but if these are painted or otherwise surfaced, check inside cabinets and lockers. Yet another clue can be steel hardware such as cabinet hinges. Screws set into wood are another good indicator because the wood will remain wet for a long time, thereby causing the fasteners to corrode to a degree far greater than a single immersion would seem to indicate. In checking on a bottom-up basis, it may be found that fasteners and hardware above a certain point aren't corroded, whereas those below that point are, thereby establishing a pattern that reveals the depth of immersion.

Detecting Prior Damage

Prior High Water Damage

Under normal circumstances, it would be expected that a boat has adequate bilge pumping and battery power to evacuate normally accumulated as well as abnormally accumulated water, but there are circumstances that may conspire to prevent this, such as that it simply doesn't occur to owners of larger boats that their boat *could* sink. This leads to the neglect of maintaining batteries, bilge pumps and drains. In my experience of having surveyed thousands of boats, it is clear that it doesn't even occur to most boat owners that they should check these systems regularly. In fact, most never do; nothing is ever done until something fails and draws their attention to it.

That something usually comes in the form of hull flooding. A pump fails and a slow leak results in water rising to the point where they can't help but notice it — their feet get wet, the carpet is floating and water is climbing up the walls! We see this time and again in the form of high water damage in cabin and machinery areas, and therefore, these signs of older water damage often serve as a clue that we are dealing with a long term problem of neglect. Old water damage does not look the same as recent water damage and therefore can be differentiated. It is normally so obvious that even a photograph will tell the story.

As boats age, the rate of leakage from above deck sources tends to increase dramatically. Leaky windows, hatches, ports, hardware and so on only tend to worsen over time. Then, too, as structures age there is a tendency for distortion that throws components and structures out of alignment, further exacerbating leakage problems. With older boats, don't overlook the possibility of very large leaks from decks and superstructures, which are usually discernible by old water damage on the interior. A good example is the case of a ten year old fifty-four footer where poor design of the superstructure resulted with the aft deck separating from the forward house molding by a good half inch. This gap occurred at a location where water ran down from the flying bridge causing the boat to partially sink. Only a smelly, rotten plywood bulkhead on the interior (underneath wrinkled wall paper) alerted the investigator that this gap could have caused the casualty because the gap was in the enclosed section of the aft deck where no rain got to it; it was not realized that the bridge deck drained in this direction.

When larger boats sink, there are almost always multiple contributory causes, the reason being that no one source of leakage, unless unusually large, is likely to sink the boat, so it is usually a combination of factors involved. These can be difficult to detect and may take considerable effort to discover and document. And because larger boats are much more expensive, resulting in very large losses, there is a much higher probability that litigation will ensue.

Prior Incidents

When boats sink, they are usually repairable and not a total loss, so that it is repaired, and goes back in service. It sometimes happens in a sinking investigation that the subject vessel had sunk - completely or partially - on a prior occasion, perhaps before the present owner purchased it. These instances are not uncommon. Since boats sink for a reason, a reason that may be design-related, and a reason that is often not remedied because the original cause was not identified the first time. This situation occurs more often with smaller boats, but I have had cases involving yachts as large as a 60 footers. Instances like this pose the issue of pre-existing conditions (pre existing the insurance policy issuance) which the owner may or may not know about, and could present coverage issues.

Cases such as this necessarily warrant investigation into the facts concerning the prior event, and highlight the fact that the marine investigator needs skills that go beyond merely investigating physical evidence. He or she needs to be a good detective as well.

In summary, there is no reason why a boat cannot be designed to withstand very heavy rainfalls without filling up with water and sinking. The fact that huge numbers of boats do survive prodigious rainfall rates - we're speaking of deluges of 10" to 20" - proves the point. If a boat does sink it is because there is a design failure, or some aspect of water tightness has been compromised by other means. Lastly, all boats leak or will leak as a result of the aging process and numerous other reasons. The purpose of bilge pumps is to remove this inevitable leakage, and to some degree provide an emergency dewatering capacity. A boat that has a pumping system but sinks anyway has done so through a fault in design or maintenance. It is the job of the investigator to find out why.

Chapter 8

Fire Investigations

Although boat fires are relatively rare occurrence, losses are usually large and investigations complex and lucrative for investigators who are adequately educated. Increasingly, marine insurers are resorting to hiring fire investigation experts, rather than surveyors who often lack adequate knowledge and training. Many of the private fire investigators (specializing in building fires mainly) do not impress me as particularly competent to handle boat fires due to a lack of specific boat knowledge. For this reason marine investigators are encouraged to get some fire training as they will be best equipped to do the job.

Boat fires bear few similarities to house or building fires because the nature of the structures is so different. This is one reason why non marine specialist fire investigators generally don't do a very good job with these investigations. Boats are very different than land based building fires, and when we add to this the fact that there are far fewer boat fires than building fires, it's easy to see why it's hard to develop a body of knowledge, as well as experience, with boat fires. The typical professional fire investigator is likely to see only a relative handful of boat fires during his career as opposed to the marine surveyor who works the waterfront and has a much greater opportunity to gain experience in boat fires. Unlike building fires — a subject on which huge efforts and sums of money have been devoted, including collegiate level disciplines — for boat fires there are virtually no studies and no body of knowledge collected. This is not to say that there isn't much of what has been learned about building fires that cannot be applied to boat fires — for indeed there is — but the application of that knowledge has to be made in consideration of the structural and environmental differences. If we understand the fundamental principles of how fires behave within combustible structures, then those same principles can be applied to the plastic, wood or metal boat.

Most fire investigators are not electrical engineers, yet a preponderance of boat fires are electrical in origin. There will come a point in most electrical fire investigations that the services of the forensic electrical expert will be needed. For this reason, marine investigators should locate and establish a business relationship with an electrical engineer or engineering firm whom he can rely on to perform this segment of analysis. This chapter does not discuss the full spectrum of fire investigation basics. Instead, it concentrates mainly on those aspects that are unique to pleasure craft.

There are numerous venues for obtaining basic fire investigation training, both in private and public institutions, including training seminars and publications. Due to litigation necessities, it is best that the marine investigator obtain some formal training because this is largely what the courts expect. Two good sources are:

The National Fire Protection Association

The National Association of Fire Investigators

Every investigator should obtain and become familiar with the appropriate sections of NFPA 921.

Kirk's Fire Investigation, first published in 1969 and now in its fourth edition, has more or less become the professional bible and is a thorough treatment of the subject by a scientist with a PhD. And therein lies the basis for a common criticism for this book that is commonly regarded as the best of its kind. At this point it should be mentioned that the tendency of scientists to explain things tends to make them far more difficult and complicated, rather than easier to understand. Science often exists for its own sake, and frequently lacks any useful purpose. This is certainly true in respect to the growing body of scientific literature in the fire investigation realm. This is not something that is useful when the results of investigations end up in litigation where complexity and scientific jargon is the bane of the trial lawyer. We don't want a repeat of the O.J. Simpson trial where jurors fall asleep listening to experts haggle for days over the validity of painstaking scientific evidence. There is no better example than this one of the pitfalls that scientific complexity poses to trial lawyers and their witnesses.[1] Technical scientific analysis of fires is mainly useful only at the margins of unusual or very costly events. It is most useful when it is capable of explaining complicated events in simple terms. Are we to be accused of being simplistic? Certainly, the reduction of complexity to explanations comprehensible to the layman is fundamental to our work.

The fact of the matter is that basic fire investigation principles are not terribly complicated or difficult to understand. This is more a matter of common sense than technicality with the exception of trace evidence science. It is no more necessary for a marine fire investigator to have a PhD in physics or even a bachelor's degree in fire science than it is for a homicide detective to be an expert on DNA. Investigators are essentially generalists who will make use of technical experts when necessary, which is often. The most important knowledge he posses is *how* to properly investigate a fire along with the legal ramifications of his work. These are inseparable subjects since we do not function in a theoretical world but the world of contentious human beings.

Much of the emphasis on fire investigation training is on the subject of arson, the intentionally set fire, by reason of the fact that arson is a criminal act and therefore poses the specter of a criminal trial and all that that implies. While arson in the realm of building fires is common, fortunately arson on boats is rare, yet training on this subject remains necessary. Moreover, it is with arson where the highest degrees of science and technology are applied to the analysis of trace evidence.

Origin and Cause

The primary emphasis on marine investigations is origin and cause. If an investigation has a shape, it is that of a funnel. It starts with a broad search for the origin of the fire, a close proximity to the exact point where the fire started. Once the origin or area is determined, the focus then narrows to the point of what exactly caused the fire. In the literature of fire investigations we frequently run across this term *origin and cause*. These two terms go hand-in-hand because they are inseparably linked. To find the cause one must first know where the fire started, not generally but specifically — the *point* of origin. Cause also consists of two elements, that of the *initial fuel* and the means of *ignition*; what started burning first and what started the burning?

While the point of origin is usually a small area, that is not always the situation, as in an arson case where flammable liquid may be liberally spread around and set ablaze. To make matters more difficult, as is often the case, a fire may spread or jump rapidly to other points, making the task of determining point of origin very difficult, if not impossible. Take the case of a building that has completely burnt to the ground. In this situation there is no obvious physical evidence to indicate at what point in the building the fire started. Thus, the point of origin can only be determined by witness accounts or good luck in locating evidence of cause. The very same situation occurs with boats every time one burns to the water line and sinks: there isn't much left to work with.

The physical properties of most small boats don't help much. First, being small, they tend to become engulfed rapidly. Boats may have a single deck or multiple decks or levels, single compartments or numerous compartments with each type presenting a different challenge. We will be dealing with everything from small runabouts to large yachts with each involving different types of propulsion. On the other hand, fires may be contained within a smaller area by internal structures, say an engine room. The smaller structure prevents the spread of the fire for a time, thus allowing for more complete burn of combustibles within that compartment. Therefore, by way of a burn being more complete the point of origin may be determined.

Larger boats, particularly those with superstructures and flying bridges have taller structures that allow for the upward burn and the chimney effect. A chimney is simply any tall confined space that concentrates and conducts superheated air upward without the ability to diffuse laterally. The chimney effect may occur within the pilaster supporting the flying bridge deck of most fly bridge sedans and many fly bridge motor yachts. The chimney causes blast furnace-like temperatures that are substantially above those of other burned areas. These much higher temperatures will cause some materials such as glass and metals to melt that otherwise did not melt because temperatures in those areas were below the melting point.

Basic Considerations

It was stated earlier that boat fires are not only unlike building fires, but there are far fewer of them. Does that mean boats are safer? No, this is probably the result of the fact that boats remain unoccupied at least 90% of the time, considering that most residential fires are caused by the occupants. While there are no statistics on boat fires, it is my estimation that the majority of boat fires occur with the vessel unoccupied, and perhaps a quarter while the vessel is underway.

In the course of boat investigations we can divide fires into two categories, near total destruction and those that are less than totally destroyed. Consider a boat totally destroyed when it burns to near the water line. Those that are not totally destroyed have at least some part of their structure remaining such as house sides and decks. There are major differences in the remains that we are left to evaluate. When all combustibles are consumed, about all we are left with are metals and a few other materials. While this chapter does not discuss the differences throughout, the reader will be aware that we have a lot less evidence to work with when near total destruction of all materials occurs.

Owing to the variety of materials used in boat construction, and their shape and design, complete destruction of the basic structure is not common. The remaining glass fibers, among other materials, tend to hold the basic shape unless the firefighters collapse it. Something under fifteen minutes is a rather typical response time and considering that it typically takes about 30 minutes to completely consume most boats, there is usually adequate time in most cases for fires to be extinguished before total destruction. This means that in a majority of cases, enough remains that we have a fair to good chance of determining cause. So what is a good success rate? Thirty percent would be good, 40% very good and 50% excellent. If one is doing better than 50% he is either very lucky or possibly too eager to be successful, rather like a zealous prosecutor that breaks the rules just to look good.

Surprisingly most boats do not sink even after catastrophic fires. This is because underwater plumbing such as hoses cannot burn completely through when full of water. However, hoses will burn right down to the water line so that sinking can occur soon after. Unfortunately, it is usually firefighters that cause most boats to sink by pouring massive amounts of water in them. Because boats contain large fuel tanks, firefighters are eager to make sure the fire is completely out and will overhaul all smoldering rubble and in the process destroy evidence. This is frustrating to investigators but unavoidable.

What is Fire, Combustion?

At this point it is useful to consider what is fire and combustion, for though these terms are similar, they are not exactly the same. Combustion and fire are technically the same as rusting steel and explosions, as they are all oxidation reactions, but are different only in terms of effect. What differentiates them is the rate at which they occur. Rusting steel does not create a fire, but rapidly oxidizing wood or plastic does. Ignition of gas vapors produces an explosion and a fire, but what is burning is other combustible materials. We all know fire when we see it since it is tangible to sight, touch and usually smell. When wood burns it makes visible fire, right? Well, not always, for combustion can occur without visible fire, which is how charcoal is made. Fire needs oxygen, but so does combustion, just less of it. Visible fire is dependent on the speed at which oxygen combines with other chemicals as a result of a certain amount of heat or energy applied. The point being that combustion may occur at very rapid or much slower speed. Charcoal is made by applying heat to wood with a limited oxygen source and thus complete combustion or consumption of the wood does not occur. Thus, the rate of burn is controlled by the availability of oxygen. This we understand by the way things burn in confined spaces, a factor that plays an important role in fire investigations.

Fire or combustion of solids occurs when sufficient heat is applied to cause the material to break down and release flammable gasses which burn. When heated to a certain point, the wood begins to break down and some components form combustible gasses such as hydrogen, methane and benzene. Other components of the material do not burn and remain as what is called *char*, the by-products of the fire. Most solids do not burn readily, but need to be sufficiently heated before gasification and combustion begins. The temperature at which this occurs is called the heat of combustion or the inflammability temperature range. Combustion temperatures are not exact numbers but ranges because several factors affect combustion temperature. These include the ambient temperature and the available oxygen supply.

Thus, for a fire to occur is dependant on sufficient heat, a combustible material and adequate oxygen. These three factors are vitally important to fire investigations and must be shown to be present in sufficient quantity to support a fire in order to prove a theory of causation.

Melting Point of Materials

All common solids will typically go through one of three types of transformations when heated:

Changing from a solid to a liquid state as when a metal, wax or ice is heated to its melting point, or the specific temperature at which melting occurs.

Fig. 8 1. Profiling this fire very quickly led to discovery of the point of origin and the cause. The burn pattern indicates that there was a very slight air flow from the port aft quarter. The fire was started by a short in a service outlet near the port aft side of the salon. Note that engine room vents are above the salon deck level. Occurring during the day, the burn time of this wood boat was only about 5 minutes after discovery.

Changing directly from a solid to a gas is a process known as sublimation. An example of sublimation occurs with dry ice (frozen carbon dioxide) when it is exposed to room temperature, or sulfur when it is heated gradually without being ignited.

Decomposition is a breaking apart of the chemicals in the material being heated. Decomposition occurs in many common organic mixtures and compounds such as foods, wood or paper. These materials usually do not melt or liquefy in a visible way, although some of the resulting chemicals or decomposition products do melt and mix with the remaining carbonaceous mass. If the decomposed mass is heated further, there is a temperature at which all the chemicals present will either melt or sublime.

Only the first and third types of transformation occur in our work. Decomposition simply means that the material breaks down into combustible and non combustible components. The phenomenon of melting plays an important role in fire investigation because materials have different melting points. Glass and metals are the main materials that serve as indicators of the degree of heat present in a given area. By knowing the melting point of these materials we generally know that a certain temperature was reached. This is particularly important when inspecting the condition of wiring as some few fires are hot enough in places to melt copper wire or at least fuse it together.

Melting points of metals can serve as a guideline as to temperatures achieved in the fire. This is often necessary to determine if melting resulted from the fire generally, or from electrical arcing that produce extremely high temperatures. Metals come in an infinite range of alloy types and percentages so we have no way of determining what alloy it is short of a costly analysis, so this is only a guide.

Profiling a Fire

The purpose of profiling a fire is primarily an attempt to narrow down the point of origin by means of analyzing the burn pattern and other internal and external factors that influenced it such as wind and structural shape, as well as how the nature of the structural materials influenced the fire. In profiling we attempt to identify critical factors that help to limit how much time we spend looking and analyzing a huge array of possibilities. Profiling a fire is a bit more reliable than that of profiling a criminal mind because we are dealing with objective evidence even though we make subjective judgements about it.

A profile is made long before the investigator ever sets foot into the chary remains. An investigator with many years of experience will need nothing more than standing there for a few minutes, or walking around the wreck taking in everything that is visible and digesting it based on his experience. A profile is not something that we need sit down and write out, but merely take the time to observe and digest what we can see, all with a view toward not wasting time. Every fire offers up something different and will produce a variety of indicators, positive, negative or indifferent. Profiling is taking the long view, as compared to the close up view we get by actually being in the wreck. It is a matter of seeing patterns and indicators that cannot be seen up close.

Was there any wind and how did that affect the fire? Wind speed and direction is key to determining the rate of burn and direction of spread. Was there an explosion? Does the degree of destruction tell us anything about the origin, or not? Did the fire vent and how. Did the vessel have shore power and what is the status of the dock circuit breakers? Equally critical to the profile is the determination of whether there were any witnesses. These are among the many things we put into a profile to help us narrow down the origin and cause.

Determining whether a boat was connected to shore power at the time can eliminate a huge number of possibilities. Checking the dock circuit breaker can provide many leads if it was tripped. Examining the shore power cord first could cut investigation time from days to merely hours.

Since virtually everything on the boat is potential evidence, the number of possibilities is huge and we don't want to have to dig and sift through all of it, if possible. Much work can be circumvented by attempting to pinpoint the origin by other means such as eye witnesses. Boat fires always attract lots of attention so there are usually an abundance of good witnesses. Try to locate and interview witness first to narrow down where the fire started.

Timing is also an important subject for profiling. If a boat burns to the water line, how long did that take? For a fiberglass boat, 20 minutes[2] is about an average time from ignition to becoming completely engulfed – wood boats, of course, go much faster – anything less than ten minutes to become completely engulfed should be considered as suspicious. If there were witnesses, try to pin down the time from which smoke was first observed until the boat becomes engulfed. If it is more than 10 minutes, the use of an accelerant is unlikely.

Fires in boats are prone to "smoldering" due to air starvation for fairly long periods of time. Eventually, the heat builds up higher and higher until a break out or vent opens up and the fire seems to suddenly burst forth with almost explosive force. This can give the false appearance that an accelerant was used, or that a minor explosion occurred. Be sure to question witnesses about whether smoke was noticed first.

Boats tend not to burn completely to the water line by virtue of the fact that the lower the fire burns toward the hull bottom the less air supply it has. Thus, as the fire nears the bottom the rate of burn slows down and usually self-extinguishes, hopefully before it sinks. Unfortunately, fire fighters tend to pour so much water on the wreck that they are the ones that usually end up sinking it.

Boat Materials

Fiberglass reinforced plastic, despite the fact that it is combustible, does not burn easily. Although the plastic is not designed to be self-extinguishing, it tends to be so, this because the flat surfaces do not ignite easily or burn freely until a certain temperature is reached. In fact, fiberglass and aluminum boats, contrary to what one would think, actually burn at very similar rates and conditions. It is essential to realize that the temperatures at which materials will burn is dependent on the size and shape of the object in consideration. A good example is that iron filings sprinkled over a candle will burn freely but an iron plate will not. Thus, mass and surface area are major factors. The scientific reasons why are far too complex to be of much value to us, yet we are all familiar with the reason why horizontal flat panels don't burn well; they don't get enough oxygen. But fragment that material in any and the availability of oxygen increases dramatically and it then burns freely. We understand that to start a fire with a match, it should be applied to the edges of a material, not a flat surface. Why? Because the edge has three sides, a smaller surface area and mass at the edge, plus more available oxygen. A splinter of wood burns easily, but a large plank does not. We can apply this knowledge toward determining how fast fires will spread, how fast up, down or horizontally.

Based on the author's testing, a resin rich polyester laminate (as opposed to one with less resin on the surface) will begin to soften at 350F and ignite at 791F. The temperature at which laminates will burn freely varies with the amount of resin on the surface and the glass/resin ratio as well as the orientation of the material, much the same as all other materials. It burns most readily in the vertical position where there is the best air supply but hardly burns at all on the upper side of horizontal. Heat build-up on the underside of decks results in the most rapid combustion and complete consumption of the plastic (that's why house tops don't last long). If the glass content is particularly

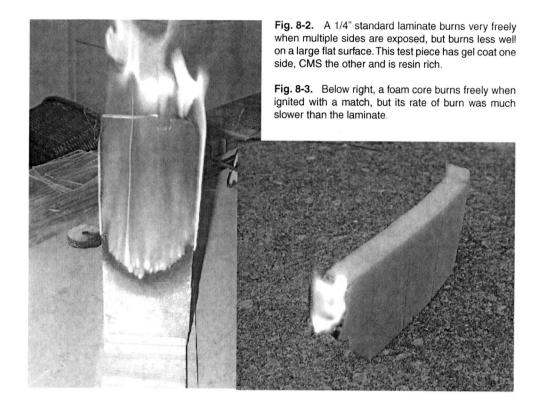

Fig. 8-2. A 1/4" standard laminate burns very freely when multiple sides are exposed, but burns less well on a large flat surface. This test piece has gel coat one side, CMS the other and is resin rich.

Fig. 8-3. Below right, a foam core burns freely when ignited with a match, but its rate of burn was much slower than the laminate.

dense as with woven roving, burn-through is rarely complete unless a constant ignition source is applied. Chopped strand mat reinforcement burns much more readily due to the lower density of glass fibers. Vacuum bagged laminates burn least well because the glass-to-resin ratio is very high.

Yet another reason why fiberglass panels don't burn well is that the by-products of soot and ash clings to, or remains on, the surface and retards the burning by depriving the fire of oxygen. This helps retard smaller fires in confined spaces that aren't well ventilated. Of course, once the fire has reached a major conflagration and the heat of ignition becomes constant, then the plastic starts to burn freely as long as the soot can rise on a column of heated air, or wind carries it away. Fiberglass panels burn most readily along edges where the oxygen supply is available from three sides and exhausts by-products readily, edges such as around windows, ventilators and the like.

Therefore, a fiberglass boat despite the fact that it is plastic, does not ignite and burn as readily as one might expect. Unlike a wooden boat or structure, fiberglass boats can "smolder" for a long time before the fire breaks out.

Subverting the resistance of fiberglass to burn is the fact that highly flammable materials for headliners are attached to the under side of decks and house tops. Typically this consists of vinyl fabric and plywood furring strips. Up to a quarter of the weight of many boats consists of plywood which is very heavy and burns nicely, thereby providing the constant ignition and heat source to kindle glass reinforced plastic (bring it up to the ignition temperature).

Glass fibers don't normally burn or melt in boat fires. In most cases the glass fabric remains completely intact except in extremely hot fires where all carbonaceous by-product is burned or carried away, leaving the fabric looking gray or white in color. In some cases it becomes so hot that the fabric fragments and crumbles. This condition often makes it easy to identify the hottest or at least the longest burning area.

Most boats are built with polyester resin and a few with vinylester. Both these plastics are thixotropic thermosets and do not melt like thermoplastic does. When heated it will soften somewhat. Core materials have been in use right from the beginning of FRP boats but today their use is more extensive than ever and includes a huge range of foam materials, most of which are PVC based[3]. Test burning of these foams reveals that most burn violently with a constant heat source applied. Remove the heat source and the fire tends to extinguish, mainly because of their location in the middle of the laminate. Similarly, one might expect balsa to burn rapidly, yet it does not. Balsa has so much internal air space that it tends to burn internally and char in a way similar to charcoal. Since both these materials are very good insulators, they will work to minimize heat transfer and minimize the spread of the fire until they are consumed, which will only be a short period of time. In the early stages they work to contain the heat generated and raise the internal temperature until the flashover point.

Lastly, we come to boats built with putty or "spray cores." These are cores of sprayed-in polyester that are porous and have a high air content. Being polyester, they are highly flammable and burn fiercely. Once these cores ignite they will burn freely, so that hulls built with this material are likely to burn to the water line very quickly. Fires in confined spaces will break out much faster than with a solid laminate or conventional cored hull or structure.

Areas of Highest Probability

It is matter of common sense to look to those areas that traditionally are the points where fires start most often. The areas of highest probability are those areas where the greatest numbers of naturally occurring ignition points are located. In addition to hot engines and exhaust systems, the bulk of the electrical system is normally centered about the engine room. The main electric panel is usually close to the engine room, and since the ABYC standard requires that the shore power receptacles be within ten feet of the main panel, these, too, are close to the engine room.

The next area of high probability is the galley where cooking and numerous other appliances are located. Stove fires, of course, usually involve eye witnesses, so determining cause usually isn't a problem[4]. Ultimately, the area of the engine room and salon is the general area where about 90% of all fires start. A common exception is when generators are not located in the engine room, or in larger vessels where there is another machinery space beside the engine room.

Fig. 8-4. Firefighters typically "overhaul" the debris to make sure the fire is out, leaving much wreckage strewn around and evidence damaged. In a situation like this, the investigators first job will be sort and segregate the large pieces which are mostly seating, and generally making it possible to move around on the vessel. Note shore cord in foreground, thrown aboard by firefighters.

This is not to say that fires don't start in other areas, just that the engine room/salon area is typically the most suspect by virtue of frequency and probability. Fortunately for investigators, if the fire started elsewhere, knowing how to profile and establish point of origin will help narrow the scope of the investigation in all but complete burn-down cases. High power demand equipment and circuits such as air conditioners, bow thrusters, clothes dryers and water heaters should also be considered as highly probable.

Initial Fuel Source

In profiling a fire, it is important to consider what the initial fuel source for ignition was. Most of the structure of an FRP boat does not ignite easily. Therefore, by identifying the areas that contain easily combustible materials from those with hard to ignite materials we may come to a better understanding of where a fire is more likely to start. Most engine rooms do not have a lot of readily combustible materials, many of which are self-extinguishing plastics, and would require a sustained application of heat to get them burning. Conversely, cabin areas with their upholstered accommodations, plywood paneling and cabinetry and other readily combustible materials, offer many opportunities for fast combustion with a low temperature combustion materials. And yet, while cabin areas contain many combustibles, they tend to lack ignition sources while engine rooms lack combustibles but contain many potential ignition sources.

A good example are the areas under open cockpit decks aft of the machinery space, an area that not only lacks easily combustible materials, but also good ventilation and numerous ignition sources.

Reconstructing Suspect Electrical Equipment and Systems

Virtually all electrical systems and apparatus must be considered guilty until proven innocent. It is good practice to work from the direction of highest to lowest probability, and to this extent high amperage draw electric devices are the most likely. For a vessel connected to shore power, examination of the entire system from boat to dock should be done first, as this is the number one probable cause. Don't forget to test the dock circuits to determine if they are wired correctly or have faults. If a vessel has not been completely destroyed and the main electric panel is more or less intact, a list of all electrical devices can be quickly made, along with the positions of all circuit breakers. But if this is not possible, a listing of such equipment can be obtained from the owner and then the excavation of debris should proceed to locate this equipment.

Moving wreckage should be avoided when it would disturb the circuitry. That is why it is necessary to have a good saber saw so as to cut away interfering debris without damaging wiring. We don't want to inadvertently mess up a shorted out electrical service outlet because we didn't know it was there.

In most cases we will not want to cut wires to remove things as it may become necessary to trace them later. It is good procedure to attempt to reconstruct the systems in a rudimentary sort of way. This can best be explained by an example. In the case of a flying bridge cruiser, the bridge deck has collapsed down into the salon area, cutting off access to the engine room, and since the fire has burned through one point of the salon decking, it is not certain that this wasn't an engine room fire. To get at the engine room, the collapsed bridge deck and helm console needs to be moved. It consists mainly of glass reinforcement, much wire and remnants of a sofa.

The investigator can't just start ripping debris out because this would be destroying evidence. Instead, unneeded debris is carefully removed and then several sheets of plywood are slipped under the bridge wreckage and then lifted up a few feet and secured with a hasty 2 x 4 framework. Now the investigator can access both the helm electricals and the engine room. In cases where there is no choice but to cut wires, using white plastic tape and indelible marker, number the cut wires consecutively for later identification and tracing.

Area Hot Spots

Degree of burn and destruction may be a good general indicator of the point of origin, but not always. Another good indicator in confined spaces is the degree of burn on hull sides. As FRP burns, only the plastic is consumed, leaving the fibers all but undisturbed. These indicators tend to be more prominent with engine room fires and fires that start deeper in the hull. Hot spots near hull sides and even overheads will display points where the plastic resin is more completely consumed. At these points the remains will appear as nothing but fabric whereas in areas of lesser burn, plastic and even gel coat may remain. Since FRP is a fairly good insulator, heat transmission through the laminate to the exterior is yet another indicator. Gel coat often displays peculiar patterns of cracking when it gets very hot without igniting. Thus, the areas of greatest gel coat disturbance on the exterior are another possible indicator.

Site Preparation

More than any other type of casualty, a fire investigation requires planning and preparation, particularly larger boats. All fires involve the layering of debris which occurs during the process of burn-down. Debris falls and accumulates in layers, and so, too, do incompletely burned parts of the structure. But boat structures, being glass reinforced plastic in which the plastic burns away leaving the fabric reinforcement, layering is much deeper and more difficult to deal with. With a wooden building, all that is necessary is to shovel up the ashes, but in a boat we have heaps of tangled fiberglass, metal, wire and hardware. These need to be moved and separated with care.

In most boat investigations the vessel will have been hauled from the water and placed somewhere in a boat yard. Large pieces of debris, such as house tops, bridge components and so on, may remain that have to be cleared away. We can't assume that these things don't contain evidence and so it will be necessary to remove them with a degree of care. The yard may have a small mobile crane, or perhaps we can use the Travel Lift to lift away large pieces of debris because it is quite dangerous to try to use manpower to move large heavy objects in a burned out boat.

Yet another consideration is what to do with the debris as we can't just toss this stuff around in a boat yard. It is preferable that, with a degree of care, the debris be set aside and then place it back in the vessel when finished.

We also need to be cognizant of the effects of rain. Not only will rain fill up the bilge with water, but it also spoils evidence. High temperatures alter the molecular structure of metals and make most of them much more vulnerable to corrosion. Post fire corrosion can seriously impede an investigation. If the bottom of the hull fills with water, we may end up with an environmental contamination problem and cannot just drain this contaminated water on the ground. I learned this the hard way when a boat yard refused to allow me to pump out a hull full of water onto the ground. I ended up having to pay over one thousand dollars to hire a hazardous waste disposal company. It's far better to not let the hull fill up in the first place. Therefore, the wreck should be covered as soon as it is secured; the cost of doing this is very modest, so there's no reason not to.

A cautionary note here: While DC current isn't going to electrocute us, DC current can cause severe burn injuries to the unwary investigator. Even worse, fuel tanks may spring leaks. One of the very first things to do on fire investigations is to locate the vessel's batteries and *disconnect* the positive cables and secure them.

Spoilation of Evidence

Though evidence handling requirements are not as stringent for civil cases as it is for criminal cases, spoilation of evidence remains a serious issue that could have legal consequences for the investigator. The fundamental principle here is that all parties to an issue have the same right to evidence as your client does, and should you do anything to deprive others of those rights, they then have the right to a claim against the investigator or whomever spoiled the evidence. Government fire fighters and investigators are immune from prosecution for despoilation of evidence, but we are not.

During the course of the investigation we need to keep in mind that the entire wreck is evidence and we do not have the right to despoil it even though we think we are finished with it. The wreckage should be treated with a reasonable degree of care so that any later investigators will not accuse us of recklessly destroying evidence. Besides, we never know when we will need to return to the wreck for additional analysis; this happens often.

This brings us to the obvious question of how long should the wreck be retained? The wreckage should be retained at least up to the point where a decision is made about litigation. Then, if litigation is initiated, it should continue to be retained up to a point where others have an opportunity to perform their own investigation. If no litigation is contemplated or threatened, then the wreck can be disposed of at any time, but remember that a defendant has an equal right to review the evidence, and should you deny him that right, this can cause serious problems for your side.

When the Vessel Has Sunk

A burned boat that has sunk poses serious problems for potential litigation due to the high probability that evidence was altered or destroyed. Even if good evidence of the cause is found, it will not be easy for a litigant to prove his case by virtue of the difficulties posed in overcoming doubt as to (a) whether evidence has been altered in such a way as to prove misleading, or (b) contributory evidence hasn't been lost. Before proffering a conclusion as to cause, the investigator will want to consider very carefully how solid his evidence really is by putting the shoe on the other foot and playing devil's advocate with his evidence.

Don't Do This

Earlier I made the statement that even professional fire investigation outfits don't always perform professionally. The following negative example is presented with a view toward learning from mistakes, in this case a bad one. This was an investigation of a total loss fire on a $750,000 sport yacht.

I had occasion to participate in this investigation that was being led by a private professional fire investigator. This firm had sent out letters to thirteen different parties

Fig. 8-5. This photograph alone was enough to sink a plaintiff's case against a defendant. There are ten investigators trampling over the wreck with no regard to what they are doing to evidence. This photo was taken near the beginning of a joint investigation.

that might have a liability interest in the matter, so that on the day of investigation, a large group of people were present, probably at least fifty. The lead investigator had failed to create a plan and launched into the investigation helter-skelter.

This was flying bridge boat on which the upper structure had collapsed all the way into the bilge leaving heaps of fiberglass, tangled wire, railings an other debris. Rather than going about it in an organized way, several men began heaving debris overboard, ten feet to the ground below. This included identifiable parts of the bridge console and deck, an icemaker and hundreds of feet of wiring. During the course of removing all this debris, there were at least a half dozen men tramping all over the boat without regard for what their feet were doing — as it turned out, destroying evidence.

Once the debris from the upper structure was cleared (apparently they concluded that none of this debris was relevant), everyone was allowed to come aboard and stomp on whatever remained of any evidence, which they did. The center of attention were the shore power connections for reasons that were unclear to me because this point was clearly not the point of origin. Nor did the components show any sign of having caused the fire.

In the meantime I noticed a set of wires running in a location where no wires should be. These wires were mostly buried in debris and were discovered because it was clear to me that this was close to the point of origin based on my profile. These wires turned out to be an extension cord that lead to a portable battery charger where it lay hidden in the sludge of bilge water, only discovered by following the aforementioned wires.

My reason for attending this investigation was by reason of my client possibly having to defend a claim of liability. I had little reason or motivation to prove the actual cause and was mainly content to let the others flounder about and create an eminently impeachable case, which they did.

The extension cord led into the engine room where the battery charger was located. The rest of the crowd was outside and apparently unwilling to crawl through the hot but wet black debris. The temperature inside the boat was around 125F, so these men were eager to get out of there as soon as possible. So was I, but I was being paid good money to do a job. I followed the cord until I found the plug end which I tried to separate but found that the thing was fused together, being only partially burned. Melting of the brass connectors indicated an obvious short that produced arcing. Equally important was the fact that this connector was laying on carpet that exhibited an obvious burn pattern (after excavation) surrounding around the plug.

At this point the lead investigator discovered me in the engine room and ordered me out. Considering the utter carelessness of this professional investigator, it didn't much matter to me what he thought I was doing since I got what I needed — solid evidence that would produce reasonable doubt about the plaintiff's theory. With a defense case, it's not necessary to try to prove causation but to cast reasonable doubt, if such exists. The investigation was concluded after three days of mostly wasting time and a total of eight hours on the boat by a large crowd of people; at no time was the engine room investigated by anyone other than myself.

Ultimately my client was named in a lawsuit by the insurer of the yacht. They falsely concluded that the shore power system was the cause of the fire when I had a solid alternate theory that a portable battery charger had apparently fallen in bilge water and shorted out because it was plugged into a circuit with a 30 amp circuit breaker. As so often happens, whoever moved the boat, disconnected the burned extension cord and threw it on the boat. When our "professionals" threw the deck over the side, part of that extension cord went with it, so no one ever noticed it. Nor were they willing to brave the claustrophobic, charred, 125 degree wreckage of the engine room.

To the extent that I was representing a potential defendant, it would not be necessary for me to produce irrefutable evidence; all that I needed would be to cast reasonable doubt on whatever the plaintiff's alleged. This position does not rise to the level of bias because the truth was not being served by this shoddy investigation.

Thus, when the lawsuit reached the point of my deposition, I was able to totally demolish their expert's report by challenging the credibility of almost every aspect of it, and then offer a more credible theory of causation, one that they had not even investigated. This was supported by testimony that the investigation ignored many other areas of possibility. The battery charger was never found by the plaintiff's expert and not mentioned in his report. This effectively destroyed the credibility of the expert.

This is an excellent example of how not to conduct an investigation. The worst part of it was that the lead investigator was just plain lazy, incompetent or both. The blackened mass of boat ruins sitting out in the sun can become extremely hot. In this case, in Florida in July, no one could stay in that wreckage for more than 10 or 15 minutes even with fans running, so there was plenty of motivation not to do a good job. If the vessel cannot at least temporarily be gotten under cover, a tent should be erected over it to prevent it from heating up in the sun. And have a few fans available.

With fire investigations, all debris is potential evidence. Debris removal or layering must be conducted with care and planning. Large pieces of wreckage are likely to have numerous wires, cables and even electronic gear attached that could be evidence. Once removed it should carefully be set aside for further examination. With boat fires virtually all wiring must be considered suspect until proven otherwise.

The Physics of Boat Fires

The tendency of science is to create complexity out of relatively simple phenomena. The subject of fire investigation has become very scientific of late, but most of this technical explanation of common events is of little value to the marine fire investigator because fires in simple structures are relatively simple events. Given that the combustible materials are known, the behavior of fire is reasonably predictable. This is important because the investigator begins by trying to work the fire backwards, from the end result to the ignitions source, rather like running a movie in reverse.

Flameover and Flashover

These two terms are used by fire fighters to describe fire behavior as it affects their safety as well as the progress of a building fire. Both these terms are relevant to fire investigations as well. As a fire burns upward within a structure, heat builds up to extreme temperatures near the ceiling. The gases released by the heat (decomposition) also continue to rise and accumulate at the ceiling level. Once these gases reach a certain temperature they ignite and a vicious cloud of flame envelops the ceiling level. That's flameover. The heat generated by this roiling gas fire radiates downward, raising the temperature of all other objects in the space until they, too, reach the ignition point. Flashover occurs when just about everything else in the room not burning seems to suddenly burst into fame and the area is completely enveloped. This is the point at which the ability to extinguish the fire before total destruction is lost.

Drafting, Vents and Chimneys

The normal process of combustible materials burning in the open is one in which the fire is a self-perpetuating cycle or system of burning. Combustion releases heat and that heat rises upward. The rapidly rising air creates a lower pressure at ground level into which surrounding air rushes to equalize pressure (nature hates a vacuum). The system is very similar to the way a hurricane works except for the rotation part. Observation of any fire makes much of this cycle obvious.

This natural drafting caused by superheated air rising within a burning structure results in numerous opportunities for vents to open up. When the vent is at the top of the structure, it is called a chimney; when toward the bottom, a vent. Examples of vents are engine room ventilators and port holes and sometimes windows. Both vents and chimneys work to control the direction and intensity of burn because they work to increase and direct air flow. A vent in combination with a chimney serves to create a blast furnace-like effect by introducing air at an accelerated rate. "Fanning the flames" is the common expression that we're all familiar with, but in this case it occurs with a self-created wind.

As respects boat fires, if one knows the configuration of the structure, then one can extrapolate from the probable areas of venting how the fire behaved.

Except for machinery spaces, boats are poorly ventilated, intentionally so. Internal spaces are intended to be water tight, which also makes them nearly air tight. The typical pleasure craft does not have any ventilation to the living spaces except for opening windows and many modern boats don't even have those. The modern "express" cruiser interior space is nearly always completely lacking in natural ventilation. In the past, contiguous bilge spaces would provide an air vent to interior spaces, but in more modern boats the bilge compartments are usually closed off so as to prevent odors from migrating to interior spaces.

If there is no ventilation whatever, such as with our express cruiser, and a fire occurs in the forward quarters, that fire will likely very quickly consume the oxygen in that area and begin to self-extinguish unless the fire opens out a vent. The earliest likely vent would be a melting plastic port hole or hatch, but if the ports are glass, it is entirely possible that the fire will self-extinguish or be reduced to low oxygen smoldering. Then, as soon as the cabin is opened up by a fire fighter or others, the sudden influx of air can result in near explosive re-ignition.

One might think that engine room ventilators would be very good at providing an oxygen source for an engine room fire. This is usually only true when the engines are running. The exception is gasoline powered boats that are required to have both intake and exhaust vents, usually a total of four. The vent assembly is usually plastic and will promptly melt and burn, opening up a much larger vent area. Most diesel boats only have two vents, one on each side and the running engines act as an air pump to pull air into the vents. Fires that occur while running are extremely well ventilated and quickly accelerate out of control. This is why automatic extinguishing systems are so important. By the time an engine room fire is noticed it is usually too late.

Since most engine rooms of larger boats are more or less closed off to other sources of air flow, the vents may do little to assist the fire when engines aren't running. This is due to baffles in the vents that will retard air flow. Being such a small space, a fire can quickly reduce the oxygen level and will behave in much the same way as trying to start a fire in a barrel that is not vented at the bottom. The fire will initially burn upward, but once that convection is well underway, the strong upward movement works against air being pulled into the base of the fire and it thus starves for oxygen. This is one redeeming factor for engine room fires rapidly going out of control when engines

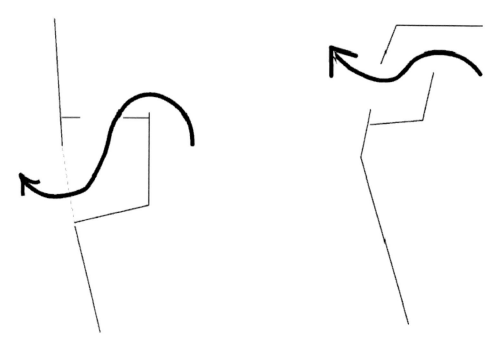

Fig. 8-6. At left is the more common style engine room vent through the hull side. This baffled box design makes natural venting difficult and will slow down a fire until the baffles burn away. At right, this less common style vent located up high provides less resistance and will vent better.

are not running. The major exception is when there is a wind blowing that will create high and low pressures on opposite sides that will facilitate a natural air flow. In this case we find that the engine room vents from one side only and rapidly spreads the fire to that side of the boat, while the other side displays little or no spreading from the vent. It is not at all unusual to see engine room fires that remain contained until extinguished and we are astonished that the fire did not escape out through the very large vents, or did so on one side only.

Of course, variations in design can produce very different results. With older boats, say pre 1985, bilge spaces were often contiguous between compartments and with the engine room bilge and thus an engine room fire would vent to other quarters. But most post 1990 boats will be found with well-sealed engine rooms, though some few do not have a full aft engine room bulkhead. When engine room fires occur in this type of boat, the fire tends very quickly to vent to other areas and compartments.

A few express cruisers will be found where the engine room vents are actually in the deck shell so that the vents are actually at the top of the engine room. In this case and engine room fire will have unimpeded ventilation and the fire will progress at very rapid speeds.

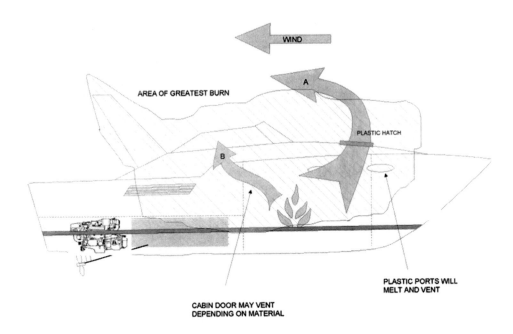

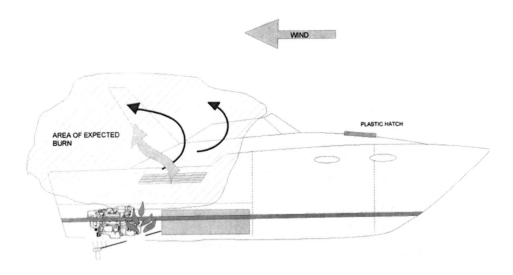

Fig. 8-7 & 8-8. These two illustrations show how the location of origin and wind affect the burn pattern. In the top illustration, a fire in the cabin will vent very quickly through plastic hatches and ports, resulting rapid spreading. Below, a fire in the engine room may or may not vent well, but in any case the wind will keep the fire confined to the stern section for a fairly long period.

Wind and Back-drafting

The flow of air around and over a burning boat, once the fire breaks out of the interior, will control the direction of burn in proportion to the strength of the breeze. Boats typically will have a much better or stronger air flow owing to the lack of impediments to the air flow such as trees and other structures. The direction of air movement is usually apparent with the remains of the vessel if it is less than completely destroyed since wind will carry the fire in the same direction as the air flow. Thus, we see the pattern of boats tending to burn to one side or one end.

Understanding how air flow controls the direction of burn helps us come to conclusions about points of origin. The point of origin would normally be more apparent if there were no air flow because then the area of greatest destruction would be clue to where the fire burned the longest and hottest. But the presence of wind can skew such conclusions by directing the fire away from the point of origin, possibly leaving that point less burned than other areas.

When examining a fire it is important to try to gain an understanding of the direction of air flow and how that determined the resulting burn pattern. *Back drafting* is a condition similar to the station wagon effect wherein the flow of air over and around a blocking object such as a wall, results in a low pressure area on the lee side of the object. This low pressure causes wind to swirl in behind the object and will draw heat and fire with it. This pattern is usually clearly represented with hull sides and superstructures wherein one side is completely burned away while the other is not. Only when there is no wind do we see boats burning down more or less evenly.

More often than not by the time we get to it the subject vessel is no longer at the burn site, but has been moved elsewhere. From the above discussion one can see why it's necessary to examine the actual burn site. Not only do we need to check on things like shore power system components but also for evidence about the wind direction. For example, port holes or engine room vents may leave burn patterns on parts of the dock. A strong wind can carry the fire onto the dock or adjacent vessels or structures and tell us much about how the fire progressed. Our goal is to try to follow the progression of burn backwards toward the source so as to reduce the amount of time spent looking for the cause.

Automatic Fire Systems

Before we go further, it is necessary to consider automatic fire systems and why they sometimes fail to extinguish fires. The primary agents are CO_2, Halon and a trade-named product called Clean Agent, which is a flouroethane. CO_2 extinguishes by means of depriving the fire of oxygen plus cooling. Other agents disrupt the oxidation process. These agents are effective only if two conditions are met: that ventilation to the area is minimal, and that the source of ignition is not perpetual. They often fail to extinguish electrical fires and will not extinguish a fuel or oil fire that is ignited by red-hot exhaust system components, or any other situation where the ignition source remains active.

The amount of air flowing through and engine room while the engines are running at speed is so great as to dilute the dispersal rate of these agent to ineffectiveness. To counteract this, the systems are equipped with automatic engine shut down systems. Unless the automatic engine shut down system functions, or the operator shuts them down, the fire system is likely to fail.

A third, and less likely, reason is that the system bottle is improperly mounted, sometimes with the nozzle facing a bulkhead, or at other times it is blocked by machinery, so that the agent cannot disperse fully.

A fourth reason is due to maintenance failure: corrosion caused the release mechanism or sensor to fail. Fire system bottles should be examined by a reliable service agency to determine how much agent remains in the bottle and/or why a system failed to activate.

Fuel Systems

Determination of the condition of the fuel tanks and distribution system is useful to the investigation for a variety of reasons. It is useful to know whether an explosion occurred or whether a fire was fuel-fed.

Contrary to myth and Hollywood movies, fuel tanks, even gasoline tanks, rarely explode. This is because liquid fuel does not burn; only the vapors do. Consider that a paper cup full of water can be set on a red hot stove burner and boiled. This can happen because the water keeps the temperature of the paper below the ignition point until the water boils away. Tanks that are nearly full are unlikely to assist a fire unless a leak develops. It is truly remarkable how often, after a serious fire, gasoline tanks remain full of gas.

Fuel tanks on many boats, particularly smaller ones, are usually located below the lowest deck so that they are not subjected to the most intense heat. In other boats, they are located aft and also usually out of the main area of fire. But some boats, mainly large ones, have engine room wing tanks that are tall and run down the sides of the engine room. This may put the tanks at or near the hottest parts of the fire where it is highly likely that they will contribute to the fire in a major way, starting off with the burning off of the tank filler hose, creating a pressurized gas vapor fire and where explosions become increasingly possible.

Fuel lines and other system components behave similarly. Of course, once the conflagration is well underway and some part of the fuel system burns away — typically the tank fill hose — vapor escapes and ignites and feeds the fire, but required fuel line anti siphon valves generally prevent this. Additionally, some sections of the fuel lines may not have any fuel in them and could burn through quickly. The evidence of a fuel tank explosion is unmistakable for the tank and any remaining structure will be blown apart and show the effects of an explosion. Look for decks to be lifted and hull sides blown outward either partially or completely.

When the filler hose burns through on a tank that is nearly empty, an explosion becomes possible but the fact remains that this rarely happens. Instead, the severed hose acts more like a blow torch from the ignited vapors and fairly quickly burns off the remaining fuel which reaches the vaporization point at only 375F. That means that if all the fuel is heated to 375F, it all will vaporize, but gasoline vaporization increases in proportion to its temperature. However, it is very unlikely that the fuel in the tank will reach that temperature before it vaporizes and is burned off. Typically the fuel is heated rather slowly and as it heats it more gradually gives off vapor which expands and vents through the tank vent or a burned fill hose which then ignites and will burn until extinguished or the fuel is expended. The net effect is that of a blow torch and will cause complete destruction of any structures in its way, including the melting of metals.

This factor makes extinguishing boat fires a bit more difficult (water won't do it) and accounts for why fire departments usually resort to using foam to extinguish this part of the fire. It is not at all uncommon to run across badly burned boats where the gasoline tanks remain nearly full, as well as fuel lines not burned through. Certainly it does happen that fuel hoses burn on the outside and become so weakened that something causes them to part and create siphoning that feeds the fire, but this is not common. This is one situation where the fire will appear to have two points of origin because the degree of burning and heat will be so extreme that it appears to be the point of origin. However, the fire already had to be sufficiently intense to burn the fuel system so that the overall direction of burn will be a clue that this is an effect, not the cause.

The state of the fuel tanks can usually be determined after the fire. Fuel tanks will often remain full of fuel even after a severe fire, but most often are found empty. A partially empty tank may have enough vapor in it to cause a low intensity explosion and in that case look for minor ballooning of the tank. This should not be mistaken for the severe heat distortion that occurs to tanks as a result of unequal heating. A full scale tank explosion speaks for itself, while nearly empty tanks are likely to be badly ballooned with severe heat distortion and melting. Aluminum tanks are normally made of tempered high grade aluminum; in cheaper boats this is not always the case. Severe tank melting without explosive damage likely means that the tank was empty. However, most aluminum tanks survive even severe fires.

Gasoline fuel systems are pressurized only between the fuel pump and carburetor or fuel injection pump, all of which will be steel or copper piping so that the only likely source of gasoline leakage is at this segment of the system. Fuel pump failures are fairly common, particularly older boats where ethanol fuel additives caused damage to older components.

Diesel fuel, of course, is even less combustible and tanks almost never explode. The systems are capable producing the same blow torch effect from burned-through fill hoses when the tank becomes sufficiently heated. Diesel fuel fires are rare and occur primarily in those instances where a leak from the pressurized side of the system occurs. Fuel injection pumps put out very high pressures so that any leak from a fuel

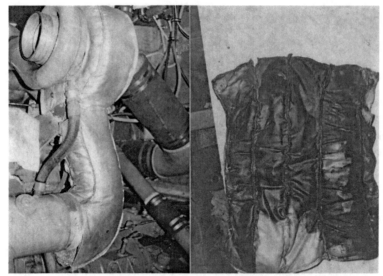

Fig. 8-9. Exhaust insulation on older diesel engines such as this Detroit Diesel are capable of absorbing large amounts of oil or fuel. Above right is a prefab exhaust blanket similar to the one at left, into which a turbocharger leaked a large amount of oil which then combusted. Because the hot exhaust provided a constant ignition source, the automatic fire system did not extinguish the fire.

line will create a vaporized spray that is readily combustible around exhaust manifolds and other hot system components. Such causes are often readily distinguishable by a spray-burn pattern since the pressurized leak will also act like a blow torch and create a very hot burn pattern.

A more common event with older boats that utilize some type of fabric wrapped exhaust insulation or "blankets" is the oil or fuel leak that saturates the insulation that in turn, acts as a wick to vaporize the oil. This will ignite at a relatively low temperature. Such fires are usually readily apparent by the obvious burn pattern (See figure 8-9). Any time there are insulated exhaust components, these should be removed and inspected for visible residues of fuel or burning.

Fuel Fed Fires

With gasoline powered boats, leaking gas is always suspect either at starting the fire or in feeding the fire. Imagine a rubber-based gasoline fuel hose such as neoprene burning through and feeding a fire with gasoline. This sounds like a very likely event, but in reality does not appear to happen often. In most cases the flexible fuel lines are found more or less intact after a fire. ABYC and USCG standards require fuel lines to be fire retardant material, and to withstand free burning for two minutes without failure. Granted, that is not very long, but in most cases all that leaks out will be that which is contained within the hose due to the frequent presence of anti siphon devices. For a fuel fed fire to occur, siphoning of fuel from the tank to the line must also occur but this is not an easy proposition because many systems have spring loaded check valves at the tanks to prevent reverse siphoning. Even if not, slow leakage of fuel from the burning hose will likely allow all fuel in the low section of fuel line to drain out slowly without causing siphoning, thus creating only a brief fuel fed fire. If you've ever tried to start a siphon, you know that it must be done quickly or the vacuum will break and the siphon fail. Were siphoning to happen, this should leave visible evidence since the leaking fuel will end up in the bilge and result in a burn pattern emanating from, or actually be in the bilge. When this occurs, the evidence is very obvious.

When investigating engine room fires and a fuel leak is suspected, excavate through the debris to expose the hull bottom beneath the fuel lines. There should be a burn pattern on the hull and stringers, as well as upward on any vertical elements such as engine blocks.

Convection

Heat rises and therefore fires burn upward most rapidly. Fires occurring on the exterior of a boat are not restrained, either by a physical structure nor by ventilation, but internal fires are. Films of fires in rooms of houses are routinely shown on television so that most of us are familiar with how fire behaves within a closed structure. Heat rises from the combustion source toward the ceiling and pulls cooler air in at the base of the fire. In an enclosed space, this creates a vertical cyclone from floor to ceiling as shown in Figure 8-10. If the oxygen source is restricted the initial fire may decline in intensity as the oxygen is consumed. This will not extinguish the fire unless there is no new source of air, but the fire will continue at a reduced rate of burning in the same way that coal burns underground.

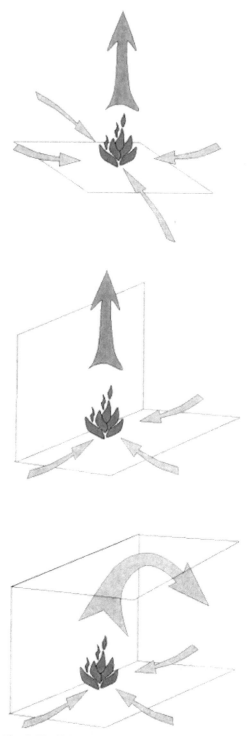

Fig. 8-10. This graphic illustrates how structures influence fires by controlling the air flow and thus the available oxygen supply, in addition to physically controlling the direction of burn until the fire breaks out of its containment.

Burn-through Venting

A fire within a structure without any vents will be contained until such time as the walls of the structure burn through and open up a greater source of oxygen. Contained fires burn much more slowly but, because of containment, the internal area heats up much more uniformly. The resultant burn within the contained area will be much more uniform and consistent throughout. Then, once the fire opens up a vent, the fire will take off in that direction because of the increased oxygen supply and burn hotter with a greater upward velocity.

Although the melting point of glass is very high at 2600 - 2900F, glass windows rarely remain in tact for very long. This is because uneven heating and stresses within tempered glass causes them to fracture, breaking into pieces. Boats usually have tempered and not safety glass. Thus broken window venting usually occurs fairly early and not much window glass will remain to tell what happened. Some boats have plastic windows that will melt at a few hundred degrees; many boats have plastic hatch covers and port holes. These will facilitate venting within minutes after the fire has started.

Engine Room Fires

It is important to understand how fires behave in engine rooms of boats with different configurations due to how the manner of venting will control the fire and rate of spread, so engine room fires tend to be ventilation controlled rather than fuel dominated. Engine room fires tend to be smoldering, slower burning fires because the potential for break out is considerably less as there are no windows to break.

Fires in engine rooms are likely to be either machinery or electrical related, although other causes are possible. Yet engine room fires on boats are unique and unlike ordinary building fires except for industrial buildings housing machinery. Not only do engine rooms have many more possible ignition sources, but also combustibles in the form of fuel and oil, including high pressure oil lines such as hydraulics. However, unless these fuels escape their normal containment, an engine room otherwise has fewer combustibles than other areas of the vessel. Therefore, it takes as much a marine expert as a fire expert to investigate.

The author has been on board vessels when engine room fires occurred on four occasions and has had the opportunity to view the behavior to some degree. Engine room fires that occur while the vessel is underway are very different from the standpoint that they are totally ventilation controlled and directed. Because engines are huge air pumps, there is a constant air flow with a consistent direction that never deviates. A pair of Detroit Diesel engines moves approximately 2000 cubic feet of air per minute. The direction of flow is from the vents to the engine air intake. Thus, a fire will tend to move toward the engine air intake and is likely to create an abnormal, or at least unusual, burn pattern

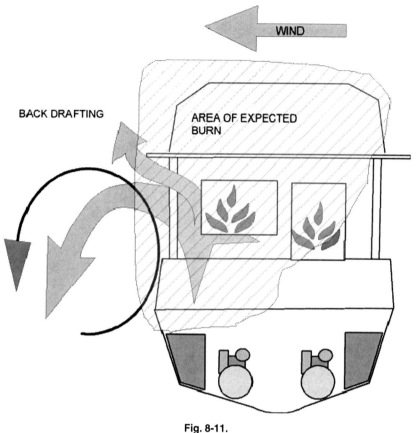

Fig. 8-11.

if the fire is extinguished before going out of control. A fire is likely to burn longer in one place and result in much greater destruction, and possibly heat generated to the extend that it leaves a very distinct pattern. Unique to this type of fire, the undersides of decks are noticeably less burned than in stationary vessel fires. This is because the airflow in through the vents and toward the engine intakes alters the normal upward convection and carries it toward the engines.

This is distinctly different than a stationary vessel engine room fire where the fire will spread in a more usual manner, going up and across the underside of the deck and seeking a break out point. Figure **8-11** shows a cross section of a typical forty foot boat. While engine room vents might be thought to provide excellent ventilation to an engine room fire, this is not always the case owing to the need to design vents in such a way as to keep water out, which may impede air flow and venting. Engine room vents are designed for engines to create a vacuum in the engine room that *pulls* air *in* through the vents due to unequal pressure. This design works somewhat to defeat a fire which is normally vented by means of convection in a sort of vertical cyclone. All things being equal, the heated air rises and tends to flow out both vents slowly and more or less equally because of restrictions — until those restrictions burn away. A strong wind coming from one side of the boat can upset that balance and serve to set up an air flow in one vent and out the other. If that happens a strong flow pattern may be established that becomes evident causing the boat to burn more toward one side, even though the fire started on the opposite side. In this case, the burn pattern may be very misleading of the point of origin.

Engine room vents are always at the top of the compartment but may be ducted down to the bilge though this is no longer usual except in gas boats where such vents are thin plastic and will melt almost immediately. In the former case, while providing an upward outlet for convection, there is no good air flow to the base of the fire down low, so the upward burn is highly restricted. If ducted to the bilge, this provides air to the base, but there is no high side outlet for convection, and thus the fire goes into a slow burn, building up heat with much less flame. Mid engine boats often have wing fuel tanks that are immediately below or in front of the vents that will not be very good at venting the fire. Instead of hot gasses going up and out, gasses have to bend around corners to escape. While these vents are large, intentionally they do not permit a free flow of air but require a decrease in pressure to bring air in.

Rear engine boat fires are significantly different than mid engine boats. For the former, engine compartments are typically much smaller and the ventilation much more direct, often with no obstruction at all. Thus, a fire in this type of engine room can burn straight up and out the vents in which case one will become the exhaust and the other the intake, feeding air to the base of the fire that may burn much faster than with a mid engine room.

Fortunately, engine room fires tend to be among the most easily determined as to causation when a vessel is running, but much less for stationary vessel fires particularly when near destruction occur. In this case, once the fire breaks out of the engine room by burning upwards, the fire becomes extremely hot, well vented and destructive.

By way of example, let's consider an engine room fire where a deck hatch has been left open, providing near perfect ventilation for the fire which burns upward with unrestricted convection. Now the engine room vents begin to feed the base of the fire and starts acting like a blast furnace and once the cabin windows go, total destruction of the vessel is almost guaranteed.

A Typical Scenario

We can get a better understanding of how this works by examining a typical example. In this case we have a 35' flying bridge sedan cruiser. The upper structure has burned and collapsed into the salon area where there is a heap of rubble. The port side is burned down to within two feet of the water line while the starboard side is intact all the way up to the house side lower windows. The cockpit deck is mostly unburned but there is almost nothing of the cabin aft bulkhead remaining.

From the remains it is apparent that the air flow was from astern and slightly to the starboard side. In other words, the wind was from the starboard aft quarter, carrying heat and flame forward and toward the port side which is burned down further because the hull side and superstructure was back drafting and the fire being carried in that direction. What does this tell us about the origin of the fire, if anything?

First, we need to know something about the wind speed since velocity of air flow has a strong influence on how a fire burns. In this instance, we know that the wind was near calm, but never-the-less flowing in a specific direction as evidenced by the direction that the fire was induced to travel.

We can rule out the fire having started anywhere near the bow and stern. How? If the fire started at the stern the cockpit area should be more completely burned. The fire would back draft off the raised transom area and ensure that the entire cockpit would burn. If at the bow, the wind direction should have worked to keep the fire contained in that area for a greater length of time because it would remain contained longer. In all probability, a fire in the bow would eventually burn through and draft in the bow area (probably the bow hatch first) keeping the fire there for quite a long time. Yes, it would back draft against the superstructure to some degree, but the fire would have to try to burn into the wind, a condition that would slow its rate of progression considerably.

With a fire of this description and conditions, experience tells us that we're not getting much help from the burn pattern unless there are other circumstances that help narrow it down, such as a lesser degree of destruction and more indicators pointing out a direction. Basically all that can be deduced from this pattern is that the fire probably started somewhere in the mid section of the boat. But there is more because we can now start working to further constrict the area by narrowing down the vertical dimension, keeping in mind that fires are three dimensional.

Of course the fire burned up, but how far down did it burn? If we can make this determination we can further limit the area to the cabin or engine room. Fortunately this is fairly easy, but it means getting dirty and doing some excavation. A quick study of the salon deck will tell us whether the fire burned up through the deck from the engine room. If not, examination of the engine room area surely will reveal whether the fire started there.

In this case, the wind direction will likely have caused the fire to burn down through the salon deck along the port side. The fire will have entered the engine room, but only partially and we can expect that the starboard side, while smoky, will not have any fire damage at all so long as the salon deck is mostly intact. Carpeting on decks goes a long way toward insulating the wood or fiberglass from burning. We conclude that the burn down on the port side of the salon into the engine room was caused by drafting, and therefore the probable point of origin is in the salon that contains the galley.

Note that on this style boat, and many others, there is a sizable void space between the hull sides and salon paneling under the side decks. This may be taken up with cabinets, but may also house engine room vent passages. This area may serve as a conduit for the fire.

Next, we'd like to know which side the point of origin was on, for this would narrow it down even further. Is that possible? The answer will depend mainly on good luck and venting. A fire starting in the salon will not have any good vents available unless a window was open, and since people don't leave windows in boats open, we can reasonably assume that they didn't. The fire in the salon is going to remain contained for a while, but most likely, because of all the windows, one of these will break and vent fairly quickly.

The fact that we have a deeper burn down on the port over the starboard side – assisted by a slight breeze — is a good indicator that the fire started on the port side and draft burned more slowly back toward the starboard side, thereby leaving it more intact after the fire was extinguished. Had the fire started on the starboard side and broke the windows out, the wind direction should have caused the fire to consume the superstructure more evenly. In that case the fire should have back-drafted off the inside of the starboard cabin side and burned down to the deck more completely.

From this we have quite strong evidence of the general area where the fire started and can begin our search that hopefully will be much more limited, saving much time working in an uncomfortable environment, to say the least.

Glass Windows

Although the melting point of glass is very high at 2600 - 2900F, glass windows remains in tact considerably longer than plastic, but for how long is not easy to determine. That is because uneven heating and stresses within tempered glass causes them to fracture, breaking into a million pieces, so wherever the first window goes, that is where the first vent starts. But that is not something we can divine. Then there is the question of whether heat broke the window or firefighters. Water sprayed onto hot glass will, of course, instantly cause it to shatter.

Layering may provide evidence as to when a window broke by its location in the debris layer. For example, window fragments on a badly burned sofa suggested that the sofa was burning long before the window broke, yet some were deeply embedded within the sofa char to show that breakage did not occur as a result of being hit with a fire hose. Glass on the cabin sole under layers of char will clearly indicate that the window broke early-on. And, of course, explosions will scatter glass leaving clear evidence of what happened even if there is no other.

Layering

The depth at which debris such as metals and other non perishables is buried can sometimes be a clue as to order of events. For something to be buried usually means that there had to be plenty of debris raining down from above, suggesting that that item was freed and fell earlier than all debris above it.

Fires burn up, but they also burn down albeit much more slowly. A fire that starts deep in an engine room burning upward behaves differently from one that starts on a flying bridge and burns down. In both cases the layering will be different based upon that which burns first.

Layering is more important from the standpoint of obtaining evidence without damaging it. An example would be a fire that started in an electric service outlet. The box, assuming that it's metal, will likely go free of whatever it's attached to; if plastic will be consumed. The connector is part plastic, which will burn away, with brass or plated steel parts that may go adrift. Short circuiting within the component will probably result in melted metal due to arcing. These parts may scatter, so it will be necessary to sift through the debris to find them. The depth to which the part is buried may or may not be important.

Excavating and Sifting Debris

Excavating and sifting is a technique that is used when the cause proves not easy to find. It's often the technique of last resort, for it means that we've reached the point of looking at little pieces. Even for easier jobs, once the origin is pinpointed it is often necessary to sift through the debris in the immediate area for clues. It is also necessary to give consideration at this point to a photography plan, making sure that if there is a pattern, we will be able to reveal that pattern and record it with photos. In the case of the burned extension cord, that wasn't easy because the burned cord occupied a large area that had to be completely clear. How we handle this depends mainly on how much room we have to work with and how much excavation is required. If there is sufficient room, one can work by moving debris from one side to another after clearing an initial area.

One of the first things to be done is to locate and secure the main electric panel and branch panels, if any. Make sure that none of the breaker toggles get moved. Photograph the panel immediately just in case any breakers should suddenly trip. Determine whether any switch position has been disturbed, either though debris shifting or by fire fighters. This can usually be ascertained by whether any of the smoke or char has been disturbed since the fire. In less damaging fires one may even find finger prints on a smoked up panel, indicating that someone has touched it. If so, then the breaker and switch positioning cannot be considered reliable.

If the area to be excavated is not too large, sifting may not be necessary and can be culled through by hand. But when it is large, it is easier to use a shovel and sifting frame covered with chicken wire. The procedure is much the same as an archeological dig where it is necessary to note the area from which the debris came. While I do not use a formal grid, I do make a quick grid sketch on paper and X it off from square to square as I go through the area. This procedure must always be used when searching for small parts such as remnants of electronics. Sifting separates the larger from smaller, and lighter from heavier particles, which are then separated, set aside, and gone through by hand picking. How you handle it depends on what you're looking for.

There are certain areas where electronics will be concentrated, navigation, appliances, entertainment and so on and other areas where nothing is expected but, never-the-less, important clues may be found because something may have fallen and bounced or was deflected to a different area. The amount of interesting debris can be very large and there are endless reasons why things end up in unexpected places. Sifting is a fairly rapid process once the large pieces of debris are removed. A typical forty foot boat can usually be completely gone through in a day.

It is good, professional procedure to go about excavating and sifting debris in an organized fashion. My method is to use an 18" x 18" sifter with 1/4" heavy wire mesh of the type used for crab traps, and crush the wood and other charred debris through it into a tub. What remains in the sifter are hundreds of screws, hardware, bits of metal, glass and a myriad of other non-perishable-by-fire objects. Amongst this we search for clues, some of which may be arced and melted copper wire.

Electrical fires start extremely hot and when involving combustible materials such as plastic leave nothing of the original plastic behind, just the metal parts. Alloys of low melting point metals such as aluminum, brass, tin and zinc may melt partially or completely and can be found as puddles of metal. Copper, on the other hand, has a very high melting point so it is unlikely to melt except through electrical arcing, which is what we're looking for.

Carpeting

Carpet lays flat on decks and because fire burns up rapidly but down much more slowly, carpeting often does not burn or melt. This is because flat surfaces don't burn well; heat rises and at the bottom level there is a lesser supply of oxygen so carpeting does not burn well. It is normal to find carpet on decks that is only singed or melted on top and is covered with a layer of debris. If we lift it up we usually find the underside is mainly undamaged. For these reasons burn patterns on carpet often contains clues as to what happened.

Burn patterns in carpet often provide proof of arson because it reveals the burn pattern where a flammable liquid was splashed around. There have been a number of cases where overheated extension cords left a clear impression. Debris tends to heap up in certain areas depending on what is above the immediate area. Decisions need to be made as to whether to excavate a carpeted area completely so as to reveal all of the carpet. I've had numerous cases where the use of portable electric devices from heaters to battery chargers and electric tools with extension cords are responsible for fires.

In another case, steel and iron tools left scattered around an open hatch in a carpeted deck got so hot that they melted into the carpet, leaving a clear impression that someone was working on the boat before the fire. The tools didn't get there by falling down from above because they were at the bottom of the debris layers.

Those extension cords will probably be laying on deck or draped over furniture on the interior. If a circuit breaker fails to protect a circuit, those wires can get so hot as to melt through whatever supports them, thereby leaving clear evidence. Extensions may enter the vessel from dockside or originate on the vessel itself. In these cases it is necessary to perform complete excavation of the deck areas.

Stored Solvents and Fuel

Most boat owners are smart enough to not store containers of solvents on their boats; most but not all. Leaking containers and rusting cans of VOC's are a common cause of fires. From paint thinner to acetone to cans of gasoline for dinghy motors, containers of flammable and explosive fuels can leak all too easily. This leakage can happen due to rusting steel containers and due to rupture caused by high temperatures caused by sun radiation. Heated outboard motor tanks of gasoline are known to build up pressure, expand and discharge the expanding fuel.

Containers are likely to be stored in lazarettes, cockpit lockers and less frequently within the cabin area. Evidence of causation is often found in the form of a burn pattern that reflects either the presence of a burning, leaking fuel, a distorted steel container or a point of origin with no discernible cause. In the case of a fire in a lazarette, we start with the fact that normally there isn't anything in this area to cause fires, and even there is, all those flat fiberglass surfaces don't offer good ignition points. If a leaking flammable fluid did ignite, there should be a burn pattern that signals the event, especially if the inner surface is painted. In this instance, complete excavation of the hull bottom, along with cleaning, should reveal the evidence. The same principle applies to all other areas of the vessel where a leaking fluid reaches its lowest point as it runs downward from the point of origin, the leaking container. In some instances the remains of a melted plastic container may be found. In all such cases, samples can be taken for laboratory analysis to determine the presence of trace flammable liquids.

Electrical Fires

The only surprising thing about electrical fires on boats is that there aren't more of them. My three decades of surveying pleasure craft and the appalling number of jerry-rigged wiring jobs I have seen indicates that far too many boat owners have little respect for electricity. In this section I have included a number of photographs of such conditions just to illustrate that the fire investigator should expect just about anything.

The older a boat gets, and the more owners it has had, the greater the likelihood that it has major electrical faults caused by substandard and jerry-rigged wiring of both high and low voltage systems. It is equally remarkable that very few electrical errors are made by boat builders, and most of those that occur are accidental rather than caused by ignorance.

Fig. 8-12. The appearance of the above shore power connector might suggest that the fire started here. However, there are some obvious clues that it did not.

Fig. 8-13. below: A quick look at the back side shows that the plastic housing is still basically intact. Secondly, the degree of destruction around the area is not sufficiently great. The cockpit side coaming at upper right has only burned to the edge of this step down. Notice how difficult it is taking a good photo when everything is black, even with good light.

Unlike house and building fires, appliance failures are much less common in boats, most likely because boat appliances are so seldom used. By far the number one cause of boat fires are faults in the shore power connection on the boat. The following is a list of common electrical faults that cause fires:

Shorepower Connection (by far # 1 cause)

High resistance wire connections

Improper wire splices/connections

Staples or screws through wiring

Exposed conductors, terminals

Engine starting circuits - solenoid failure

Battery cable arcing

Electric motor lock up

Failures in bow thruster circuits

Main circuit board fault

Circuit breaker failure

Transmission overheat

Ferroresonant battery charger fire

Transformer overheat due to low voltage

In the past, fires were occasionally caused by low voltage in the dockside system caused by the voltage drop occurring in excessively long wire runs. Low voltage to electric motors causes them to work harder, generating more heat. This problem is now rare because most marinas now use transformers to maintain voltage over long distances.

One of the very first things that needs to be done with all fire investigations is to locate the main circuit panel and insure that whatever remains of it does not get disturbed. Circuit breakers are made of a fire retardant plastic often survive the fire in their original form. Even if the plastic has burned, it can often be determined whether the breaker was in the ON or OFF position. This information will be exceeding important to the remainder of the investigation.

The Chicken or the Egg?

One of the more difficult aspects to deal with is the issue of secondary short circuiting. This happens because the fire burns the insulation from conductors which then short against themselves or other metal objects. How does one know whether a short circuit started the fire or occurred after it started? The answer is that this is the investigator's art, his job to make that determination. Unfortunately, there are no clear-cut answers since every situation is different; it's mainly a matter of extrapolation from whatever evidence we can glean, and certainly the condition of the circuit breakers will be a major factor. It is important at the outset, for both AC and DC systems, to make a determination early on as to whether substantial secondary arcing has occurred. The key indicator will be when there is more than one breaker that is tripped. Find out if the owner is in the habit of keeping breakers turned off.

A burnt panel that remains more or less intact is very delicate because the burnt plastic, when disturbed, will tend to crumble. After locating and excavating the panel with great care, before touching it carefully photograph it from a number of angles since taking pictures of blackened debris is not easy and those multiple angles are needed in order to capture detail. Our primary interest at this point is the determination of the position of the switching and circuit breakers.

At this point the panel is left where it is since it will likely be necessary to trace wiring.

Circuit Breakers

The function of circuit breakers is not widely understood; most people assume that they provide all means of electrical protection, but that is not the case. The only function that a circuit breaker provides is that of *over-current protection*. Circuit breakers cut off the power supply when the rated capacity of the breaker in amperes is exceeded. They do not protect against low voltage and electrical faults unless the fault results in an increased flow in excess of the breaker's rating. That would exclude all high resistance conditions that result in circuit overheating and arcing, that instead of increasing the flow, actually reduce it and therefore the circuit breaker provides *no protection* for this condition.

Over current in a wire causes uniform heating of that conductor, assuming that the wire is in no way impaired. The only way that localized or point heating could occur is if a condition exists that would cause high resistance which causes heating at the point at which the resistance occurs and for this reason arcing and heating at loose or corroded connection will not trip a breaker or blow a fuse.

In a more perfect world, circuit breakers and other forms of circuit protection would never fail, but for a variety of reasons they do. Circuit breakers can become corroded and refuse to function. People foolishly subvert circuit protection in various ways, installing equipment without circuit protection; circuit protection rating is frequently improperly matched to the potential load. Circuit protection, particularly fuses, will not function properly when the size and distance of wiring is not correctly determined.

Circuit breakers also only protect the circuit downstream of the breaker. A boat's main high voltage circuit breaker does not protect the shore power cord and connections; unfortunately, the boat has to rely on the often questionable condition of the dock circuit breaker to perform that function.

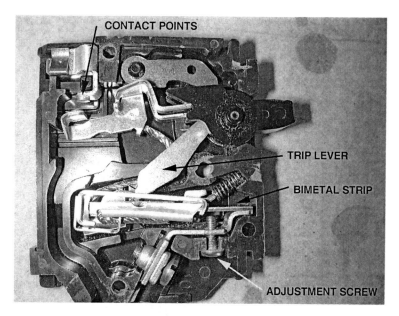

Fig. 8-14. Thermal Circuit Breaker

There are a large variety of different types of circuit breakers and fusing devices in existence but only a few are ordinarily found on boats. The primary fusing on both AC and DC systems will use Molded Case Circuit Breakers, referred to as MCCB's, Combined Switch Breakers that are intended to be used as on/off switches as well, and self-resetting types - usually the push button variety. Other means of protection are fuses and fusible links.

The three types of circuit breakers commonly found on boats are the plain thermal and magnetically controlled breakers plus the combination thermo-magnetic type. The later type combines the virtues of both basic types, fast response to over current and temperature. Thermo-magnetic breakers are considerably more expensive and are not often found on ordinary boats, but are commonly found on larger yachts where cost is less of a concern. Thermal breakers are typically of a bimetal type which uses strips of different metals clad together. Since these different metals react to heat differently and have a different expansion rate, the strip will bend when heated, the idea being that this will cause the spring loaded mechanism to trip. There are several obvious shortcomings of this type, one being that the ambient temperature can seriously affect the trip temperature, often resulting in nuisance tripping. Higher quality breakers have built-in compensators for this, whereas cheaper breakers do not. The second problem is that the life span of this type is in proportion to the number of times the breaker is tripped since the bimetal strip will eventually become permanently weakened and distorted and then fails to close, i.e., remains in the tripped position. Of course nuisance tripping is not a fire hazard, but some of the things people do to stop it are.

Nuisance tripping is also caused by high power equipment such as air conditioners where the start up amperage can be as high as 500% of running amps, but more usually on the order of 150% to 200%. To overcome this problem, circuit breakers are designed with a brief tripping delay. The inherent danger in this comes from the greater degree of arcing that will occur in a high resistance connection when the current flow is briefly doubled.

The number one cause of circuit breaker failure to open on boats is water and resultant corrosion. Whether a breaker is thermal or magnetic, it is predominately a mechanical device with a number of working parts and springs. These parts are mostly plated steel so that if water gets inside them the result is predictable. Contact points can fuse closed, springs stick, parts corrode and refuse to move or break apart and jam the mechanism. And because boats typically have a lot of breakers, there is motivation for builders to cut cost by buying the lowest cost breakers.

Forensic electrical engineers warn that there are huge numbers of electrical systems that are improperly designed. The primary reason for this stems from nuisance tripping of breakers resulting from failure of how to design a system that is not subject to nuisance tripping which occurs either because of ambient temperature-related problems and/or lack of understanding of the performance of the devices on the circuit. Rather than properly resolving the problem, the proverbial penny in the fuse holder for circuit breakers is simply increasing the rating of the breaker and thereby create a danger. Boats are particularly prone to nuisance tripping due to the common problem of damaged dockside systems. Shore side receptacles are, more often than not, in poor condition and never get serviced until complete failure occurs. If we go down the dock at any marina looking at all the outlets, we're likely to find numerous outlets that are blackened by electrical arcing, a clear indication that something is wrong. High resistance at a dock connection likely means a low voltage or amperage condition on the vessel that can cause an over-current condition that the breaker senses and trips. The boat owner, frustrated by this, attempts to resolve the problem by upping the breaker rating by another five or ten amps.

As systems on boats become increasingly complex, and the resultant power demands ever higher, so does the requirement of providing adequate circuit protection. While the marine investigator isn't necessarily expected to understand these technicalities, he does need to know how to recognize when such problems may exist.

Circuit breaker failures are usually not obvious because as installed in the panel, the backside is concealed. Whenever an electrical fault is found that caused arcing that is the suspected cause, the breaker should be pulled and inspected. Most MCCB's consist of two halves of molded plastic held together by rivets. They are made of high temperature plastic that will usually survive a fire at least to some degree. This type of breaker can be opened up by drilling out the rivets. Those that are glued together have to be carefully cut apart with a saw. An examination of the internal workings may reveal whether there was a breaker failure and the cause of it. Look for fused together contacts, evidence of corrosion and broken parts. The extremely high temperature of the fire may have caused damage to internal parts, so it will be necessary to try to sort this out. Certainly bimetal sensor strips are likely to show permanent distortion of the strip, so its condition will be inconclusive unless supported by other evidence. Residual corrosion is usually the deciding factor.

A final and very common mistake that electricians and others make is to wire in multiple devices on single circuits. Some seem to think that a 20 amp circuit breaker is capable of protecting multiple devices up to a twenty amp draw. A 20 amp breaker isn't likely to protect a circuit with a 7 amp device.

Engine Starting Circuits

It was not until around the mid 1980's that we began to see some type of circuit protection on engine starting circuits. Obviously, providing circuit protection to the starter motor positive cable is not practical because of the sudden, high amperage current. But fires caused by a fault within this line are not common, the more common cause being a fault that causes either the solenoid or bendix gear to remain engaged. Solenoids are risky because of their susceptibility to corrosion and heat distortion. Therefore, by fusing the solenoid, a much higher degree of protection is provided to the starting circuit. Both fusible links and circuit breakers are commonly used, but because these circuits and batteries are usually located deep in the bilge and near shaft glands, corrosion is a continual problem.

Typically starting circuit breakers are steel bodied and when they corrode they can go adrift or fall apart, creating the potential for a short circuit, as can the solenoids themselves. Check all electrical circuits and contact points for evidence of arcing.

Battery chargers are dual voltage and high amperage devices, typically delivering anywhere from 20 to 50 amps DC, rendering them vulnerable particularly because they are so often exposed to sea water. Despite the fact that chargers typically have double circuit protection, severe corrosion can defeat both sets of circuit protection. The battery charger should be considered highly suspect in any major boat fire.

Electric Bow Thrusters

High amperage draw electric motors provide lots of risk of electrical fires since these units are located deep in the bilge below the water line and in a wet environment. The idea of using an electric motor for this application is a bad idea and the number of fires that have resulted proves the point.

Some of this risk has been reduced by running these motors from a separate set of batteries located nearby, eliminating long runs of heavy cable. The shorter the run of cable between breaker and motor and batteries, the more likely a breaker will sense overheating in a cable. A big motor protected by a 20 or 30 amp breaker poses the problem that fire starting ground faults that are well below the circuit breaker rating. A fifteen amp short circuit is more than capable of starting a fire but will not trip the breaker.

Low level arcing in the corroded connection of a high amperage cable can generate tremendous amounts of heat, as can mere high resistance. Because of this, high amperage cable arcing is far more likely to start a fire than lower amperage. Then there are the usual problems associated with solenoid failures, the same as with main engine starting circuits. Magnetic solenoids are made of steel which is subject to rusting, causing the solenoid to hang up. To prevent this, the solenoid itself must be fused close to the solenoid.

Electrical Arcing

Electrical arcing occurs when the normal flow of current jumps across a break in the metal to metal contact in a circuit such as a loose or corroded connection. Unless of very high amperage (20 amps or more), 12VDC arcing itself is unlikely to start a fire, but the potential increases as voltage rises. The increased resistance causes the generation of heat. If the resistance is very high, the conductor will get hot enough to melt, even burn, the insulation. At this point a direct short may occur should the wire come in contact with a ground.

Electrical arcing in high voltage circuits becomes hot enough to melt metals at the contact point so that arcing is likely to destroy the contact point and circuit continuity. But before this happens it usually sets the insulation and surrounding combustibles afire, or creates a short circuit. Note that plastic wire insulation is only fire resistant, not fire proof. The common rating is to 105°C which is only 221°F. While it is self-extinguishing, it will continue to burn as long as the ignition temperature is maintained.

A direct short circuit (unrestricted amperage) in a 12VDC wire will almost instantaneously raise the conductor temperature to several thousand degrees (copper melts at 1981°F), depending on the amount of metal to metal contact. The insulation will instantly melt and combust with a high probability of creating more ground faults. This is a situation that is often found when unfused leads are taken directly off of batteries or a lead is taken off the main panel buss with no branch circuit breaker.

Wiring in boats is required to be the flexible, stranded type because solid wire is not flexible and poses grave problems with connectors and terminals going loose, plus breakage caused vibration and fatigue. Occasionally solid cable is encountered when after market alterations or additions are made. Any time solid conductors are found on a boat they should be highly suspect.

High resistance overheating commonly occurs with a smaller wire joined to a larger wire and in conjunction with a high resistance connection in the smaller wire. Large wire/small wire joins usually will not heat up enough to cause a fire unless the former situation exists or this is a very high amperage circuit. But it's a very different situation when we're dealing with high voltage since the total power flow is so much higher and the margins for error much less. Even minor corrosion on a high voltage connection is potential trouble, but when combined with an undersized wire, the result is usually a fire or major ground fault.

Thus we can see that fires can start at electrical connections for two reasons, (1) reduced surface-to-surface contact causing overheating, or (2) that corrosion prevents surface contact altogether can cause arcing or, as often happens, both conditions exist simultaneously in which case major arcing occurs.

It is widely believed that conventional thermo-magnetic circuit breakers should protect against this eventuality, but the fact is that the purpose of circuit breakers is to protect against over current, that is, protecting against more current flowing through a conductor than it is intended to handle. Over current in a wire causes it to heat up and melts the insulation. That same over current heats up the bimetal element that trips the breaker. Unfortunately, low level arcing can take place well below the threshold point of where a breaker would trip.

Electrical arcing and ground faults are the primary reasons for sifting debris since trace evidence of that arcing may be found in any type of electrical device. Some of the more common faults that cause arcing and ground faults are:

> Corroded connections at shore power receptacle (#1 cause)
>
> Staples and screws driven through wiring
>
> Chaffing caused by inadequate securing of wires
>
> Wires pass through holes in metal frames with sharp edges
>
> Spade connectors become loose
>
> Wire nut connections come loose
>
> Wire nuts fill full of water and corrode
>
> Butt connectors trap water and corrode
>
> Unsecured wires with splices laying on metal chassis especially air conditioners
>
> Wiring in contact with hot engine parts
>
> Short circuiting across gang connectors
>
> High resistance across splices due to corrosion
>
> Electrical tape used to make splices in hot machinery spaces
>
> No ground or bond on electrical chassis

It should be noted that the majority of these common causes can occur just about anywhere in the boat. However, in terms of frequency, DC arcing is far less a factor than AC arcing except in high amperage circuits.

These pages contain photos of dangerous electrical conditions, presented here to illustrate the wide variety of ways that electrical fires can occur, and the difficulty of discovering such elusive causes.

Fig. 8-15. A water leak onto this steel circuit breaker box has rendered the circuit breaker inoperative as the rust scale has jammed it. The circuit is a windlass that now has no protection.

Fig. 8-16. Electric shore power cable retractor twists 250VAC cable, tearing the connections out of main panel.

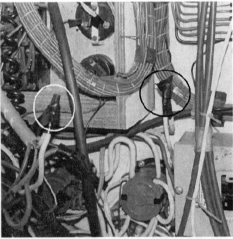

Fig. 8-18. The backside of this panel revealed amateur high voltage wiring containing two taped high voltage wire connections. Note that tape is going loose.

Fig. 8-17. A deck leak onto the circuit box of this 50 amp windlass also caused the breaker to fail.

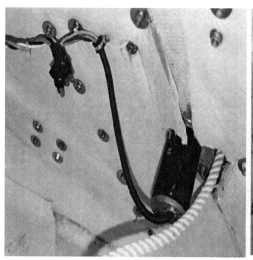

Fig. 8-19. Anchor windlass connected with wire nuts and electrical tape. Underside of deck is upholstered with foam and vinyl.

Fig. 8-20. Amateur installation of battery and inverter system in an unventilated compartment within living spaces. A multiple outlet extension cord is used for high voltage distribution. Hydrogen gassing from batteries is likely to damage these components.

Fig. 8-21. The engine starting circuits for this boat are attached to the side of battery box and are only one inch above the water-flooded deck. Behind these cables are two push button type 40 amp steel circuit breakers that are completely destroyed by corrosion.

Fig. 8-22. Years worth of jerry-rigged wiring and substandard splices are directly in contact with leaking fuel valves.

Fig. 8-23. A close look at this shore power receptacle provides an easy clue as to the probable cause of this fire. Note the water line and corrosion inside the cover, revealing that it had been filled with water.

Shore Power Connections

Corroded and damaged connectors are the most common cause of boat fires. Shore power cable male ends along with the female receptors deteriorate over time for several reasons. One is the arcing that occurs when they are disconnected with current flowing. Corrosion in sea water environments are the other. Both these conditions degrade the surface mating area and result in high resistance and/or arcing. Shore cables are rated at either 30A, 50A and 100A with each having a different type of connector so that a 30A cable can't be plugged into a 50A receptacle. Yet with even a 30A cord with the dock fused at 30A, the amount of current is easily sufficient to heat up a high resistance connection to the point of starting a fire.

Unfortunately, resistance heating is not protected by circuit breakers because the heating is localized at the connection; thus, neither the shore breaker nor boat breakers are of any help. Recovery of the shore cable and boat receptacle is critical in all cases, but when connected to dock power after the fire, fire fighters aren't likely to be considerate of destroying evidence. Usually they just tear the remains free and where the metal parts end up is anyone's guess. Sifting the debris is necessary to attempt to find the surviving parts. If we're lucky, they're still clinging to the wire ends.

Also check the shore cable ends for evidence of having been stressed such as the cable being too short or having been pulled for any reason. The plastic twist-lock end will, of course, burn away on 30A cords but 50A cords have a metal sleeve that may be damaged or distorted by mechanical stress. Alternately, the connector tangs may all be bent in the same direction. If they are, place the tangs in their normal position to establish whether the cable had been stressed in one direction.

Electric Motor Fires

Neither AC or DC motor fires are common unless in conjunction with circuit breaker or solenoid failure, by reason that internal shorts result in such high ampacity of the circuit which then exceeds the circuit breaker rating. If it doesn't blow the branch circuit line it will probably blow the main. Motors seized up by corrosion are common and are quite capable of starting fires if the circuit breaker fails. Fortunately, circuit breaker failure is also rare.

Faulty Electrical Devices

Cheap foreign made electrical control devices such as switches and circuit breakers are now flooding the country. The author's experience with the frequent malfunction of these things in consumer products has led him to collect, examine and test a number of these devices, with the conclusion that many of them are poorly designed and faulty manufactured. There are also increasing reports of such products from China and other Asian countries that bear false certification and approval labels such as *CE* and UL. That such devices finding their way onto boats can be expected to cause an increasing number of fires.

Faulty switches and improperly designed switches are a potential cause of fires. The switches themselves don't cause fires, mainly because most switches only have positive wire connections and no grounds, so there is little potential for a ground fault. However, should a switch that controls a motor stick in the ON position, the danger becomes obvious. The most common faults are switch terminals that are too close together so that if they get bent (a distinct possibility on a boat) they may come in contact with each other, permanently closing the circuit. Turning the switch off will have no effect.

Other troublesome switches are cheap cam action switches that rely on the spring tension of metal contact levers. Actuating the switch moves a cam that straightens the tensioned contact level, completing the circuit. This unidentified switch was found in a bench grinder in the engine room of a boat. The captain stated that after purchasing the machine, it never worked. Planning to return the grinder to the retailer in the near future, a fire occurred in the engine room several days later. The cause was traced to the sliding contact lever in the switch that had gone adrift, causing the motor to inadvertently start up and run for an unknown period of time, perhaps as much as 48 hours. The Motor was not designed for continuous operation, overheated and set a cardboard box on fire.

Cheaply made push button circuit breakers pose an even greater danger. Figure 8-24 on next page is such a breaker which was dismantled for evaluation. It is a bi metal thermal type controlled by a tiny copper spring; the device is in no way water resistant, and yet was installed in an instrument panel in the horizontal position. The contact points are held in place by spring pressure of the tensioned bi metal element. The spring wire is a mere 0.012" so that sea water corrosion could easily dissolve it. This spring, which didn't even exert one ounce of pressure is supposed to actuate the push button

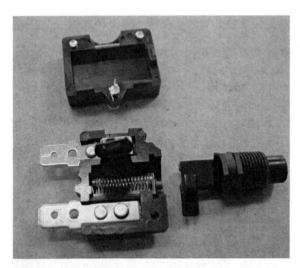

Fig. 8-24. Typical circuit breaker found on helm panel isn't water proof and is easily damaged by water.

which has a thin plastic tab that slips between the contact points to open the circuit. The internal cavity is capable of filling up with water and the spring pressure is far too weak to overcome the effects of even mild corrosion. The end result is that the switch will turn ON but will not turn OFF.

Unapproved Electrical Devices Used on Boats

Few boat builders these days will resort to the use of unapproved electrical devices ranging from electrical equipment to circuitry components. Three features differentiate marine approved devices; (1) corrosion resistance, (2) ignition protection, and (3) shock load resistance. Ignition protection is most important on gas powered boats, while corrosion resistance and shock load resistance are important on all boats. Boats are subject to repetitive cycle shock loads or pounding, especially high speed power boats. And as boats keep going faster and faster, maintaining electrical system safety becomes increasingly difficult. Even so, electrical system failures are only a common cause of fires in proportion to the age of vessels.

Most unapproved electrical devices are added to a boat after purchase. Everything from toasters, coffee makers to garbage disposals and fans. Most of these devices have ungrounded, two wire cords. They are more of a shock hazard than a fire hazard. One of the more frequent causes of fires is the cheap electric fans made in Asia that are found on boats in large numbers and which either don't have UL approval or have a falsely acquired UL label, something that is all too common with cheap foreign imports. The fans almost never have ground fault bonds, are made with mainly steel components, with flammable plastic housings. When motor lock up occurs, overheating and a fire can start by ignition of the plastic or surrounding materials. The very low amperage draw of these small motors means that a severe ground fault is unlikely to trip the breaker before it starts a fire. Boat owners are known to turn these fans on in a futile effort to reduce mildew and leave them running for long periods of time unattended.

Fig. 8-25. In a fire believed to be caused by a multiple outlet "power strip", a copy of the destroyed device was obtained, dismantled and examined. What was found that the positive and negative terminals were within 1/8" of each other and that any heavy shock load could have caused the terminals to contact each other. The self-contained circuit breaker did not function when a direct short ignited the plastic case which is highly flammable.

If the fan is mostly plastic, all that will remain will be the wires and the small motor so that only sifting the debris will likely find it. However, either the wires or the motor are likely to reveal whether there is a fault in any of these components. Therefore, when combing through the debris, all remains of appliances and unidentified electrical devices should be set aside for further study.

Faulty cheap electrical devices are also frequently found in the form of cheap accent lighting such as fluorescent lights with solid strand wiring and all steel components and other decorative lighting, most of which was never intended to be used in vessels. The author has had two cases of fires being started by wires cutting on razor sharp edges of steel lighting fixtures because the internal wiring of these fixtures is not secured.

It should be noted that the larger the yacht, the greater is the potential or likelihood that non marine approved devices are used for interior decoration and the like. Things we might never think of such as 120VAC electric devices to raise and lower hidden television sets, electric door openers, drapery and blind opener drives and a nearly endless array of possibilities. Or how about the indoor spa with non marine pumps installed in the bilge? Who would ever guess that an owner-hired contractor installed a 24/7 electronic surveillance camera would set the yacht on fire, yet one of these did just that. The small drive motor was not weather proof, was wired into a 30 amp circuit and seized up and started the fire.

Multiple Outlet Extensions

Extension cords are a common cause of fires usually by virtue of low level arcing, high resistance heating at connections, and underside wiring relative to size of the source circuit such as an 18 AWG cord on a 15 or 20 amp circuit. Household type extensions (cheap 2-wire) usually carry the warning that they should not be used when frequent flexing occurs. This type usually becomes brittle with age. Many of these cheap wiring devices are foreign made and fail to meet standards and are found to have low melting point flammable insulation and undersize wire.

Cheap foreign made "power strips" have been found with very bad design and substandard materials. In the case of one fire, the positive and neutral terminal strips were less than 1/8" apart so that any distortion of the plastic housing could cause a direct short. In addition, the plastic housing was not high temperature, self-extinguishing plastic and burned readily when tested. It was equipped with a switch and circuit breaker of dubious quality. An exact copy of the burned up power strip was purchased at a drug store for $10.00, thus the cost of the circuit breaker and switch had to have been less than $1.00.

Owner Installed Inverters

Inverters have gained increased popularity and such systems are often owner installed with all that that implies. From the numerous such systems that the author has seen, it's fair to say that at least half of them have major faults from batteries installed in unventilated compartments, no primary circuit protection on the DC side and extension cords used instead of dedicated circuits with the only AC side circuit protection on the inverter itself.

A typical example is a sail boat with four 6V batteries plus an inverter installed beneath an interior seat absent any ventilation and no circuit protection beyond the branch breaker powering the inverter.

Flammable Plastic Conduit

There is a type of ribbed plastic conduit, black in color and split lengthwise so that is really chaff protection, that is highly flammable and should have been banned long ago. The ribbing of this material facilitates its rapid burning so that it actually acts like a fuse when ignited and will spread a fire that otherwise might not spread. See Figure 8-26 on opposite page.

Examining the Electrical System

With a boat that is totally burned down all that is left is a heap of rubble. The prospect of finding the cause seems remote. Since most fires involve smaller boats, the prospect may not be as difficult as it might seem. The fact is that most of the electrical system survives to a considerable degree. Most of the wiring will remain, absent insulation, and in a tangled mass. Everything burnable is gone yet most of the metals remain but tangled up with a mass of glass fibers. If we need to get into the electrical system in detail, it becomes necessary to separate the wheat from the chaff, so to speak. Once the glass fabric is gotten out of the way, the remains of the electrical system are actually easier to access in most cases than before the fire, though the current condition of it is

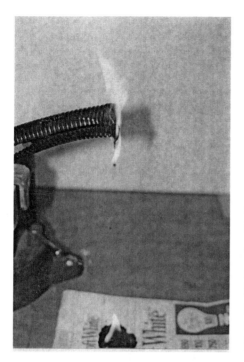

Fig. 8-26. Black ribbed plastic conduit commonly used on boats burns fiercely when ignited and behaves like a gunpowder fuse, rapidly spreading fires. Notice flaming drips of melted plastic.

not exactly favorable. Even so, it is easier to search for ground faults and arcing.

The type of wiring rated for marine use has a thermal rating of 105C or 221F before the insulation begins to melt. Thus, in most boat fires there is nothing of the insulation left unless the fire was extinguished early, which is rare.

Heat and chemicals generated during the fire can cause stranded copper wire to begin to disintegrate. This is distinct from melting as the wire will be found to crumble when bent but short circuiting and arcing evidence will remain obvious in the form of beading, and this is what we are looking for. And since wiring tends to be run in multiples, the prospect of examining it goes fairly rapidly. Copper wire often gets hot enough to just begin to melt, but not completely. The result is that stranded wire strands lightly fuse together and make the wire very stiff. When bent it will often just break or crumble. This condition will exist throughout substantial lengths of wire. Conversely, a dead short can also heat wire up to the melting point. This is distinguishable by only a single wire in group that shows signs of melting, combined with the fact that at the shorted point the wire has become beaded at the break. The remainder of the wire, upstream of the power source, if it can be found, will not have these characteristics.

Items of electrical equipment tend to be concentrated at load centers, control stations, galley, heads and similar groupings. Larger yachts will have a scheme of 120VAC service outlets, grouping of switches such as in galley, heads — all of which makes it a bit easier to examine it all. These points are identified by the wire runs that lead to them. Depending on circumstances, it's a good idea to try to sift the debris at deck level in these areas.

The Only Cause

One of the larger problems that we have with fire investigations is not finding a probable cause, but one of proving that it is the only cause. Conclusions of cause of

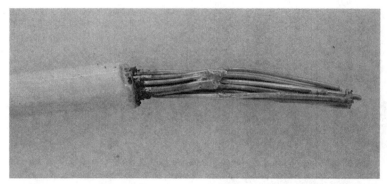

Fig. 8-27. This is the typical degree of melting that occurs when a 12 volt circuit shorts to ground.; a 120 VAC circuit will burn away completely.

a fire are easier to attack because it is very difficult to eliminate all other possibilities, because it is difficult to determine, yet alone account for, all possibilities. With fires, the possibilities are endless, whereas with a sinking much more limited. It is therefore a matter of greatest importance to try to account for as many of the major possibilities as possible. When challenged, it's nice to be able recite a long list of everything that was examined and considered. When we cover the major points of the major systems, this will usually be sufficient to overcome any attempt to discredit.

Melted Conductors: The Chicken or the Egg?

One of the more difficult and frustrating aspects of electrical fire investigations is the determination of what happened first. The question arises because, as a boat burns, normally at least some part of the electrical system is energized, if not all of it. Then there is the matter of both AC and DC systems. As the wiring insulation and other components burn, electrical conductors become exposed and some of these may short out, leaving what might best be described as false evidence.

A good example of this is wires in a bundle where the insulation burns away. If a hot wire contacts a ground, the result is inevitable and obvious. Direct short circuiting of hot wires typically creates arcing that is so hot that it melts the copper. The melted wire ends become molten, causing a bead of copper to appear on the ends that is very distinguishable. Higher amperage 12 volt arcing is typically accompanied by splattering of the molten metal (**Fig. 8-27**). Beaded or balled copper conductors are not *prima facie* evidence of the cause. When this evidence is found, it becomes necessary to determine whether the fire caused the arcing or the arcing caused the fire.

Copper wire can melt from the heat of the fire though this is not normal because most fire temperatures are below the melting point of copper. Yet localized hotter spots can occur but fortunately it is usually possible to differentiate between melting caused by an arc and that caused by general heating. Localized melting occurs over a longer length of the wire than does arcing. Globules occur when heating happens over a larger area; globules tend to be flat and irregularly shaped, whereas when beading occurs, the bead

Fig. 8-28. Close up of a Leviton 125 V. receptacle showing how the push-in connection relies on a single spring-tab. Notice how the multistranded wire has slipped off to the side so that only a few strands of the wire are engaged. The same can happen to solid wire, which is not permitted on boats. The device is labeled "SOLID WIRE ONLY".

will have a sharp definition point; the transition from unmelted to melted whereas local melting has a gradual transition. Further, since wire is extruded, it has die marks on it much the same as bullet rifling so that it is possible through microscopic inspection to determine approximately how hot it got. A metallurgist can make these distinctions through microscopic analysis.

Service Outlets & Switches

Loose connection arcing tends to be very distinctive in the form of ragged pitting and melting, sometimes with metal splatter apparent. With this condition it is best to attempt to find both parts of the connection — wire and terminal, both parts of a receptacle, etc. This is particularly important where "push-in" connections on service outlets are suspected. Push in connections should never be used on boats because of the vibration and pounding forces of boats can easily loosen them. The author has actually witnessed a service outlet failure with push in connections while underway in a boat. In this case the metal barb that grabs the wire within the push in socket arcs and melts or burns away, allowing the captive wire to go free and cause a direct ground fault. This then set the surrounding wood paneling afire. Dissection of the badly burned service outlet clearly revealed the melted retainer barbs.

In the above instance the vessel was underway with the generator running. An icemaker was plugged into a service outlet when this fire occurred. The obvious question was why

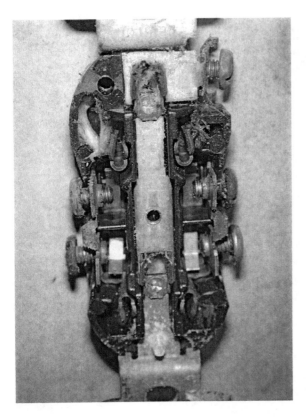

Fig. 8-29. Most of the metal components of a standard service outlet are steel with the exception of the two terminal strips. Even the screws are steel and subject to rusting. This one, located in a cockpit, had three insect nests in it which, when wetted, caused a short. View is from backside.

didn't the circuit breaker trip? The answer was that the ampacity of the short was below the threshold of the breaker. The fire was actually started by up to 30 minutes of arcing which set the plywood into which the receptacle and box was mounted afire *before* the wire went completely adrift. In this case it was easy to determine the sequence of events because the fire was promptly extinguished, and because I happened to be sitting in a chair and observed it happening.

All boats that have 115VAC service outlets are residential grade only as there are no known "marine" grade devices. The vast majority of these will have push in wire sockets. In addition, some of the metal parts are brass and others are steel, the later of which includes the terminal screws (plated) and grounding frame. Figure 8-28 on previous page shows why push-in sockets are dangerous in boats: the wire can easily slip away from being held by the barb. Additionally, push-in sockets are only supposed to be used with solid and not stranded wire but sometimes this is ignored. Moreover, the conductor strips are positioned about 1/8" away from the steel chassis or frame. A few drops of saltwater inside can easily create a ground fault. As for the wire barb, this is an unreliable design at best, but the plated steel connector screws pose a serious hazard when water rusts the steel and creates a very high resistance connection.

All of the plastic junction boxes and outlets that we tested when heated with a blow torch proved to be self-extinguishing when the flame was removed; they did not burn readily and thus it is unlikely that an outlet itself will be the ignition source. However, plastic wiring insulation burns much more readily and is not self-extinguishing . Service boxes will contain heat causing higher than normal temperatures.

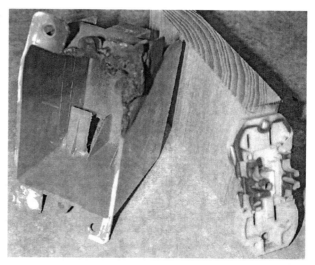

Fig. 8-30. Plastic receptacles and boxes are usually made of self-extinguishing plastic as this shorted out receptacle indicates. While this was a serious short, it did not cause a fire because there were no nearby combustibles.

The response time of circuit breakers may be too slow to prevent major short circuiting from melting conductors. In other cases the ampacity of the short may be below the threshold of the breaker, yet when arcing of any degree occurs this is very unlikely to trip the breaker.

When the point of origin appears to be a service outlet, check for the following:

1. Wire is misaligned with push in barb - look for arcing on the edges of the contacts

2. Socket barb is broken off or bent.

3. Wire came loose from attachment screw; look for arcing around terminal screws

4. Water damage and insect debris

5. Service outlet box mounting tabs broke due to fatigue.

6. Remnants of highly flammable ribbed plastic conduit that is often used in boats.

It should be the goal of the investigator to go over as much of the wiring as possible, searching for short circuits which are more or less obvious, but tedious to find. When found, mark these points with tape and when finished the short circuits will be numerous or not, and may or may not reveal a pattern. We then compare this evidence with the position of the circuit breakers in an effort to understand what went on with the electrical system. The objective is simply to determine whether whatever short circuiting evidence we find happened before or after the fact, whether it was cause or effect and thus have some basis for establishing inclusionary or exclusionary evidence.

For example, the interpretation of whether only one short circuit or extensive short circuiting is found will be dramatically different. If only one or a few are found, these can be fairly quickly evaluated as to whether one or more is the cause. Whereas massive short circuiting will suggest that something is wrong with the basic design of the system circuit protection. Experience indicates that massive short circuiting occurs more often in older boats where corrosion in circuits impedes the functioning of breakers and fuses.

When short circuiting is the result rather than the cause of the fire, this often occurs in massed wire bundles where the situation is readily identifiable. Wires in boats don't normally chaff against each other sufficient to cause damage to the insulation, especially in bundles or conduits. On the other hand, wire insulation more often becomes damaged where it passes through objects with sharp edges or is generally harder than the insulation itself. It's not unusual to find wires pinched between structures.

High Resistance Heating

Overheating and melting of insulation due to high resistance is common but does not often start fires because this predominantly occurs in low voltage circuits that people treat more cavalierly than high voltage. High resistance connections cause only localized heating of the wire. Tests show that resistance heating unless extreme, is usually insufficient to ignite wire insulation. High resistance usually doesn't end up tripping the circuit breaker or fuse unless occurring very near the device. High resistance heating usually does not result in starting a fire because equipment failure usually occurs first, and because of a scarcity of easily ignitable materials.

One instance where resistance or overcurrent heating can cause a fire is when multi stranded wire connections are made without proper terminals. A typical example is when someone tries to connect a wire directly to a wing nut stud on a battery and only a few strands end up making contact, or it later comes partly loose. With the current flowing only through a few strands, those strands may suffer over current heating under a high amperage load. With low power DC equipment (under 10 amps) conductor overheating is very unlikely. In fact, a test performed by connecting a 5 amp bilge pump with but one strand of a #14 AWG wire produced no heating at all even with the pump under load.

With high amperage DC and even low amperage AC circuits, the story is altogether different. Remember Ohm's law, $P = I \times V$ where power in watts equals current in Amps x voltage in Volts and Watts is the measure of total electrical power or energy. Five amps at 115 volts (575 watts) is nearly ten times as powerful as 5 amps at 12 volts (60 watts) and will produce far greater heat when high resistance or arcing occurs. In the same experiment as above, when using 115 volts instead of 12 volts at 5 amps passing through a single strand resulted in the strand becoming instantly red hot.

Another common cause of electrical fires results from making high voltage wire connections by twisting two stranded wires together and wrapping with electrical tape.

All electrical tape is subject to the adhesive softening with an increase in temperature and going adrift. Fire tests of tape reveals that some are self-extinguishing while some burn readily. UL approved 3M tape is three times as costly as cheap unbranded tape. When the taped twisted wires loosen, arcing occurs causing localized heating with likely loss of insulation or ignition of the tape.

Explosions

Explosions on boats are fairly rare with the most common being the gasoline vapor explosion. Gas vapors can be very dense so that the resulting explosion is very hot, hot enough to start fires by the heat generated alone. Highly flammable materials such as paper, fabric and thin plastics near the vapor concentration point are prone to ignite. The majority of gasoline explosions result in fire due to the fact that leaking fuel is usually the source of the vapors. This ignites the leaking gas or gas residue and makes a fire all but inevitable.

The statement that liquid gasoline does not burn is basically just a technicality since gas vaporizes so rapidly, yet alone when heat is applied, that the end result is that it certainly appears to burn when, in reality it is the vaporized gas immediately above the liquid that is burning. On the other hand, diesel fuel oil cannot be ignited in liquid form and does not vaporize sufficiently at ambient temperatures that it cannot be ignited until it is heated to its vaporization temperature.

There have been many recorded instances where gas vapor explosions did not cause a fire, but these are a distinct minority. These are more likely the consequence of early ignition of a newly started leak that ignited before a significant accumulation of liquid gas or residue occurred, or a very slow leak. Gasoline explosions tend to produce more heat than outward explosive force. In this regard they are distinctive from LP gas explosions that are far more violent but produce less heat and are less prone to start fires depending on the state of the liquefied petroleum container. If that container is breached, a major conflagration will occur. If not no major fire may result. Therefore, a gasoline explosion is typified by only moderate blast damage but a roaring conflagration afterwards. In a few cases, only blast damage remains.

The fire resulting from explosive damage to fuel system components such as tanks, filters and fuel lines that result in escaping fuel is usually catastrophic, resulting in total destruction of the vessel. The fuel fed fire happens so fast that there is almost no chance of extinguishing the fire before it burns itself out. In this regard gasoline explosions are unique in appearance and timing. Since both gasoline vapor and liquid are heavier than air, the fire is usually rooted deep in the hull.

The majority of gasoline explosions result from leaking aluminum fuel tanks that leaked as a result of corrosion. Tank corrosion almost always occurs on the bottom side due to entrapment of water against the tank, the result of improper tank mounting.

A secondary cause of corrosion is galvanism wherein another metal is in contact with the tank. When explosions occur and the amount of fuel that leaked is substantial, the fuel tank bottoms should be inspected. Heavy corrosion pitting clues us into where that leak might be. Note that a leak on the bottom of the tank only needs an invisible pin hole due to the weight generated pressure of fuel within.

Battery Explosions

Lead-acid battery explosions are fairly common and are caused hydrogen buildup in cells that have lost electrolyte. These explosions do not normally cause fires and the damage is usually confined to the battery and plastic shrapnel damage. Substantial hydrogen generation in a small compartment can cause much more violent explosions. It so happened many years ago that I was in the engine room of a fairly large yacht when a battery explosion occurred. I had just finished checking a bank of four 8D batteries that were hot from overcharging and had moved away so that an engine was between myself and the batteries when it happened. The blast knocked me silly with an instantaneous flash that was very bright yet there was not enough heat to burn me, but I did get a piece of plastic shrapnel in my elbow. Pieces of plastic casing were imbedded in overheat insulation and the battery charger casing was deeply dented where a piece of shrapnel hit. Yet there was no sign of burning even near the batteries.

Batteries should not be installed within living quarters in places where there is inadequate ventilation as they often are in sail boats. The placement of batteries under berths and in small, unventilated compartments can result in hydrogen concentrations to the level of high explosiveness. Besides the explosive damage, the risk of fire is from damage to nearby electrical systems that short out. Thus, batteries that are found to be fragmented after a fire may have exploded.

Lithium battery explosions are now becoming so frequent that they are garnering quite a bit of attention, especially after my local fire chief and his assistant were seriously injured when their battery powered CPR device exploded while changing the battery, causing severe burns and blowing the two men over. This incident has been followed by many others, but the notable feature here is that not only do these small batteries explode with great force relative to their size, but the explosions are hot (up to 1800F) and can cause fires. The reason for these explosions, beyond lithium compounds being very dangerous stuff, is not known at this time.

This problem is likely to be short-lived as there are already efforts underway to redesign these batteries so as to prevent these unfortunate possibilities. In the meantime, lithium battery explosion fires remain a distinct possibility.

L-P Gas Explosions

These are even more rare than gasoline explosions, but are so violent that they are unmistakable. Pieces of the boat may be thrown hundreds of feet away, something that I've never seen with a gasoline explosion and only with L-P gas and water heater explosions. As mentioned earlier, whether a fire is started depends on the concentration of vapor and depending on what happens to the liquefied petroleum container. If it is ripped violently away from its moorings, the gas lines are likely to be severed, thereby ensuring a fire. The origin of this fire is likely to be localized near the tank or in the vicinity of the fuel distribution piping.

The vast majority of L-P systems are in sail boats that have poorly vented interior spaces, so it doesn't take much of a fuel leak to create explosive concentrations. If there is anything left of the wreck, the first indication is likely to be that the deck is separated from the hull.

L-P tanks are required, if contained within the hull, to be mounted in air tight compartments ventilated to the exterior because regulators vent to the atmosphere and will create a build up of vapor. This requirement is often not met by boat owners that retro fit their boats with L-P systems. L-P gas is lighter than air and disperses very rapidly and will turn the entire boat into a bomb, hence the tendency of the entire boat to blow apart.

If a fire ensues the chances of finding the cause declines dramatically as evidence of leaking system components is destroyed. Regulators are aluminum and promptly melt, flexible gas hose burns away and heat will destroy any chance of proving gas burner or valve leaks. Even so, evidence of damaged gas hose may remain so that care should be taken to protect and examine as much of the hose as possible. The most likely points for hose damage is in way of a gimbaled stove and near the tank. If a fire does not ensue then every aspect of the system is more or less available for evaluation. Suspected hose damage can be differentiated from fire damage by laboratory analysis.

Machinery Fires

Engine room fires that occur while the vessel is underway are ventilation fed fires. While we don't think of them as such, engines are great air pumps moving many hundreds and even several thousands of cubic feet of air per minute. Thus, these fires are fanned by vigorous air flow that readily vents fire inhibiting fire by-products. Once they start, they can quickly go out of control, hence the need for automatic fire extinguishing systems that we will consider a bit later on.

Propulsion and internal combustion engine related fires are most often caused by (1) exhaust system failure or design problems, (2) engine overheating and (3) combustible materials inadvertently coming in contract with hot engine components.

Prior to the advent of water cooled turbochargers, turbos were the number one cause of fires in diesel powered boats. Because non cooled turbos are no longer being made — since around 1985 — as a cause this only exists in older boats.

Fig. 8-31. Working in a burned engine room can be particularly tough as this melted mass of wires situated above an engine under a fixed deck. Since it was clear that the fire started in this area, part of the deck was carefully marked and cut out to expose the area of interest without damaging evidence.

But exhaust system started fires remain a frequent cause of fire due to failure to inspect and maintain many other engine exhaust system components that are not water cooled. This often includes a portion of the exhaust manifolding leading up to the turbocharger, as well as piping leading from it. Non water cooled exhaust system components must be adequately insulated both from the fire hazard and personal injury standpoint.

Exhaust Insulation

Beginning around 1990 we began to see a new form of exhaust insulation that utilized a high temperature plastic resin in conjunction with carbon or glass fiber. This type of insulation, called "hard wrap" by one of its inventors, has a great advantage over "blanket" type insulation wrapping which has a strong tendency to fragment and generally break down over time due to low frequency exhaust system vibration.

Propulsion engine exhaust can run up to 1400F, so hot that cast iron turbochargers will glow cherry red in a dark engine room. Just aft of the manifolds or risers, the exhaust pipe temperature typically runs around 1000F. Good insulation can bring that down to just a few hundred degrees, but as the insulation deteriorates it routinely rises to the range of 600F, the combustion temperature of many oils.

Blanket type insulation is usually wired in place with wire wrapped around metal hooks. Over time as the insulation is removed and replaced it typically becomes less well fitting and typically after about ten years it will be found to be quite loose, elongated rather like a rubber band hanging off a hook too long, and not tight at joints with large gaps. The danger here is to anything that inadvertently comes in contact not only with the exposed parts, but also with insulation that is radiating temperatures of around 600F. Of course, there is rarely much space between the engine and the deck above — and all the wiring and plumbing hanging off the underside of that decking. It often happens that the heat melts or otherwise loosens wire clips attached to the underside and in turn, this drops down onto the hot exhaust component, possibly starting an electrical fire when a short circuit occurs.

Deteriorated Exhaust Components

Since the major parts of marine exhaust piping are water cooled fiberglass on conventional inboard boats, exhaust piping fires almost never occur. The lone exception is the gas inboard or stern drive engine that utilizes a rubber type exhaust sleeve joining two other components together such as the riser and exhaust pipe.

Cast iron exhaust riser failures occur with great regularity. Corrosion scale, over time, blocks off the coolant water passages, thus restricting, or even completely blocking off, the cooling water. When this happens an exhaust system fire is almost inevitable. First, a hole is burned in the hose then, once the exhaust gases are escaping this usually sets the engine compartment on fire.

Since this type of fire occurs with the boat underway, most of the time the fire is detected and extinguished before the fire goes out of control. But not always, and when a boat is badly burned, if the exhaust hoses are also badly burned to the point where the source of the fire is not self-evident, one should remove the engine exhaust risers and check for blockage.

Gas powered boats all more or less have similar systems, but when it comes to diesel powered boats, systems vary widely and system failures occur for equally diverse reasons.

Oil or Fuel System Failures

One of the more difficult causes of fire to discover is when a pressurized oil or fuel line or hose ruptures or leaks. This can be a steel fuel oil line compression fitting failure, a corrosion hole or a failed hose that either directs a stream of oil onto a hot engine component such as an exhaust manifold. Lubricating oil does not combust until at least 600+F and fuel oil just slightly below that and by itself does not burn well. But the flash point of oils is much lower so that if the rupture results in a fine spray or vapor, hot engine components can easily ignite it.

Fire System Failures

It is not uncommon that automatic fire systems fail to extinguish or even suppress a fire. Engine room fires are particularly insidious and difficult to put out due to the ventilation situation and high temperatures created by a contained fire plus high ambient temperatures. System failures occur for many reasons, the more common of which are failure to maintain and improper installation.

There is a tendency for the ventilating systems of engine rooms to defeat oxygen reducing extinguishing agents including Halon, CO2 and the fluoroethanes, the so-called "clean agents". When engines are running, the air flow rate is likely so high as to render these systems ineffective. Therefore, for the systems to function, Halon and fluoroethanes require an automatic engine shut down system. CO will automatically stop engines due to instantaneous oxygen depravation and do not require a shut down system. The other types will not stop engines and therefore require a shut down system.

FE241 is a dangerous chemical named chlorotetrafluoroethane that should not be touched or breathed, a heavier than air gas that functions by reducing oxygen content in air. It is a severe health hazard so all precautions should be taken to ensure that an undischarged system does not accidentally discharge while investigating.

Halon is a chlorinated fluorocarbon (CFC) and is not toxic to humans but can cause suffocation and frostbite if a system is discharged in a confined space. Halon is no longer permitted to be manufactured but is permitted to remain in service. Existing systems can be recharged with recovered Halon. Safety measures need to be taken when working in a fire damaged confined space to prevent accidental discharge. In open spaces there is little risk.

All of the approved agents are very effective and will extinguish an oxygen-fed fire; these systems will not extinguish electrical arcing fires or prevent high temperature reignition as from red hot exhaust systems and other metals. They will not extinguish fires inside of exhaust hoses or fiberglass pipe or smoldering fires with a self-contained oxygen source such as balsa wood.

Since most automatic systems have manual modes activated by means of a pull cable, accidental discharge can occur by inadvertently pulling on the cable.

The majority of systems found in boats today are what we might call self-contained/portable. That is, they are easily removed and installed and not permanently fixed. Most are boat builder installed, but many are after market installations by boat owners or others, thus increasing the potential for improper installation. The primary reasons why systems fail are as follows:

Engine shut down system fails

System improperly installed

System capacity is undersize.

Failure to maintain

Engine shut down failure can result in fire suppression failure. A typical pair of 400 HP engines can move air as much as 2,000 cubic feet per minute and that rate is twice cubic air space that the system is likely designed to handle. Thus, running engines will evacuate the released agent to an ineffective concentration in a very short time.

Improper installation includes the system being inadequate for the size of the space, two units used for one space, or the discharge nozzle is blocked or misdirected.

Failure to maintain can result in anything from leakage and depressurization to water exposure and corrosion related failures.

Other Causes

Fires start on boats from many causes, some predictable and not hard to discover, while others are bizarre, and certainly unexpected. For that reason alone, the cause may be hard to find if severe fire damage ensues. The case of a faulty bench grinder switch cited earlier is a good example that, had there not been a partial witness, it is unlikely that the cause would have been discovered.

Halogen Lamps

Halogen lamps emit a very bright light and have become very popular as overhead recessed lighting in boats. Unfortunately a halogen light bulb can reach temperatures of 1,200 degrees F. The glass shield that surrounds the bulb reaches temperatures of 800 degrees F. Both of these temperatures exceed normal ignition temperatures of many combustibles that are usually found near halogen lamps. Compare this to a 100 watt incandescent bulb, which reaches temperatures of 475 degrees F.

Halogen lamps are routinely installed in vinyl headliners where there is also plywood backing or furring. These materials are combustible at around 600 - 800F. Moreover, marine grade wiring is rated for 105C or 220F temperature service, temperatures above which the insulation begins to soften and melt. Halogen lamp parts usually survive a fire with the remains consisting of the bulb and a 2" diameter glass disk. Lamps installed in overheads that start fires usually result in fires that are extinguished long before massive destruction of the vessel occurs. Point of origin quickly is narrowed to some part of the upper structure and will often end up burning a hole or vent through an upper deck or housetop.

Enclosed Lighting Fixtures

Enclosed lamps will contain the heat build up resulting in much higher temperatures that could reach ignition point of surrounding materials. In boats we commonly find DC lighting fixtures with discolored and melted lenses that occur with the use of the manufacturer supplied bulb. These don't normally cause fires, but when someone decides to up the wattage of the bulb beyond the manufacturer's recommendation, fires can easily start. These are almost always ceiling or wall mounted fixtures where the burn pattern will be obvious if complete destruction does not occur. One clue is that the circuit was energized and therefore melting of the wire insulation has a good possibility of creating a short. The remaining question will be whether the lamp started the fire or the short. Arcing or fusing of the conductors near the bulb and fixture will be a good indicator.

Clothes Dryer Fires

Mid size and larger yachts often have electric clothes dryers. Fires can occur due to improper installation and venting as well as ignition of lint build-up in the vent system. Also look for water entry through the vent duct and resultant corrosion-related problems.

Stove Fires

The vast majority of stove fires occur with someone present, so there is little doubt about the cause. However, there is one situation where stove fires can occur with no one present. Many, if not most boats, have electric stoves that have covers on top. Very often, and foolishly, these are wood or plastic and therefore if the burner is accidentally turned on, the result is inevitable. The Princess electric range was manufactured with a wooden cutting board built into the stainless steel top. It also has an automatic cut off switch to prevent the burner from being turned on, but there is a record of these switches failing to operate for a variety of reasons. Since the switch is bent metal, it can be pushed aside so that the top does not engage it.

It is also fairly easy for someone to accidentally bump against the front or top-mounted switches and inadvertently activate a burner, or simply fail to turn it off completely. Similarly, with some cook tops, it is possible to place the cover over the burner without engaging the cut off switch. The author has personally witnessed this happening on a number of occasions.

Hydraulic Stabilizer Fires

Stabilizing systems use high pressure hydraulics and hydraulic oil that can get very hot as a result of pressurization. Typical operating temperatures run around 150F for short term operation but can go much higher with long term operation. Lightweight hydraulic oil is extremely combustible when vaporized, as from a system leak. Sparks or hot engine exhaust systems could easily ignite it after gallons of the oil has been sprayed around the engine room. This type of cause results in an immediate conflagration and is typified by the captain stating that the fire gave no warning before the vessel was engulfed, but is likely to be mistaken for a diesel fuel fed fire.

Search for samples of hydraulic oil residue in any remaining debris that is likely to retain such residue. In most cases, a fairly large number of samples from different areas will be needed because oil residue in engine rooms is hardly uncommon, but hydraulic oil all over the place is. Also obtain a sample of oil from the reservoir as a basis for comparison.

Lightning

While it is entirely possible that lightning could cause a fire on a boat, the author has investigated hundreds of lightning damage claims and has never seen, nor heard of, lighting starting a fire on a boat. The reason for this is that there are usually too many good low resistance pathways to ground, such as masts, outriggers top frames and railings. For lightning to cause a fire there needs to be high resistance in whatever is conducting the charge. Plus, the duration of the charge is so brief that there is insufficient time for great heating to take place. In most cases there is even little visible evidence of the event, the most common being shattered antennas. Even though fiberglass antennae have very high resistance (except for the small, internal conductor), I've never seen one burn.

For lightning to cause a fire, a low temperature combustible like paper, fabric or wood needs to be included in the pathway but such an occurrence is extremely unlikely on a boat, as compared with a lighting bolt in a dry forest passing through pine needles or dry leaves.

The issue of whether lightning could cause ignition of fuel vapors in a fuel tank is frequently raised. There is one recorded incident of this happening where a tuna tower leg terminated within inches of a fuel filler deck plate of a gas powered boat. The tank exploded but the boat did not burn and clear evidence of the lightning strike told the story.

Three Red Flags of Arson

Arson cases are usually highlighted by prominent red flags. People who burn their own property to collect the insurance (or for any other reason) are financially desperate and probably not thinking rationally and tend to give themselves and their motives away. The difficulty with committing arson is a matter of not being seen setting the fire or leaving clear evidence. Obviously, if the boat owner was seen aboard the boat shortly before the fire there is immediate suspicion. Therefore, most arson cases occur at night when there are no witnesses, which is the first red flag. The next red flag is financial distress as indicated by a bad credit report. The third flag is a fire that suddenly engulfs and consumes the entire vessel, as when an accelerant is used. When a witness states that a fire seemed to blossom just a bit too fast, suspect the use of accelerants.

When these three factors are present, the odds are very high that arson was involved. The odds are equally high that there will be no evidence and the arson cannot be proved, yet alone who did it. Even so, that does not prevent us from trying.

A fourth red flag that is applicable to boats only are open hatches. Hatches are not normally left open for a variety of good reasons. Exterior hatches will allow rain to enter and interior deck hatches left open are dangerous. Therefore, if hatches are left open, it is usually for a reason. One good reason is that open hatches will provide ventilation to an enclosed space, allowing a fire to burn much faster than an enclosed space and people generally understand this. If open hatches are found, this may be a clue to arson.

If an accelerant is poured throughout the interior of the vessel, the windows opened and then ignited, the vessel will be consumed within about 15 minutes. That is not enough time for a fire department to arrive (after being notified) and get set up. The boat will burn to the water line and probably sink whereon all evidence, if there was any, is likely lost.

However, most arson attempts are not this successful because starting a conflagration such as this with volatile liquids is not easy, and neither is getting away unseen and uninjured. Therefore, most arsonists will resort to some other means than personally setting the fire. In some instances they hire others to do it; in others they attempt to use some sort of delayed ignition method. Less sophisticated methods utilize space heaters, trouble lights placed on oil soaked rags or the use of high voltage light bulbs. The later method, if cleverly done, will produce almost nothing in the way of evidence in a severe fire. For example, a 100 watt bulb will produce a maximum temperature at the top of about 475F, not enough to combust paper or cotton. But wrap that bulb in insulating cotton fabric and the temperature can rise to the ignition point. Therefore, look for lamps that are out of place as a possible indicator.

If the use of flammable liquids fails to result in total destruction of the vessel, the chances of finding evidence are good, either in the form of trace volatiles or in burn patterns that burning liquids create.

To give an idea of how difficult it is to prove an arson case, out of dozens of instances where arson was apparent, in only two cases was it sufficiently proven that the insured did it that the claim was dropped, denied, or not filed at all. If the local fire officials are not only competent, but also interested, the marine insurance investigator should make every effort to work with them. Some fire officials will work with us while others will try to hold us completely at arm's length, allowing no input from us. When working with fire officials it should be kept in mind that they are always the lead investigators, and that our role is secondary or supportive at best. Moreover, fire investigations at some point become criminal investigations since most fire officials do not have police authority, the case has to be referred to police detectives, but police are even less prone to work with us than the firemen. Unfortunately, arson cases are so difficult to prove that police agencies show little interest in investigating them even when the arson evidence is obvious. Bear in mind that because this is a criminal matter, the "beyond reasonable doubt" standard must be applied.

As the insurance investigator, we have certain abilities that neither the firemen nor the police have (and vice versa). The police can't demand documents except by court order for a search warrant. We have the leverage of the clause in the insurance policy that requires the insured to cooperate with us, and provide documents. If we need the cooperation of government officials it's a good idea to explain this to them as it has a way of altering certain insular attitudes they commonly posses. Nobody has to cooperate with the police, but if the insured wants his claim to be paid, he does have to cooperate with the insurance company.

In the event that compelling evidence is obtained without police assistance, consideration must be given to notifying the police. In many states we are compelled by law to do so, though such laws aren't often enforced. However, we must bear in mind that this is a business relationship between ourselves, the insurer and insured. Therefore, the primary responsibility for the evidence obtained rightly belongs with the insurer and that police notification should only take place with the client's approval.

(Footnotes)

1. An even more important issue surrounding the dependence on high technology is the issue of cost where, even in the public sector, the enormous cost of providing high tech answers is straining budgets of all types of investigative agencies.

2. If that seems like a long time, consider that in most cases, fires start long before the first visible flame is seen.

3. PVC when burned releases hydrochloric acid which is extremely toxic and deadly when inhaled.

4. Exceptions are stoves with covers and safety cut off switches that are known to fail.

Chapter 9

Machinery Failure Analysis

The insurance industry has great need for competent machinery damage investigators and the field is wide open for anyone who would like to specialize in this area. More marine insurance claims are filed for machinery damage than any other type of loss. While machinery failure analysis is vast subject on which there is very little published literature for pleasure craft engines, this chapter can only begin to provide an overview of the basic issues that the pleasure craft m

arine surveyor encounters. Anyone wishing to enter this field will find it necessary to establish his own program for self-education that can be attained in many ways, but none of which have been consolidated into a general program.

This chapter is designed to help get would-be failure analysts started by providing an overview along with essential fundamentals, but is by no means a complete text on the subject. The main item of interest is, of course, propulsion engines. A significant number of clients requiring these services are boat owners with warranty disputes who need the assistance of an expert. Machinery damage is among the most difficult types of claims to investigate and requires the greatest degree of technical knowledge and skill. That is perhaps why there are so few investigators who are expert in the field or specialize in this area. There are also very few firms that specialize in machinery failure analysis; of those that exist tend to deal primarily in heavy machinery and systems and industrial issues.

The investigation of machinery damage is a technical specialty that may not be amenable to a generalist surveyor/investigator, for it requires significant mechanical experience. A fundamental knowledge of gas and diesel engines is required. Yet the marine investigator is often assigned machinery cases and usually finds himself forced to rely on the opinions of repairers as to causation. Repairing an engine and analyzing failures are not the same thing so the repairer usually isn't the best person to rely on. It is also worth noting that many repairers have become familiar with insurance and know that they have a much better chance of getting paid if the loss is covered; hence, they have a bit of a conflict of interest.

The marine investigator should at least be familiar with engines and the primary reasons failures occur. While this is a subject that could literally fill volumes, this chapter will touch on some of the basics that will help anyone who wishes to add machinery damage analysis to his resume get started. As with most technical subjects, the reader will find that education is a never-ending process because the products that we deal with are constantly changing and is encouraged to seek out the training seminars that are made available from time to time in his area.

The Internet now contains extensive information on this subject[1], as well as providing sources for education including web sites, books, and training seminars. In addition, many engine manufacturers offer periodic training venues. Check with dealers and manufacturer web sites for information about the availability of such courses. A number of engine and parts manufacturers provide excellent failure identification photos in the form of charts or posters, companies such as Detroit Diesel, Federal-Mogul, John Deere and others which I am unable to reproduce here[2]. There is so much available on these web sites that a significant amount of self-education can be had from these alone.

Historically, when dealing with machinery damage claims marine surveyors have placed a great deal of reliance on engine repairers, mainly because they lack adequate training on this specialty. The problem with attempting to rely on repair firms for information, including dealers and independents, is that these people have a loyalty to the manufacturer of the products they service, and are generally disinclined to critique faults in design or manufacturing. Making sure that they get paid is another motivation for being less than candid. Although I have been forced to rely on a number of independent mechanics over the years, I've always run into problems with them not wanting to be critical of manufacturers because, even as independents, they still are reliant on manufacturers for parts, service bulletins, general information and specialized equipment — all of which is likely to be withheld should the dealer or manufacturer become displeased with the independent.

One may become qualified in Federal courts as an expert simply by virtue of experience, which has to be fairly extensive. As mentioned elsewhere, expertise is not restricted to formal education. Far from it, self-education is recognized and accepted so long as that form of education can be demonstrated. Having conducted numerous investigations, engine surveys and attending numerous repair seminars or similar will usually suffice. Keep in mind that everyone starts with no experience and no education and can only obtain it through persistence and determination combined with liberal doses of time.

One of the first things that anyone who wishes to become a machinery failure expert has to do is to obtain the owner's and repair manuals for the most common types of machinery that will be investigated. These, fortunately, are fairly few in number. Owner's manuals are important from the standpoint of the recommended maintenance procedures that can serve as a guide for us to check whether such maintenance was performed.

He will also need to cultivate relationships with repairers as an additional source of information that will be indispensable to his work. Indeed, most of the knowledge that I possess comes from years of badgering service managers and repairers with questions at every opportunity.

When manufacturers have problems with their products, almost inevitably they end up issuing bulletins to dealers and repairers. These are supposed to have limited access, but if one thinks like an investigator instead of a mechanic or surveyor, one will find ways to get copies of these documents which should be saved in a file. To be successful, you'll need to train yourself to be constantly alert for opportunities to obtain these documents which will become extremely useful in the future. It's like opening a savings account for small weekly deposits that seem insignificant at first, but grow into a sizeable account with the passage of years. Start collecting those documents now and in ten years you'll have an entire library at hand. The usefulness of these documents can last for decades, so the effort pays long-term dividends.

By way of illustration, I collected information on Detroit Diesel engines for over twenty years so by the end of that time there was almost nothing that went wrong with these engines that I didn't know about, even though machinery damage analysis was not my primary line of work during all those years. Though my frequent contact with repairers and engine surveyors I was able to accumulate this information that filled several 3" thick ring binders by making it a point to ask for this information on virtually every opportunity I got. Thus, if I wasn't an expert on some point myself, I certainly knew who was; it is just as important to know who knows the answers as it is acquiring knowledge yourself.

Insurance Coverage Issues

The reason that the investigator should be familiar with insurance coverages is not that the investigator makes coverage decisions, but that he is familiar with them so that he can provide the company decision maker with sufficient information. In other words, we need to know what questions *will be* asked so that we can provide the answers. Keep in mind that the company adjuster is not an expert, is usually completely ignorant of the subject, and will be relying heavily on the investigator for answers that often have to do with cause/effect relationships.

It is not the intent of most marine insurers to provide machinery breakdown insurance in the same way that the so-called "extended warranty" contracts do. If insurance companies did that they would, in effect, be providing a warranty for manufacturers,

Fig. 9-1. A good working environment is essential to not only to the investigator, but also to ensure that repairs can be done properly. "In-frame" overhauls increase labor time and tendency for error and should be avoided when possible. Above, the engine is removed to the repairer's shop where there is plenty of space and everyone can take their time doing the job right with the right equipment.

thus removing the responsibility for product reliability from the maker and assuming it themselves. Extended warranty contracts are actually forms of insurance and not a warranty, and are regulated by most state insurance departments. All risk yacht policies typically provide coverage for loss or damage resulting from *external causes*, or the wording may include the phrases "sudden and fortuitous." Both these terms are taken to exclude internal causes such as breakdown and wear and tear.

External causation would include things such as damage caused by taking on bad fuel, debris in outside cooling water, operator error (excluding failure to maintain), latent defect and the normal array of casualties that injure the vessel. As we can see from this, most engine failures result from internal causation, and there are not many possible types of external causation.

Machinery damage claims provide a wide open arena for differences of opinion, debate and legal conflict owing to the high degree of esoteric technicality, general lack of analytical skills available and institutional bias. Yet for many of these same reasons, such disputes, while frequently litigated, rarely end up in court.

The repairer, that is, the mechanic, rarely if ever has training in failure analysis, yet because he is the one person with the greatest access to, and familiarity with, the broken machine or engine, whatever pronouncement he makes as to causation is usually accepted as an expert opinion when, in fact, the mechanic's expertise is in the area of repair, not analysis. The marine investigator will run into this problem frequently because repair mechanics are frequently involved in claims to some degree. Some will proffer opinions and some will not; some will admit that this is not their job, while others will vociferously inject their viewpoints or that of their employer. Thus the investigator not

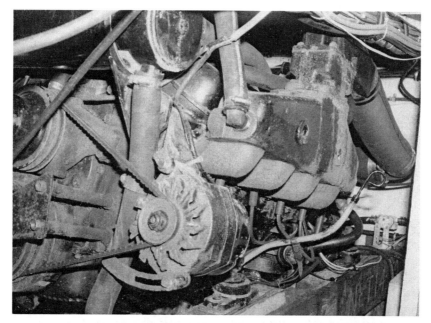

Fig. 9-2. Unlike road vehicles, marine engines operate in an environment that may be unique to each engine. The above engine displays not only serious neglect, but examination of the vessel revealed that the engine room bilge was constantly filled with water, creating a very wet environment, reflected by the very rusty condition of the engine. This was simply the result of a failure to maintain a bilge pump that hadn't worked for years.

infrequently finds himself at odds with the repairer.

It is the role of the investigator not only to determine causation, but to interpret that causation as it relates to coverage. That is to say that merely to affix the cause generally is insufficient because it requires his technical expertise to interpret the event properly; therefore, it becomes his duty to become familiar with the various coverages so as to help insure that the coverage decision is correctly determined. This is because when the client has no knowledge of machinery whatsoever, the client isn't going to be able to interpret what we are saying to him or her. Many insurance claims supervisors are women whose knowledge of engines is zero, so this should effectively make the point. The person making the coverage decision is likely to not even be able to understand what the investigator is talking about. There will be many instances where the investigator is effectively but indirectly making the coverage decision (or at least educating his client how to make that decision), hence his need to be able to do so without any bias, and to effectively be able to understand the both the word and intent of the policy language. This point touches directly on the issues of primary or initial cause as well as contributory causes which can make coverage decisions complex and difficult.

This confronts directly on matters of *initial* and *ensuing* damage as when a design or manufacturing fault results in catastrophic engine damage, i.e. it blows up or flies apart. Some types of coverage exclude the initial damage (cause) but not the ensuing damage. It then becomes necessary to separate the two events. In other cases all forms of internally caused engine damage are excluded, but when the engine blows up, shrapnel goes through the bottom of the boat and sinks it.

Coverage exclusions such as wear and tear have been written and interpreted in two ways. Some policies exclude machinery damage from internal causation period. Others will cover only resultant damage from a failed part. An example would be when a deteriorated hose results in loss of engine coolant with subsequent overheating damage; the deteriorated hose would not be covered, but all other damage would. One type of coverage would exclude any damage resulting from deterioration, while another type would not pay for the deteriorated part, but would pay for the ensuing additional damage. It is the investigator's role to make these determinations.

Warranty Claims

The objective of assisting a client with a warranty claim is to convince the manufacturer to honor the claim without having to resort to a lawsuit. In a majority of cases this will be successful when sufficient proof of a fault can be provided.

Most people would probably assume that a warranty claim can only be made if it falls within the warranty period. This isn't necessarily true. A manufacturer does not have a right to sell defective products (which is technically fraud when he is aware of the defect) and in most cases a warranty merely reiterates what is legally required of them, albeit to a lesser degree. If a manufacturer has knowledge of a defect and fails to notify the purchaser, that purchaser still has a right to a claim against the manufacturer. This is why we hear of manufacturers making good in instances where the written warranty has expired.

Over a period of decades, owner's experience with warranty claims is highly variable. What a manufacturer sees as the value of his goodwill is usually dependent upon his profitability. In other words, when times are not good for them they tend to put up more resistance or restrictions on paying claims in order to boost profits. Moreover, at the rate that manufacturers change ownership, there is no basis for consistency. In a few instances a manufacturing error may be so widespread and costly that it threatens the future of the company (or its CEO) that the company denies the problem altogether. The Firestone Tire Company is a good recent example.

Whether it is a warranty case or not, it is useful to make an effort to determine how widespread the problem is. This can bolster a case in several ways. When a defect is recurrent throughout the product line, this is an indication that the manufacturer is aware of the problem. If the defect is isolated, an out-of-warranty claim becomes much harder to advance because the manufacturer can dispute the nature of the cause. But when it is widespread, it is much more likely that others have knowledge about the nature of the problem, and this may make it easier and less costly to track down.

A good example of a successful "warranty" claim is the case of a 1996 Sea Ray 330 Express which was a rear engine boat with an underwater exhaust system. My client, and numerous other owners of this model, suffered from recurrent engine seizures when water backed up through the exhaust and filled the engine. The builder alleged that the problem was due to out of warranty corroded exhaust risers. Indeed, the entire boat was out of warranty.

First, the exhaust risers were removed and pressure tested and proven not to be faulty. In this case I judged that this would not be enough evidence to achieve the client's goal. Next, I measured up the boat, engine installation and exhaust system and produced a scale drawing from which the heights above water line could be established at various degrees of trim and conditions. From the measured drawing it could be determined that a mere 12 degrees of transverse list would put water into the engines. Moreover, a copy of the engine manufacturer's installation specifications was obtained which indicated that the engine installation did not meet those specifications. The minimum recommended height above water line was 12 inches whereas the builder only allowed 8 inches. Armed with this evidence, the builder backed down and footed the bill for two new engines and a redesigned exhaust system.

It wasn't long after this case, that I ran across many other owners of this model with the same problems but with different results. Several managed to get rebuilt engines out of Sea Ray, but then their engines continued to fill with water. I ran across one owner that had his engines rebuilt twice and had filed suit against Sea Ray after they refused to resolve the problem a third time.

This Sea Ray case illustrates another important point. The more evidence we have, and the more convincing it is, the more likely that the manufacturer is to settle the case. He will be looking at the issue from the legal standpoint of whether he could defend a lawsuit; we should be looking at it from the standpoint of whether we could win one.

Latent Defects

Marine insurance policies usually have a clause relating to latent defects. When there is coverage, the insurance does not cover the latent defect itself, but only resultant damage caused by a latent defect. A latent defect is defined as *an unknown defect not discoverable by such inspection or test as the law reasonably requires under the circumstances.* Latent defects can include defects in materials, design and workmanship. For a detailed discussion about latent defects, see Chapter Four.

Latent defect is occasionally alleged as a cause of engine failure though it's a lot more difficult proving the nature of the defect than merely making the assertion. Latent defects in the manufacture of engines — owing mainly to automation — are rare. More often the defect is a matter of faulty design rather than the actual fabrication of component.

Investigation

First Things First

Before plunging into an investigation willy-nilly, it's wise to first establish the environment in which the incident occurred. We'll want to know whether the failure occurred as entirely an internal event with no outside factors, or was the failure initiated, or contributed to, by an external cause?

The investigation should begin with questioning of the boat owner about the repair and maintenance history of the engine, frequency of use and the circumstances under which the breakdown occurred. Each type of occurrence, from spinning a bearing, burning a piston or severe overheating, demands a particular set of questions. This is then followed by examination of the vessel's engine room to determine if there were any other factors involved. This could include anything from inadequate ventilation, saltwater spray, or a general lack of maintenance. If the lube oil in one engine is like sludge, the other is likely to be the same, and so on.

The owner's response to questioning should be listened to carefully, not only for what he says but the way he says it and what he does not say. It's possible that he has had a long-standing problem that he doesn't want to admit to. Indeed, with careful planning of questions, it's possible to learn more from this interview than from the engine itself. Here's how that works.

First start with a detailed questioning about how he maintains his engines; the objective is to find out whether he is knowledgeable or not. If we determine he is very knowledgeable, and then move on to detailed questioning about what happened, and his answers are vague and evasive, then we have a clear indication that he knows what happened but doesn't want to tell us. Why? Probably because he believes that what he thinks is the cause that will not be covered by insurance. You can't get a much better verbal clue than this. Conversely, if you determine that the owner is mechanically ignorant and says he doesn't know anything from anything, he's probably telling the truth. Think of this like a doctor questioning a patient about his symptoms. Once this is done we can now move onto the actual inspection of the engine.

The Operating Environment

In most cases this means the engine compartment of the vessel. Questions for you to consider will be : Does the engine compartment have adequate ventilation? Is the area free of contaminants? In one case, a deteriorated carpet padding on the deck above was found filtering down through the engine hatch edge gaps and going straight into engine air intake. Are there any water leaks putting water onto or into the engine? Is the propeller shaft slinging bilge water around? And so on.

Aside from the condition of the engine itself, the condition of the engine room will tell a lot about how the engine was maintained. If the engine is already removed from the vessel, it is necessary to go to the boat and examine the engine room.

Be alert to the fact that other factors may be involved. These include but are not limited to:

- Propeller size

- Exhaust piping size, location

- Broken muffler baffles causing exhaust restriction

- Improperly designed underwater exhaust systems

Excessive exhaust system back pressure due to undersize pipes, mufflers or bad design is occasionally the direct cause of engine failure.

Investigation Procedure

Legally, the burden of proof for proving the cause of loss lies on the insured. Most insurance companies, however, will not take that approach. Because of the high costs involved, the investigator should establish with his client who is to pay for engine removal and tear down costs. Should it be the case that the loss is not covered, we want to avoid a dispute. In most cases the surveyor will be utilizing the services of the insured's selected repairer, giving him instructions on what he wants him to do. If so, that can create a clear estoppel situation because the surveyor gave the order. Therefore, he must not only make clear who pays for what, but also make clear that these efforts are limited to investigating causation and are not an admission of coverage.

Starting with a failed engine that remains in the boat, the question may arise as to who pays the cost of the investigation. This would include removal of the engine, transport to an appropriate facility, and the labor cost of dismantling. Because the burden of proof is on the insured, this is normally his expense; when in doubt, and before giving any advice to an insured, it is best to consult with your client.

It is highly desirable that the investigator should be present during the tear down. If possible, he should also inspect the engine room before the engine is removed, but if not, he should inspect at the earliest possible time, the purpose of which is to examine the engine room for any condition that might have caused or contributed to the engine damage. Failing to do this before examination of the engine parts wastes time and risks errors.

TIP: Be sure to inspect the area under the engine which is often found to reveal evidence of leaking fluids.

Layout and Mark the Parts

My procedure is to make arrangement with the repairer to dismantle the engine in my presence and lay it out in order on the floor with each part in its proper position so that it can be correctly identified. The reason for this necessity is that if the parts are not in their proper order (as when you have the usual bucket of parts) it is impossible to discern patterns from wear or overheating. Lacking this, an investigation becomes badly flawed. Once all the parts are laid out, I mark the major parts such as pistons and bearings with identification since during handling they're likely to get mixed up. I use a Magic Marker or Dremmel tool and scribe the number in so that it is permanent and doesn't get accidentally removed, such as will happen with chalk or grease pencil.

In larger yachts, the process is to perform what is called an "in-frame" overhaul where the engine remains in the yacht. This makes our job considerably more difficult due to a lack of space, and the need to take greater care to not get parts mixed up. We need to be present at least at the outset of tear down to make sure that the mechanics don't just throw parts in pile. If possible, get the mechanic to perform any dismantling. It is best that the investigator not do any dismantling himself so as to avoid later being accused of causing any damage. However, if you cannot avoid doing it yourself, make sure you know what you're doing and document your actions in the file.

Once dismantling is accomplished the parts are then analyzed for faults and patterns. Most major engine failures result in a pattern of evidence left by the initial fault. The nature of this pattern (such as carbonization, lack of lubrication or overheating) usually provides a clue to the initiating cause.

From this description, the reader will discern why following this procedure will lead to the most reliable result. This is not to say that in cases where the investigator is presented with a pile of parts, he will be unable to make a determination; only that it will be much more difficult with less reliability.

While good photography is an important part of the investigator's work, the difficulty with photographing engine parts is the fact that it isn't possible to completely photograph everything from all sides. Because of this problem, critical damaged parts that are evidence should not only be photographed, but saved and stored in a safe location. All too often, parts left in the care of a repairer end up getting lost or discarded, so it's best that the investigator take possession of them and store them in a safe location until such time as the case is resolved.

Engine Failure Analysis Fundamentals

Considering the typical V-8 gas engine or the marine diesel, we see that there are literally thousands of possibilities for why things go wrong. The odds for finding the exact cause of an engine's demise is about the same as that of determining a serious boat fire is about 65%. Or, to put it another way, I am successful at determining the exact cause of failure a little more than half the time. As investigations go, these are not bad odds.

Fig. 9-3. The accumulation of salt on the flame arrestor and inside the carburetor leaves little doubt about why this engine failed.

Engine failures occur due to an abnormal condition; in the proper environment with good maintenance and conscientious operation, failures should not occur short of some manufacturing defect. Engine failures normally result from faults in the following primary categories of causation:

- Cooling system

- Lubrication system

- Fuel system

- Aspiration system

- Engine overload

When investigating the cause of engine failure, all aspects of its operating systems must be examined to determine whether its condition was a contributing factor.

It should be noted that engine failure often occurs from faults in more than one of these categories. With the exception of piston failures, the usual causes or basis of engine failures for gas and diesel engines are generally not the same. This is because diesel engines are much more sensitive to faults and lack of maintenance, whereas gas engines tolerate considerable neglect. However, the basic principles of failure analysis are very much the same.

In most cases, engine failures are progressive events that begins from a root cause that leads to degradation of other parts or systems that then fail and can be likened to a chain reaction. A failed part or component can never be said to be the cause of engine damage by reason of the fact that something caused that part to fail[3]. It is that "something" that we seek to find. Piston or bearing failure is never a proper conclusion because it neglects to address what caused those parts to fail. Inadequate maintenance is the predominate reason why engine damage occurs in an estimated 80% of all cases. With marine engines, which are modified automotive engines, faults in marine conversions and installations

Fig. 9-4. The cause of this engine failure would be elusive if one did not carefully examining all parts. The burn - like pattern at the lower right of this cylinder liner is the result of a leaking liner seal, dripping coolant down into the crankcase. The streaming water marks are clearly visible. The lower end of the liner protrudes into the crankcase.

are also frequently implicated.

An important reason why we are not always successful at identifying a specific cause for the demise of an engine stems from situations wherein multiple lesser faults combine to place so much stress on the engine that the cause of its ultimate demise cannot be specifically determined. Instances occur in which poor maintenance combines with an otherwise non fatal fault to produce an ultimate breakdown in which the non fatal fault is merely the "last straw." Such cases are easy to visualize but hard to prove conclusively.

Marine engines are much more heavily loaded than their cousins, the automotive engines, which are powering vehicles that roll on wheels, a factor that presents much less of a load than that of a boat plowing through many tons of water. This factor alone accounts for much of the lower reliability of marine versus automotive engines. The higher load means that marine engines are far less tolerant of any shortcomings in the fundamental operation systems. The diesel engine does not tolerate faults in its fuel system; a lack of maintenance even for relatively short periods typically leads to serious internal damage. And because of the high loads, marine engines are always vulnerable to overheating; minor cooling system faults easily lead to overheating and damage.

On performing an engine failure analysis, it is not sufficient to merely seek the failed component within the engine. Instead, the engine must be viewed as a whole, the sum of its parts combined with the environment in which it operates, along with the degree of care it did or did not receive. In pleasure craft, the most frequently occurring

Fig. 9-5. Bulging cooling system hoses may be a good indicator that there is blockage within the cooling system.

cause of failure is lack of proper maintenance. The manufacturer's recommended maintenance routines will be contained in the owner's manual which should be examined by the investigator. Take note that as engines become increasingly "high tech," proper maintenance becomes increasingly critical.

This is closely followed by, and often in conjunction with, high speed, high performance diesel engines that push the limits of how much horsepower can be squeezed out a basic engine block. It naturally follows that the higher the horsepower-to-displacement ratio, the more critical maintenance becomes. Due to higher speeds, greater loads and increased operating temperatures, high performance diesels are vastly less tolerant of substandard maintenance conditions than their lower powered cousins. We must also understand that the failed component(s) is rarely the cause of failure but usually the symptom of the overlying cause. In all cases we must ask what caused the failed part to fail. Only rarely will the cause be defect of that part.

In addition to the basic internal combustion system, engines are dependent upon four subsidiary systems: air, fuel, coolant and lubrication. Each of these must supply the right quantity in order for the engine to function properly. However, that quantity is completely dependent on the amount of LOAD the engine is subjected to. When the load is increased (as with a boat with a fouled bottom or props) the demands on the lubrication, cooling and aspirating systems are likewise increased. Should there be fault in one or more of these systems, damage is bound to occur.

Of course failures usually occur from combinations of faults that typically result in a chain reaction of cause and effect so that the proverbial question of which came first, the chicken or the egg, is always present. The goal of machinery damage analysis is the determination of the initiating event or combination of events. This is rarely ever easy, which is what makes machinery failure analysis so challenging.

The approach to analyzing a failure must be organized, systematic and thorough, starting with a more or less standard procedure involving the process of elimination. Unfortunately, by the time the surveyor is brought into the picture, it is often the case that the engine has already been torn down and sometimes repairs are already completed.

The surveyor is shown a pile of damaged parts from which he is expected to affirm the alleged cause. This, of course, is impossible, so that when encountering this situation, all that the investigator can tell his client is that the evidence has been destroyed, and in an insurance case, the insured failed to provide the insurer with the opportunity to inspect the damage. Do not make the mistake that you can pass judgement on a pile of parts minus the rest of the engine. There is no opinion that anyone could draw about the cause of failure in such a case that would stand up in court; the best one could do would be mere speculation.

Failure to Determine Cause

As mentioned earlier, experience indicates that failure analysis is successful in about 65% of all attempts. The success rate is not higher because all-too often a combination of factors is too complex, or events of conditions were involved that cannot be discovered. Or we are faced with the situation in which we cannot determine which of several conditions occurred first in a chain of events. Of course, as we see demonstrated on television every day, there is almost no limit to the very expensive, high tech analytical machinery available to us. Thus, we have to accept the fact that, despite our best efforts, the cause is not always discoverable within the parameters of reasonable efforts and cost.

Overheating

Overheating is the fundamental cause of most machinery failures and can be in the form of either:

(1) *systemic* failure, which is a global[4] cooling system failure ranging from pump failure to loss of coolant, or

(2) *localized* overheating which is the most common form.

The cause of localized overheating does not necessarily result from cooling system malfunction, but can result from causes ranging from local lubrication failure to induction system faults such as a clogged intercooler and others. Excessive friction results in overheating, but in ultimately a lubrication failure, yet a lubrication failure can be the result of excessive heat. The subject of overheating can get a little complicated and here we'll examine some of the fundamentals.

Overheating and Thermal Expansion

All metals when they heat up will expand, but some more than others. Aluminum lies at the top of the list of greatest expansion rates while iron and steel are at the middle, thus these two metals have greatly differing rates of expansion. Pistons expand greatly while cylinder liners and blocks much less so. Engines are designed to account for these

Fig. 9-6. This is an extreme example of a fouled intercooler as it is about 80% restricted. The end result was complete destruction of the engine. The oil sludge came from a leaking turbo bearing and contains a high percentage of salt. It takes far less than this to result severe overheating and damage.

expansion rates so that at the recommended operating temperature, all parts should fit just right.

Aluminum pistons in a cold engine are undersize, but when they become too hot they expand to oversize. If the whole engine overheats, the cylinder bores will also shrink or distort, thus an expanded piston and distorting cylinder are guaranteed to result in piston failure. Most of the cooling to a piston is by means of the oil bath from the underside so that should the cooling system fail, the iron block will begin to heat up more rapidly than the pistons. Yet contact heat transfer in way of the rings will result in oil break down and ring friction soonest. A clogged or corroded oil cooler will result in higher oil temperatures, probably leading to oil viscosity[5] reduction.

Global overheating also affects the crankshaft bearings which will be kept cool a bit longer by the oil, but once the oil temperature rises substantially then thermal expansion of the crankshaft, rods and bearings begins to have an effect which will be dependent on the state of wear. Less wear and these parts will seize all the sooner. Global overheating generally does not affect camshafts and lifters.

Fig. 9-7. Clogged oil cooler due to fouled cooling system.

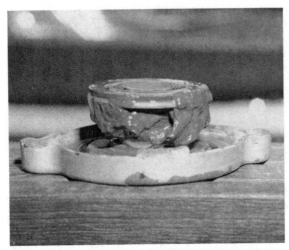

Fig. 9-9. The devil is in the details as shown by the above damaged cooling system cap that would not allow the coolant recovery system to function. Don't overlook the little things.

Fig. 9-8. Cap is loaded with iron oxide sludge, clear evidence of failure to maintain the cooling system.

Thermal expansion due to cooling system inadequacies has been shown to be prevalent with many high speed, high horsepower engines where engines have been souped up beyond the ability of the cooling jackets to provide adequate cooling. Nearly all engine manufacturers have been guilty of pulling too much power out of their engine blocks at one time or another.

Improper Cooling System Maintenance

This is one of the leading causes of engine failures thereby creating the need to examine the cooling system closely. Closed marine cooling systems have two sides to them, the closed and open sides. The open side is subject to fouling from foreign material (calcium, silt, biological matter) plus galvanic/electrolytic corrosion of the heat exchanger core. Even small amounts of scale build-up on tube bundles will have major effect on heat transfer capabilities.

Gas engines will have three coolers (heat exchange, oil and transmission coolers) while diesel engines have up to five coolers. Thus a cooling system failure affects more than the just the basic engine cooling, but everything else that is dependent upon it. Each of these coolers is separately capable of failure and leaking coolant into the oil or fuel or vice versa.

Failure to maintain the proper ratios of corrosion inhibitor will result in the build up of iron oxides within the system, causing a reduction of heat transfer capabilities of the cooling jackets. Knock out a freeze plug and check the passages for sludge and iron scale. Excess ratio of ethylene glycol can cause coagulation of the coolant that severely retards heat transfer. This is noticeable by the presence of green slime. Check for rusty sludge build up at upper surfaces of heat exchanger tank, in coolant recovery bottle and pressure cap overflow passage.

Fig. 9-10. The heat exchanger on this engine had been leaking salt water into the cooling system for a long time. Knocking out a freeze plug, we find the bottom end of the block is completely sludged up over three inches deep.

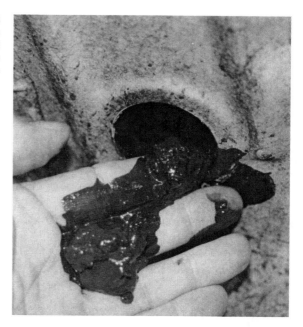

The presence of carbon or oil in the cooling system is indicative of leaking gaskets, cracked castings, or leaking coolers. Large amounts of oil probably means a corroded and leaking oil cooler core. With Detroit Diesels, check the copper injector tubes which are flared into the heads and are occasionally subject to cracking or corrosion damage.

Many global overheat conditions are either directly or partly the result of improper cooling system maintenance. This is especially true for high performance and high horsepower engines that are more or less operating "on the edge" of safe power parameters.

When an engine, by design, is generating a bit too much heat for its cooling system to handle, it won't take much in the way of reduced heat transfer to send the engine into overheat condition. Thus cooling system maintenance becomes critical. The most common cause is system corrosion caused by the adding water to the system, and not coolant mixed at proper ratios. Most boat owners will simply top off with water, so that over time the coolant ratio declines to corrosive levels. This results in the build up of rust scale within the block that can severely retard heat transfer.

Another problem is with localities that have very hard water with excessive amounts of dissolved calcium. This results in a build up calcium deposits on copper cooler cores.

Stray current is yet another cause, wherein less noble metals such as aluminum and zinc anodes corroding will create deposits of oxides of these metals on cooler cores the same way as zinc anodes do to propellers.

Most of these problems are readily discernible by careful inspection of the various cooling system components, including water jackets in the block and manifolds. If possible, obtain a sample of the system coolant for analysis.

My perusal of a number of engine manufacturer's owners manuals reveal that they do not contain adequate or proper advice about cooling system maintenance. For example, the manual (1998) for the Yanmar 6LP-STE engine, which has an aluminum heat exchanger tank combination manifold does not specify that anything other that water needs to be added to the cooling system, except in freezing climates where any type of antifreeze is recommended. It comes as no surprise, then, that many of these engines have experienced severe cooling system corrosion.

Conversely, the Crusader Marine engine manuals recommend a precise 60/40 ratio of ethylene glycol antifreeze and warns against adding water directly to the system, and that the coolant be changed *annually*.

If the sludge within a cooling system is orange-brown in color, it's probably iron oxide and will be magnetic. Test with a magnet. If black, it could be oil or carbon and can be determined by feel. If a gelled green slime, this indicates an excess of antifreeze that has coagulated.

Causes of Failures

Coolant Related Failures

Operation in the marine environment raises the potential for water being the cause of failure. The source of water may be external or internal. Condensation appearing inside an engine, or the associated rust patterns such commonly found on the underside of valve covers, is usually the result of water in the oil. The amount may not be enough to become visible through emulsification, but is detectable in an oil analysis. If it was salt water, a strong presence of chlorine will be found.

Water related corrosion usually leaves telltale evidence in a variety of forms. Condensate has a tendency to migrate upward and will usually manifest itself in the form of rust spots on the valve train and corrosion on the underside of valve covers. When water gets into cylinders it will leave corrosion stains on liners and walls even after the engine has been run. Leaking head gaskets leave traces on cylinder walls and a clear trail of migration under the gasket surface, so be sure to examine the faces of both parts. Leaking manifolds and risers show rust stains inside manifolds and cylinders. Water in the oil forms acid that attacks bearings and is readily distinguishable by a metallurgist.

Sea water run through cooling systems – as with open cooling systems or failed coolers and heat exchangers — results in heavy rust scale build up that inhibits heat transfer through the cylinder wall and heads. The result is unequal heat distribution, cylinder distortion and cylinder head cracking. Scuffed or seized pistons are very common in older salt water cooled gas engines which can be said to have reached the end of service

 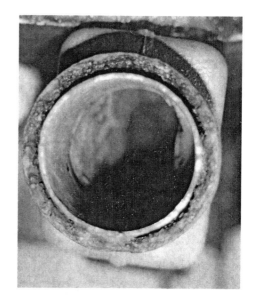

Fig. 9-11 & 9-12. The Crusader riser on the right has nearly 90% blockage of the water jacket which reduces water flow through the cooling system, resulting in rising engine temperatures. Left, both these Mercruiser risers have severe scale and about 50% restriction, but both were corroded through the casting, allowing salt water into the engine. This is the number one cause of engine damage among gas engines.

life. This is usually due to heavy scale build up in cooling jackets that inhibits heat transfer (**Fig. 9-11 & 9-12**). Cylinder walls and heads then develop hot spots and valve damage occurs. One distinguishing feature is that little or no oil burning appears on underside of piston crown, but ring/land damage is prevalent throughout.

If the engine has a plastic coolant recovery bottle, a quick check will revel whether the cooling system is dirty, oily or full of carbon.

Fig. 9-13. This internal view of a cylinder block water jacket was taken with a bore scope. Engine is a Caterpillar 3208 run without an anticorrosive coolant in the system, just water. The heavy rust scale seen here resulted in chronic overheating due to inhibition of heat transfer.

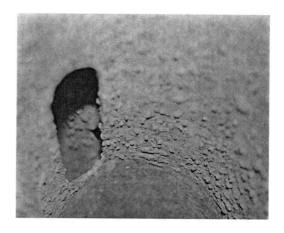

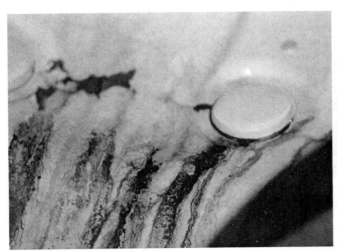

Fig. 9-14. This cylinder block crack between freeze plugs is indicative of freeze damage. The fact that oil is leaking out means that the block is cracked through the other side of the water jacket as well, into the oil gallery. This was a failure to provide proper antifreeze protection. Another good clue is that the boat was moved from Florida to New York during winter.

Exhaust System Faults

Water backing up through an engine exhaust system is a fairly common occurrence. However, for a variety of reasons, this gets blamed for a lot more cases of engine damage than actually occur. Water backing up through the exhaust would be, in insurance parlance, an external event and therefore covered but for one thing. For water to back up through the exhaust usually means that the system is not properly designed since it is possible to design a system where this cannot happen except from extreme events such as storms. Even then, the vast majority of boats won't suffer such damage. On the other hand, a faulty exhaust system design is a latent defect and would be covered by some policies.

All sorts of internal problems such as cracked castings, corroded risers, leaking gaskets and coolers are blamed on water up the exhaust, but fortunately, in most cases, the truth of the matter is easy enough to track down unless the evidence has been destroyed. Since the water came up the exhaust, or so it is alleged, there should be a trail of evidence. It is easier to begin by trying to verify the allegation than to look for other causes. Start by questioning the boat owner about the period of time leading up to the event, how was the boat used and in what circumstances. Next, examine those components that can rust – risers, manifolds, turbochargers – and look for the rust trail. A sizeable amount of water entering an exhaust manifold will fill it up, leaving a rusty water line on the interior. Measure the effective height of the exhaust riser above the normal load water line. Is it reasonably high, or is it obviously too low? Are there mufflers or surge extensions on the line? What is the condition of the muffler baffles and are they damaged or missing?

In the typical twin engine installation, the outboard bank of cylinders is more in line with the exhaust pipe than the inboard bank, which extends off the "Y". Invariably, it will be only the outboard bank that is affected if water up the exhaust is the true cause (unless it's an unusual system). If there is water on the inboard side, but not the

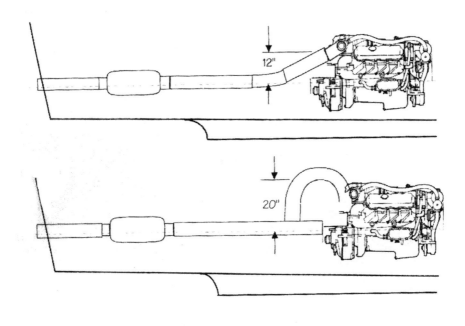

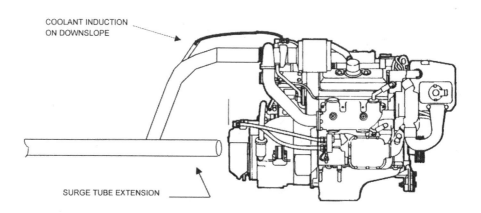

Fig. 9-15 & 9-16. The top drawing illustrates a faulty exhaust system design where water entry into the engine is inevitable over time. With the two lower designs it would take an extreme event to overcome the designed-in protections.

Fig. 9-17. The two primary indicators of disuse are piston ring rust marks as shown above, and rusty flutes on exhaust valves. Each ring mark indicates a point where the engine had stopped in the past and was allowed to sit for long periods without starting so that surface rust developed on the surface as gravity pulled the oil away. A normal cylinder will not show these rings.

outboard, it's a sure bet no water came up the exhaust, so look elsewhere. If no such evidence turns up, then chances are that water up the exhaust is not the cause.

With gas engines, most of the time the problem is discovered when the owner goes to start the engine and it won't crank, either due to being seized or being hydrolocked. It is fairly rare for gas engines to kick over with water in a cylinder and bend a rod. This is not, however, unusual for diesel engines with their much more powerful starting motors and the fact that they usually kick over in less than a full revolution. Bent rods are common with diesels and catastrophic engine failure often results before the problem is discovered.

It is usually much harder to track water in the exhaust after an engine has been run for a period of time because the rust trails will get covered up with exhaust soot rather quickly. Try scraping the soot from the inside of the manifold to see if there is rust under it. No trails will likely remain in the head, but pitting on the exhaust valves is a possibility. Note that the valve chamber in the head should be expected to fill up with water on any valve that remained closed. Look for a water/corrosion line on the valve stem at the anticipated level.

Corrosion caused by exhaust system aspiration. A boat that is docked in a position stern-to the waves for lengthy periods are subject to wet salty air being forced through the exhaust system and through any open valves. This causes rapid but rather light surface corrosion on the cylinder walls and exhaust valve seats. This leaves telltale ring marks on the cylinder walls as shown in Figure 9-17.

High exhaust system back pressure is a fairly frequent contributory cause of diesel engine failures. Excessive exhaust pressure usually results from undersize exhaust piping or mufflers, and occasionally exhaust system piping design. The exhaust system is part of the aspiration system — air-in, air-out — so it should be obvious that because hot exhaust gasses are not being evacuated as rapidly as they should, higher internal temperatures will result and the engine performance will suffer. The primary effects of high exhaust pressure are usually mid to long term in the form of piston and exhaust valve burning and greatly reduced service life. It is often a primary cause of engine failure.

Low Fuel Lubricity

A relatively little-known problem is poor lubricity of diesel fuel. When diesel fuel is refined, it normally has inadequate lubricity. Therefore, nearly all refiners will add something to increase lubricity since for fuel injectors and pumps to function properly, lubricity must be at a certain level. The problem comes when a distributor dilutes it with a less costly fuel to increase profits. Lubricity then falls and injection system failures then occur. The premier failure feature is piston failure.

Moreover, according to some researchers, efforts to lower sulfur content also lowers lubricity. And since sulfur leads to air pollution problems, efforts are afoot to reduce the sulfur content of fuels. Therefore, fuel quality related problems are likely to increase in the future. Presently there are no standards for fuel lubricity but efforts to create standards are underway. One of the main problems is that tests for lubricity are time-consuming and too expensive at the moment to be commonly conducted. The investigator should stay alert to new developments in fuel testing for, should a new, cost-effective test method be devised, fuel lubricity testing should become a standard element of diesel engine failure analysis.

A lack of lubricity results in friction and wear of injector parts. This typically leads to a sticking and leaking injector that, in turn, leads to piston failure. Solution: whenever piston melting is involved, have an injection shop or metallurgist examine the injectors for wear and sticking.

Machinery damage investigations nearly always involves the chicken-or-the-egg question of which came first. The difficulty is one of attempting to separate that which caused the problem from the resultant damage, and this is rarely ever easy. In the case of machinery such as engines that self-destruct, evidence of the cause may be completely destroyed, seriously damaged or altered, or it may simply be impossible to differentiate between the cause and the effect. Because of these problems, investigations of machinery damage tend to have a lower success rate than many others.

Lack of Use

It is hard for laymen to appreciate that lack of use is extremely damaging to marine engines but it should be easier to understand with a good appreciation of just how terribly corrosive is the saltwater marine environment. It was discussed earlier how aspiration through the exhaust system causes internal corrosion and its effects. It is entirely true that a fresh water environment is less corrosive, though not always due to the presence of salt. Colder climate fresh water use results in substantially longer engine life, by the calendar rather than hour meter, mainly because boats are laid up and out of commission for a large part of the year. Being hauled out, the exhaust pipes are not subject to the effects of surging water.

When saltwater is vaporized from spray, the salt separates out and becomes airborne. On a day when the sea is rough, there is so much salt in the air that it can be seen as a cloud of mist along the beach. The same thing happens from the spray that the boat throws, much of which will be taken in through the engine room vents. Thus, sea water boat engines will be ingesting salt crystals plus water vapor in varying amounts depending ventilation system design and whether or not the engines have good air filters. Gas engines almost never do. Salt in a cylinder, of course, is very abrasive and will lead to accelerated wear and corrosion.

Internal engine corrosion can occur when an exhaust system is situated at or near the waterline so that water is surging in and out of the exhaust pipe almost continuously. This pushes wet, salt-laden air into any cylinder in which the exhaust valves are open. In a matter of weeks rust can form on the cylinder walls. Each time the engine is started, the rings scrape on this abrasive oxide, and the process is repeated over and over until excessive ring wear occurs. Most often the first sign of a problem becomes evident with low compression and poor performance due to corrosion on exhaust valves and seats. Later on, excessive ring wear kicks in.

More frequent use goes a long way to alleviate the excessive wear by (1) oiling the cylinder walls and (2) removing light surface rust before it becomes more damaging. Tests have shown that gravity and evaporation can remove oil from cylinder walls in 2-3 weeks; the recommended frequency of engine operation is once per week.

Engine Overload on High Performance Diesels

The top cause of boat engine failures is failure to maintain the engine properly. The second most common cause (particularly diesel engines) is from squeezing too much horsepower from a basic engine block.

The concept of a high performance diesel engine is in direct conflict with the benefits boat owners think they are getting from diesel power, specifically, longevity, reliability and economy. There is a limit to how much power can be extracted from a given size cylinder block without sacrificing reliability and engine life. The more horsepower that is pulled out of an engine, the shorter it's service life will be as a result of increased temperatures, stress and more rapid wear. When we think of high performance diesels as similar to racing engines, we can get a better understanding of why a high performance diesel doesn't last for 3,000 hours. Why do modern racers rebuild their engines after every race? Because of the terrible heat, stress and damage caused to the engine by squeezing the maximum amount of power from it. So, why should high performance diesels be much different?

The greater the number of revolutions it makes, the more wear will occur over a given period of time. Chronologically, a diesel that turns 3400 RPM will wear 42% faster than an engine that turns 2400 RPM because the pistons are going up and down 42% more! This increased wear is inevitable and unpreventable, but that is not the only negative factor.

As boat owners want to go faster and faster, engine manufacturers often compromise common sense and raise power ratings to a point where the engine either becomes unreliable or has a vastly reduced service life. Most boat owners seem to think that these high performance engines should last for many thousands of hours; rare is the engine that ever does. The primary reason why "premature" engine failure occurs with HP engines is the inability of the cooling system to remove the additional heat generated from burning larger amounts of fuel. It is possible and not uncommon for manufacturers to exceed that limit.

What happens is basically this: Horsepower is increased to the point where the cooling system can no longer provide adequate cooling for the entire engine. This does not mean that engine coolant temperatures (as generally measured by a sensor immersed in coolant) can't be kept within limits, but that the cooling jackets in the engine — which are limited in size by necessity — can no longer provide adequate or even heat transfer to *all* areas of the cylinder block or head. Some parts of the block are going to be hotter than others, so the problem becomes one of localized overheating. When uneven heat transfer occurs the cylinder block, heads or manifolds can become distorted resulting in uneven wear to a degree that can be catastrophic, even result in cracked castings, but more often detectable uneven wear. Typical evidence is the cylinder that wears out of round which should be readily evident on close examination.

The case of the 12V92 Detroit Diesel at 1300 hp is a classic example of this problem wherein the upper sections of the cylinder liners would go out of round, leaving a wear pattern that was very distinct where piston rings gouged scallops in the cylinder walls. The source of the problem was ultimately traced to the fact that the engine was generating more heat than the cooling system could remove. Unfortunately, cylinder block heat distortion is not always this easy to detect, and can involve cylinder heads, valve train, gasket problems and even crankshaft misalignment. Whenever failures involving high performance diesels are encountered, excessive horsepower should be suspect. Abnormal wear patterns are typically indicative high horsepower premature failures and excessive wear.

So how do we define high performance? Whenever the horsepower to displacement ratio is greater than a factor of one 1.00 (horsepower divided by displacement), I consider that to be high performance. A 500 c.i.d. engine should be able to put out 400 hp with reasonable service life, but is likely to be unsatisfactory at 500 hp. This number is based on experience to the extent that engines below this factor of 1 have a much higher probability of an adequate service life while those above that number tend to demonstrate substantially reduced service life. While I do not have any hard data, my experience suggests that a reasonable service life for a marine diesel in pleasure craft service would be approximately 2,000 - 2500 hours with adequate maintenance. The median is probably closer to 1,500 hours. For high performance engines, this number comes down to around 1,000 hours and often much less. Service life is defined as operating hours between major overhauls (It is useless to talk about averages since there are too many variables involved that prohibit defining what an average is.)

The fact of the matter is that the investigator of diesel engine claims will frequently be up against the question of failures involving high performance diesels. The controlling factor will usually be a matter of the degree of internal wear versus engine hours. He will also find it useful to examine the service history of the engine where a pattern of premature failures may exist.

Propeller Overload

Diesel engines are designed to operate at specific speeds under specific load conditions. While this can be a very complex issue, for our purposes we need to understand that overload conditions with boat engines derives mainly from improper propeller selection. When a propeller is too large in diameter or pitch, it will not allow the engine to turn up to the full rated RPM, an indicator that the propeller is placing too much load on the engine. This will result in a condition of over-fueling, incomplete combustion and carbon build up with all the attendant problems described above.

Improper propellering is the hidden fault for the investigator since it is very hard for him to make this determination. The only way for him to do is by means of research against the size props that similar or identical vessels are using, or possibly with the boat builder. It is not unusual for boat owners to experiment with propellers to try to make their boats go faster and thus inadvertently overload their engines. Evidences are excessive carbonization, exhaust smoking and propensity to overheat. Look for heavy exhaust soot on the transom as an indicator.

It is imperative that the engines turn up to *exactly* their rated RPM; fifty or one hundred RPM off is not close enough. Question the owner about top engine speed, propellers and symptoms. Any time overload is suspected it will be useful to try to check the current propeller size against what the boat came with originally. This may be included in the owner's manual or obtained from the builder directly.

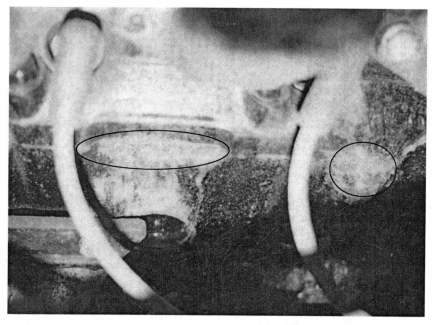

Fig. 9-18. Head gasket leaks on a 454 gas engine to the outside of the block leaves telltale evidence even before tear down. In this case, the engine marinizer did not use proper marine gaskets on a salt water cooled engine.

Failure to Change Oil Filters

With both gas and diesel engines, the failure to change filters eventually results in the filter being plugged up to the point that the by-pass valve is opened, putting the filter completely out of the loop. At this point, the build up of carbon and other debris in the oil occurs rapidly. With gas engines, this is exacerbated by the crankcase rebreather. With diesel engines the carbon content increases dramatically, raising the viscosity and degreasing overall lubrication. The passages through the crankshaft are the first to be affected and bearing damage is usually the first thing to occur. The physical evidence is unmistakable because it occurs more or less evenly throughout with every bearing and every piston. And, if that does not tell the tale, the condition of the oil will.

Manufacturing/Design Errors

Failures may result from faults in design or manufacturing and though they are not common, typically appear in large numbers. The most common types of design failures involve cooling systems and the use of aluminum components that are essentially incompatible with this application. Two other recent instances involve piston failures in M.A.N. diesel engines and cylinder head failures in Caterpillar 3116 engines. Normally such failures occur very early on with the introduction of a new model but the problem is soon detected and remedied by the manufacturer. But not always. Sometimes the manufacturer goes into a state of denial and tries to deny and conceal the problem. Of course, when the manufacturer owns up to a problem, there is little reason for us to get involved, so in most cases of manufacturing error we run up against a manufacturer that is unwilling to admit to the problem.

Unfortunately for us and boat owners, manufacturers and their repairing dealers have the ability cover up such errors through denial and withholding of information. This is a problem that the investigator will run into repeatedly. The first hint that we get that we may be facing a serial failure usually occurs when we hear through scuttlebutt — sources such as yacht captains and boat yards — that a particular failure has occurred on multiple occasions. Invariably we run up against the problem of affiliated dealers and repairers being unwilling to divulge any information about such problems because to do so threatens their relationship with the manufacturer. Even independent repairers (who depend on dealers for parts and support) are usually unwilling to admit that the problem exists.

This state of affairs leaves us with the only option of independently proving that the fault is the result of a production or design error, a prospect that can be quite expensive — but not always — because occasionally the fault is easier to prove. A recent example involving Z-F transmissions will illustrate.

In this case a number of grounding and striking submerged object claims came my way in which only moderate running gear damage produced cracked and shattered aluminum gear casings. The first three were instances where the gear casing had simply cracked, and though I was suspicious and didn't think that this should have happened, I wasn't motivated to fully investigate. These were all gear boxes behind 1,000+ horsepower engines.

Eventually a fourth case came in where the gear box had shattered into several dozen pieces. It looked as though it were made of glass and hit with a hammer (Fig. 9-19). This case drew a lot of amazement; no one, including myself, had ever seen a transmission so totally destroyed. Examination of the gearbox, or what was left of it, suggested that this was not a design fault for the break up of the casting followed no pattern. The casing fractured through thick as well as thin sections. Sudden stoppage of the propeller shaft apparently torqued the box apart.

The history of severe groundings, such as hitting reefs at high speed, is that cast iron gear casings have been known to fracture, but this is rare. Frequently large diameter shafts are twisted right off with little or no damage to the gearbox, so why were these Z-F gear casings breaking up?

Fig. 9-19.

One clue was that while the gear case carried a Z-F name plate, cast into the casing was "MPN-Italy", indicating that the gear box was not made in Germany or by Z-F.

A metallurgical analysis was performed on the aluminum casting in which the metal was assayed as "Class D" casting alloy on a scale of A to D with the later being the least desirable. The characteristics of class D casting alloy is that it is cheap, weak and brittle. The gear box should have been class A material.

With the Caterpillar 3116 engine cited earlier, proving a manufacturing error was far more difficult where there was a variety of different types of failures to cylinder heads, from cracking to dropped valves. Once again the basis of the problem was traced to engine parts manufactured in Italy, in this case the entire cylinder head. The difficulty here was that a much more costly analysis needed to be performed on relatively low value losses. In most cases the client preferred to just repair the damage than go to the trouble to make a recovery. The knowledge of exactly what was wrong with these cylinder heads was so closely held by Caterpillar that even after years of questioning repairers, I never did find out.

Manufacturing errors involving GM V-8 gasoline engine blocks are very rare and are more likely to involve engine marinizers.

Engine Damage Due to Sudden Stoppage

During my career as an insurance investigator I have investigated dozens of engine damage claims wherein the boat owner alleged that engine damage was caused by hitting something or grounding at high speed. These were cases where engine damage was alleged to be the result of sudden engine stoppage. Even though there was no apparent damage to the engines, the owners demanded that the engines be torn down to inspect everything. In some cases the insurers foolishly obliged, but are under no obligation to do so because the burden of proving his damages belongs to the insured, no the insurer. In no case have I ever found damage occurring to an engine under these circumstances. Transmission damage, certainly, but not engine damage. The major part of the shock of sudden stoppage at high speed is born by the clutches, the output shaft and the transmission casing which have fractured occasionally. Expect the coupling bolt holes to be elongated or deformed.

All large diesel engines have very heavy duty drive dampner plates so that there is thick rubber insulating the flywheel from the drive plate. Gas engines have shock absorber springs in the pressure plate. Damage would first have to occur to the dampner before engine damage could ensue. Most often, drive dampner failures are due to age and fatigue as this component does not last forever. High speed groundings have completely torn bottoms out of boats without causing engine damage from sudden stoppage of the propeller. View any such claims with skepticism. If the insured demands an engine tear down without direct evidence of damage, it should be done at his own cost.

Useful Data on Electronic Diesels

Diesel engine systems are being increasingly computerized, the main thrust of which is increased power and efficiency. Unfortunately, these benefits come at a high cost to owners and insurers because not only is the component cost very high, but also the cost of labor to service these high tech systems.

Large engine systems such as the Detroit Diesel DDEC and Caterpillar systems operate from a central computer system. These systems operate from an array of sensors that monitor temperatures and pressures and store records of same in the CPU. Such data is often used in conjunction with warranty claims and so manufacturers and dealers like to consider this data as confidential information. Typically this data is only available with the manufacturer's diagnostic equipment and software, without which no one can access the data.

Obviously, this raises some interesting legal questions about to whom this information belongs and who has a right to it. If such data were readily available to the owner and others there'd be no problem but my own experience is that while Detroit Diesel[6] usually makes it available, Caterpillar does not. A similar situation also exists with fuel injected outboard motors.

This computerized data is extremely useful for evaluating machinery damage claims because not only does it record overheats, but the actual location where it occurs. It detects loss of oil pressure and internal aspiration pressures and thus is an excellent diagnostic tool — if those in possession of the diagnostic software are willing to make it available.

On Chickens and Eggs

No other types of investigations are so plagued with the question of which came first, the chicken or the egg, as is machinery damage analysis. Engine failures usually display any number of damage types and evidences, and this makes it difficult to figure out what happened first. The solution to this problem is patience and diligence.

It is a general principle or rule that the causes of engine failures do not originate within the engine but normally from some outside circumstance such as a failure to maintain properly, or some event external to the vessel such as grounding. The problem with most faulty failure analysis is that the analyst concentrated on the engine damage and neglected to consider all the systems and the environment. Therefore it is essential that all aspects of the various systems be examined, and that each system be considered in its entirety.

For example, a severe engine overheat situation will need to have the cooling system examined, not just the engine components, but out to the engine intakes on the bottom of the hull. The same goes for the aspiration and exhaust systems. An investigator cannot say he had done a thorough job until he has examined all of each system. In most cases this will answer the chicken or the egg question.

Even so, some cases will involve more than one cause so that we will need to answer the question of whether one cause led to the other, did both contribute concurrently, or is one primary over the other that is merely contributory. Such questions are always relevant to the determination of insurance coverage, as well as other issues. If these questions cannot be answered with certainty, the investigator must say so in his report.

Components and System Failures

Cylinder Bore Distortion

Most of the literature that I have reviewed about piston scuffing – quarter point and so on – attributes the various patterns to piston overheating. While this is to some degree true, most such analytical advice fails to take into account the effects of cylinder block distortion. This only occurs under global overheat conditions, and therefore the effects of distortion should appear more or less the same in all cylinders. This will occur in situations of heavy cooling jacket corrosion, and since the heat transfer has been reduced for an extended period of time, pronounced ring wear should also be evident.

Piston Scuffing

Piston overheating and failure is by far the most common form of engine failure which can occur globally or in isolation, factors which provide valuable clues as to what the cause is. Isolated piston overheating points to a particular source within that cylinder, whereas global overheating suggests an overall systemic fault. However, the subject of piston failure is complex, and there is a long list of identifying factors some of which are clear cut and others nearly hopeless in identifying the cause because there are multiple possibilities.

We start with the fact that piston expansion due to excessive heat is going to produce increased contact with the liner, usually resulting in melting from friction which produces even more heat. Melting will probably cause detonation, which in turn will hasten the demise of the piston.

Piston scuffing can occur for many reasons and the investigator's primary job is to find the initiating cause by a process of elimination or association such as linking one fault with another. Whether the damage has occurred with just one piston or one bank of cylinders is often the defining clue since causes may be local or global.

Engine Top End Overheating

Top end over heating is the result of operation with low coolant levels in closed cooling systems. The cause may be a matter of neglect or a faulty system pressure cap. Many, if not most boat owners rely upon the coolant recovery bottle to judge whether the system has adequate coolant. This only works when (1) the pressure cap functions properly or, (2) the small orifice in the neck of the heat exchanger tank isn't clogged. The result is that the system is low on coolant and they don't know it.

Top end overheating can result in cracked heads, galling of valve stems & guides and valve burning or breakage. Usually, no piston or cylinder damage occurs. In older, abused engines, the damages and evidences are so extensive that long term neglect and degradation is the only thing that can be determined with any degree of certainty, there being no one particular cause other than general neglect.

Open up the heat exchanger tank and check for water lines that may indicate a long-term, low coolant condition.

The wrong thermostat or a malfunctioning thermostat can result in an engine running at excessively high temperatures. This causes abnormally high piston and liner temperatures that cause both to go slightly out of round. The end result is piston scuffing, metal transfer (piston to liner) and inevitable failure.

Operating without a thermostat in cold water will result in uneven heating and heat distortion related wear, quarter point scuffing and possibly cracked heads, poor combustion and carbon build up. Engine failure would not be an immediate result.

Piston Crown Overheating

The piston crown overheating occurs when the piston rapidly overheats. The galling is confined to the area from the rings on upward or perhaps just slightly below. This is normally a global condition affecting all pistons more or less equally. The causes are limited to:

- Too much fuel (always a global condition)
- Too little air (always a global condition)
- Exhaust restriction/excessive back pressure (always a global condition)
- Engine timing (always a global condition)
- Injector timing (may be only one cylinder)
- Lack of piston crown cooling (global or local depending on oiling system)

Too much fuel in conjunction with insufficient air produces serious exhaust by-products so look for exhaust soot fouling on the boat exterior as an indicator.

Exhaust restrictions usually result in valve burning as well.

Bad injector timing produces a lot of carbon.

Lack of piston crown cooling is always evident by a pattern of burned oil on the underside of the crown that will be very obvious. If cooled by a stream of oil, check the nozzles for restrictions. Check all pistons undersides for consistency of burning.

Piston Crown Melting An extreme local overheat condition, usually the result of bad air/fuel ratio which is also the result of an exhaust restriction. Complete a full check of fuel induction and exhaust system. Protective carbon usually burns away completely. Patchy carbon loss is probably due to detonation.

Piston Crown Holed Detonation in diesels and preignition in gas engines is the sole cause of extreme melting and holes in piston crowns. If only one piston, have metallurgist check others for signs of melting. Check all manifold vacuum hoses for leaks.

Quarter Point Scuffing

In this condition scuffing on the piston occurs at four evenly spaced points in a vertical line from top to bottom. It's primary cause is a general cooling system failure which can include corrosion or sludge on cooling jackets.

Piston Ring Groove Collapse

When rings are seized within the piston grooves, usually the first, without any carbon build up, the cause is detonation, usually accompanied by some form of cracking and/ or melting of piston crown.

Center Point Scuffing

Galling at only one point on a piston skirt regardless of vertical position usually indicates an insufficiency of the cooling system, usually in high performance engines where the horsepower exceeds the systems ability to maintain even temperatures. This is usually accompanied by very abnormal ring wear showing up on the liner and rings. This condition can also appear as a result of heavy loading of a very cold engine or racing a cold engine after start up where no other symptoms appear.

Other Piston Damage

Most other kinds of piston damage are readily identifiable such as foreign material, excessive wear from dust and debris, exhaust valve failures, wrist pin adrift.

Broken Piston Rings

Broken rings occurring in conjunction with severe piston galling damage is not indicative of anything for the galling probably occurred as the result of the broken ring. First, eliminate all other possible global conditions. There are three primary causes of broken piston rings:

- Detonation/preignition; generally occurs in conjunction with piston crown melting no matter how slight. This is the number one cause of broken rings. Groove distortion from ring hammering should be present.

- Excessive carbonization leads to extreme piston groove distortion and melting; ring grooves are impacted, some rings may be seized.

- Over-revving – no other symptoms present.

- Improper installation, excessive wall clearance

- Improper break in (when engine hours are low)

Micro analysis of ring lands will usually yield clues – is there any melting? Inquire whether engine was ever rebuilt as errors may exist; check ring specs against manufacturer requirement. Check ring gap and piston-wall clearance. Check cylinder-liner bore.

Excessive Ring and Cylinder Wear

Excessive ring and cylinder wear, when it occurs without similar wear to other parts, is most likely the result of lack of use wherein the cylinder walls rusted and the rings scraped it off repeatedly each time the engine is started. This is a condition that is often see with boat engines that are operated infrequently. It is usually accompanied by excessive rusting of valves and seats. Evidence of such rust probably won't show in the cylinders although it is occasionally evident by a series of concentric rings on the cylinder denoting each time the engine was stopped for a lengthy period. More likely, however, there will be evidence of rust corrosion on some of the valve stems below the guides. This is likely to appear on some, but not all valves. If the engine had been run hard recently before failure, the only other evidence would likely be corrosion to the valve head seat areas. Look for excessive wear in these areas.

TIP: Some engine manufacturers (Detroit Diesel is one) put ring wear grooves in their rings so that the amount of ring wear is visible or measurable. Otherwise, it is very difficult or impossible to measure ring wear without a specialized instrument.

Excessive wear occurring generally throughout the engine, particularly on cam shafts, and valve lifters is a likely indicator of failure to change oil and filters. With gas engines this is easy to detect because the end result is a build-up of gums and varnish in places where it shouldn't be present, especially valve lifters; cam and lifter wear will probably be excessive as well, along with acid damage to bearings. Accumulations of sludge with engines without emission control is not common. Cut the oil filter apart and check for clogging. Check or test the oil cooler for restrictions and clogging. Check air intake, intercooler, flame arrestor for signs of foreign material (debris).

One of the better indicators is to judge the amount of wear relative to total engine hours, and in consideration of what the anticipated service life between overhauls is. Excessive wear appearing in an engine with only 800 hours, be it gas or diesel, is abnormal. We need to keep in mind also that just because the engine oil is relatively

Fig. 9-20. The abnormal injector spray pattern, both right and left, is a good indicator of causation. Note the great difference of carbon built up between these two pistons. Both of these cylinders are suffering from a leaking head gasket, but the one on the left is into the water jacket that had salt water in it.

clean at inspection time does not mean that engine service was not neglected previously.

Worn, Leaking Injectors

With a properly functioning diesel, the injector spray pattern appears symmetrically on the piston crown rather like a flower. Pattern is dependent on the number of spray orifices, so be sure to check number of orifices against "flower petals". When this pattern varies widely between pistons, it is an indication that there are injection problems. When no pattern exists at all, it is because detonation has blown all the carbon away.

An injector that is not working properly but throwing streams of fuel into the cylinder will cause severe damage. If it leaks onto the piston crown, it may burn a crater in the crown or in severe cases, a hole. Often, a bad injector will wash the lube oil off part of the cylinder wall resulting in ring friction damage. This is ascertained by associating a faulty injector with a particular cylinder where this sort of ring galling has occurred.

Whenever suspicious spray patterns appear, injectors should be sent off to a qualified injection shop with a request for a report on each.

Engine Carbonization & Detonation

Neither carbonization nor detonation are themselves primary causes but, rather, are secondary symptoms; both are abnormal conditions that are the result of yet another cause. When carbon and detonation have been identified, we need yet to identify what caused these conditions.

Fig. 9-21. Extreme carbonization built up below crown, impacted first ring groove and jammed ring tight in groove. At this point direct contact between piston and wall begins resulting in piston slap and metal transfer.

Fig. 9-22. In the larger view below, note how carbon has built up between first and second ring. In this case, the carbon is due to prolonged and excessive idling, otherwise this piston would have been destroyed if run at high speed.

Carbonization

Carbon normally burns or fuses into the piston head and is not easily removed. The pitted, orange peel-like texture of piston heads is the result of this burning and is completely normal and the color ranges from orange-brown to black.

Carbonization is herein defined as *excessive* carbon build up within the combustion chambers as a result of incomplete combustion; it does not refer to the normal amount of carbon that is ever present in all engines. Carbonization results primarily from over-fueling, insufficient air, or prolonged low speed idling in diesels and any other condition that results in incomplete combustion. In a properly tuned engine, heavy carbon build up is not normal. An even and normal layer of carbon across the piston head helps protect it from heat. Over time, that carbon may become hardened and burned into the aluminum (as seen by the pitting of the surface). Later the carbon builds up to a heavier layer and may begin to flake away because it is not fused into the aluminum. This, in turn, causes uneven heating and heat distortion because obviously, the thicker the carbon, the greater its insulating capacity.

Carbonization problems typically begin by reducing engine performance resulting in increased heating. This then accelerates the carbon build up rate. Eventually, pieces of carbon will become red hot; detonation may come and go. Carbon begins to flake off and likely will end up lodged between the piston and cylinder wall or on a valve seat. This begins the process of piston crown edge melting and cylinder wall scuffing or even valve pitting. These are conditions that rapidly worsen until piston or some other failure occurs.

Detonation

Detonation occurs in gas engines primarily as a result of low octane fuel or a bad air/ fuel ratio (lean). But when it occurs in a diesel the cause is usually the result of red hot carbon deposits that ignite the fuel prematurely or unevenly. Carbon is protective of aluminum pistons, indeed necessary, in moderate amounts but harmful in large quantities. Aluminum alloy pistons melt at a mere 1500 degrees while the combustion temperature of fuel is around 3,000 degrees. The aluminum piston dome does not melt due to a protective carbon layer that forms almost immediately and fuses right into the aluminum where it will remain unless detonation burns it away. Carbon does not burn until nearly 3,000 degrees, so as long as the carbon layer exists, it prevents piston melting.

Detonation starts from the fuel pre-igniting from a hot spot in the combustion chamber such as those red hot carbon deposits. Secondary ignition later occurs at the normal combustion timing because detonation combustion is not complete. During detonation the almost instantaneous ignition of the fuel/air mixture causes rapid shock waves that pound against the sides of the combustion chamber and piston. These shock waves produce the knocking sounds we may hear in our automobile engines but are less likely to be heard in boat engines and not at all in diesels. Shock waves that are strong enough to mechanically "ping" the walls of the combustion chamber are strong enough to carry away the protective carbon layer.

Without a carbon layer protecting the aluminum piston, the surfaces are exposed to the combustion flame which may then melt through the piston crown. Melting may also occur on the edge of the piston next to the cylinder wall where pressure waves reflecting off the wall combine and amplify the pressure at specific locations. The pressure of combustion blows the molten aluminum away. Sharp edges in the metal such as at the edge of the piston and along valve cut-outs in high compression pistons, or high dome pistons are difficult for carbon layers to provide protection and are usually first damaged by detonation.

If the detonation is minor, or doesn't last long, the result is that carbon deposits in the area of boundary layer failure are burnt off the surfaces leaving bare aluminum. If the conditions that cause detonation are quickly terminated, such as a power change made by the operator, little or no engine damage may occur and the carbon is reestablished.

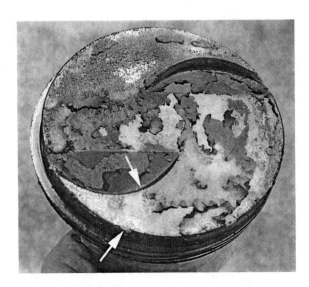

Fig. 9-23. Early phase detonation damage. Carbon layer is partially burned off and melting is occurring at high points.

Detonation Damage

With more severe or prolonged detonation, local temperatures melt the aluminum causing holes in the piston. With any engine type, burning of holes into or through the piston first requires the destruction of the boundary layer and a burning off interceding carbon layer. Evidence of boundary layer destruction by detonation is identified by the complete removal of carbon deposits in areas normally observed to contain carbon, typically showing bright metal while all else is carbon covered. This flaking away is often localized and close to the outside edge of the piston dome.

Detonation damage is not limited to burning of holes in pistons or the combustion chamber (typically between the valve seats). The rapid increase in pressures can overload the rod bearings causing lubrication failure and possibly bearing failure. Piston ring breakage is common. There could be other hidden damage caused by detonation such as over-stressing of the crankshaft or propeller shaft.

When detonation occurs with the piston on its upward compression stroke near the top we have a condition of force against force. These forces can be up to three times the normal force of combustion and are extremely damaging. Damage may result to valves, pistons, rods and bearings and head gaskets. Unfortunately, detonation damage is almost impossible to prove unless piston melting occurs, but telltale signs are lack of carbon and a lack of other faulty conditions and occurs with old as well as new engines. Deformation of ring grooves without other associated wear indices is another indicator.

The key indicator is that most carbon layers are blown off piston crown with patches of bright metal showing, often with melting present. Micro analysis will revel that melting has occurred. Detonation is often a local condition wherein frequently only one piston suffers severe melting damage or is holed. This becomes prima facie evidence that detonation is the cause. In gas engines excessively hot spark plugs or spark advance can also be a cause of piston melting. However, this will lead to a global damage condition affecting all cylinders so that when occurring to only one cylinder, ignition timing can effectively be ruled out.

Leaking injectors which drip liquid fuel on the piston crown can also cause piston melting and holing. Therefore, when limited piston damage occurs, it is necessary to

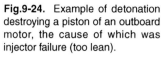

Fig.9-24. Example of detonation destroying a piston of an outboard motor, the cause of which was injector failure (too lean).

examine the injectors for signs of damage.

Outboard Engines Failures

The leading cause of outboard engine failures is pre ignition and detonation. These are similar phenomenon with differing causes but the same end results: acute engine damage and ultimately failure. The damage caused consists of thermal fatigue, ring land damage/compression (stuck rings) and piston crown erosion and melting.

The primary causes are (1) incorrect fuel octane, (2) poor quality fuel, and (3) excessively lean air/fuel ratio. The later is usually caused by fouled carburetor jets and vacuum leaks. Yet another possible cause is improper wiring such a switched spark plug wires or reversed wires from trigger to switch box or coils. This is identifiable by the detonation damage only occurring to a few cylinders. Cross firing is yet another cause, due to either old ignition wires or excessive salt and moisture.

As with all other engines, detonation in outboards is usually caused by excessive carbon build up which is readily discoverable as a cause. Based strictly on scuttlebutt on the waterfront, along with limited personal experience, Mercury fuel injected engines in the period 1999-2001 were plagued with carbonization problems. Other possible causes are wrong spark plugs and plugs with broken ceramic and an engine run on gasohol (gas + ethyl alcohol).

Valve Failure

Valve failure is a more common occurrence with gas engines but not diesels. The main reason is higher engine speeds, timing problems, and increased heat and corrosion. The cause of valve failures is usually readily identifiable by metallurgical analysis as long as an undisturbed piece of the broken part is available. Valve failures occur for three primary causes, impacts, corrosion and fatigue.

Fatigue is fairly common with older engines that have been worked hard or poorly maintained. Fatigue fracturing is readily identifiable by naked eye if you know what a fatigue fracture looks like.

Impacts occur primarily due to engine over speeding that causes the valves to "float", that is, the valves are going up and down so fast that the spring hasn't adequate time to close the valve fully and it is struck by the piston. In this event, a dent is left in the piston crown. Impacts may also occur due to weak valve springs, pointing out that spring tension should be measured for every valve failure case to determine whether spring tension was a factor. Also, pounding marks should be evident on the rocker arm and stem head.

Corrosion may cause pits that create a stress riser that initiates a fracture, typically occurring around the seat area, again readily determinable through metallurgical analysis. Corrosion shows up mainly in seat land areas of valve and seat.

Valves are supposed to rotate, but once they gain a little wear they often stop rotating. This shows up on the stem tip as a "bow tie" wear pattern whereas a rotating valve displays concentric circle pattern. A similar non-rotational pattern is likely to show up on the valve land and seat.

Other secondary causes are valve stem retainer or key failure (usually obvious), may be a defect or the result of valve floating from weak springs or over speeding. Fractures at the keeper groove are usually caused by over speed or wrong ignition timing.

When excessive guide wear occurs along with valve breakage, check for excessive wear in other engine parts. Also examine seat for uneven wear or build up of deposits. An unevenly seating valve will cause it to be slightly cocked causing wear to one side of the guide, will stop rotation and result in breakage at some point below the guide whether of the stem or flute. Lack of lubrication will show up as galling in the guide area.

If the investigator is present at tear down he will have the opportunity to layout the valves as they were with each cylinder. If not, then it's difficult to try to figure out where the valves were located. This is important in order to determine whether compression was occurring. As a general rule, compression loss means less complete combustion which can be expected to translate to greater carbon build up. When valves and seats reveal incomplete seating, general symptoms of incomplete combustion should be expected.

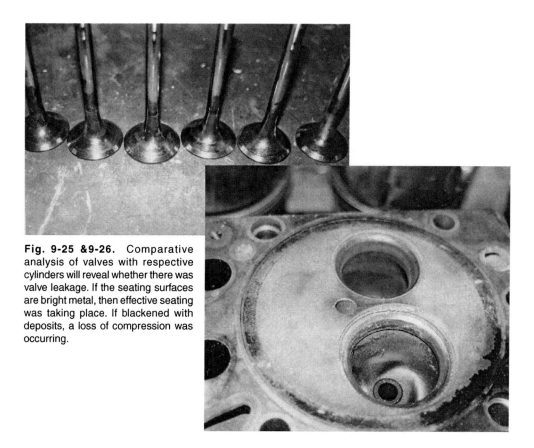

Fig. 9-25 &9-26. Comparative analysis of valves with respective cylinders will reveal whether there was valve leakage. If the seating surfaces are bright metal, then effective seating was taking place. If blackened with deposits, a loss of compression was occurring.

Excessive Wear Rates

It is oft stated by many experts that engines in boats don't wear out; instead they die of neglect and abuse. This is particularly true of gas engines and moderate horsepower diesels. However, high performance, high horsepower diesels are often an exception to the rule. With gas engines there is also an exception, which is when engines are subjected to excessively heavy loads as when gas engines are powering a larger vessel that should probably be powered with diesels. Very heavy loads result in excessive wear rates along with other problems, such as those caused by lugging which occurs when the load is so heavy that the engine has trouble turning up to speed. Prolonged lugging inevitably results in abnormal combustion, overheating and reduced service life resulting in premature failures.

Excessive ring and cylinder wear relative to total engine hours, absent any other major faults, is an indication of (1) excessively high load, (2) excess horsepower, or (3) poor maintenance. Failure to perform oil and filter changes at proscribed intervals will usually show up in the crankshaft bearings as well as cylinder wall wear, camshaft wear and sludge and varnish build up in gas engines.

When unusual wear rates are encountered, consider whether engine power is adequate for vessel size and weight. With high performance diesels, also consider whether excessive horsepower is to blame, in conjunction with indications of over loading or lugging.

Gas engines are more prone to damage that results from incomplete combustion that causes a power loss. Any power loss in a larger boat is immediately evident by a loss of speed; in most cases the boat owner will increase throttle to make up for this. With a diesel engine black exhaust soot would result, and since boat owners don't like to leave a cloud of black smoke, the problem usually gets corrected rather quickly. But gas engines won't leave a cloud of black smoke, so the problem is much less evident. The net result is unrecognized overloading that, if allowed to continue, will eventually wreck the engine by various means from carbonization to detonation to fatigue.

The Cylinder Head Dome

The normal appearance of the head fire deck or dome is variable, depending on how much idling was done before the engine was last run. Any carbon build up on a properly operating engine will quickly burn away at speed. The color should range from rust - orange to black. A light coating of carbon is considered normal. If the color ranges from whitish to light tan, and the pistons also show clean aluminum, this indicates excessive heat and may be due to global overheating or detonation.

Blown Head Gaskets

Blown head gaskets are most often the result of overheating and secondarily due to either salt water in the cooling system or failure to maintain a proper coolant. The result is that corrosion erodes the head surface under the gasket surface. The result is that on the compression stroke, combustion by products escape into the cooling system. The first indicator will be carbon in the cooling system.

Problems with leaking head gaskets tend to go on for a long time, causing major damage to various systems until, ultimately, catastrophic engine failure occurs. For this reason, careful examination of the gaskets and both of the mating surfaces should be made. The evidence of leaking gaskets becomes obvious to various degrees as shown in nearby photos. Leakage may occur between cylinders or migrate to cooling jackets. If the later, then supporting evidence appears within the cooling system.

Be sure to examine both sides of the head gaskets and to line them up in the original installed position, then compare the patterns between the various mating surfaces of the head and block. Leaks can occur on either or both sides of the gasket.

Piston Ring Blow-by

As ring wear increases, or scratches occur in liners, the amount of combustion blow-by into the crankcase increases. This puts exhaust by products directly into the engine oil, raising acidity, and increasing varnish and sludge. The increase of soot in the oil raises viscosity, filter plugging and general reduction of oil flow and distribution. Piston ring blow-by shows up as dark patterns on piston skirts.

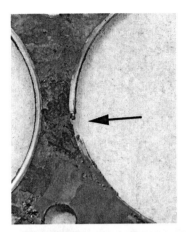

Fig. 9-27 & 9-28. Be sure to examine all sides of the head gasket and cylinder head for evidence of leaks. As shown in these photos, leaks are usually obvious. The erosion of the metal ring at left indicates the presence of water from the cooling jackets. Match the gasket with the head as it was originally installed, to see he full pattern.

Diesel Soot

Soot is formed during the combustion process and enters the crankcase with combustion gas blow-by. Soot is 98 percent carbon by weight, and has an original size of 0.01 to 0.05 micron, but tends to agglomerate to form larger particles in the crankcase. Soot levels generally increase with engine hours and fuel consumption. Excess soot increases the oil's viscosity, leading to higher temperatures, power loss and the risk of lubricant starvation, especially at start-up, but its worst damage is increased wear rates. An oil's ability to disperse soot is critical to prevent soot-polishing wear caused by the effects of soot on the oil's antiwear additives. If wear occurs in the valve train, fuel economy will suffer as injection timing and valve timing will move from their optimum settings.

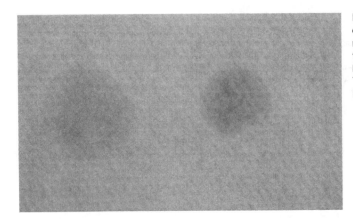

Fig.9-29. Paper towel test for oil viscosity. Drop on the left is new oil; on the right oil with only twenty hours time (gas engine) but note the difference in diffusion. The used oil spreads significantly less well.

Some mechanics learn to perform quick preliminary viscosity tests by placing a drop of oil on a paper towel and observing its ability to spread. This is only a preliminary indicator and must be done with the same type of paper every time. Of course, heavily sooted oil resists spreading. Before performing this test, test the flow on paper with clean new oil of the same viscosity as a benchmark by which to judge. Droplets must be placed at the same time.

Viscosity Thinning Damage

Understandably, many people become confused about the meaning of the term viscosity. Viscosity is the ability of a fluid to resist flow. Thus, a high viscosity oil is thicker than a low viscosity oil.

Reduced oil viscosity is primarily caused by fuel dilution resulting from fuel injector damage. At its worst it can be detected by feel but normally requires a viscosity or other tests. Oil viscosity failures usually result in catastrophic engine damage unless the symptoms are recognized early. Extreme wear, scoring, galling, ring seizure, severe bearing damage and valve train damage are universally present.

Viscosity Increases

Primarily a function of soot contamination, viscosity increases as temperature decreases. Thus, it is critical that the correct oil weight for temperature environment be selected. High viscosity results in a degradation of oil distribution, particularly to cylinder walls and the undersides of piston heads which are cooled by either oil splash or spray nozzles. Thicker oil splashes less well but nozzles will clog when oil gets too thick. Look for burned oil on undersides of pistons.

Bearing Damage

There are literally dozens of different conditions that can cause bearing damage and failure, and we'll only consider the major ones here. Color poster charts of typical bearing failure causes are readily available from bearing and engine manufacturers. When removing bearings from the engine, be sure to mark their position. Lay out in order both rod and crankshaft bearings together and analyze the overall pattern of both.

Any time bearing damage is apparent, regardless of whether it is cause or effect, the bearings along with a sample of engine oil should be sent to a metallurgist for analysis. Also, check the bottom of the pan and other engine locations for evidence of sludge: obtain samples if present. The metallurgist can readily identify the cause of most types of bearing failures through simple micro analysis. The cause of the bearing damage is likely related to the overall engine failure. Engine lubricants over time naturally turn acidic despite the addition of alkalines to help prevent this. That's why operating times between required oil changes for diesel engines is rather low. Acidity can reach such high levels that it becomes destructive of bearing and other components.

Engines normally develop condensation in the crank case shortly after startup. With longer operating times, it is evaporated away, so here again we see how short term operation can cause serious damage over time. When water is introduced into old, highly acidic oil, the results can be fatal.

Normal Wear. Wear is evenly distributed, little discoloration, few foreign particles. May show small hairline cracks on surface. Use plastigauge to measure wear.

Particle Contamination. External contaminates embedded in engine bearings usually results from failure to maintain the oil system, but it can also result from degradation or flaking of internal parts such as ring plating. Test the flow of the oil filter. If clogged, oil was by-passing and no filtration was occurring. Condition of oil is further evidence. Infrequent oil/filter change, dirty environment. Send to metallurgist who may be able to identify the material.

Fatigue/overload. Worn area on the top rod bearing only or lower crankshaft bearing only. Detonation, lugging engine, incorrect propellering.

Dealignment. Very uneven wear on both shells. Most likely bent rod, irregular side loading on piston (combustion restriction) or overhaul/manufacture defect. Possible crankshaft thrust bearing wear/failure.

Oil Starvation. Friction burns bearing up. Badly mutilated fusing. Lack of oil, clogged filter/failure of by-pass valve, blockage in oil passage.

Cavitation/erosion. Erosion and pitting on bearing surface. Often looks like electrolysis, eroded areas are bright. Acids, coolant, fuel contamination. May be in combination with overall engine wear. Send to metallurgist for analysis.

Distorted Engine Block When laid together, an uneven wear pattern is evidenced across all bearings. Extreme wear varies between upper and lower bearings, centers and edges or side to side.

Distorted Crankshaft. Unexplained wear on both upper and lower halves, concentrating at either the center or end bearings but not both. Overloading and high speeds; prevalent in high performance engines: too much power from the engine.

Transmission Failures

Transmission failures occur for a variety of reasons, including wear and tear, fatigue, design error, improper engine installation as well as selection of the wrong transmission. The later can include selecting the wrong reduction gear ratio as well as an undersize transmission. The first thing to do in every case is to check whether the manufacturer's power rating is borderline or exceeded by engine horsepower.

Historically, transmission failures have often been caused by engines mounted on stringers that are flexing. This causes the engine and shaft to go out of alignment and places great stress on the gear box. Interview the owner and ask whether there is a history of prior failures, engine mount failure, chronic stuffing box leakage, breaking or bending shafts and general alignment woes. If two or more of these problems have existed, it is likely that an unstable engine foundation is the problem.

Except for the Z-F problems mentioned above, transmissions in recent years have had fewer design-related problems than in the past when they were rather numerous, say pre 1990. Since independent transmission specialists don't sell many aftermarket transmissions, these folks tend to be forthcoming about disclosing which models seem to have problems, so don't hesitate to ask around for advice.

Alignment related problems tend to place heavy stress on the output shaft and bearings so that when rear bearing failure is involved, alignment and engine foundation including bad mounts should be suspect.

Laboratory Analysis

Oil Analysis Fundamentals

Oil analysis was originally developed as a diagnostic program to detect wear problems in machinery before serious damage ensues as an on-going monitoring program, and as a means of performing proper maintenance, not as an analytical method for failure analysis. Even so, there are many aspects of oil analysis that can be adapted and applied to failure analysis.

The basis of oil analysis is the identification of particulate matter that is suspended in oil. Particulate matter may be heavy enough, such as wear metals, that gravity will force it to settle out, which is why it is imperative that samples of oil sump heavy sludge be obtained for analysis as well. A magnet can be used to collect larger particles that are then analyzed by microscopy and other methods.

Contaminants may enter the oil from within and from without. Internal contaminates are usually wear metals, combustion by-products and self-contained coolants. External contaminates can consist of just about anything else. Engines, of course, may be built of varying materials but generally marine engines consist of a basic package of iron, chrome, copper, aluminum, lead, tin, nickel, molybdenum, antimony, titanium, and manganese. Silver may also be present. In addition to these, and complicating matters considerably, other elements are found that are part of the oil additive packages, chemicals added to improve the performance of the oil.

Particulate matter is expressed in microns, a millionth of a meter or 0.000039" and are invisible to the eye. Oil analysis results are expressed as PPM parts per million or $1/1000^{th}$ of a percent. Commercial oil analysis uses Atomic Emission Spectrometers that detect particles in the range of less than 5-10 microns and will not pick up larger particles. As wear increases in an engine, the size of wear particles increases so much of suspended wear metal will not show up. Because of such very small particles, our oil collection methods must be absolutely clean to avoid contamination.

If oil analysis is available from a metallurgical lab, it is advisable to obtain from this source rather than a firm that only does oil analysis. The reason, of course, is that a metallurgical lab is capable of doing far more work which you are likely to need. FAA certified labs are located in nearly all major cities across the U.S. and many other nations as well.

Wear metals in engines come primarily from pistons, rings cylinder walls and bearings and will be dependent on the make up of these components. Bearings contain lead, tin and copper and the degree of wear is indicated by presence of these metals as they appear in that order in the bearing sandwich of metals. Cylinder wear will yield iron, chrome and aluminum. High amounts of aluminum show up with piston skirt scoring and piston melting detonation. Very high copper (150-500 ppm) very likely comes from oil cooler tubing, especially if salt water has gotten into the oil. Usual heavy bearing wear values are under 100 ppm because this wear occurs slowly.

When considering high iron values, pay close attention to whether there is high wear on any one particular component such as cam roller, rocker arm, etc. that may be skewing the interpretation. In other words, is the high wear metal the result of a local or global wear condition or both?

Wear metal analysis is not merely a matter of determining PPM, but when particles or fragments are larger, the size and shape of the particles becomes important. Gears and roller bearings, for example, are subject to flaking action so that when flakes are found it is usually possible to determine exactly where they came from.

Contaminant elements typically consist of silicon (Si), potassium (K), sodium (Na), chlorine (Cl), boron (B) and molybdenum (Mo). Silicon comes from abrasive dirt, sodium from sea water and potassium from coolant, as do M and B.

Oil additives consist of a wide variety of elements including:

> Calcium
>
> Magnesium
>
> Phosphorus
>
> Zinc
>
> Sodium
>
> Boron
>
> Molybdenum
>
> Barium
>
> Silicon
>
> Copper

The oil analyst has data on various oils that tell him in what proportions these additives should exist and thus can identify many oils from the results. This is why it can be very misleading for an amateur to try to interpret an oil analysis.

There are a lot of things that can go wrong with oil analysis, which is why it is recommended primarily for long-term review and not short term. Therefore, for our purposes we interpret the results with a much broader factor for possible error and should not make any close tolerance judgments.

Water contamination is a common problem with marine engines that is unlikely to show up because high operating temperatures evaporate it away. If it is sea water or from the cooling system, salts and glycols will remain to tell the story. Not all labs test for glycol, so be sure to ask in advance.

Fuel dilution is something we want to know about with all oil analysis and is determinable through gas chromatography, IR and acoustic wave technology. Again, be sure of what your lab's capabilities are.

The same goes for soot which we definitely want to know more rather than less precisely. Engines manufactured after 1998 all inject higher levels of soot into crankcase oil due to EPA mandates. The allowable rate of soot is 3% so much higher levels will indicate either delayed oil changes or increased levels of wear.

Oxi-polymerization is what happens to engine oil and is the result of oxidation due to high temperatures. In a normal engine this rate is very slow. Oxidation causes polymerization and an increase of viscosity. If you're ever burned cooking oil in a frying pan, then you've witnessed polymerization. That yellow stuff stuck to the outside of the pan is polymerized oil. Combined with soot, old polymerized oil can have greatly reduced lubrication properties, increased viscosity and is indicated by TAN (total acid number) of your report. Compare the TAN number against the viscosity value. High soot and high viscosity combined with a high TAN means that the engine oil is long overdue for changing.

How we can use any of these findings for engine failure analysis depends on our specific situation and in most cases will serve as supporting, not primary evidence. To the extent that failures are often the cumulative result of failures to maintain, the proverbial chicken or egg question can frequently be resolved by a combination of visual examination, oil and wear metals analysis that will demonstrate that maintenance failures were a long standing problem that ultimately culminated in complete breakdown.

Oil Analysis

All engine failure investigations should include a lube oil analysis, which is inexpensive and can be very revealing. Oil analysis can be used for any machinery that has a lubricating system, and can be had in two degrees, basic or comprehensive and the later should be the type to obtain as this checks for all types of wear metals and other chemicals, including engine coolants and water, whereas the basic type is a bit too limited. **Table 9-1** on page 337 is an example of a more comprehensive analysis. Some of the results even an amateur can interpret, while other elements require an expert. With an oil analysis we're basically looking for two things: the presence of foreign material such as water, glycol, sodium and chlorine, and the relationship of wear metals, the later of which can only be interpreted by a knowledgeable expert. With diesels, percent of carbon content is a major issue.

One difficulty in interpreting oil analysis wear metals is that the amount of wear metal is heavily dependent on how long the oil was in use. If the owner can provide the number of hours on the oil, this will be most helpful and this information should be provided to the oil analyst.

Fuel dilution of crankcase oil is an occasional common problem with Detroit Diesels, usually caused by a broken or cracked injector jumper line, but also may occur with four cycle diesels due to leaking injectors. In this case, piston crown damage should also be present, probably along with liner scoring.

Examine the Oil Pan

Before the engine is completely dismantled, the oil pan should be carefully removed, the oil drained off, and the bottom of the sump examined for debris. If there is a substantial amount of debris, sludge or metal filings, this should be collected in a clean container and sent off to the lab for analysis.

Coolant Analysis Similar to an oil analysis, the contents of the cooling system may provide valuable evidence. A system without a corrosion inhibitor obviously will suffer from corrosion related problems and the analysis will verify that. The analysis will also reveal things like salt, chlorides, iron oxides and other oxides of metal along with an array of coolant additives.

Intercoolers and Flame Arrestors

Flame arrestors on gas engines will collect large amounts of foreign material, as will intercoolers on diesel engines that lack good air filtration. Samples of this debris should be obtained for lab analysis. Also check the turbocharger vanes: are there white deposits on them? If so, it's probably salt. Salt is responsible for rapid ring/liner wear but is rarely fatal in moderate amounts.

Detroit Diesels have the blower-fed scavenging system so that over time oil and foreign material collects within the scavenging ports. This is one of the major sources for excessive wear of rings and liners. Chunks of sludge can break off and lodge in piston gaps above the upper ring or within ring groove causing local piston burning or ring damage or breakage. Have a sample of sludge analyzed for excessive amounts of salt.

Other Analytical Techniques

There are numerous other analytical techniques available for worn and failed components, some available at reasonable cost while others may be found to be cost prohibitive. Most of these techniques are very effective for the determination of causation of failure. Water, for example, doesn't have to be present in oil to identify corrosion damage to bearings. Metallurgical analytical techniques have advanced to the point where almost any type of failure mechanism can be identified. The primary limitations now are those of cost. The beginner is urged to become personally acquainted with a full service lab and learn the range of techniques available and cost feasibility. A personal tour will be a fascinating experience that will give him a far greater understanding than mere words can convey.

Knowing Who To Ask

It was mentioned at the beginning of this chapter that it is just as important who you know as what you know. The reality is that no one can know everything he needs to know and still find time to earn a living. This deficit is fulfilled by making it a point to cultivate acquaintances and friendships with those who have the ability to provide us with the answers we need without having to pay for it. When our own personal expertise fails us – as it often will – we do not hesitate to turn to those who can provide the expertise we lack.

Oil Analysis

		MTU 183T93 Port	MTU 183TE93 Starboard	Marine Gear Port	Marine Gear Starboard	Kohier 9.0 EOZ	Kohler 18.5 CCOZ
Al	Aluminum	10	5	3	3	4	2
P	Phosphorus	978	323	914	885	862	994
Pb	Lead	2	1	121	52	2	2
Mo	Molybdenum	16	10	13	1	5	9
Ag	Silver	0	0	0	0	0	0
Cr	Chrome	5	5	0	0	7	0
Si	Silicon	5	3	6	7	12	4
Cu	Copper	2	1	48	28	3	0
Na	Sodium	5	9	5	4	6	3
Sn	Tin	1	1	2	1	0	1
Fe	Iron	70	32	21	9	17	7
Ca	Calcium	2301	3231	2372	1143	1573	2380
Zn	Zinc	1149	379	994	945	1017	1143
K	Potassium	4	1	2	2	2	2
Mg	Magnesium	21	28	64	897	759	40
F	Fuel	N	N	N	N	N	N
W	Water	N	N	N	N	N	N

Table 9-1.

(Footnotes)

1. On everything from motor cycles to aircraft engines.

2. olor photos are essential but are cost prohibitive to reproduce here.

3. The exception would be a manufacturing defect.

4. Global means a system wide failure that affects the entire engine, such as with complete loss of cooling system coolant.

5. Viscosity is the resistance of a fluid to flow. A reduction in viscosity means that the oil gets thinner, more fluid, which is the definition of oil viscosity breakdown.

6. Detroit Diesel keeps records of every engine they manufacture going back decades and in most cases they have willingly provided me the information for the asking.

Chapter 10

Fraud Investigations

Although this chapter examines fraud investigations primarily from the stand point of insurance claims, fraud exists in all areas of economic activity. Boat owners are deceived by repair firms and vice versa. Boat buyers are deceived by boat sellers. There essentially is no limit to the kinds of situations that the marine investigator may be called on to investigate.

Fraud investigations rarely start out as such, but become fraud investigations as the result of uncovering evidence or indications of fraudulent activity related to some other line of work that the surveyor is engaged in. A pre purchase survey once morphed into a stolen boat investigation; a boat owner requesting assistance with a boat yard dispute ends up as a major fraud investigation; the investigation of a stolen boat for a client turns into a case of business partner fraud. The possibilities are nearly endless.

So why should marine surveyors get involved with fraud investigations? Why aren't such matters simply turned over to police professionals whose job it is to deal with such matters? The obvious answer is that police agencies show no interest in investigating what they consider petty crime; they have bigger fish to fry, so if the job is to be done at all, it has to be done by other professionals.

No marine surveyor who handles insurance claims can escape the issue of fraud because he will encounter it frequently. Insurance fraud is a rampant problem for the insurance industry, the rate of which grows every year, now estimated at nearly 85 billion dollars annually. The South Carolina Attorney General's office estimated in 2002 that the insurance costs of the average family are increased by $1030.00 annually as the result of insurance fraud. Fraud is as rampant in marine insurance as in every other kind of insurance.

Most people believe that insurance fraud is a victimless crime, and surveys taken reveal that one in three see nothing immoral about "padding" insurance claims. In fact, many see it as an entitlement for having paid premiums. Insurance fraud is defined as misrepresenting the truth in an effort to obtain an insurance settlement to which one is not entitled. By the laws of most states, property insurance is required to reimburse for the dollar value of a loss, not more, not less; the policy holder is to be made whole, not to profit from a loss. This is the principle of indemnity.

The marine investigator is in a good position to help do something about fraud while earning a living because fraud investigation is a natural outgrowth of normal claims work that many surveyors perform. It is true that most claims offices, when hiring a surveyor, don't expect to be hiring an investigator. However, the surveyor will find this is a role that he can easily slip into, expanding his work and income with little or no transition time, and that his clients will readily accept these services.

Phony small boat theft claims are a common type of major insurance fraud, along with willful destruction of the vessel to collect the insurance money. Fraudulent boat theft claims occur both on an individual as well as organized crime basis. Not only are boats stolen from honest owners, but dishonest owners "steal" their own boats, while still others make a career of crafting phony claims. In some parts of the country, small boat theft rings pop up from time to time, especially for outboard motors. And then there are the insurance scam artists that find ways to purchase insurance on boats that no longer exist. Some even steal the identifications of boats owned by unsuspecting owners.

However, major boat theft is not the primary type of marine insurance fraud; rather the major dollar amount of fraud is committed by ordinary policy holders with all the usual self-justifications for doing so. Common fraud is committed with every type of claim starting with misrepresenting the degree of damage to outright fraud in the representation of damages and dollar values of loss, such as the intentional seeking of the highest estimates. This we could call "petty" fraud were it not for the high dollar amounts involved. This type of fraud is normally handled by the claims person[1] that never leaves the office, which probably explains why so much of it goes unaddressed.

While petty fraud is a crime of opportunity — the insured finds it convenient and justified to inflate his claim — major fraud is distinguished by being premeditated, planned in advance. Insurance companies are far more eager to go after this type of fraud than they are common fraud because there is less of a stigma of attacking their customers. Premeditated fraud is committed by both policy holders and non policy holders such as repairers and liability claimants.

How individual insurance companies deal with fraud is highly variable and ranges from ignoring it (it's easy for them to pass the losses on to policy holders) to making serious efforts to combating it. The marine surveyor should not make the mistake of automatically assuming that a new client company will be eager to combat fraud; he may find himself doing something that is very unwelcome to his client. It is always necessary to discuss this issue with the client in advance of starting investigations. Some companies will not want to discuss the issue, and when brought up, dismiss it with vague reactions. Take this to mean that they'd rather you didn't concern yourself with the matter.

There is a difference between routine investigation on a insurance claim where fraud is not suspected and one where it is. That is, a normal claims verification process is not an investigation in a formal sense, though investigative work is certainly involved. A fraud investigation does not become such until there is strong evidence that fraud has been committed, at which time the investigator, adjuster or surveyor should discuss the issue with the client and obtain approval to begin investigating. The reason for this is that the actions undertaken in a fraud investigation will become obvious to the insured, and are likely to evoke a reaction; the insurance company may want to issue a reservation of rights letter in advance. Solving fraud cases is usually a matter of outwitting the insured, which means that the investigator will be aggressively challenging the insurance company's customer, a situation that embodies some inherent legal risks unless handled properly.

Role of the Marine Surveyor

The marine surveyor that handles marine claims is the first line of defense for insurers and any other types of clients he is working for. He is the one most likely to first suspect fraud, and because he is the man-on-the-scene, and already in possession of much information, he is the one in the best position to investigate. Many claims handlers are reluctant to get involved, either because they don't know how, are afraid of consequences, and probably both. Fortunately, a little knowledge goes a long way and this chapter provides an overview of the types of cases encountered, issues involved and the means of investigation.

The newcomer to investigations will find that fraud investigations can be time consuming and require a great deal of forethought and planning. Success is determined not only by the evidence that is found but also how effectively it is used. Like panning for gold in a stream bed, if there is one flake of gold there must be more and, hopefully, a few nuggets as well. One bit of evidence can be used to pry out others. Evidence consists not only of things but that which people say and do, so getting perpetrators to say things they don't intend to say is a major objective. The chapter on interrogation techniques deals with this subject extensively.

A fraud investigation may be technically said to begin the moment the surveyor suspects that something is not right, and from that moment on he makes an effort to find out what it is. It may begin with a suspicious document, apparent false statements, altered identification numbers and a host of other things that are a tip-off that something is amiss. Curiosity leads him to dig a little deeper whereon his suspicion is strengthened.

At this point he notifies his client who advises him whether to go ahead and complete an investigation.

A cautionary note here: an investigator should never launch into a full-scale investigation without his client's knowledge and approval. Full-scale investigation here means going beyond the normal claims verification process, to actively suspecting fraud and setting about obtaining proof.

The various types of fraud obviously require different approaches because they involve different types of claims and individuals that range from first-party insureds to third-party claimants and career criminals, from vessel damage to liability property damage to personal injuries. To defeat the crime of fraud it is necessary for the investigator to out-think the perpetrator, to spot and expose his weaknesses and exploit them. Each type of fraud typically has a pattern or profile so that familiarity with the pattern is the essence of exposing the scam. A few of these profiles will be described in this chapter.

For perpetrators to succeed it is necessary for them to anticipate where the investigator will looking, and to be able to cover their tracks without making mistakes or leave evidence; few possess the ability to do so because most fraud attempts are first time efforts that are rife with mistakes and stupidity. It is a different story for those perpetrators who make a vocation of fraud, who learn to become proficient at it. Fortunately, in the marine business we will not encounter many of this type.

As with all types of investigations involving policy holders who are the customers of insurance companies, fraud investigations require the same diplomatic skills that need to be applied to every type of claim. Someone suspected of fraud must be treated as innocent until sufficient evidence is obtained. Always the investigator is aware of the policy holder's propensity to sue over even the flimsiest of motivations, and does his best to not needlessly raise his ire. His attitude is never confrontational because he catches more flies with honey than vinegar. There is the need for frequent consultation with the client to avoid going off into deep water without floatation support.

The Risks

No doubt some readers will be wondering what kind of risks are involved with fraud investigations. The risk of encountering violence is very low, but that statement must be tempered by the qualifier "when the investigator uses good common sense". He ought to be able to identify a career criminal or an individual that is prone to violence; the warning signs are usually very obvious, such as demeanor, modes of dress, language and so on. It is not a myth that many crooks look like crooks, though there are certainly many exceptions to the rule. Violent people, however, are almost always sending out hostile vibes so that we learn to steer a wide circle around them.

Our work is a business, we are not law enforcement, and there is no sound justification for carrying on an investigation that poses obvious hazards to ourselves. If there is danger involved, we should inform our client and recommend that the matter be referred to law enforcement.

One other area of risk is the legal one, the risk of being sued, which is a risk that exists with all areas of involvement with insurance claims on behalf of a company. If an investigator gets sued along with the insurer, if it is possible, the insurer will usually provide the investigator with a defense. Unfortunately, some lawyers will try to separate the investigator from the insurer by charging him with a separate issue that is contrary to the interests of the insurer, so that the insurer will be unable to do so.

Surplus Lines Insurance

Surplus lines is a nice name for what essentially amounts to insurance for high risks that most mainline insurers don't want to deal with. The marine business, being inherently risky, involves a lot of surplus lines, most of which is handled by foreign markets such as "Lloyds" along with a host of "offshore" companies operating out of island nations and all that that implies. The hallmark of surplus lines is that it generates a disproportionate amount of fraud and litigation.

If you like doing investigations, some of the better surplus lines companies can offer a steady flow of work, since this type of insurance produces large numbers of claims with unquestionably the highest rates of fraud. However, surplus lines are often more or less exempt from the bulk of insurance regulations that other companies must abide by, a factor that poses some economic risks to service providers such as problems getting paid. Historically, there has been a significant amount of fraud perpetrated by surplus lines companies that are foreign corporations governed by the dubious laws of an island nation. Beware that fraud can be a two-way street! Do some research on the client before getting in too deeply.

Another risk posed by working for foreign insurers is that they are usually not familiar with the laws of the state in which they are operating. If they violate state guidelines and get sued, usually the surveyor will be named along with the insurer. This can be avoided by making sure that foreign clients obey state laws such as time limits for paying/denying claims, reservation of rights, fair claims practices and so on. In other words, be a good advisor to your extra national clients.

Red Flags for Common Insurance Fraud

Marine investigators encounter fraud not only when working with insurance claims, but also in many other situations such as the fraudulent sale of vessels. Fraud occurs just as often in first party claims as it does third party (liability) claims.

Fraud occurs in all types of insurance claims from misrepresentation of damages, such as when a repairer colludes with a boat owner to inflate a claim, to hiding, altering or destroying evidence. The most common type of fraud is misrepresentation of a claim in which the insured either lies about the cause of real damage or intentionally causes the damage, to claims for loss of items that never existed, in which the insured or claimant is hoping that no one checks too closely.

Boat owners have made claims for theft of dinghies and outboard motors in which a most rudimentary investigation found the allegedly stolen items in or behind the insured's garage, hidden on the grounds of the yacht club and so on. In one case, an allegedly stolen outboard motor was found being offered for sale at a marina. In another case a marine electronics outfit engaged in a long-term lightning damage scam against many insurance companies. When a boat owner suffered a legitimate lightning strike, the electronics retailer offered to split the profits with boat owners when adding very costly pieces of equipment to the damaged list that the boat owner did not have on their boats. He even went so far as to drill holes and install brackets for the equipment that didn't exist to make it look like it did. The electronics retailer fraud was finally proven when an investigator realized that the bracket for a piece of equipment that he was familiar with did not fit that item and the boat owner couldn't prove that he ever owned that equipment. Thus, careful checking of simple facts is as likely to reveal and prove fraud as anything else.

The most common indicator of small claims fraud results simply from the investigator not believing the insured's story, whether it's a matter of the facts that don't add up, or he simply has a sense that the claimant is lying.

The number one red flag for major fraud is financial distress. People with serious money problems will do strange things, stupid things, too. Things like sell their boat and claim it stolen so that a simple check with the state reveals the transaction. Then they present you with a color copy of the title thinking that you can't tell the difference. You probably can't, but we have other ways.

If you are working for an insurer, be sure to consult with your client before attempting to obtain a financial report. They certainly have the means to do this and will probably want to do so, but will likely want a signed non waiver agreement first. Regardless of the type of situation, if fraud is suspected, the client should be consulted immediately. Do not proceed with the investigation before getting approval.

The following points are widely regarded by insurers for claims of all types as indicators of possible fraud:

- The time line doesn't add up.

- Unable to provide receipts.

- Claimant is elusive or hard to contact but has no problem reaching you.

- Claimant is unusually knowledgeable about insurance claims.

- Claimant conspicuously avoids using the mail and always delivers documents personally (doesn't want to commit felony mail fraud).

- Excessively pushing for rapid settlement. Willing to accept smaller settlement rather than produce documentation.

- Too many large purchases by cash.

- Insured bombards you with paper work, attempting a snow job.

- Excessive justification.

- Excessive contact from claimant, claimant is overly helpful.

- Addresses are always P.O. Boxes

- Handwritten business documents, hastily prepared word processor or spread sheet documents: receipts and invoices not from established businesses but fly-by-nights.

- All witnesses are related to claimant.

- Unable to provide specific dates or time lines; dates on documents don't make sense.

- Late reporting of claim.

- Witness attitudes don't seem right, excessively biased or effusive, wordy.

- Supporting documents reveal a bias, eager to prove a point.

- Repair facility is overly friendly toward claimant in correspondence.

- No official report filed for incident when required, or filed late.

- Immediate representation by a lawyer; lawyer is very demanding.

We will discuss these indicators throughout this chapter, with illustrating examples.

When Overstatement Becomes Fraud

The marine surveyor/claims handler has to confront on an almost daily basis the issue of when overstated claims become a matter of fraud. Overstatement of the dollar value of losses, even when premeditated, isn't regarded by insurers as fraud, mainly by virtue of the fact that premeditation is too hard to prove. Since policy holders routinely inflate the extent of damages and value of their claims, the insurer's response is simply the claims handler or adjuster who's job is to bring the adjustment back in line.

Overstatement becomes major fraud when the perpetrator engages in significant falsification of documents, material facts, or engages in collusion. This type of falsification provides material evidence that can be relied upon for whatever action the insurer decides to take. This may take the form of making claim for equipment or property that never existed or was not owned by the claimant, alteration of documents, willful destruction of property that was not damaged by the casualty, and damage to property caused by an unrelated event.

Because petty fraud is so commonplace, it does not rise to the level of warranting serious investigation until (1) a certain dollar value threshold is reached and, (2) the probability of success seems likely. Insurance companies generally avoid chasing rabbits down deep holes because digging them out becomes too costly and the end result too doubtful. For these reasons any marine surveyor who proposes to perform investigation work should make it a point to consult with his clients in advance so that he has a solid understanding of when they want to investigate and when they don't.

The Uses of Evidence

Once the evidence has been obtained that a fraud has been committed, there are several uses that can be made of it. The obvious one is to turn it over to law enforcement for prosecution. Most of the time it is used by an insurer to deny a claim. Another is to present the evidence as means of forcing the claimant to modify or withdraw the fraudulent claim. This later use is a common and effective application of evidence stemming from investigations. The reality is that insurance companies are not particularly motivated or interested in prosecuting fraudsters; if they can avoid being the victim of fraud by some other means, they'd be most happy to go that way.

When the Insured Has a Lawyer

There will be occasions when the insured or claimant immediately obtains a lawyer, raising questions in the investigator's mind as to why. This is a legitimate question since retaining a lawyer for an insurance claim is not normal. After all, this is not a criminal investigation. Many investigators are intimidated by lawyers, not the least because lawyers make concerted efforts to intimidate.

A lawyer representing an insured has no need to be hostile or demanding to the investigator or claims handler, but when he is there are grounds for suspecting that the hostility and aggressiveness is a cover for a scam. Until a claim has been denied or otherwise disputed, there is no cause for adopting an adversarial demeanor. That it exists suggests that something is being hidden.

It is very rare that an insured will hire a lawyer during the claims process, but it will not be rare for third party claimants. The investigator should never feel intimidated by either an insured's or claimant's threat to hire a lawyer. The reality is that a lawyer isn't much help to an insured or claimant who is making a claim. The lawyer is as much bound by the insurance contract as the insured and company are. About the only significant effect he can have is to be obstructionist and delay the claims process which hurts no one but the insured. If we know the law, and work scrupulously within its boundaries, having to deal with a lawyer can accrue to our benefit because it is far more difficult to explain legal and contractual points to an insured than to a lawyer. We can say things to a lawyer that it would not be wise to say to an insured. I wouldn't tell a policy holder that he's making an idle threat, but I'd have no problem saying that to his lawyer!

Investigative Tactics

Hostile Third Party Lawyers

Lawyers that represent third party and personal injury clients are a special breed. While they posture as champions of the weak and poor, their behavior is rather like that of the carrion scavenger, sitting on the high wire awaiting some road-kill. As daily reading of the newspapers reveals, there are also large numbers of them that directly participate in fraud schemes, particularly involving injury claims. As investigators we must take care to avoid moral indignation at the tactics they employ which consist of bullying, intimidation, bluff and bluster. Many of them are highly experienced at their "art" of trying to get the target insurance company (or anyone else for that matter) to settle quickly under threats of suing. They will often employ ruses based on false quoting of insurance law and regulations, mixed with threats of "bad faith" suits, but mostly it is pure bluff and bluster contained in their threatening letters. All letters received from lawyers should be forwarded by fax to the client immediately[2].

Most company claims adjusters are too well trained to fall victim to these tactics but some aren't. A marine surveyor will be perceived as a particularly vulnerable target, for the lawyer does not expect him to have any training at all. The lawyer's efforts will therefore be to try to keep the investigator fearful of all sorts of dreadful consequences should he make a mistake or not permit a fast settlement due to the need for investigation.

These lawyers are not to be feared since behind every instance of bullying and bluster lies a lack of substance to the threats. This is why it is so vitally important that any surveyor who handles these kinds of claims know and understands the insurance laws of his state thoroughly, for without knowledge of the law the claimsman will become intimidated by these threats.

Nor does the investigator need to employ any subtlety with these characters. The best approach is the offensive one of making it clear that their claim will be routinely investigated like every other such claim, and that the time it takes to accomplish that will be within that prescribed by law. Since most states don't set a time limit for third party claims, the claimant is now at a distinct disadvantage. Note that with states that set time limits for first party claims, that time limit is only for admitting liability, not actual settlement and payment, which is where the bad faith issues arise. Bad faith is only an issue in third party claims where a company denies liability in a case where clearly it is liable, or causes financial injury by taking too long to pay.

A strategy that I like to employ with particularly obnoxious lawyers is to sucker them in a bit by at first appearing ignorant and intimidated. This just urges them on to greater abusiveness by giving them a false sense of control. This is particularly useful when you believe that the lawyer is assisting his client in fraud. Making them feel more secure increases the chance of their making arrogant mistakes. Then, at a certain point, Walter Mitty morphs into Dracula.

With small to medium size cases (property damage, not injury cases where damage awards are possible) there is no need to conceal one's evidence or knowledge derived from the investigation. As evidence accumulates indicating probable fraud, a good tactic is to dribble that information out to the lawyer in ways that are as equally devious as the tactics he uses. Lawyers who take these kinds of cases are usually doing so either on a contingency basis or basis of very small fee plus large percentage of the settlement. It is therefore in the lawyer's interest to inflate the claim as high as possible and sometimes they will violate law or legal ethics in doing do.

It is my experience that when dealing with aggressive claimant lawyers, that when they are presented with indications that my investigation is producing results unfavorable to their client, they begin having second thoughts about whether they want to continue pursuing the case when it appears as though they might not get paid, or if fraud may be revealed. Very often, a single, solid — but by no means conclusive — bit of evidence is occasionally enough to cause them to ditch their clients. Bear in mind that unscrupulous lawyers are equally unscrupulous with their own clients. Their Achilles heel is that they don't want to get near a court room despite their threats.

Tactical Delay and Exposure

This tactic is designed to progressively weaken the resolve of a suspected claimant or lawyer engaging in fraud, by means of taking time with the investigation and, at the same time, slowly revealing our evidence to the claimant or lawyer in bits and pieces, a standard police tactic. This can be done over the phone and in person. If I can arrange an interview with a claimant in his lawyer's office, and in doing so carefully reveal a bit of evidence that I have, that is the best way. Perhaps it is a document and I try to put him on the spot with it.

> Mr. Lawyer, you submitted on behalf of your client these receipts for out of pocket medical expenses. Despite my having told you that we would not accept photo copies, you sent photo copies anyway. See these copies here are very weak, some of the print can't be made out and particularly the receipt number. I took these copies back to the pharmacy and asked them to trace them and they came back and told me that they have no record of such purchases being made by your client on these dates. Can you explain this? Perhaps you can encourage your client to find the originals.

> You mean he made copies and but lost the originals? That's interesting!

If you have solid evidence, do not be shy about using it to best effect. The idea is to create the impression that his case is *slowly* falling apart. Slowly because time is money and we want him to think he's wasting his. We can use that to advantage by stringing things out, within legal limits, of course. Naturally, this tactic works best when we feel certain that we're dealing with fraud, not merely resorting to a bluff as he is.

At some point we will request a statement from his client. A claimant does not have to give us a statement, but a refusal to do so looks bad for him. This should never be done until an investigation is well advanced and we have some solid information to work with. During the course of that interview the piece of evidence may be revealed and questioned loosely. If this produces some lies, so much the better, but don't push it too hard. Keep it fairly light and non aggressive. Several weeks later in a phone call with the lawyer another bit of evidence is revealed. This is done with little or no fanfare, as if accidentally dropping a piece of paper on the floor. We do not try to brow beat the lawyer with these bits, but rather let the idea unfold and blossom in his own mind. In this way we are denying him the opportunity to refute the evidence, while raising the question in his mind of how much more evidence we have. It will become apparent to him that we are dribbling evidence to him and this strengthens his misgivings; he knows we are confident of our position.

Injury claims on party fishing boats, a.k.a. "head boats," are commonplace. In one such case a woman claimed to have broken her foot on a badly located cleat, placed on a high traffic deck. The first indicator that the claim probably wasn't legitimate was the fact that she was already represented by a lawyer. The second indicator was that she had not informed the boat captain of the incident. The third indicator was that the alleged date of the incident was two days prior to the date she first sought medical attention. That's a long time for a broken foot.

With party boat claims, it's always useful to check with any other boat owners in the area to see if this person had made claims with them. In this instance, the claimant had, so now we have a solid indicator that we have a fraudster on our hands. The attorney strongly resisted allowing her to give a statement. The investigator's response to this was, *You mean you expect us to pay a claim based on unsubstantiated verbal allegations? You know better than that. Either your client gives us a statement or we turn you down.*

Under threat of denying the claim, he finally relented. Apparently, the lawyer did not rehearse his client very well because she testified that she was walking on the deck from the stern toward the bow on the starboard side, opposite to the side where all the passengers were fishing. Her story had a gaping hole because it was her left foot that was injured, but the cleat in question was on the outboard side of the deck. If her foot had hit the cleat, it would have had to have been her right foot that was injured.

The advantage of working with a lawyer is that we can say things to him that we can't say to a claimant, such as, *Based on the investigation I've done so far, I'd say that your client's case is pretty weak. Are you sure that your client has what it takes to go advance a claim?* A statement like this amounts to a polite challenge, and perhaps a warning that the investigator knows more than he is letting on.

The objective with such tactics is to get the lawyer to fold his cards without ever our client having to issue a denial of the claim. Keep in mind that fraudsters are just as likely to lie to their own lawyers, and the lawyers surely know it. If our case is strong, the claimant will simply go away, not to be heard from again. This is by far the best possible outcome we could produce for our client who will little comprehend what we have done. Therefore, do not be shy about explaining it to him. Be sure to stick a feather in your cap when successful.

A Stolen boat case:

> In a stolen boat case involving a bit of amazingly good luck, I was spending the weekend in the Bahamas when I happened to observe the stolen boat in question entering Bimini harbor. It was readily identifiable due to the boat name in two-foot high letters painted on the side; incredibly, nothing had been done to conceal the name. Equally fortunate was the fact that I had a good camera with telephoto lens at hand, taking a series of photos of the boat not only entering the harbor but docking at a pier/warehouse and unloading large plastic-wrapped bales in broad daylight (presumably marijuana). There were four men in the boat but since I had never met the insured, I did not know if he was in the boat.

> A week later I arranged to take a sworn statement under oath from the insured at his lawyer's office. I brought one of the two dozen photos I had taken with me. As soon as I saw him in person, I knew the man was a drug smuggler and could be the violent sort. The investigation was young, not even two weeks old, so I did not mention the photo or seeing the boat, proceeding to take the statement as if I knew nothing. As we were leaving the conference room, when no one was looking, I left the photo on the table. Of course, during the interview I identified the insured as one of the men in the boat. Neither the lawyer nor the client was ever heard from again. Naturally, the photo had a camera date on it.

While this was a rare bit of very good luck, it does illustrate how effective this tactic can be, although in most cases it is not this easy. Notice how the revelation serves as a subtle accusation without having said a word, something that is very important when dealing with an insured like this one. Because of the photo, he's not about to accuse me of anything. Nor is he about to initiate a suit against the insurer because the photo says it all.

The same tactic can be used with phony documents. Simply mail a copy of it to the claimant anonymously, or leave a copy isolated on a table or desk in plain sight where he will see it. That will get him thinking because you let him know what you know or suspect without ever saying a word.

Attacking the Cover Story

While the odds are usually stacked against him, the one great advantage that the fraud investigator does have is that petty crooks are inexperienced with their crimes and are vulnerable, much like the recidivist burglar who gets caught over and over with the same stupid mistakes. Most scams are revealed, not through major discoveries, but by the relentless review of the small details of the case.

That vulnerability lies in lack of expertise in concealing their crimes. Investigators are detail oriented, fraudsters aren't. Tactical delay and exposure works particularly well in cases where there is a significant paper trail where the details don't match up. Perpetrators do not expect to be confronted with evidence against them. At least not during the investigative phase; instead, they are prepared to challenge a claim denial with a premeditated cover story that cannot be predictive of what evidence will be uncovered and used against them.

When there is a significant number of documents that contain evidence, these can be used to sow confusion and break down a claimant's story. The perpetrator's premeditated cover story will be based on how he thinks the investigation will unfold. He cannot know what kind of evidence we will uncover and is defenseless, but for off-the-cuff lies, against its use. When confronted with it he has to ad lib a lie and is thus likely to make a mistake.

Revealing/Hiding an Investigation

A hunch becomes a suspicion when multiple indicators are present to suggest something that is more than a guess, but less than proof. It is the convergence of multiple indicators that usually forms the threshold for launching a serious investigation wherein it may become apparent to an insured that he is being investigated. Here we must make the distinction between total vessel theft claims and most other types; the total vessel theft is *always* seriously investigated because, if phony, constitutes a major fraud. The insured will (or should) automatically assume that his claim will be looked at closely. The investigator's approach will be straightforward and without any concealment of his intent, for there is no need to do so. With other types of claims the investigator will want to keep his intent and efforts concealed most of the time for reasons that are necessary with lower value claims.

Letting it be known that an insured is under investigation obviously carries with that revelation certain negative effects. Not only could the insured become more defensive and less cooperative, but is likely to bring additional pressure on the investigator such as from producing agents. At this point, it is best that an insurer send out a reservation of rights letter. For other types of losses it is best, whenever possible, to avoid giving the appearance of overtly conducting an investigation. This is not difficult and is attained primarily by good diplomatic skills and asking questions in a non threatening way that does not betray suspicion.

Insurance fraud is committed by people of all social and economic strata and not just "criminal types". What motivates even well-educated and apparently financially comfortable people is, of course, financial troubles that lie below the surface of appearances. If you don't know your client's policy about getting financial reports on insureds, be sure to ask since this is critically important and ought to be done for all boat theft claims.

Paper Trails: The Case of the Scheming Lawyer

Imagine a lawyer who commits fraud. Because he's a lawyer, he thinks he's very clever, what with his lawyerly skills and all.

> In one of the most humorous cases I've ever run across, a lawyer boat owner was a claimant against my client boat yard, alleging that my client was responsible for sinking his yacht. His allegation was that improper wiring caused electrolysis that resulted in a sea cock failure.
>
> He thought he was being very clever by documenting everything he did and every phone conversation he had with a confirmation letter. He thought he was covering his behind. Apparently he was not a trail lawyer, for he failed to recognize that his verbosity — diarrhea of the mouth when dictating letters — would end up providing proof of his fraudulent claim. When all the letters were put together and analyzed as a whole, it was found that he made the proverbial Freudian slip by revealing certain dates that provided proof that his case was fraudulent. These dates led to the obtaining of proof that a failed sea cock was not the cause, but that the actual cause had been covered up by the lawyer.

Note that reviewing a group of documents such as letters as a class constitutes a distinct analytical technique, in this instance comparing the statements made by one person over a period of time. But while we won't often see this exact situation, it can occur in other ways with other documents and situations. It also points up the importance of keeping notes of the things people say to you. The review of correspondence for evidence and clues is an important part of the service that the expert witness provides and should not be overlooked. In large cases trial lawyers will usually prepare chronologies of correspondence; even in our work on small cases we should do the same.

When dealing with a large number of documents, a good analytical technique is to sort them out by categories and review them as groups, comparing the information in one to the others as in the case of the letters mentioned above.

Paper trails don't always provide direct favorable evidence but often subtle clues. We need to train ourselves to learn how to read them. So how is that? At first one can only learn to come by them through patient study of the documents you have at hand. Study them patiently, read them more than once. As they say, time can work wonders, and in time you'll become adept at seeing these things quickly; they will jump right off the paper at you, slap you in the face and say SEE!!! THIS IS IT! I'm not resorting to hyperbole here; practice and patience develops the skill needed to sniff out this sort of thing. With a bit of experience you'll begin to do this automatically and learn to evaluate documents quickly and accurately.

False Documents

Altered Documents

Another common fraud that is perpetrated is by the submission of false documents, whether faked entirely or merely altered. When document fraud occurs, obviously it is rarely with original documents and usually with copies, typically poor ones. Thirty years ago, copy machines weren't very good and bad copies were common. Today, there is no excuse for poor copies. Today's copiers and scanners make it possible to easily create forgeries that are hard to detect. Alteration of original documents is more difficult and apt to damage the paper or leave obvious traces.

The necessary proof for document fraud is usually obtained by going back to the source of that document and obtaining an original copy and comparing it with the one submitted.

A common method of submitting false receipts is to use old cash register tapes that don't contain a description of the product, remove the date and photo copy them. It is common for claimants to copy several receipts on a single sheet and submit that. Such a document is far too easy to falsify and should never be accepted. Thermal printed tapes are weak to begin with, but copies are far worse.

Even inexpensive copiers nowadays often have reducing capabilities and this is an excellent way to conceal inexpert alterations. Enlarge the document, alter the numbers, then reduce the copy to normal size and the obvious alteration disappears!

Large chain stores often have long, multi-faceted tapes about 4" wide up to two feet long. Such tapes can be cut with scissors to eliminate unwanted information such as product itemization and dates to reveal just the total. This type of fraud can be revealed by going to the store in question and looking at their receipts to see what has been altered. One can also ask them to verify the copy you have. If the product was purchased with a credit card, as it usually is, then demand to see the credit card company statement.

Pay attention to fonts or type face on machine receipts which should be consistent on each. Different fonts on sections of the receipt may be a tip-off. Also check the details from receipt to receipt, such as different credit cards used, name on card, card numbers, signatures and control numbers.

In most cases these methods of fraud are rather easily exposed by going back to the seller and comparing records.

Faxes

One way to ensure that altered documents cannot be detected is to send them only by means of fax.

> In one instance, a boat owner submitting a claim for damages submitted a fax of an estimate with the numbers altered by $20,000. In another, someone making a claim for theft of electronics went out and purchased electronics one day at one of those marine superstores, and returned them for full credit the next. Then he submitted copies of the receipts with altered dates (copied before the return) and submitted those as proof of claim by fax. Unfortunately for him the investigator went to the retailer that sold the electronics and compared their records, whereon they revealed the return. This clear-cut fraud case was turned over to the state attorney general and the good fellow ultimately went to prison.

The quality of facsimile machine documents is so bad that faxed documents should be considered unacceptable. It's almost impossible to detect falsified faxed documents because the resolution is so poor; these should never be accepted as evidentiary documents, not even for a small insurance claim. Claimants should be required to mail documents, despite the grumbling this frequently produces. Then, should the documents arrive by Federal Express or personal delivery, it is reasonable to become suspicious. Is that person trying to avoid committing mail fraud? Why would he spend $11 for special delivery, or deliver it himself when a 37 cent stamp will save all that time and money?

Boat Repair Fraud and Collusion

Throughout my career I have frequently encountered fraudulent activities with any type of job involving high dollar value boat repairs, refitting and rebuilding. This has been a two-way street in which repairers as well as boat owners, even yacht captains, were the perpetrators. I've had several large cases where the boat owner conspired to create a liability claim against the repairer. But the fact remains that the largest number of fraud cases are those involving insurance claims in which either the repairer, the boat owner, or both, are determined to profit from an insurance claim.

Hidden Damages

Large losses such as sinkings, fires and collisions present situations in which assessing all the damages is difficult. The issue of hidden damages is a legitimate one, which is what makes boat repair fraud so difficult to prevent. Boat repair fraud is covered in this chapter since discovery of the fraud typically occurs during the claims handling process, or even at the end. Thus, it is usually something that catches the surveyor by surprise.

While surveyors do their best to nail down repair costs with estimates and contracts, our best efforts don't always succeed owing to the assertion that the repair cost of some things cannot be estimated until the job is started, the damages "opened up".

This places the surveyor in the impossible position of having to constantly monitor the repair process; the repairer is well aware of that fact and therefore seeks to exploit it. The end result is that he is faced with an invoice in the end that is substantially higher than the estimate. Most states have laws that make this illegal in the automobile and home repair business, but not in marine.

This is a very old tactic that has been highly refined by those who engage in it and is difficult to defeat. To give an idea of just how difficult it can be, consider that I once encountered a high end boat yard, one that routinely exploited insurance claim repairs, who brought their attorney to a repair cost negotiation.

While the boat owner may or may not be participating in this scam, the effectiveness is predicated on the fact that the *boat owner*, not the insurer, is ultimately responsible for payment of the repair bill and the repairer relies on him to put pressure on the insurer to pay. Should the surveyor agree to leave certain "open" items on the damage report subject to later evaluation and estimation, the door is left open for the repairer to exploit it. Then there is the issue of "hidden damages that may be discovered during the course of repair." By far, this is the most widely exploited situation over which the surveyor begins to lose control.

The idea behind this technique is that the repairer believes that once they have the boat in their yard undergoing repairs, the insurer and boat owner is now at the yard's mercy. There are a number of boat yards in South Florida that are masters of this technique. Every surveyor who ever had to deal with these outfits dreaded the prospect, knowing what was coming but believing that there was nothing that they could do about it. This is a type of fraud that can succeed *only* if the insurer provides the opportunity for it to succeed and declines to stop it.

> In one case a boat yard strung out a large damage claim to the extent 37 new items totaling more than $150,000 over the original contract in which the surveyor needed to return to the vessel numerous times to inspect these "newly discovered" damages, and obtain new estimates on each one. The new findings are dribbled out a few at a time, and in each case the alleged "damage" is debatable. The repairer's strategy was to overwhelm the surveyor and insurer with a blizzard of paperwork and wearing him down by creating as much extra work for the surveyor as possible, stringing it out over a long period of time so that he ultimately gives up trying to manage the costs.

Over the years this technique has proven effective. It is a tactic that is well known among contractors of all sorts, and has attained it highest degree of refinement from those firms that perform government contracting, which many boat yards do.

Along with this, the tactic of obfuscation may be employed wherein a revised estimate is issued that is unclear about the nature or extent of the additional repairs. This obfuscation then gives rise to yet another additional damage claim in what amounts to a sort of pyramid scheme.

It must be understood that when the insurer acknowledges the possibility of hidden damages (as when the surveyor mentions this in his damage report), the estimate or contract is rendered invalid and becomes an open ended document: thereafter all elements of control are lost. The only solution, then, is to demand that, as the repair expert it is the repairer's responsibility to account for *all* the damages. The notion of considering hidden damages at a later date must be *flatly rejected* and should be placed in writing. If the insurer declines to take this position, then there is nothing that the surveyor can do to assist the insurer in controlling costs because he has no control, no authority and no leverage.

If it is necessary for hidden areas to be opened up, or components dismantled, in order to assess the full amount of damage, then these things should be done. But under no circumstances should a major insurance repair job entertain the idea of additional hidden damages.

From the foregoing it can be seen that the traditional marine insurer practice of hiring a surveyor to assess the damages places the insurer in a difficult position. The difficulty is that the insured or repairer can challenge the surveyor's assessment without end. It would be far better for the insurer to require the insured to assess his own damage, and for the insurer to do the challenging. In the above instance, that is the way the case started out, but where they went wrong was in not settling and paying the claim until the damage repairs were complete, thereby providing the insured and repairer the opportunity to keep building up the claim.

Collusion is a crime that can only happen when someone provides the opportunity; once the scam is given the opportunity to begin, it is very difficult — if not impossible — to stop it. In the above mentioned case, the yard involved had a lawyer backing them up. In most cases we can see collusion coming because the outfits involved usually have a reputation for it.

Only the insurer can make the decision to resist the scam and if he's not willing to do that, then he should just go ahead and pay whatever is demanded of him. Unfortunately, the internal politics of some insurers is such that they have aided and abetted such scams, giving rise to boat yards that perfect the technique of exploiting all insurers.

Repairer Takes Up the Insured's Cause

A very common fraud indicator is when a boat yard or more likely, a small time repair shop or shade tree mechanic "goes to bat" or takes up the claimant's cause. A typical example goes like this:

Dear Mr. Snidely:

I have become very concerned about the condition of your boat and I strongly recommend that so and so must be done to your boat immediately because if you don't, bad things will happen. Your insurance company should know this and I do not understand why they are delaying payment of your claim. Etcetera . . .

In this instance, the tip-off is that this is not normal business behavior and indicates that the repairer is taking an *unwarranted personal interest* in the boat owner's affairs. Why? But also note that the repairer either exaggerates or misrepresents the situation by engaging in hyperbole. Reputable business people don't do that sort of thing because they have no desire to involve themselves in the owner's affairs, yet alone in fraud. This sort of letter, note or memo is occasionally seen from small time operators and it is an indicator of possible collusion that should be taken seriously. That is, the service provider is looking out for his own interest by trying to ensure that the boat owner can make a recovery under his insurance that will help line his own pockets, or at least pay his bill which may be inflated. Documents like this constitute good evidence for a trial lawyer.

String-Along Claims and Other Scam Tactics

A string-along scam is part and parcel of the above technique, but is also a common technique of claimants building up the dollar value of a claim slowly through frequent revelation of newly discovered damage or items, or feeding invoices to the claimsman one-at-a-time. The perpetrator's idea is to wear down the claimsman's will to resist by presenting him with lots of extra work, involving much intentional confusion, hoping that he'll just give up and recommend payment of the claim. The fact is that the technique often works with overworked claims people. Business people tend to be exceedingly good at this because it's a common business tactic of which defense contractors are masters. The corollary to this is the blizzard of paper scam in which the claimant tries to overwhelm the claimsman with confusing paperwork. This may be augmented by the pestiferous phone caller technique in which the claimant calls the claimsman many times a day, every day. This is part of the technique of frustrating the claimsman and wearing him down. All of the above are indicators of fraudulent intent, usually on the part of a premeditating scam artist.

Insured as Contractor

Another version of this scam is the insured who either wants to make repairs himself, or he tells the insurer that he knows all the right contractors to use who can make the repairs for much less than a boat yard. This type of claim almost always turns into a nightmare. The best way to prevent it is to not let it get started. These types of scams are premeditated fraud wherein the insured expects to profit either by (1) making cheap, substandard repairs and pocketing the difference or, (2) using contractors to inflate the repair cost beyond control, sometimes through phony invoices.

This scam is often hallmarked by numerous handwritten invoices that are progress billings. The insured expects progress payments by the insurer, and submits progress summaries along with the payment requests. To confuse the issue further, the insured makes purchases and performs some labor himself; thus efforts of the insured are commingled with that of his "contractors."

If the insurer or surveyor allows this to happen, he's going to find himself with a full time forensic accounting job trying to sort out a deliberately created mess of confusing paper work.

The only way to avoid this scam is to prevent it from happening at the very beginning. If an insured wants to make damage repairs himself, that's his right. But the insurer should not put itself in the position of being a forensic accountant. Instead, the loss should be settled on the basis of a professional estimate or repair contract *before* the insured begins repairs.

Sworn Statement in Proof of Loss

The use of a Proof of Loss form can be an effective tool at this point. The adjuster can simply send a proof of loss[3] form to the insured. The proof of loss form ties the claimant down into making a written claim demand which, if falsified, serves as de facto evidence of fraud when other evidentiary facts exist. Its effect is generally to make the insured think about what he is doing and hopefully realize the risks to which he is exposing himself. Many state laws require the insurer to supply this form.

It should be clear from the foregoing that the best way to deal with this scam is to leave the burden of assessing damages with the insured and his repairer. In this way, the surveyor's role becomes one of confirming or denying that alleged damages exist, along with determining the reasonableness of the repair cost.

A Case of a Professional Fraudster

One of my most memorable cases was a large yacht loss of dubious circumstances. The yacht was a rebuilt 55' sailing yacht of somewhat questionable pedigree that may have burned once. The issue was hurricane damage that the owner was repairing himself with numerous contractors. The insurance company adjuster had completely lost control of the claim because he never established any control at the outset. The insurer had agreed to make progress payments, something that proved to be a major blunder. The second mistake was a failure to nail down the damages and the third was the failure to establish the total dollar value of the loss before repairs began. This lead to the a situation where the insured could milk the insurer mercilessly. And he did but he got greedy and went too far.

The insurer realized what was happening far too late. When the case was referred to me, it arrived in a large carton weighing 20 pounds and containing more than a thousand documents. Long before analysis of all the documents was complete, the methodology of this con artist became clear. It was both sophisticated and complex, using an accounting system that made each document in some way linked to every other. Part of the trick was to use frequent summaries with running totals and considerable overlap. On top of that, numerous changes were incorporated in such a way that rendered the whole mess nearly incomprehensible. I was stunned to think that the insurer could have allowed such scam to go on for nearly a year during which time the "loss" grew by over 400%. By the time it was referred to me the insurer had paid out $430,000 in "progress" payments. At the end I estimated the real damage value at $87,000, so he had bilked the company to the tune of $343,000.

It was obvious that we were dealing with a master fraudster here and so I recommend a background investigation on the individual that was carried out by a private investigator. Many interesting things turned up, beginning with the fact that the man was a retired high ranking military officer that had long worked in Pentagon procurement and accounting systems. Additionally, he had once been brought up on Federal fraud charges but was acquitted.

Now we knew why the scam was so sophisticated; here was a guy that had plenty of experience at hiding huge sums of money in piles of documents. But, however clever the strategy, it was badly flawed because once anyone gets beyond being overwhelmed by the huge amount of paper and the apparent unintelligibility of it, a painfully obvious pattern emerges: The whole mess was, itself a clear intent to defraud by virtue of its unintelligibility along with excessive numbers of changes. The methodology was far beyond anything a reasonable person would do intentionally or by accident. With his professional background the whole thing was completely out of character.

When I counted up the actual invoices, there were 191 of them. Over 1000 pages of paper, many containing incomprehensible handwritten explanations, were sent to the insurer that had no demonstrable reason for existence other than to sow confusion. Normally, a reasonable person would just total up the invoices. But what this person had done was to make "constant adjustments and corrections" in the form of summaries.

Not surprisingly, this claim bore many other hallmarks of fraud: at least 75% of the documents were copies, not one original; nothing was ever mailed, always hand delivered. Of the monies paid him, I estimated that only $35,000 were put into repairs. What ultimately sent him to prison was that I was able to prove that many of his invoices were fraudulent. The vast majority of them were of the handwritten variety on standard office supply forms from one-man type shops of dubious reputation and in some cases didn't appear to exist. When law enforcement finally went after them, several turned state's witness to avoid prosecution themselves.

Preparation for turning the case over to law enforcement involved demonstration of the pattern of premeditated intent. Hundreds of pages of documents had to be analyzed and sorted in such a way that the method could easily be demonstrated. This huge mass of documents was later turned into a slide show that revealed the same pattern and methodology used over and over again so that a jury had no trouble convicting him of insurance fraud.

Obtaining direct proof of fraud when it exists is usually not difficult and a single altered document is often all the proof needed. But equally often it's a matter of circumstantial evidence. Defense lawyers would have us believe that circumstantial evidence is of no value when the fact is that most criminal convictions are based on circumstantial evidence. A single circumstance is not good evidence. When dealing with circumstantial evidence, we need a preponderance of circumstances sufficient to remove reasonable doubt. The following is good example of both direct and circumstantial evidence in one case:

> A vessel is reported stolen. The owner stated that he was delivering the boat to a repairer on a trailer and parked it on the street in front of the repair shop, after dark, on a Friday night, knowing that the repairer did not do business on the weekend. The investigation later developed that: the date on the boat's title had been altered by three years; the owner had no equity in the heavily financed boat that was worth less than the loan balance, and the owner was behind in his payments; much false information had been provided on the insurance application.
>
> The repairer stated that the owner did not inform him that he was dropping the boat off on Friday but was told it would be Monday. Had he known that the customer would do that, he would have advised him against that. No witnesses could be found that ever saw the boat at the time and place the owner said he delivered it. The owner failed to make a police report until Monday morning when he also called the repairer and asked how the repairs were going.

None of this evidence taken alone would have been sufficient for the insurer to deny the claim, but taken together is sufficient to make a clear and convincing case, not the least because the insured did not act like a prudent uninsured by leaving the boat where he did. In this case the insurer didn't have to deny the claim because the investigator confronted the insured with overwhelming evidence and the insured decided against pressing his claim. Believing this to be fraud, in essence the insurer dared him to sue. He didn't.

The salient point here is that in many instances, while fraud may not be absolutely proven, absolute proof isn't always needed, just a very strong preponderance of evidence. Claims may also be denied for other reasons such as cited above, or when the investigator runs across evidence of other crimes, an event that is not unusual. Knowledge of other crimes can be used to defeat claims simply by the investigator revealing that he knows it. One should never threaten the use of this information as that could be construed as blackmail. Mere revelation of the knowledge to the claimant is often enough to make the claim disappear.

The investigator must be exceedingly careful in such situations that he is not dealing with a violent person as this could result in serious retribution. A criminal background check should first be made. Find out what kind of person you are up against before employing this tactic as you don't want to confront someone who might try to harm you.

When Control is Lost

By contract and by law, the insurer is only obligated to pay fair and reasonable repair costs. The difficulty is with defining "fair and reasonable". The problem with repair estimates is that they are just that — estimates, and to work a claim from one is to essentially lose control. Competitive bids are a far better way, but such bids may be difficult to obtain. Though bids will always be higher than estimates, the benefit is that of achieving control. When dealing with very large losses, one option is to pay good money for a thoroughly detailed estimate and contract bid on very large losses. Note that in large claims it is necessary that a fixed price contract be backed up by a detailed cost breakdown because the contractor must be able to show how he arrived at his bid. It is of no real value to us if we don't have it because the veracity of the bid can be argued. Hard facts and numbers are needed to successfully argue a point.

> By way of example, in a case where a large yacht insured for $1.2M had partially sunk, an insured and his repairer presented the insurer with a $900,000 estimate - that's estimate, not contract. I felt that this was excessive and so arranged to pay a top flight boat yard $3,000 to make an iron-clad, detailed contract bid which came in at $550,000. In a case like this it is imperative that the credentials of the estimator be impeccable and that he is willing to do the job for the amount stated, hence a contract, not an estimate. In this case the estimator and I spent three days aboard the vessel with an assistant and a computer spread sheet detailing every nut, bolt, screw and wire clip. The estimate on which the contract was based ran to 40 pages of detail. In this way, our documentation was nearly unimpeachable.

This procedure is absolutely necessary to stave off litigation in troublesome cases. The claim was settled, a proof of loss signed, and a check issued before repairs even began, successfully averting a costly scam. The claims handler must become resigned to the fact that large losses are temporary full-time jobs that require extreme attention to detail and great patience — all the attributes of a good forensic accountant.

The Stop-Loss Technique

This is a method designed to resolve the problem when the surveyor gets stuck with an open ended contract with a hidden damages clause. With this technique, by the time the claims handler has his second or third new estimate for undiscovered damage, he's going to know that he's got a problem. To succeed the client has to be willing to back him up. The surveyor has tolerated the additions up to this point, but now he asks the repairer, *Will there be any more undiscovered damage?* If their answer is that they don't know, can't be sure, or something equally vague, this is the clue as to what is coming.

The surveyor should then go back to his client and explain that they are being scammed, and propose this method of stopping it. The surveyor then advises the repairer that he can't have them wasting his time anymore if they are incapable of assessing all the damages. *You (the repairer) hold yourself out as repair experts. I cannot accept the notion that you are incapable of documenting all the damage. If you can meet this requirement, then we can continue. If you cannot do that, we will seek a repair contract elsewhere and settle the claim based on that.*

Then with no further discussion, he leaves, no argument, no further discussion at this time. To do otherwise will show weakness and you'll be dragged back into worthless discussion in which you can only lose. The objective is to put the ball back in the repairer's court by refusing to accept the notion that this expert repairer is incapable of discovering all the damages, *now!*

This is going to ruffle their feathers, causing them to call the insured and make all kinds of accusations against the surveyor. The insured will call and raise hell. The surveyor must stand his ground! The principle behind this is that the only contractual obligation of the insurance policy is to reimburse the insured for the dollar value of his loss, not to supervise repairs or allow oneself to be manipulated like a puppet on strings. The insured is obligated to present his loss — all of it at one time — and not in bits and pieces strung out over six months.

It should be emphasized here that there is a reason why marine insurers get themselves into this pickle. It is that they are far more deferential to their rich customers than they are to Joe Six Pack with his eighteen foot outboard. Joe doesn't have his shopping centers or multi million dollar business insurance insured with them whereas Cabernet Conrad does. At this point, the insurer needs to decide whether he wants to continue doing business with this shady character. If they're not going to stand up to him, then it's no longer our problem.

Understand that both the insured and the repairer will engage in a strategy of trying to put the responsibility on the surveyor. *You* are holding things up, *you* are not doing your job, and so on, trying to make you feel guilty or defensive. If you accept this, you are sunk.

If the insurer is willing to back you up, now's the time to unspring the repairer's trap. The claims adjuster must answer the insured by calmly explaining to the insured that it is his responsibility to assess his damages and present his claim in full. He has chosen this yard to do that on his behalf, but if they're not capable of doing that then perhaps he should find someone who is. You've got other claims to handle and you're not going to go back to that yard every time they find something that they should have found at the beginning. That is *their* job, not yours. Advise the insurer that they should write the assured, enclosing a blank proof of loss asking him to present his claim *in full*.

Now the responsibility is back on his shoulders where it belongs. Inevitably he'll go back to the repairer where they'll probably conspire up a huge list of new things totaling many thousands of dollars and mail it to you. At this point presumably all the hidden damages are now exposed and you can now bring in another repairer to make a second estimate. The effect of this is to demonstrate that you have no intention of being defrauded and that their scam is failing. Whether at this point they are ready to punt remains to be seen, but now you are going to tell them that it is the insurer's intent to settle on the basis of the estimates to date. This may induce him to punt or push it to the limit.

Bizarre Happenings

The use of boats for smuggling contraband has a long and colorful history in this country even in recent years. From the whisky smugglers of the prohibition era to the peak of the days of the drug trade, hallmarked by the Colombian Cocaine Cowboys that wreaked a course of havoc through the Bahamas, Florida and the Gulf Coast, to the smuggling of refuges, then and now, the use of pleasure craft plays a prominent role in illicit activities. These boats are often insured and the damages sustained during their illicit commerce may be presented as insurance claims.

In 1986 I was assigned an insurance claim by Chubb & Sons on a Hatteras sport fisherman said to be at our local Hatteras dealer for repairs. The odd thing about it was that no cause of loss was given nor any description of damage on the loss notice. However, the name of the insured corporation sounded familiar to me but I did not place it until later. The next day, on my way to breakfast, I stopped by the dealer (who hadn't opened up yet) to see if the boat was there. It was and what I saw was stunning. The boat was full of bullet holes and the cockpit and bridge was smeared with blood. Arriving at my office I did a bit of thinking and then some digging through old file records and found that the name, Foxfire International Investments, appeared on another of our files. The outfit was owned by Colombian national Carlos Lehder, head of a faction of the Medellin Cartel, the infamous drug lord who now resides in a U.S. prison after being captured in 1987, convicted and sentenced to 155 years.

A day later a story appeared in the Miami Herald about a shoot out between drug smugglers and the Bahamian Defense Force in the Exuma Islands, the details of which suggested that this was the boat involved. It was. Needless to say I was not too thrilled to be involved with people who use automatic weapons against military forces in protection of their trade. The boat was also full of spent 7.62 mm high velocity brass cartridges, which is what AK47's use. And these people had filed an insurance claim for the damages resulting from a gun battle? Incredibly, they had! Needless to say, there was no issue here as damages sustained in gun battles are not covered. As an aside, Lehder's common law wife, Coral Marie Talavera Bacca, was recently revealed to be, until 2001, a manager for insurance giant AIG. In this business one never knows.

This was one of the more extreme, though not the only such, cases that had come across my desk. And while cases like this are far from common, the probability of a marine investigator running across similar bizarre cases during a career is rather high. It pays to be alert to warning signs of trouble and when the potato is too hot to handle, drop it[4].

Vessel Theft Fraud

Legitimate total theft of vessel claims are distinguished by certain characteristics; all the documents seem to be in order, the facts of case line up with the insured's story, there is no indication of financial distress, the insured is forthcoming with information and the investigator is left without suspicion.

Fraudulent theft cases are hallmarked by the exact opposite of the above factors wherein some of the facts don't line up, the insured's story seems improbable or is filled with gaps, requested documents are said not to exist or are slow in coming, and there is the suspicion that the insured may be financially distressed.

Total theft of vessel investigations are, as often as not, predominately paper chases since something as large and expensive as a boat or yacht can be expected to leave a large paper trail, a trail that starts with the ownership documents, police or Coast Guard reports and moves along to the trail of records maintenance, repair, fuel and dockage purchases and so on. Field work consists of tracking down potential witnesses and frequently obtaining formal statements which will be essential for a claim denial.

Indicators of Vessel Theft Fraud

Boats that are really stolen are stolen for four main reasons:

(1) For use in money, drug or human smuggling. Larger boats stolen for these purposes are normally used for a one-time run and then abandoned and so are often recovered.

(2) As a means of escaping the U.S. undetected. As a boat outbound to another country these usually are not found. Even when found they are often very difficult to recover from some third world nation.

(3) For parts or engines. Usually found stripped, abandoned. Pros normally perform very careful removals as opposed to the cut and rip method of the petty thief. Disconnected rather than cut wires, cables and hoses will indicate a pro.

(4) For resale and conversion to cash. Boat theft rings specialize in high value small boats and come and go periodically, but I've never encountered one that specialized in larger boats because they are just too easily identified and found.

Theft of vessel claims have some fraud indicators that are different from ordinary claims fraud, though many will overlap. Some of these are easily defined while others are more difficult to describe, mainly that "sense" that something is not right, whether it is the behavior of the insured or a combination of factors. Good investigators develop hunches, but hunches are not something that materialize out of thin air; a good hunch is based on indicators that convey a possibility. Among the more obvious indicators are:

- Insured is overly friendly and helpful, but then starts pushing for rapid settlement and becomes hostile when that doesn't happen.

- Value of vessel doesn't match owner's profile

- Value of items lost or stolen are inconsistent with value of vessel. Example, $8,000 electronic item on a boat worth only $40,000.

- Vessel insured above market value

- Vessel had no security whatever, i.e., trailer parked on street

- Date of loss very close to policy inception or expiration dates

- Insured always delivers documents in person and not by mail

- Details and dates are always vague and never definite

- Submits supporting documents that are always poor photo copies, often illegible

- Blank receipts, no sales tax or wrong tax calculation

- Receipts, invoices without dates

- Handwriting similar on more than one invoice

- Can't provide invoices for large purchases

- Doesn't comply with document production request

- Old invoices printed on new paper when it should be yellowed

- Two different handwriting examples on same document

- Vessel is for sale

- Expired registration

- Vessel not used for long time

- Multiple party ownership

- Avoids meeting with investigator, doesn't show up, cancels meetings

Proving fraud is always a difficult proposition, but obtaining irrefutable, actionable proof is not the only possible objective, as was illustrated in an earlier example. Good investigative work may result in the insured withdrawing the claim if he sufficiently fears exposure.

Theft investigations usually start with the premise that fraud is an ever-present possibility so that one of the first things to do is obtain the ownership and purchase records. These will include title, if any, federal and state registration and original purchase records. The original bill of sale is particularly important since the identification contained therein can be checked against all other documents. While this won't disprove the absence of any alterations, it's an important step. One should not take possession of a boat title or original records at this time but simply inspect the original documents, make note of any irregularities on it and photo copy it. Photocopies of titles as proof of ownership should not be accepted as proof of ownership unless verified through the state agency.

Small Boats

Many outboard boats are stolen just for their motors, equipment and hardware and then the boat is left abandoned in some remote area. In this instance, it's probably a legitimate theft, though one should still be alert for indicators. In South Florida entire boats are stolen, placed in containers or aboard small ships and shipped to South America. In the west they are taken to Mexico. Check with local police or marine patrol for advice on whether known theft rings are currently operating.

Fraudulent activities involving small boats are widespread and commonplace, so one need be alert from the beginning in such cases. Good investigators begin to develop an intuitive sense about cases commonly based on the behavior of the boat owner or irregularities in documents and circumstances involving the loss. For example, stolen trailer boats tend to fit a common pattern: the boat was parked in a place where there is little or no traffic, no security, few possible witnesses, it occurred at night, and it involved behavior not consistent with reasonable and prudent behavior. A common example: the trailer-boat was parked on the street or in large parking lot. A reasonable and prudent person knows that anyone with a trailer hitch could drive off with the boat in a matter of seconds and would not place the boat in such locations.

One of the most common profiles for small boats involved in fraud cases is that the pedigree of the boat is questionable. That is, either the age of the boat, or who built is in doubt. This often includes "rebuilt" older boats where the work done on them is substandard or at least not at a professional level. The boat has been repainted and the H.I.N. number is no longer there or is obscured. The boat hasn't been used in a long time, or the rebuilding job hasn't been finished.

Most policies insuring trailer-boats these days have a clause requiring demonstrable anti theft measures such as trailer hitch or wheel locks, being chained up and so on. The lack of any such measures may void the coverage.

Example

> In one of my more unusual cases, a supposedly ten year old 24 foot Sea Ray was reported to be stolen and recovered in a vandalized condition. Someone had completely stripped the boat of anything of value. The boat was insured at a higher than market on the basis that it had been completely rebuilt and refurbished. Oddly, the insured was the one who made the recovery. The so-

called refurbishment of this boat was very poor, there were significant alterations and the hull number was no longer present for reasons unknown, plus
there was no engine to have a number. The mistake that the insured made was
that there was once a registration number in tape-on registration numbers on
the bow that had been removed. Sunlight caused fading of the paint so that
the numbers could just barely be made out. When those numbers were run
through the state's computer, it came back as the registration to a twenty year
old Renken that had been reported stolen eight years prior. When asked to
see the boat's title, the insured said he lost it but was applying for a duplicate.
Checking back with the state again produced no title application. End of claim.

Example

In another exemplary case, an older boat was reported stolen from an owner's
home and was later recovered from beside a busy highway a little more than a
mile from the insured's home. He claimed that the trailer had a hitch lock on it
that was no longer present, but the hitch lock was not in place when recovered
and there was no evidence of its forceful removal. The boat disappeared from
his driveway, in a fenced yard, overnight and was recovered by police within
24 hours. The fence was said to have a gate that was locked with a chain, but
the owner couldn't produce a cut chain or lock.

The boat was found on the side of a very busy highway. The insured did not
make a police report, claiming that he hadn't time. Two engines and some of
its hardware and equipment was missing, all of which had been carefully removed. The location where it was found didn't make sense because the thieves
that stripped it certainly wouldn't strip the boat on the side of a busy highway.
Normally they take the boat to a secure location where their activities won't
be seen. The thieves certainly wouldn't then take the boat and dump it where
it was found; if they were going to dump it, they'd do it in a remote location.

This prompted the investigator to dig a little deeper. The outboard motors were
about 12 years old and possibly in poor condition. This owner had owned the
boat for six years, half its life. Records of engine maintenance and repairs were
requested but the owner couldn't produce any. The investigator then canvassed
the local repair shops where upon he hit upon one marina service manager that
stated that the owner had brought the boat to their facility a year previously for
repair of a power head that was blown due to leaking head gaskets. The other
engine also had problems. The boat owner made an insurance claim through
a prior insurer but the claim had been denied. The owner could not provide
any proof that the prior engine damage had been repaired.

Now, let's summarize the situation. We have a twelve year old boat with what appear to
be worn out engines that was purportedly stolen and stripped of its engines and some
hardware, but the boat is found abandoned. The boat is not in very good condition.

Does it make sense that a thief would steal a boat for twelve year old engines? No, in fact, all indicators point toward this being a fraudulent claim since none of the evidence confirms the insured's story.

The basis of the claim denial was the failure to comply with the requirement for a locking device. But while this was not a rock solid basis for denial, the decision was heavily weighted by the other evidence that was fairly strong; this was not the kind of case that a plaintiff would want to go to court with.

Tracing Larger Boats

Vessel theft fraud involving larger vessels is not common, but you may be assigned to actually stolen larger boat cases.

Larger vessels are usually stolen for use in some illicit activity such as smuggling, and typically only take place along national borders for a variety of reasons, not the least of which is the international change of jurisdiction. Boat thefts on the West Coast (excepting San Diego area) are uncommon because there's no place to hide. But it's a different story in the east and south where there is an endless maze of waterways along with quick refuge to foreign countries like the Bahamas, Mexico, Cuba and other islands where even if you do locate the boat, recovery will be difficult.

When larger yachts are stolen, if the notice of loss is promptly given — say within 24 hours — it is worthwhile and the chances for recovery considerably higher. The assumption is that the boat departed on its own bottom which, if that is the case, should make it easier to trace. Starting with the place where it was docked, we attempt to establish a time line. By knowing approximately when last seen, and knowing what speed it was capable of making, range circles can be plotted on a chart to indicate how far it can go within 24, 26, 48 hours and so on. If we can get ahead of it, assuming that it is going to run as far as possible, or for a border, we can notify bridge tenders, and local law enforcement authorities to be on the look out (BOLO) for our boat.

When assigned a fresh boat theft, one of the first things to do is to obtain a description of the vessel, along with any distinguishing characteristics, a photo, the registration and hull number to relay to authorities. The boat name will assuredly be removed or covered up, so distinguishing characteristics are important.

If the vessel is of substantial value, say $500,000 or more, it is worthwhile to hire an aircraft and go look for it. I have successfully recovered several large yachts this way.

A boat that can comfortably cruise at 25 knots can do 600 miles in 24 hours in open water. A twin engine aircraft that cruises at 180 knots can do that in three hours, so there's the advantage. Then, too, is the consideration of our boat's fuel range, information that the owner can provide. Where would it have to stop for fuel? Thieves may want to avoid confined waterways during daylight hours and will most likely head for open waters if possible. Otherwise they may try to move only at night if conditions permit. The point here is that the investigator must know his local waters and try to second guess the thieves thinking and route.

Before setting out, however, you will need to have in place a plan for how you will recover the boat if you find it. On my first-ever attempt to locate and recover a large yacht, I hired an aircraft at considerable expense, spent two days searching and actually located the boat. But I failed to plan for what to do next so that by the time we landed and local law enforcement was contacted and they got their show on the road, my yacht was long gone. Thus, I found it and lost it. When hunting an actively fleeing yacht, it is necessary to make arrangements for radio or phone communication with local law enforcement such as the marine patrol or Coast Guard, U.S. law enforcement will usually be very cooperative owing to the prospect of making a front page arrest. Foreign law enforcement may be more problematical.

Be prepared for your failures to outweigh successes because attempting to locate the boat is a long shot. With an aerial search it is imperative to prepare the time/distance circles to define the search area. It is not difficult to determine how far the vessel can travel in a given period of time. Then determine all possible directions of travel. Which is most likely? For what purpose was the vessel most likely stolen? The answer is usually determined by what kind of illicit activity has been going on in your area.

Coordinate with the aircraft pilot the fuel/time/distance limitations and begin the search from the aircraft maximum fuel range unless you intend to refuel. In other words, work back from just beyond the farthest distance that you think the vessel could have traveled. The local geography will suggest what is the best search pattern. Open ocean is the worst due to the huge expanse of empty space without distinguishing characteristics. All will depend on how much time you plan to spend in the air — and how much money to spend. In this way, as you run short on fuel, you terminate the search while closest to home base where the boat is least likely to be.

Ownership & Registration

It may be hard to believe, but is very true, that state boat titling agencies have very weak verification controls so that scamming the system is not particularly difficult. Titling and registration issuance in many states have been farmed out to independent contractors, a situation that aids and abets fraud in a variety of ways. We hear news reports about this happening with motor vehicles rather frequently, but the boat scam artists rarely seem to get caught.

It might seem improbable that a boat owner would attempt to alter boat titles and registrations, but it happens all the time. These documents should be examined carefully for evidence of alteration and then checked back with the issuing agency. It happens that someone at the state agency stole a stack of blank titles and has sold them. The important point about stolen blank titles is that they are not entered into the system so that when you check, nothing shows. Also, check the type fonts on the suspect title against the type of printing found on a legitimate title.

Next, we want to see the original purchase documents. The reason we want to see these is so that we can cross-check hull and engine numbers. In more than one astonishing case, a stolen boat was used as the basis to make a stolen boat claim. In other words, the boat thief is also the insured who is collecting twice for the same boat, after he has sold it but reported it stolen! In this instance, the stolen boat was recovered so that not only was the claim denied because a stolen boat can't be insured, but the insured was arrested for felony grand theft.

Insurance frauds committed on a repetitive basis either individually or as a group, have used a wide variety of methods of creating fraudulent titles and other documents. Some have managed to obtain blank state titles but most often there is always some excuse as to why they can't produce a title, or the title is a color photocopy that has been altered. Such frauds are easily discovered and proven by obtaining all necessary records from the state or federal agency that issued the documents. Such cases are hallmarked by the absence of a bill of sale.

A more common scam is to purchase old, derelict boats that roughly match the description of a newer boat; then, alter the hull number to match the older boat, leaving the year obliterated by paint and filler, or alter the year number on the title.

In the case of most non organized crime false thefts, the owner is motivated by acute financial troubles and has actually sold the boat he is trying to collect insurance on. If he's selling to an unsuspecting victim he's going to get caught because the new owner will want to obtain a new title and registration. Is there any way he can sell the boat without getting caught? Only if the investigator fails to check with the state, for it is unlikely that a police agency will check. It is doubtful that many states flag titles of stolen boats (Florida does), so it's up to you to check.

At one time Florida had a provision for titling home made and rebuilt salvage boats that provided means for criminals to create titles for boats that did not exist, or to title a boat as something it was not. These are the infamous Z boats, named for the letter Z in the prefix of the hull number (FLZ). Some states may still have such provisions, or there may be loop holes in whatever provision they have. Some state titling agencies are very cooperative and will provide all the information you need while others, like California, will not provide any information without a signed affidavit from the *owner* and police, which renders the California agency useless to independent investigators. In this state only a police officer can make these checks, so it becomes much easier to perpetrate this fraud.

The above referenced provision led to a situation where scam artists would obtain old or wrecked boats, claiming that they had been rebuilt, creating phony bills of sale or builder's certificates of origin, and obtaining new titles with late model HIN's. The boat would then be insured and get "stolen" with all the documentation appearing to be in order unless one checked with the state titling agency. States that have this provision add the letter Z to the hull number such as FLZ or GAZ.

Thanks to the efforts of the International Association of Marine Investigators, the tactics of marine fraudsters are being discovered and disseminated amongst police agencies nationwide. Those areas with heavy boating activity and official marine patrols will have officers who are members. This has served the purpose of making police much more aware and cooperative with private marine investigators. The beginner is encouraged to join IAMI and become acquainted with his local marine patrolmen.

Financing

Financial records provide another good avenue of investigation. Just because a boat is financed doesn't automatically signal that it is legitimate.

In one theft case in which the behavior of the insured caused me to be suspicious, but without any direct evidence to that point, I decided to go to the firm that held the mortgage and asked to see their paper work. The insurer has the right to see these documents because the lender is a loss-payee and a co-insured. Unexpectedly, the lender produced a somewhat different set of documents that those provided by the insured.

The lender produced a Manufacturer's Certificate of Origin that the insured did not have, but the MSO produced a slightly different Hull number (two digits transposed) than that shown on the title. The boat couldn't be checked because it was gone. Earlier I had called the State and verified the information on the registration, but not the title because I didn't have the title at that time (my mistake).

I was completely baffled by this anomaly. I then called the titling agency and was told that the title number was "not issued." It later was disclosed that this title was one among many blank titles that had been stolen from the agency – there is no title check for registration issuance, so the state didn't pick up the stolen title number. Further investigation revealed that the dealer that had sold the boat in another state had recently been indicted and convicted of selling stolen boats and motors, but was now defunct. This had made news even in the local Florida papers as it was national chain dealer. The insured apparently had heard that the dealer had been caught, and was fearful that the boat he now owned was also stolen.

If discovered, the insured would lose the boat and he would be left with a large mortgage to pay and no boat. While I suspected that he found a way to get rid of the boat, and file a fraudulent claim, I was never able to prove this. The insured and lender both lost out anyway because one cannot legally insure stolen property, even if one is a victim of fraud. The lender and the insured filed suit against the insurer and lost because both had failed to perform due diligence. The proof of illegitimacy was contained within the documentation had they but checked carefully.

The lesson learned here is that it is necessary to cross-check all documents; the investigator needs to determine what official documents exist, and who possesses copies or originals, and then proceed to cross-check them. Possessors of official document copies can include:

Owner	Lender
State government	Federal government
Seller	Broker
Dealer	Manufacturer

Fictitious Boats

Incredibly, some states, such as Alabama, still do not issue boat titles. Boats from non title states provide an excellent opportunity to sell stolen or fictitious boats in other states provided someone is foolish enough to buy a boat without a title. In states like that, possession truly is nine tenths of the law.

It is not only possible, but fairly easy, to obtain a title on a boat that originated in a non title state, in a state that does issue titles. In most cases all that is required is:

(1) registration slip

(2) bill of sale

(3) a tracing of the HIN

Fake tracings of HIN's are easy to make, as are phony bills of sale. A registration slip can be forged. States that don't title boats will issue registrations on just about anything because all they're interested in is the fee. Some states even contract out registrations to private contractors so there is no problem for con artists to get phony registrations for a boat that doesn't exist, then get a title for it in a titling state, insure it and report it stolen.

Every stolen boat case should get a complete title check. If your state won't release this information, try going to the local marine patrol office with your case and see if they won't get the title information for you. As most states have IAMI members, they may be glad to help.

Develop a Profile

Beyond tracing the official record of a vessel, about all we have to go on are other records, the existence of which we aren't aware of. By developing a profile of a boat we can get a very good idea of what records should exist, and then ask the owner to produce them. For example, a diesel boat should have its oil and filters changed every 100 hours, a gas boat every two hundred. Diesel oil changes are expensive so the owner should have some record of this. The inability to produce maintenance records casts suspicion.

Next, we can ask the owner how often he uses the boat; then ask how many hours per year that comes to. If he says 300 hours, find the hourly fuel consumption of his engines, then figure the approximate amount of fuel he should have burned. Does he claim the federal fuel tax deduction? If so, let's see the records. Where does he buy his fuel? When was the last time? Will that retailer search his records?

Outboard boats circa 1999 and later probably have computerized engine controls that have a CPU that records vital engine information. Find out who the servicing dealer is and whether they have serviced the engine and have a CPU download on file of his engine data. Here's where developing good relations with local marinas becomes indispensable for trying to get this information. Because he was a customer, they may resist giving it to you. If so, you still have the option of demanding this information from the insured.

The same applies for many electronic diesel engines where this data is probably maintained directly by the manufacturer; all the larger electronic diesel engines record this data. The larger and more costly a boat is, the greater the paper trail it creates and the avenues available for investigation. The more we question the owner and learn about the boat, the more avenues we can open up. Keep in mind that boat owners attract a lot of retail business attention. A boat owner who doesn't cut an economic swath through his marine community probably has a dead or fictitious boat:

- What equipment has been purchased recently?
- Who did you buy it from?
- Recent repair work and who did it?
- Recent maintenance and who dit it?
- Fuel and oil records
- Routine engine service, warranty claims, etc.

These are by no means the only possibilities. Each case has a unique profile that requires creative thinking and digging, digging, digging.

All states issue annual registration decals that are to be affixed to the vessel. Always take note of whether the registration is current as this is very often a good first indicator that all is not well. A boat without a current registration raises the question as to *why?* Usually it is because the boat isn't being used and an unused boat is usually an unwanted boat. Also be alert to boats that are insured as pleasure craft but have a commercial decal.

Federal Documentation

Most marine lenders will require federal documentation for vessels valued at $150,000 and above. This gives them a first preferred ship's mortgage, which is important to them.

Federal Documentation is handled by the U.S.C.G., Department of Transportation and its usefulness for our purpose is the recording of liens. An abstract of the document can be obtained on any vessel which will list the history of virtually all liens on that vessel, past and present, as well as any arrests and attachments. The easiest way to obtain an abstract is to go through a documentation service where the cost will be about $75 - 100. All that is needed is the documentation number. Any vessel that was ever documented is still on record.

Witness Canvassing

One of the more laborious investigative tasks is witness canvassing, which often has to take place in the claimant's neighborhood, so that you are questioning possible friends and acquaintances. People are generally reluctant to say anything negative about people they know. A good investigator is never content to take canvassing subjects at their word, but will go further in evaluating body language and demeanor. The unusual behavior of potential witnesses can be a tip-off that something is not right.

Canvassing is extremely important when total theft of a trailer boat from a residence occurs. Take note of all the homes that have a line of sight to the location of the boat, for these neighbors will have a higher probability of having seen the boat. If the boat is highly visible from the street then anyone could have seen it. In canvassing, we always start with the most likely witnesses first since canvassing can involve a lot of people and we want to play the highest probabilities first.

Most people are not particularly observant of what goes on around them so that the likelihood of coming up with a witness is low. Even so, the occasional hits we get on canvassing are usually enough incentive to motivate us to do it. Sometimes there is a person who, for whatever reason — perhaps he or she is the neighborhood busybody — tends to be observant of what is going on around them. And sometimes that person doesn't like the insured and is willing relate what he saw. And there is always the rare case where a witness saw the insured, or a thief, drive off with the boat, never to return.

Fixing the last time the vessel was seen is critical in the same way that time of death is important in homicides. A witness could place the boat in a location after the time the boat was reported stolen, or the last time it was seen could place the insured in proximity to it.

Another fertile area for canvassing is boat yards, marinas and other repair facilities, something that can usually be done by phone. The objective here is to determine whether the facility has any knowledge of the boat such as having made an estimate for repairs that the owner could not afford to accomplish.

Alteration of Official Documents

As discussed earlier, people making fraudulent claims often alter documents; sometimes they're very good at it, but more often alterations are rather obvious. When an insured has done this, usually he will make the alteration on the original and then send the investigator a color photo copy of it. Or he may even make a copy, alter that, and then photocopy it again. That's why poor copies of documents are a red flag. There is no reason for an insured to provide a bad copy of any document other than to try to hide something.

If it is suspected that a copy is being submitted as an original, distinguishing a fake from a real document such as a title usually comes down to the type of paper and type face. If in doubt, contact the appropriate state agency and ask if they can make the identification for you. If it proves a fake, they will likely turn it over to state investigators to finish the task for you. Altering an official government document is a crime additional to the fraud committed, but not necessarily independent of it.

Lightning Strike Fraud

False claims alleging lightning strikes are common and becoming increasingly so. Such claims are usually motivated by the ailing finances of the owner and are made obvious by several factors. First, there is no evidence of a lightning strike, followed by the "damaged" items being rather old.

Lightning, in and of itself, passing through metal does not cause damage to the metal. If it did, then all electrical wiring would become damaged the first time it is used. Lightning can cause damage when it meets high resistance, whereupon the item it is passing through instantly heats up and will burn. Electronics are full of resistors large and small, so that when lightning passes through circuit boards or resistance coils, the end result is severe heating or even a small electrical explosion as resistors blow out. Single side band radio tuner boards are a prime example of a circuit board that will explode when struck. At the very least, the part gets hot enough to leave evidence as to what happened. Radio antennae have a tremendous amount of resistance built into them so that when struck by lightning, antennae tend to blow apart, as do circuit boards.

Antennas are both grounded and have high resistance at the transmitter end, making them a prime target for lightning. When struck, the internal resistance is so great that the electrical charge breaks out through the fiberglass where it meets the resistor, usually leaving a shattered antenna. However, the antenna cannot carry the whole charge so that most of it continues on its path to earth outside the antenna jumping off to things like towers, masts, outriggers or even through air. The main part likely goes straight to the water outside the vessel. If a tower or mast is grounded, this will carry the main charge within the vessel to the ground point. If not grounded, it travels outside. This is what so often explains the differences in the amount of damage to electrical equipment.

I've had numerous claims involving extensive electronics mounted in an aluminum cabinet attached directly to a tower that was not grounded, and amazingly, many components were not damaged. Radios and radars, because of their antennas, rarely survive a lightning strike.

Just because electrical equipment is not functioning is not proof of a lightning strike. Neither does an allegation of lighting; just because someone alleges lightning, doesn't mean that it happened. The burden of proof is on the insured to prove causation.

I have never seen a legitimate lightning strike that did not leave some evidence in the form of burning, smoke or blackening somewhere, usually within electronics circuit boards, particularly radios that are attached to antennae. If there is no damage to the radio or antenna, then lightning probably didn't happen. When investigating lightning claims, all reportedly damaged components should be dismantled and inspected internally. In many cases corrosion will be found as the cause of equipment failure. In particular, check the electrical couplers to the antenna or power supply source where high resistance arcing may show up.

As mentioned earlier, double check the veracity of model numbers and types of electronics with brackets and connectors. It is all too easy for the insured and his repair outfit to substitute a costly late model gadget for an old, obsolete one.

The claim is very often made that, because the vessel's sea cocks are grounded or bonded, lightning passed through it/them and caused damage to same. This is a bogus claim whether made in ignorance or intentionally. People have even claimed that propellers, shafts and even engines were damaged by lightning. No such claim has ever been proved. I have heard stories of lighting blowing sea cocks out of hulls, or blowing holes in hulls, but I have never actually seen such a thing

Injury Claims - Medical Bills

Rarely do marine investigators become involved with injury claims and medical costs, mainly because most lack the training and experience to do so, and such claims are not assigned to them. However, this can be a very good avenue of business to develop because these claims rarely ever settle quickly and offer good, long-term work. Some marine insurers have their own experts on staff because they deal with other lines of liability insurance, but many do not.

Third party injury claims are the ones that are most likely to involve fraud. The insured's boat threw a wake that caused someone to fall down in another boat and be injured, but no one witnessed the event. That person immediately retained a lawyer, one of those guys that advertise on TV that spouts off about knowing your rights, which, translated means "I will squeeze the maximum number of dollars from that rotten insurance company."

Injury investigations are conducted the same way as any other type, starting with gathering the facts of how the mishap occurred, but then a second phase begins with examining the facts surrounding the injury. As with other types of fraud, medical fraud raises all sorts of warning signs, usually starting with a sense that the claimant or his attorney is not being straight with you. The pattern of events and behavior of people doesn't fit with that of people who are being forthright.

It often starts with the usual hostile and threatening lawyer letter that is notably lacking in specifics. The medical diagnosis is vague and generic such as chronic pain and headaches, a chiropractor instead of MD is involved, a small, private clinic instead of a hospital, only soft tissue injury is involved, few or no witnesses to the occurrence of injury, medical records, bills are poor photo copies and so on. In other words, there is a notable lack of provable specifics combined with suspicious presentation of verification. The differences between a real injury claim and a fraudulent one are like night and day because the real one leaves little doubt of its veracity while the other bristles with question marks.

Insurance fraud "mills" involving lawyers, doctors and clinics are very common with Jones Act cases involving shipping and commercial fishing, but the pleasure craft surveyor is most likely to encounter them in events involving small marine contractors such as dock and piling companies. There are numerous lawyers who specialize in this type of case because the Jones Act throws the door to this kind of abuse wide open since vessel owners are saddled with limitless liability for seamen. These scams are well established in all ports involving commercial fishing and other maritime activities and will often venture into the area of pleasure craft. These lawyers often have paid informants in hospitals and clinics who notify them as soon as a potential injured client arrives. Therefore, the first red flag is that the lawyer signed up the client within hours of the accident[5]. Be sure to compare the date of hospital admission with the date the lawyer was hired.

Another identifying characteristic of these injury scams is that small clinics, rather than major hospitals, are involved.

As with all other types of claims, overblown injury claims become fraud issues only when evidence presented by the claimant is suspected to be false. Matters of moderately overstated costs and injuries are treated as matters for adjustment.

I have defeated many phony injury claims by simply shadowing the claimant and observing his activities. In a case alleging a severe back injury in which the only diagnostics done were by means of X-rays (which are not adequate for this type of injury), by asking around the waterfront where the seaman work I was told that he was building his own boat in a nearby yard. There I found the seaman unloading 80 pound sheets of plywood from his pick up truck and photographed him doing so. A private investigator was hired to observe and photograph his work for several more days at moderate cost. Armed with these photos, the phony claim was easily defeated.

The Achilles heel of any lawyer that is pressing a fraudulent injury case is that the last thing he ever wants to do is to litigate the case. That won't be true if any aspect of the injury is real. Therefore, one of the best strategies for defeating fraud cases is simply getting enough evidence to expose the fraud and either force the withdrawal of the claim, or opting out for a very small settlement. Experience shows that when there is a lawyer that is involved in "mill" type operations, exposure will usually cause him to settle quickly and reasonably or disappear and never be heard from again.

As with other types of fraud, tactical delay and stringing out exposure of phony evidence works well as psychological weapon to instill doubt and fear of exposure. Whereas dumping a whole load of evidence on him gives him the opportunity and incentive to try to justify it all at once. However, such tactics must be carried within the guidelines of applicable fair trade practices legislation.

Although the investigator may not know anything about injuries, medical diagnosis and medical bills, analysis is not much different than for boat yard bills, and is not difficult to learn. For more difficult cases, there are numerous services that provide analysis of both bills and diagnosis at a reasonable cost. I have used these firms frequently over the years with considerable success.

Resource

IAMI

The International Association of Marine Investigators offers annual and regional conferences to further the training and knowledge of private industry, as well as public law enforcement personnel. Founded in 1986 when Major Dave MacGillis, of the Florida Marine Patrol, organized and published the Vessel Theft Investigators National Roster. This roster was intended to assist investigators combat marine theft, a high profit, low risk crime that was out of control, by providing contact persons from various agencies involved in marine theft investigations.

State Insurance Departments

Some states have very active insurance departments, and because insurance costs are becoming an increasingly critical problem, more and more states are taking an active interest in combating insurance fraud. Establishing contact with, and getting to know, state insurance investigators in your state can be of tremendous assistance to both you and them because this is one way for them to develop information and leads.

However, it is necessary to be very careful about giving names of insureds because an insured is your client's customer and we do not have the authority to report suspected fraud without the client's approval. Toward that end, when talking with official investigators, the marine investigator may relate a current case without giving the name of the individual involved. He may ask questions about a certain clinic, or an ambulance chasing lawyer or doctor with a view toward finding out if they have any information on these people.

Getting information from official investigators is usually a matter of subtle trading of information. As cops, they too, have to be very circumspect and dare not go on record with incriminating statements. But once a relationship is established, if you can provide good information to them, they will usually reciprocate with generalities and disguised language.

For example, the marine investigator asks the state investigator whether he has any indication that such and such a clinic or doctor is running a fraud mill. If he doesn't, he can flat out say no. If he does, he might respond with, "Nothing specific." Such an answer means that he *has* heard something.

In a case involving stolen outboard motors, a Marine Patrol officer was asked whether he had any evidence of a certain boat dealer being connected with stolen motors. The officer didn't answer, but went back to his office and returned with a copy of a year old newspaper clipping describing a story in which the same dealer in another city was implicated in selling stolen motors. The officer went back to his office without having said a word. A short time later the marine investigator passed information to the Marine Patrol officer that led to a major crime ring bust involving that dealer. Needless to say, that marine investigator's relationship with the Marine Patrol was sealed.

Ultimately, getting information from government investigators is a matter of building a relationship and trust. Without this they're not going to talk, but it is well worth the effort to take the time to build these relationships if we want to be successful investigators.

(Footnotes)

1. Claims person, claimsman and adjuster all refer to the insurance company employee that assigns the job and supervises the surveyor's work.

2. A good procedure for self-education is to research each questionable item as it arises so that over time you will come to know the law as it is called into play.

3. The proof of loss form is a standard claim form by which an insured makes a claim demand, requiring signature and notarization.

4. Since those days the drug trade hasn't gone away, it has gone invisible. Now that we are a nation that does not enforce its borders, the importation of illicit drugs pours in from every corner and is more likely to be encountered in a truck than a boat.

5. In some states, including Florida, it is illegal for a lawyer to solicit a patient in a hospital. If you discover this, it is an excellent way to defeat the lawyer.

Chapter 11

Interrogation Techniques

Interviews, interrogations or taking statements, regardless of which term we use, means the same thing. It is a process by which we obtain information from witnesses. I deliberately chose the term interrogation because it conveys the sense of trying to extract information from people who may be reluctant to give it. Verbal information that constitutes evidence amounts to around one half of all evidence obtained during investigations, yet my experience is that the vast majority of marine investigators do not take formal statements. The end result is that their investigations are incomplete.

There are probably a number of reasons why they don't. In some states, licensing is required and they don't have the appropriate license. But probably the main reason is simply fear because they have no training, and because they are afraid of confrontations. This is much the same phenomenon as stage fright.

Certainly if one has never done it before, the prospect probably seems a little daunting, but the reality is that it is easy, far easier than one might imagine. Let's first start with the understanding that relatively few people ever refuse a request to give a statement. Secondly, including witness statements with an investigation report provides credibility that it would not otherwise have. Teaching yourself how to interrogate people effectively will improve your investigative effectiveness very substantially.

Throughout this chapter I discuss interrogation techniques primarily from the standpoint of interviewing policy holders or insureds, but not without recognition that the investigator will face many other kinds of subjects who are too numerous to deal with individually. Some investigators will do nothing but insurance work, while others won't do any at all. While interrogation techniques remain essentially the same no matter who the subject is, it should be recognized that insureds, as interview subjects, have to be treated differently than other types of witnesses because they are customers of our clients.

The development of effective interrogation techniques is essential to conducting successful investigations. A skilled interrogator can extract information from a hostile or reluctant witness where the unskilled interrogator comes away with little or nothing — the difference can be that great.

For most people who desire to get into the business of marine investigations, the idea that they would have to become a good interrogator probably never crossed their minds. That was certainly my case, but a time came when one of my insurance cases involved a death, and I was faced with the stark reality that I had inadequate skills to do what I had been tasked to do. Moreover, I was faced with interrogating a man who was suspected of murder[1] and I was terrified at the prospect. There was little choice but jump in and do the best I could, come what may. The task ultimately proved much easier than anticipated.

I should point out here at the beginning that, although I delve into some sophisticated techniques, in the vast, vast majority of cases there is no need to get clever where simplicity will do just fine. Be sure to understand the difference and don't make the mistake of getting fancy when it is not necessary. Only when we get involved with serious cases involving reluctant or devious witnesses are such tactics necessary.

A simple rule is this: *It is always better to underplay a situation than to overplay it.*

Getting Started

There is only one way to learn this work and that is to jump right in and start doing it. Do not, at first, be too concerned with the results; learning these skills takes time. Prepare your list of questions, and then just go ask them. As we engage in the process, new questions will come to mind; follow whatever new line of questioning that offers. Since we are likely to get sidetracked this way, it's best to write out a list of questions at first.

The appropriate attitude for conducting an interview is to simply be yourself. It is completely unnecessary to engage in play-acting. As we shall soon see, it is usually better to appear stupid and inept than smart.

Also avoid trying to use advance techniques until such time as you lose anxiety and become comfortable confronting people face-to-face. Do a moderate amount of preparation but avoid excessive preparation; filling your head with too many details is not helpful.

In naming this chapter, I have deliberately used the term "interrogation" because that's what it is, though the techniques employed are soft, not hard. It should go without saying that our methods are not the stuff of movies and television. Were you to view a video of my interrogations, you would see that they more closely resemble a normal conversation but for the fact that I am asking all the questions. This is about how to extract information from people who might otherwise be reluctant to give it. The investigator downplays the offensive nature of it by calling it an interview which, of course, implies willing cooperation. Interviews are not always given willingly but in some cases are compelled by an insurance contract. In most cases our interviews of persons are very ordinary and without any great significance to them. Of course, some few of our cases are not ordinary, cases where large amounts of money are hanging in balance along with possible civil or criminal litigation undercurrents.

A condition of most insurance contracts requires the insured, when asked, to provide a statement either under oath or otherwise. The best person to obtain this statement is the one who investigates the casualty. The marine investigator will be exposed to a very wide range of situations and personalities, and while it would take several volumes to thoroughly discuss this subject, this chapter will highlight the basics.

Effective interrogation of persons is an art simply because many people are reluctant to speak with strangers. Therefore, he who knows how to get reluctant witnesses to talk has a great advantage over those who don't. There's nothing like coming up against a witness whom we're sure has the information we are seeking, but who cleverly avoids divulging it. And because we are usually dealing with moneyed persons, our subjects are usually more sophisticated than most.

Fraud is a common element in the marine investigator's work, but whether that fraud is petty or major, it will have a major influence on interviews and statement taking. Whenever fraud is suspected, our work becomes greatly complicated and has to be adapted to fit the situation. It is fair to ask why can't we just ask honest, straightforward questions and be satisfied with the answers we get? In most cases we do just that, but experience teaches that some of persons we question will not, for whatever reasons - rational or otherwise — respond with straightforward answers. The shrewd investigator is one who knows how to coax information out of reluctant witnesses. And since we have no official authority whatsoever, we must get them to cooperate willingly.

Understand that interrogation techniques demand appropriateness to the status of the individual being interrogated, as well as the seriousness of the issue at hand. Keep in mind that investigations can involve anything from mere property damage claims to major fraud cases to wrongful death cases and even criminal activity. On several occasions I have had to do interviews of convicted felons in prison, something I'd never imagined having to do. And although quite scary, it turned out not to be as difficult as I had imagined, and in each case I was more successful than I had expected.

Sooner or later we all end up working with litigation cases that will provide learning opportunities. A good way to improve our abilities is, whenever possible, is to obtain actual transcripts of depositions and study them carefully. These can usually be obtained from any attorney that we are currently working with. It won't matter where the deposition comes from, our own cases or one we know nothing about, just get your hands on a few and study them for what they have to teach. It is very easy to discern the competence level of both the questioner and the questioned, and what makes them good or incompetent. With study, we discern their strengths and weaknesses.

The Art of Listening

Studies have shown time and again that people are generally poor listeners when they are engaged in conversation with others. The simple reason

for this is because people can't listen when they're thinking about what they are going to say while the other person is speaking; people simply do not listen.

It is vitally important for the investigator to become a good listener. The way to achieve this goal is to practice *not thinking* while the other person is talking. Concentrate on what the person is saying and not what your mind is trying to throw at you. Listen and observe body language. This can be done without staring at the person by learning, at times, to use peripheral vision, looking up, down, or aside short of the degree to which vision of the person is lost. Or by diverting attention away from the person frequently, but just as frequently returning to eye contact.

The Basis for Conducting Interviews

Interrogations are conducted for one of two reasons: for the purpose of determining insurance coverage, anticipation of litigation, or both. Since litigation is possible with any investigation, no matter how mundane it may seem, interviews and statements should always be taken seriously. Doing a good job requires preparation and at minimum should consist of reviewing the file and making note of the most important points to cover.

How important is this witness or statement? The more important it is, the more time we need to spend at thinking about how it is to be conducted. An important question to ask ourselves is whether this is the right time to be conducting the interview. We can't do a good interview unless we know what questions to ask, and we won't know what those are until we're well advanced in our investigation. Therefore, the greater part of good preparation is waiting until the right time to conduct the interview. For casual witnesses this is usually unnecessary, but is especially necessary for reluctant witnesses.

Types of Interviews

Interviews and formal statements are not the same thing. For our purpose, interviews are *informal* questionings of persons in person or by telephone, but are not recorded. Formal statements are either tape recorded or hand written statements, sometimes even with a court reporter. Recorded statements can be taken in person but will more often be taken over the phone to save time and cost. These techniques will be discussed later on. Formal statements can also be taken under oath as specified by most insurance contracts. What does "under oath" mean? Swearing an oath simply means that the person consciously and deliberately makes an assertion that what he says is true and is done by a certified court reporter who renders the oath. It means that he has considered the matter as opposed to speaking "off the cuff"; it is a formal statement of the highest order.

Statements under oath are normally only taken when a claim denial and litigation is anticipated, and only in consultation with the client. The procedure involves hiring a court reporter who then administers the oath. The investigator then proceeds to ask his questions; it is just that simple. However, court reporters may be used to record lengthy interviews simply as means of dealing with the transcription problem. In this case, no oath is administered. When I use a court reporter, I am always careful to put the subject at ease by telling them that the purpose of the court reporter is because I don't have the staff available to make long transcriptions; further that they may have a copy of the transcript if they wish.

The difference between a formal statement and a deposition is that the later is a direct component of litigation; it is sworn legal testimony intended for use in court. The formal statement is for the purpose of deciding insurance claims as well as determining whether litigation is necessary. Only rarely are statements taken by investigators used in court proceedings.

For our purpose there are two main subjects of interviews, witnesses and insureds. In some cases they are participants in the event. Witnesses don't normally have a personal interest at stake and normally don't lie or withhold once they agree to a formal interview. Witness statements are usually taken as soon as the witness is identified. The exception to the rule is when we just don't know enough to ask pertinent questions. The best technique for statementizing witnesses is to first run through the interview verbally. Then it is gone through in more detail while it is being recorded. The reason for this is to avoid long, rambling answers by the witness, which are costly to transcribe and deal with. Doing it off record first gives us the opportunity to eliminate windy answers and irrelevant questions without being made to appear manipulative. The result is a briefer, more succinct statement.

Should a witness launch off into a rambling answer, don't hesitate to cut them short, politely asking them to get to the point. You have the right to ask them to keep their answers brief prior to getting started. Some people will prattle on and on, but this isn't helpful to anyone, so do your best to keep prattle out of the statement. Feel free to interrupt them if they get windy. Some insureds, in particular, tend to over explain things. It may seem like a strange thing to say, but some people get a little too cooperative!

Informal insured interviews are often done in stages as questions arise and need to be answered. Normally, the investigator does not record these as statements, but merely makes notes on what was said of importance. It is a waste of time to take a full, formal statement at the outset of an investigation because we do not yet know enough to conduct a good interview. The result would be an incomplete and inadequate statement.

The primary purpose of a formal statement is to create a written record upon which the claims examiner can make a coverage decision. Investigator statements don't often end up as admissible evidence in trials, however that is not an excuse for not following the proper rules of evidence.

Informal Interviews

The informal interview is conducted without tape recording or other means of keeping record of the interview other than occasionally taking notes if the situation permits. It is the most casual method of interviewing a subject and should be conducted that way in all cases. Casual means that it is so informal that the subject hardly even notices that it is an interview; it's just someone asking him a few questions.

The purpose of doing the informal interview is to find out what the subject knows and what it's value may be without going through a formal interview. It may well be that the investigator, after getting the basics, will want to convert to a formal statement then and there; that is always an option, but generally we don't do that because, if the witness turns out to be important, it is still too early and we don't know enough to do a thorough interview. Coming back to the well the second time is rarely a problem after an informal interview. The one thing we want to avoid is the failure to ask important questions because we took a formal statement too early, and then have to try to do that second time.

Informal interviews may be done over the phone or in person as the situation demands. After an accident, we may be canvassing an area for witnesses, in which case we ask everyone we find whether they saw or know anything. In the case of an insurance claim, our first phone call to the boat owner becomes an informal interview. The objective is to obtain as much information as possible.

Before taking notes in front of the witness, be sure that this isn't going to cause an unwanted reaction. Taking notes begins to give the sense of being formal or "official." Do it only with very comfortable, forthcoming witnesses. Preface the act with, *Would you mind if I took a few notes?*

In other situations we may have received advice that a certain person, say, a boat yard employee, was a witness or has knowledge. In this case we seek the person out at his place of employment and attempt an informal interview on the spot. Depending on what he says, this may be but a preliminary to performing a formal interview on tape.

With the informal or preliminary interview, the first objective is getting the person to cooperate, knowing that there are some people who do their best to avoid getting involved in anything. The minute they sense an investigation they clam up. With this possibility in mind, the investigator's initial behavior should be to avoid the appearance of conducting an investigation. If it is a casual witness, I initially avoid introducing myself and just start asking questions in a most casual manner. *Say, were you here yesterday when. . . ?*

Remarkably, most people will answer quite a few questions asked by a stranger before they think to ask him who he is. At which point I apologize for not introducing myself and make the introduction while carefully gauging the subject's reaction. If there is no sense of reservation, I proceed with my questions. But, if I sense reluctance, I ask, *Do you have a problem with answering a few questions?*

The reason for doing this is that I want to confront a reluctant witness at the outset, and not waste my time getting evasive or dishonest answers. This forces the witness into taking a firm stand at a moment that he was not prepared for this. If he becomes hostile, nothing has been lost because I wasn't going to get anything out of him in any case. In the vast majority of cases the witness will relent by saying that he doesn't have a problem answering questions, even though he clearly does. This forces him into a more cooperative mode despite his attitude and results in more forthcoming answers.

In the above situation I am careful to not take notes in front of the witness because doing so will be just more intimidating to him. This mandates a very soft approach in which the negative line of questioning – *I don't suppose that you were in a position to have seen . . . . ?* — is likely to be more effective than the direct question, *Did you . . .?* Here the objective is to just get the subject comfortable and talking. Don't drive to the heart of the matter first, but begin with peripheral questions. A witness like this is probably susceptible to patronizing so take any opportunity to play to his ego.

With any witness, it is best to first try to nail down that person's position to make observations. Was this person in a position where he could actually observe what you are now asking about? *Where were you standing? What were you doing?* These are good opening questions. You don't want to find out later that the witness's line of sight was marginal, at best.

If the witness provides valuable evidence, we will probably want to come back and take a formal statement at a later date. We often don't know at early stages how useful a witness's information will be. At that time they will frequently say, *But, I've already told you what I know.* This provides the basis for why I do not tell them that I will be coming back for a formal statement; I don't want to give them time to formulate an excuse.

Statement Format

A recorded statement, whether in person or over the phone, should follow some simple rules of introduction and conclusion as follows:

> This is David Pascoe, Marine Surveyor, about to interview Mr. Jim Jones at his home in Miami. Today's date is April 2, 2003. Mr. Jones, are you aware that this conversation is being recorded?

Do I have your permission to do so?

Mr. Jones, please state your full name for me.

The subject of this interview is the claim that you filed with Gigantica Insurance company for the theft of your yacht. I am going to ask you some questions and if you don't understand the question, you will tell me so before answering, okay?

Upon conclusion of the interview, close in this way.

Mr. Jones, I am finished and don't have any further questions. Is there anything that I asked that you didn't understand, or anything that you wish to add or clarify?

Thank you, I will now turn the recorder off.

To save yourself time and embarrassment, always test the recording level at the location where the interview is being conducted, and at the distance it will be placed in relation to yourself and the subject. Make a quick test recording and then play it back. This applies to both in-person and telephone interviews.

Unless yours is an extremely serious case, you may, if necessary, turn the recorder off or pause it prior to the completion of the interview. But for a serious case where the tape could possibly be evidence, it is best not to turn the recorder off or pause it.

Conducting Interviews & Timing

From a strategic standpoint there often arises the question of when is the best time to conduct an interview. Only you can answer that question by your knowledge of where you stand with the investigation. It should be obvious why timing is important. At the beginning of an investigation we know little or nothing and therefore won't have many questions to ask. The more we know, the better the interrogation will be. Some of our investigations will involve wrong doing or untruths told by the insured - or others - and we'll want to pin him down as to what he purports the facts to be. We will want to (and I use this term advisedly) "trap" the subject with his own statements. In this context the word "trap" does not mean trick someone into saying something they don't mean; it means trick or motivate them into inadvertently telling the truth, or otherwise revealing the untruth.

There will be times when we know that the subject is lying and will want to use our knowledge of the truth to goad him into making certain admissions. *Did you know that such and such was happening? Did so and so ever tell you . . .* In the hands of a skillful interrogator, our knowledge can be used to gain admissions that would not otherwise be made. If we merely drop the hint that we know the truth, perhaps we can get the subject to contradict himself, or change course. We can use any sleazy yet legal tactic that a lawyer would use. If we think that the subject is lying, our customer-client courtesy is abandoned. But we don't want to become confrontational until such time as all necessary cooperation has been attained because once the cat is out of bag, so to speak, we are now in an adversarial situation and all cooperation ends. To this end, the taking of statements comes closer toward the end than the beginning of an investigation.

Statements can be taken either by voice recording or in handwriting. The later method, of course, is not amenable for a statement that is going to be longer than a page, and where the investigator feels it is important to get a signed statement quickly as in the example below. We would want a signed statement in more serious cases where we don't want to leave the statement open to challenge. Obviously, getting a signature on a recorded statement is more difficult and time consuming because it first has to be transcribed, then taken back to the witness for signature. This is usually not done unless there is a perceived need for doing that. An injury case would be a good example of where it would be needed.

Handwritten statements are basically summaries of an interview in which superfluous talk and the questions are left out; only the heart of the matter is written down. One can make them as short and to the point as possible and do not need to read like fine literature. Typically the handwritten statement is used when the amount of information that the witness can offer is either limited, or is easily condensed, as in the following example:

> My name is Mary Miller, age 34 and residing at 454 Bakers Lane, Muscogee, Alabama. I am a school teacher and was off for summer vacation when on June 13, 1999 I observed the vessel AQUIT-ALL leave its dock at 8:30 PM with three men on board. I don't think I have ever seen any of these men before and I didn't recognize the boat owner. This dock is directly across the canal from my home, no more than 30 or 40 yards from my kitchen window. I have never met this neighbor but have seen him many times, and don't know his name. They only moved into that house about three months ago. The men caught my interest because it was raining and cold and I wondered why anyone would be going out in this weather when it was just about to get dark. They loaded a large, wooden box on board. Its dimensions were about 2' x 2' x 4'. I don't have any idea of what might have been in the box, but it took all three of them to carry it, so it seemed very heavy. The following morning the boat had not returned, nor did I ever see it back at that dock again.
>
> Signed, Mary Miller

If the investigator doesn't have reasonably good handwriting, then he should use a recorder. Before buying a recorder, test it to make sure that it picks up voice at a distance of at least ten feet. Most statements will be taken sitting down at a table that may be large. Inexpensive recorders are unlikely to be adequate.

Recording & Transcription

Effectively recording interviews and transcribing them requires proper equipment. Standard pocket recorders pose certain problems and hazards, among which is the fact that they run on batteries and all too often the batteries fail us at the worst possible moment. And we forgot to bring spares! Secondly is the problem of fidelity; inexpensive pocket recorders have poor fidelity so that often words can't be understood. Even the best of equipment produces these problems so I recommend against them. If you intend to use a pocket recorder be sure to test it before you buy.

Next is the matter of transcribing interviews. Transcription equipment and someone to do the transcription is needed since trying to transcribe from a pocket recorder is very difficult and time consuming. Dictation-transcription equipment is expensive (mine cost $800) and I resolved many of these problems by purchasing a single machine which is used for both recording and transcription. I take the whole machine (It's about a foot square by 4" high and weighs 12 lbs.) with me because it fits easily in a brief case, has superior fidelity and runs on AC power so I don't have to worry about batteries. It's equipped with a telephone adapter and foot pedal accessories and uses standard cassettes.

Court Reporters

Sometimes serious cases warrant the use of court reporters for taking statements under oath and otherwise. Sworn statements under oath should always be done with a court reporter. The cost of court reporters is reasonable enough (usually $125-$200) that they are very convenient for complex cases, particularly when you don't have your own secretary capable of dealing with long transcriptions. When there are multiple witnesses to be interviewed, I attempt to schedule them all in the same day to minimize cost.

The insured or witnesses are usually taken aback at the mention of "court reporter" so I do not tell them in advance. Whether they come to my office or I go to theirs, the court reporter is always a surprise. If it's not a sworn statement, I patiently explain to them that they will not be under oath and that I do it this way simply for convenience and because it is cost efficient. They're still edgy, but rarely do they resist. *"Oh, don't let the court reporter here upset you. You are not under oath here. This is just a much more efficient and cost effective way than using tape recordings."* Then be sure to tell the reporter not to make the subject take the oath.

When using a court report I find it necessary to put the subject at ease by being very friendly, smiling a lot and cracking a joke if possible. I start the interview with puff ball questions first and keep the tough ones for near last.

Time and Place

When arranging interviews, we usually have to go to the witness's premises where a problem of control may arise. Subjects can thwart us by using two tactics: cutting us short on time or with constant interruptions. Businessmen in particular are very good at using these tactics. The following incident will get it clearly fixed in your mind what can happen when we don't control an interview.

On one occasion, to take a recorded interview I arrived at the subject's office where I was kept waiting for at least a half-hour. After being shown into his office, the interview was gotten underway whereupon the phone started ringing and the man engaged in a fifteen minute conversation, completely ignoring me while I sat there waiting. Clearly he was hoping I'd get frustrated and just get up and leave. When I didn't, and the phone call was finished, he stood up and announced that he had to leave immediately, and did, unceremoniously leaving me with my mouth agape. This person was not refusing to give a statement, merely making it impossible to do so by devious means. While this is not a usual experience, this extreme illustrates the kind of tactics we can come up against.

Doing interviews in homes and offices frequently poses problems such as ringing phones, barking dogs, crying babies, loud televisions and all sorts of interruptions. At the time of arranging the interview, advise the subject that you need a quiet location without interruptions. Ask if they can provide that. If not, ask them to come to your office. Prior to entering someone's office ask the person if he can instruct that he is not to get any phone calls or interruptions, or turn his phone off. Don't be reluctant to be assertive.

Attitude

The old saying that you catch more flies with honey than vinegar is quite applicable to conducting interviews. We should consider how the interviewee will react to our demeanor, first being cognizant that the individual is likely to be rather uneasy to start with, so it behooves us not to antagonize the situation with a cold, overly professional demeanor. It is disarming to be friendly if you can do that without appearing patronizing or phony, but it is better to be professionally casual rather than personally friendly since you are clearly not personally acquainted and to act that way will be obvious. The Columbo character is a good representation of professionally casual.

When it comes to taking statements and conducting interviews, there is, of course, no better teacher than experience so that until one has a few of these under his belt, it is best to just ask one's questions in a straightforward manner and not attempt to be clever about it. After having gained some experience, one will discover good reasons for clever planning. That is, good reasons for asking questions in a certain order or questions phrased in a deliberately crafted manner, but before attempting this the interviewer needs to become sufficiently experienced and comfortable himself. In all probability, the beginner will be just as nervous as the interviewee, so any effort to manipulate the interview is not likely to come off well. Don't attempt to be a good actor before you know how to act; if you do, you'll just look foolish. Start by being yourself first, then add to it as you gain experience as experience will teach you when to act and not to act.

Background Information

With first and third party claims (claimants making a claim for loss or injury), one should obtain background information from the subject[2]. This should include things like occupation and employment, marital and family status as well as any other relevant information such as where the person lives and with whom. Marital status is particularly important for large claims such as total losses; if the insured is involved in divorce, there could be serious implications for paying a claim on disputed property. If this is an injury claim, questions concerning medical history are in order. This sort of personal information often becomes relevant in ways that are hard to anticipate, so I'll give an example:

> In a statement given on a claim for a stolen boat (that turned out not to be stolen) the insured stated that he was an employee of a certain company. On his insurance application he gave something entirely different. On checking, it turned out that he had not been employed by that company for at least the last four years. He was unemployed and in serious financial trouble, a relevant fact that goes to motive. The false information given on the application was relevant only to serve as an indicator that something was seriously wrong, and led to continued investigation.

With an insured, asking questions about the history of the boat, its purchase, maintenance and repair history is equally useful with any type of case. *Have you had any major engine problems in the last few years?* The engine problems question is a good one because engines are the most costly aspect of the vessel and could be an indicator of financial distress. It is also possible at times to prove his answer, and should you discover evidence to the contrary, he has trapped himself and you now have two pieces of evidence instead of one, the recorded lie plus the truth.

Preparing Questions

Can you read words on paper upside-down, across a table? Perhaps not, but some people can. If the hand writing is reasonably good, I can do it, and, it's not necessary to be able to read every word to be able to discern the nature of what is on the paper I'm looking at. The novice investigator will have a need to prepare written questions that he will need to refer to in front of the witness, but he won't want the witness to be able to read them.

Use this simple technique that lawyers use, which is to write out the questions on a legal pad but not on the first page of the tablet. Have something irrelevant there on the first page or few pages — perhaps old notes. In this way one can merely lift the first page as needed to refer to the questions, but the subject on the other side of the table won't be able to see them.

Don't Be In a Hurry

One of the worst mistakes an interrogator can make is to be in a hurry to get the interview finished quickly. The witness is likely to pick up on this, and will resort to the oldest trick in the book — the delaying tactic. If he thinks you intend to wrap it up quickly and he intends to be evasive, he'll simply hold out knowing you'll soon be on your way.

A good technique is to adopt a forced attitude of not being in a hurry, in fact, behaving as if we intend to camp out for the entire day. Once inside the witnesses premises, deliberately start to slow down. If we're going to be sitting at a table, we make a show of slowly getting ready. It's best to bring a brief case and use that as a prop to slowly shuffle through it pretending to look for something. Make a show of sitting down, getting ready and shuffling through notes, but do it in a way that is friendly and not officious.

Toss in some lines of casual conversation to put the subject at ease and to delay. Walking into a room, look around for something of interest that you can comment upon, say a big marlin up on the wall, a trophy or some display object. Such comments slow things down and put the subject more at ease.

The attitude that we want to project is one of being friendly, intelligent, thoughtful and have all the time in the world. In other words, once we have sat down, it becomes clear that we are here to do a job and we're going to be thorough about it, not just proffer a quick question and answer session. We may have told this would only take fifteen minutes previously, but now he's facing a different reality.

Avoid firing off questions like a machine gun. Take time with each question, pausing after each answer to consider its meaning and what your next question should be. If you are concentrating on the next question on your list, you are likely to miss an important opportunity — *listen to the answers!* It is a strange thing, but most people are uncomfortable with even short periods of silence in the presence of others; they feel compelled to fill the air with words. If we have this tendency, we need to train ourselves to not only become comfortable with silence, but to use silence as a tool. Use the prop of shuffling through papers if necessary, but find a way to give yourself that time to consider what the subject has said.

The Pregnant Pause

While we're on the subject of silence, let's consider something you already know about but probably have not fully considered, the pregnant pause. It is that wordless look of anticipation by the questioner that the witness has more to say after he has given what he thought was a complete answer. This is a most fundamental technique of interrogators, especially trial lawyers and is really very simple. The essence of it is an expectant expression on the face of the questioner who gazes directly at the subject, as if to say *And?* or *What else?* This technique will elicit further explanation from the subject almost every time. As with any manipulative technique, it must be used sparingly or the witness soon catches on. Of course, it works best when we have reason to believe that the witness is holding out, or simply isn't very talkative or verbally skilled.

Casual vs. Personal Witnesses

For our purposes there are two basic types of witnesses. The casual witness is one that has no personal interest or connection to the subject, whereas the personal witness does have some type of personal relationship with the subject of investigation. A casual witness can be someone who, merely by circumstance, has knowledge of an event, such as a bystander, a bridge tender or gas dock attendant. This is the easiest type to deal with. The personal witness is one who knows the insured, may be a friend, neighbor or business associate and who, for personal reasons, would want to protect the insured for reasons rational or irrational. The personal witness may be an injured party or have any one of a wide range of financial interests that creates a bias that may not be immediately apparent. The point here is that we are attempting to identify whether the witness will have reason to cooperate and tell the truth — or not. Sometimes it won't be clear in advance what the witness's motives will be, as when there is a business connection in which subject is merely an impersonal customer of the witness, i.e., he purchased an item. Certainly it will make a difference in the reaction if that item cost $10 or ten thousand dollars.

Casual witnesses must necessarily be treated with a great deal of deference because they are under no obligation to cooperate; they must be made to want to cooperate. Experience shows that most people will voluntarily submit to giving statements with little resistance, but some few people are just plain ornery. We can try to break down that resistance by carefully explaining why we want their statement and what it will be used for. Some people are afraid that they will be dragged into court as witnesses, so if that is unlikely, it's a good idea to tell them so. Dispel the notion that their cooperation is going to inconvenience them. There is no reason to not be forthright:

> This is a normal part of an insurance inquiry and your statement, along with several other witnesses', will be used by the insurance company claims examiner to determine whether (a) the claim is covered or, (b) our insured is legally liable for damages (or whatever the case may be).

Or,

> If you provide me with your statement, there is little likelihood that you'll be bothered any further. This should be the end of it.

The insured, though he's required to cooperate and provide a statement, must be also be treated with some degree of deference. If he's not guilty or suspected of perpetrating a fraud, then he's a valued customer and it's up to the investigator to discern the difference and adjust his approach accordingly. However, a good interrogator can be very tough and effective without being the least bit unpleasant, and this is what we should strive for in all cases.

No one is born with good interrogation skills; these are learned techniques, though some people may seem to be naturally better at it than others. Some aspects of these skills can be taught while others can only be acquired through practice and experience.

Good technique is all about the ability to motivate the subject into providing answers to questions that he may not want to answer.

Some witnesses (not referring to an insured here) may be reluctant because they have a negative attitude about insurance companies and sometimes this is made obvious. If a witness is critically important, we can try to break down that resistance by appealing to the witness's sense of fair play. In this case, I will usually go into a little spiel about how the insurance company cannot evaluate the situation fairly unless witnesses are willing to cooperate. I explain how insurance is a form of socialism that everyone who buys insurance is paying for indemnification for certain, but not all, types of losses; that if some people abuse that contract, we all end up paying for that abuse unfairly, and then our insurance rates will go up. I explain that my obligation is to discover the truth, whatever it may be. The implication is that I'm doing him a service by keeping his insurance rates down!

If one engages in this sort of appeal, it is extremely important that you not be perceived as suggesting that the insured has engaged in foul play. On the contrary, we should try to make it appear otherwise.

There will also be instances where a witness's relations with the insured or boat owner is such that there is a likelihood of his being biased, as when that witness is a close neighbor of the insured or the subject being investigated. This needs to be taken into account beforehand and means need to be developed for dealing with it before doing the interview. It is usually fairly obvious when a witness is covering up, or being evasive, for a friend or acquaintance and the investigator needs to be prepared to try to trip up the witness if he thinks he's not telling the truth. When a witness evades or lies under these circumstances, it is usually an ill-considered lie or evasion, and probably easy to defeat. Of course, one does not confront the witness with his lie directly, but tries to gently reveal it or cast doubt on the original statement. Give him the opportunity to save face and change his answer gracefully. The important thing is that, if there is reason to believe that the witness will color the truth, then to be prepared to coax the witness to tell the true story.

During the course of an interrogation a good interrogator will use more than one technique as the situation demands. The first and most important aspect is to develop a non-threatening attitude; the first approach to the subject is to be friendly and casual. Since most interviews are conducted in the subject's home or office, an effort is made to compliment the subject based on something that catches his interest within the subject's home or office. Note that if one comes on as gruff and officious, this creates an air of suspicion and resistance. On the other hand, one should not go to the opposite extreme and appear gratuitous or patronizing. The Columbo technique, discussed further on, works particularly well with insurance investigations.

Reluctant Witnesses

Anyone who spends a significant amount of time investigating marine casualties will soon discover that possessing great technical skills is not enough. It is equally important to develop the necessary skills to deal with people effectively. There is often more to be discovered by or through persons than through physical evidence. And, people being what they are, obtaining and evaluating verbal evidence can be difficult at times.

The first difficulty is that most verbal evidence involves ordinary, mundane, everyday events that people are not prone to remember. The vast majority of our everyday activities are soon forgotten because they are of no significance, but only the means to an end. Secondly, people are generally reluctant to "rat on" another person. It's the *I don't want to get anybody in trouble* rationale. The mere fact that an investigator is snooping around asking questions about an event that involves a person with whom the potential witness had contact, carries with it the suggestion that the person may be in some kind of trouble. The vast majority of potential witnesses in these situations will become circumspect and try to avoid answering truthfully or completely. Very few ever readily volunteer everything they know without some inducement.

The difficulties are compounded by the fact that the witness has perhaps done business with the individual being investigated, so there is a natural reluctance to say anything negative about a customer. Thus, getting witnesses to cooperate can be like pulling teeth, and they may only do so willingly through the application of good interrogation skills. One approach to a potential witness that has done business with the subject is to make an appeal to his sense of fair play similar to the following:

> I understand why you're reluctant to talk about your customer, but let me point out that neither you nor I know how whatever knowledge you possess will affect Mr. Smith's insurance coverage. You should not make that judgement because what you know could lead to his claim being covered as well as not being covered. It could well be that if we don't discover the facts, his claim will not be covered, so I would ask you to tell me what you know and let the chips fall where they may. It's not our business to try to influence the outcome of an investigation.

The above response to a reluctant witness is both the truth and an effort to establish the integrity of the investigator. This is a very common situation with boat yards, marinas and other repairers for whom the subject was a prior customer, and whom they would like to retain as a future customer. Keep in mind that when an investigator comes around asking questions or asking for documents, it is likely that the first thing that goes through the witness's mind is a vision of being called to testify in court, and what the consequences of that might be. He may be thinking less about his client than he is about being inconvenienced by being dragged into this affair. The fact that you are asking questions tells him that this is a serious matter.

When questioning a potential witness, it is very important to be observant of that person's reactions. We will already have a good idea of what his attitude is by his reaction when we called to set up the appointment. The investigator cannot be observant if he is overly focused on himself, the questions he is asking and the information he is hoping to obtain. It's necessary to free up the mind by writing down our questions as an easy reminder so that one can concentrate on the individual, and not solely on the questioning. If resistance is detected, then we need to go to work on breaking down that resistance, and not continuing to bombard the witness with yet more questions that he doesn't want to answer. That just won't work because it's all too easy for the witness to get rid of the investigator by saying that he doesn't know or remember, a tactic that most reluctant witnesses will use.

No form of coercion that you might think of is going to work. The approach as given above is the best one can do. Under no circumstances should the investigator attempt to coerce answers by the use of false statements or trickery.

There will be instances when it becomes clear that the witness is not telling the truth or is evading while he is pretending to be cooperative. Confronting untruth or evasions head-on will get us nothing but more resistance. The way to deal with this is to gently redirect the question in a casual and non threatening way. Sometimes this isn't possible and we have to accept our defeat. The trick is knowing when and not carrying the effort so far as to become annoying.

Another useful technique to use with reluctant witnesses is to pointedly stare at the person when asking the question, never letting your eyes wander from his face. Doing this suggests that you already know the answer to the question and you're making it obvious that you're checking to see if he's telling the truth, that you will know if he's telling the truth. This may induce a person to tell the truth that would otherwise lie or evade. Aside from his answer, what is his body language telling you? This is an intimidating tactic that has to be used with caution and only as a last resort.

Exposing the Lie

If we shouldn't confront a lie or evasion directly, then how should we do it? As an example, let's say that we have a witness to an event in which timing is critically important. In response to a direct question, the witness tells us that he didn't see what we are asking about. That seemingly leads us to a dead end. Since the witness has told us enough that we have reason to believe that he isn't telling the truth, we'd like to try to break him down.

To avoid confronting the issue directly, redirect the line of questioning to go back over the story. Perhaps it's a matter of the witness's position and line of sight. Go over the story in greater detail, one step at a time in such a way as that his answers put him in a position where it is obvious that he should have seen the event and noted the time. Then we pop the original question in modified form: *What you have told me so far puts you in a position where you should have seen whether anyone was on the boat. The time was shortly before the workday ended and you clocked out. That would be about four o'clock, right? Are you sure you aren't mistaken about not seeing anyone? Please think carefully. Could someone have been on the boat at that time?*

Handling it this way gracefully traps the witness without a directly confronting an evasion. What we are saying is that his first answer doesn't seem logical because it contradicts other statements he has made. Give him an easy out by suggesting that perhaps he made a mistake, or had forgotten.

The Unobservant Witness - I Don't Remember

There will be some cases in which a witness account is vitally important, but for whatever reason we are not getting the answers we think we should. This would be in a case where the subject says he doesn't recall and we believe him. In such cases, good investigators are never satisfied with just one attempt at asking a question; if it is important enough, they'll come back to it again and again until they're satisfied that no answer will be forthcoming no matter what they do.

Because people are focused on their own affairs and not those of others, witnesses may be witness events and actually observe them, yet have little or no recall of the event afterward. Imagine how cluttered up our minds would be if we stored in memory virtually everything that our eyes see like a video tape! We practice selective memory by necessity, but we also know that under hypnosis, some people can be made to recall events that they could not consciously remember. This is one of the most frustrating aspects of working with witnesses. But the reality is that people often know things that they are not consciously aware of.

When encountering witnesses that we think should have observed something but have no memory of it, there is no use trying to pressure them to recall for pressure will produce the opposite of the intended result. We've all had this experience of forgetting something and not being able to immediately recall it. And the harder we try, the less likely we are to bring it back. Yet later on when we're not trying to remember, the thing suddenly pops into mind. How? Why? We don't know, but we do know that's the way it happens. One technique that good investigators use to prod memory is a questioning technique that minimizes pressure by presenting the question in *different ways at different times* during the interview. Take that same question and later reinsert it in a line of questioning that is totally unrelated so that it just sort of pops up out of nowhere.

Testing Recall

When encountering *I don't recall* answers, place a star next to your note so that you remember to come back to that question and ask it again.

Bracketing is a method to be used to attempt to discredit a deliberate dodge. In this situation we bore in on closely related events that the witness does remember, eliciting a number of positive responses. We try to bracket the event with questions that elicit positive responses, so that when the *I don't recall* response pops up where it apparently shouldn't be. It doesn't fit because the witness remembered everything but the key question. While we may not be able refresh his memory, it may become possible to make it clear that the answer is an evasion.

Perhaps you can tell me how it is that you can remember A, B and C, but you can't recall D? Did they not all occur at about the same time? It seems to me you have a very good memory but yet on this very important point you have no recollection. Why is that?

It seems to me that you should have been in a position to actually see it.

This makes it clear that we don't believe him without actually saying so, and effectively traps the subject with his own evasions. Notice that this line of questioning won't have the same effect as asking *Why don't you remember?* which is more confrontational. Worded in this way, we first compliment him on a having a good memory, but go on to say that it doesn't make sense that he can't recall this point. Unless he is a very good liar this is likely to leave him stammering.

The reason for doing this is to highlight an evasive answer. As stated previously, a lie or evasion can be as good as a positive or truthful response if the issue comes to litigation. Though we think that the witness has not told us the truth, we want that untruth or evasion to be made clear in the record of the investigation for future triers of fact, the court.

This is a technique that has to be planned in advance until one gains sufficient experience to be able to do it on the fly. The interrogator will generally know in advance which questions are likely to draw the *I don't recall* answer, and he is likely to have enough knowledge to create bracketing questions in advance. Notice here that it's best to do the bracketing *in advance* of the critical question so that the witness doesn't catch on. The point being to show that the witness has good memory of other details at the approximate time, but for some peculiar reason cannot recall the answer to the seminal question.

A last ditch technique, after getting the "I don't recall" answer more than once, is to call that witness on the phone at a later date. This is only used when we believe that he honestly doesn't recall. During the interim time period, the witness's mind is likely to be subconsciously working and ultimately deliver up the memory as unexpectedly as it normally happens in everyday life. But if we don't call again, the witness certainly isn't going to call us and say, "You remember that question you asked me the other day . . . ?"

Accepting the Lie

Occasions will arise when we have to take a statement from someone whom we know, or at least suspect, is guilty of making a mistake. Or perhaps he simply has knowledge that he is unwilling to divulge, yet we believe that we know what that knowledge is. We know in advance that this person will make a denial or avoid the question if it is asked outright. The thing to do is put ourselves in the subject's shoes and ask ourselves how he's going to react to the question. Will his answer be an admission of liability? If so, how will he answer? Obviously he's not going to tell the truth. If that is the case, can his false answer benefit us?

Witnesses that go on record with falsehoods may be of great benefit to us when we have contrary evidence. The benefit is advantageous when the untruth serves to reinforce a larger untruth for which there is unimpeachable evidence to the contrary, as when a witness that is marginally involved is participating in supporting a fraud. So the question to ask ourselves is whether the lack of candor will benefit our case by discrediting the witness. When it comes to an insured, and we have other evidence to the contrary, then we may accept the evasion or falsehood as given. Keep in mind that a witness that goes on record with an answer would have a hard time changing his answer during litigation testimony without suffering some degree of discredit.

Mirroring Technique

The technique of mirroring is one of adapting oneself to the subject's attitude or demeanor based on the idea that he will respond better to his own personality type. Psychological studies say that this is effective. My own experience is that sometimes it works and others I have no way of knowing if it did or not, particularly with the unpleasant types. The idea is that if the subject is a rough, tough, gruff guy, one more or less mirrors this personality type, or at least doesn't meet him with a smiling, gratuitous demeanor; don't meet a stern face with all smiles. If the witness is being hard-nosed, he is doing so for a reason; mainly to try to intimidate you and get you to back off. You may eventually wear him down with kindness, but that will take a while. If you are naturally the affable sort, stow it and act officious; don't smile, be polite but humorlessly correct. Conversely, don't greet a bright, sunny person with a stone face, but respond in kind; be more kindly, more personable. If, during the course of the interview, the subject's demeanor changes, you change with it.

It is important for success to be ware of the various types of personalities one will face. As a rule of thumb, persons who are not guilty of anything have nothing to hide and thus have no resistance to answering your questions; conversely usually those who are guilty (in action or intent) usually do. But, there are always some people who are suspicious of the intentions of others and will resist answers to your questions even though they may have no reason not to answer fully. Some people are always grumpy and uncooperative. Some people have guilty personalities. Then there are those who are accomplished liars that can laugh and smile and feed you endless lies without flinching. We may not always be able to read truth or lies through the physical demeanor of the individual. While these can be clues, it is actually the truth in his words that we ultimately seek. The investigator will face every conceivable personality type, and to be effective, experience is the only effective tool.

Evasiveness

A witness that gives evasive answers demonstrates a degree of bias. Evasion can take the form of either incomplete answers or misdirection. The most common misdirection is answering a question that was not asked, or just saying something that is irrelevant. Politicians are masters of this deceptive art and we're all familiar with them. Incomplete answers can be attacked directly because the witness has given us that opening by at least answering partially:

> Perhaps you didn't understand my question: Did the boat return to the dock on Saturday, the same day that it left?

However, sometimes attacking a complete evasion head-on will only strengthen the subject's resolve to avoid answering or make him hostile. The better way to deal with misdirection is to let the evasion stand for the moment and come back to it later. If we can anticipate what questions the subject won't want to answer, then we can devise a strategy to overcome or extract an unexpected admission. Plan to ask each key question at three different points in the interview. Then, plan to phrase the question in different ways so that it is less recognizable. It is difficult to explain this technique, but as one gains in experience and faces these situations, you will come to intuitively understand them. Should you intend to confront the witness head-on with evasion or misdirection, do it at the end of the interview so that any hostility that results doesn't turn him uncooperative.

From time to time we run across the subject that is truculent and very evasive. A subject that is excessively evasive is actually telling a story that he doesn't know he's telling. This is a person that is clearly dishonest and his evasion will speak for itself, so there's no need to try to coerce or manipulate him. Ask your questions and let his words stand as given.

Testing for Truth

There will be times when it becomes apparent that an insured is not telling the truth, and a time when it becomes necessary to make a judgement whether that dishonesty is intended to cover up something that is highly relevant. I have run across numerous instances when I have caught the insured lying for no good reason that I could perceive, but later discovered the reason. I've had boat owners lie when they thought that a particular cause of loss might not be covered, when in fact it was, and their lying, their creation of a different story threw the claim into the realm of not covered; in other words, they lied themselves right out of being paid for a loss because their belief was erroneous. In one case, a man accidentally sunk his own boat, then lied about the cause, not knowing that his insurance covered his error because it was not intentional.

Hopefully, this will give an idea of the many peculiar reasons people tell lies. In the above instance I turned off the recorder and gently informed the insured of the facts, whereupon he sheepishly changed his story to the truth. In this case it was not in my or the client's best interest to let the claim be denied because the insured was lying as the result of a false belief.

When an insured is lying for no apparent reason (as when you don't suspect him of fraud), it's wise to try to figure out why. Continued investigation may disclose the reason.

Trapping

Trapping a witness in a lie is a tactic used by trial lawyers for the specific result of discrediting him in front of a jury. We don't have jury so that all we are interested in are the answers that the subject gives. When we get a lie but have evidence to support the truth, this provides the means by which a lying witness can be trapped. However, trapping is something that should be done only with already hostile witnesses by preplanned design where the end result can be used to advantage. There will be those instances where one expects the witness to lie, and in which we already know the truth, or have evidence of it. Direct confrontation, no matter how subtle, is likely to have consequences on the remainder of the interview. Once a witness has been trapped, cooperation may cease and the interview will be essentially over. Don't do it unless you have a good reason for doing so, and fully understand the consequences that are likely to follow.

Trapping is also done in situations where we want the subject to know what we know about him, such as that he has committed fraud.

The employment of the technique involves allowing the witness to spin his yarn without challenge. Then, when he has finished committing himself, the falsehoods are challenged based on known facts. But, there must be a conscious objective for doing so because in most cases the challenge will be pointless and not achieve anything.

The Turning Point

There comes a time in some investigations when the insured or other subject becomes suspected of engaging in unlawful, or dishonest activity. This usually begins with telltale physical evidence or suspicious behavior, but then is exacerbated by suspected or provable dishonesty. At this point the subject becomes a suspect and our attitude toward him naturally changes. No longer is this a routine investigation, but is now one in which serious consequences are likely to arise, for others as well as ourselves.

The gathering of verbal evidence changes from ordinary interviews and statements to interrogations. The distinction between the two is essentially one of the seriousness and intensity with which it is conducted because, at this point, litigation becomes very likely with possible criminal overtones. This is no longer business as usual.

It was iterated previously that the most important interrogations should be done at the right time, a time when we have sufficient information by which to formulate the basis of effective questioning. At this point in the discussion, it should be very clear that the application of good interrogation techniques is completely dependent upon what evidence has been gathered to date. Without it, we have no basis by which to make judgments on whether witnesses are being truthful or not, beyond our intuitive senses.

Big Lies, Little Lies

Most people are not good liars, at least not good enough before an experienced investigator. However, many are skilled at telling simple, short lies, but rare indeed is the person that can effectively spin a long tale without leaving glaring contradictions. That said, it follows that it's not easy to trip up a subject when conducting an interview over a relatively simple matter, yet the longer the individual's involvement or story (assuming that the story isn't true), the more inconsistencies there will be to exploit.

We have mentioned this case case in Fraud Investigation chapter and the following is the full story of the case that will illustrate not only how complicated stories can get, but how much easier they are to exploit:

This investigation began with a policy holder reporting that his boat was stolen. The boat was a custom built parasail boat of considerable value. The insured initially related that he made arrangements to take his boat back to the builder (who was located nearby) for some kind of repair. Being a trailerable boat, he says that he dropped the boat off at the builder's shop on Friday. On Monday afternoon, he calls the builder up and asks how the repairs are going. The builder replies that he can't make repairs until the customer delivers the boat. The insured says, "But I dropped it off to you on Friday, what do you mean you don't have my boat?"

The builder stated that he was on the premises until 8:00 Friday night and stated that no boat had been delivered to that point. His place of business was in a known high crime area, and had tall fencing with razor wire on top. On questioning, the insured admitted that he parked the boat on the street but at 6:00 PM and said he didn't think it was necessary for him to go into the office to tell the owner that the boat was on the street. "I figured he'd see it and bring it inside the compound." This was beginning to look like a trumped up bailment situation.

The boat builder also suspected the same thing and not only consented to a recorded statement but also gave me his entire file to look over. The builder told me things about his customer that only made suspicions worse, such as the insured bounced a check given as a purchase deposit; that the insured had tried to get the builder to inflate the purchase price to create a false down payment, which he refused to do.

I had the insurer run a credit history on the insured; the results indicated that he was in serious financial trouble. A number of documents were collected, including title, registration and insurance application. The later indicated that he was an employee of a certain company which, when I checked with them, found that he had last been employed with that company more than four years prior. For some strange reason the insured lied about this on his application, but he also lied about the purchase price, inflating it about 20%.

About a week later the boat builder called me and said that on a business trip to Mexico, he found a hatch cover to the insured's boat laying beside the road some four miles from the border. It was identifiable due to obvious uniqueness. He then told me that he recalled that the insured had had a fire on his boat about a year ago which he didn't know anything more about. Continued investigation turned up information that this boat had been located in another state for a while and I got the name of the marina. Questioning people at the marina turned up a witness who remembered the fire incident by saying, "Yeah, I remember. That was the guy that tried to set his boat on fire by setting a trouble light on a pile of oily rags." They couldn't prove arson because the boat owner said that the light must have fallen down from where he had set it. That didn't explain why he went away leaving the light on.

A quick trip to the nearest fire station turned up some very bored firemen who were more than willing to talk. A copy of the fire report concluded: suspected attempted arson. The case was not referred for prosecution.

The insured filed a claim for smoke damage to his engine compartment as the rags were smoldering but had not yet erupted in flame. A small claim was paid before the fire investigation report was released a month later.

At this point, what do I have? Suspected arson, not provable; lying on an insurance application, material and immaterial; and the insured in a position in which he probably can't prove his loss. He could offer no proof that the boat was where he said it was, but if he left it on the street in a known high crime area, he's guilty of gross negligence. No reasonable person would leave property worth $130,000 in this location at night. Even so, what evidence I have is not rock solid by any means. All avenues of investigation have been exhausted so I decide to go for a statement under oath and try to get him lying.

By this time the insured has been issued a reservation of rights letter and has hired a lawyer who sends me threatening letters. The statement was set to be taken in the lawyer's office, at which time he was notably more subdued. I spent two days preparing this interrogation, knowing that the insured would be well-prepared by his lawyer. There were four main areas of interest for exploitation: the arson attempt, the current alleged loss, the hatch cover by the roadway (which he wasn't told about), and the false statements on the insurance application.

My questions were laid out according to the four categories and then shuffled like a deck of cards, the objective being to keep the subject completely off guard as to the order of questioning. In this way, he couldn't anticipate where the line of questioning was going. By the expression on his face, a number of my questions clearly stunned him. The statement lasted for two-and-a-half hours, during which time the subject became extremely nervous, broke out in profuse sweating, and completely lost control of his story, expanding his lies many times over. At one point his attorney slumped in his chair and stared at the ceiling in complete surrender. There was nothing he could do to help a lying client.

With all those lies contained within a statement under oath, the insurer now had no hesitation to deny the claim. However, that might not be necessary. By law, the insured can be required to file a signed Proof of Loss. When the interview was over, I pulled the document out of my brief case and placed it front of the lawyer, telling him to have it filled out and sent to the insurer's office, whereupon they would *consider* payment of his claim.

I rightly predicted that the lawyer would advise the insured not to file the proof of loss, withdrawing the claim by default. He knew that I was coming close to proving fraud and probably advised his client not to do it. Thus, no denial was ever issued because a formal claim wasn't filed and the insured couldn't counter-sue: a perfect outcome.

Here's a case where the insured ultimately did himself in because he couldn't keep track of his lies. Without that Statement under Oath, the insurer probably would have elected to pay the claim rather than risk losing a civil suit. Thus the sworn statement proved to be the deciding factor. Granted that the investigator was the benefactor of a lot of good luck, but that is true with all successful investigations.

This brings up another point that I should mention. In the above case I had an important witness (the boat builder) who was somewhat hostile to the insured. One need be very careful about this kind of bias that is opposite what we normally encounter. Fortunately, this person was an honorable man who was obviously very careful about what he said about the insured, understating rather than overstating the truth. Not all people are so honorable or careful.

Out-of-Sequence Questions

It is logical for us to ask our questions in a chronological order, but not necessarily effective, particularly with a reluctant witness. In following a logical line of questioning, it is easy for the witness to anticipate what the next questions will be. Trial lawyers use a technique of dropping *out-of-sequence* questions at unexpected times in the hope of eliciting an unguarded answer. In this respect we have an advantage that the trial lawyer does not have since he is not permitted to badger the witness with the same question repeatedly. With this technique, the repeated question is phrased in a different way and inserted into a line of questioning where it is unexpected.

This method can be carried to the extreme where there is no logical order of questioning, which is useful with the hostile witness that we suspect is not telling the truth. A witness that tells too many lies naturally has trouble keeping track of them, and thereby becomes more amenable to forgetting what he has said earlier. I use this technique in fraud cases where I feel certain that the witness has committed fraud. Virtually all my questions are out of order in an effort to keep the subject off balance. This method frequently produces Freudian slips. It cannot be done ad lib and requires careful advance planning.

Misdirection involves grouping questions in such a way as to attack the central point from different directions or lines of questioning, either in a physical or chronological context or both. It is essentially a much more complex and advanced version of out-of-sequence questioning and often used as a means of challenging suspected lies or evasion.

Leading, Wordy and Clever Questions

If you have ever testified in court or given a deposition, please don't make the mistake of attempting to copy tactics used by lawyers. An investigator who tricks a witness into an untrue answer accomplishes nothing except diminishing himself. The only craft for us to use is to elicit the truth, not the answer we want to hear.

A leading question is one in which the question contains the answer. Leading: "Was the car you saw leaving the scene dark blue?" Non leading: "What color was the car you saw leaving the scene?" A negative leading follow-on: That car wasn't dark blue, was it?

Those are obvious examples, but complex questions can be leading without being obvious.

There is also a right way and a wrong way to ask questions:

> *You didn't notice what color his shirt was, did you?* [Suggests the answer is "no"].

> *What color was his shirt?* [Neutral]

The first of these is the wrong way because it is a form of leading question in that it also suggests the answer. This form makes it too easy to answer "no" whereas the later makes the subject think about it.

> *My understanding is that you observed the explosion when it happened, is that correct?* [Suggestive]

> *Did you see the explosion at the moment it happened?* [Neutral]

This type of question might at first appear to be leading, but it's not since all it asks for is a yes or no answer. Now consider the following sequence:

Q. What color was the other boat?

A. Umm, I think it was blue.

Q. Would that be dark blue or light blue?

A. It wasn't dark.

Q. Could it have been gray?

A. No, definitely blue but possibly grayish.

Q. How about blue-green?

A. More like the color of the sky.

Notice how this line of questioning works to narrow down a vague answer while at the same time assists with better recall.

On the other hand, the negative leading question can help get the answers you're looking for when used in the right way:

Q. I don't suppose that you were actually looking at the boat when hit the dock?

A. Actually I was.

Q. But you didn't actually see what the operator was doing at the time?

A. Yes, I could see him very clearly.

Q. But you couldn't see his hands?

A. I could see that one of them was around the shoulder of a woman standing next to him.

Notice how this line of questioning causes the witness to give very firm answers. Now that you've set the precedent, it will be very hard for the witness to be evasive. This type of questioning works best with a witness that is somewhat reluctant or less than forthcoming.

The following question, with no preliminaries, asserts the presumptive fact that the witness directly observed the explosion without having to ask directly, and without his express assertion. Asked this way, the witness is unlikely to challenge the assumption, and when answering affirmatively, prevents him from saying later I don't recall or didn't see it.

At the time the explosion occurred, what did you notice about the color, smoke or force of it that caught your attention?

Conversely, if you are the witness, be sure to challenge and part of the assertion if it is not true.

After opening with questions identifying yourself and the witness we next have to transition into the subject at hand. There are a variety of ways to do this, but the method chosen should be based on the particular circumstances. If we have a reluctant witness, don't give him the opportunity to give you one word answers unless that will suffice. It may be better to start with an open-ended question such as:

Q. My understanding is that you were standing on the dock when it happened, is that correct?

A. Yes, I was.

Q. Tell me everything you saw at that time?

A. Well, I saw this and that.

Q. Anything else?

A. I saw the other thing.

Q. And then what happened?

Notice how in this exchange the questioner has the opportunity to ask three open-ended questions in a row, with the objective to keep him talking, in the hope that the subject will say more than he intends to say. Open-ended questions need to be used with reserve because, if asked too often, the ploy becomes obvious and the subject starts to resist. If you've ever been a witness in court, you know how troublesome and frustrating open ended questions can be. *Mr. Witness, please tell me everything you know!*

A good technique is to start off with opened ended questions and then work to refine the answers, followed by another open ended question, and so on. Follow this method until you exhaust the subject. With this method, one can go into an interview with only a few major points and fill in the rest with whatever additional questions the subject's answers suggest.

Keep in mind that the evasive subject will recognize that the open question puts him in a box. Eventually, it needs to be followed up with specific questions, especially if the subject is being expansive. Then save the open questions for the time when he withdraws again and starts feeding you short answers. If you go too far with open questions, he'll probably shut you down with *I don't know* or *I don't remember.*

The essence of the good interrogator is that, through his experience, he learns to *read* and *play* the witness like a piano.

Statements Under Oath

A statement under oath, as its name suggests, is serious business and is only used when a client demands it. This will usually be done in consultation with the insurer's attorney, although without his presence. It is not good form for an insurance company to use a lawyer against an insured as this gives the appearance of ganging up on the insured, so the investigator is the best choice for taking the Sworn Statement. And because it is usually only done when coverage is seriously in doubt, it is likely that the insured will have engaged an attorney at this point and the taking of the statement will more or less come to resemble a deposition. During my career, I have taken little more than a dozen Sworn Statements, and in each case it was because fraud or criminal activity was suspected, and only once was the subject not represented by a lawyer. Though the lawyer does not have the right to cross-examine, he does have the right to object to your manner of questioning and to counsel his client about how to answer, or to advise him not to answer at all.

Some points to remember are: (1) The interrogator should appear to be totally neutral and betray no emotion whatsoever; never become agitated or angry by anything the lawyer does. (2) If the case goes to litigation, as it probably will or you would not be taking the sworn statement in the first place, you need to be thoroughly prepared; the lawyer will be helping the witnesses to not give the answers you want to get, so this is no mere question and answer session. (3) Do not engage in banter with the subject; if he is not answering the question or is evading it, state that he has not fully answered the question and ask it again. If he still doesn't answer, state for the record that you think he hasn't answered the question. *For the record, I have asked this question three times and Mr. Smith still has not answered the question.* Then move on because the lack of an answer is now an answer in itself. The most common mistake of the inexperienced is to let evasive answers pass. This probably happens because the interrogator isn't listening closely but, instead is thinking about his next question and fails to pick up on the evasion.

Order of Questioning

It stands to reason that if the interviewer begins to bore in and starts to ask questions that will make the subject (particularly an insured) uncomfortable at the outset, then the subject is going to be resistant and probably hostile throughout. This interview would not be conducted, were it not for the fact that there is some question as to whether insurance coverage will apply, or perhaps it will end up in litigation; you know it and the interviewee knows it. Hostility and resistance that spoils an interview can usually be avoided by starting with the softball questions first. We are likely to have an idea whether the interview will be long or short based on the nature of the case. In some cases there will only be a few important questions that need be asked, so there's no reason not to get right to them, but in cases that are complex, it's best to sketch out the order of questions.

A good investigator with plenty of experience becomes adept and can play most witnesses like a piano. The technique involves something of a one-man good-cop/bad-cop routine wherein questions are grouped in such a way as to put the subject at ease before springing the hard questions on him. We should remain aware that our line of questioning always reveals the direction our questions are heading unless we do something to conceal the direction, and there are good reasons that we should avoid revealing our thoughts before certain other questions are asked and answered. There are instances where one single question will shut a subject down, making him unresponsive or resistant to answer anything further. This is especially true when there exists the possibility of wrongdoing, which is no stranger to insurance claims.

Therefore, it becomes necessary to conceal our thoughts until the right moment. This is accomplished by making a list of questions, considering their impact, and then placing them in a suitable order. Is it necessary to write out all questions? For the inexperienced the answer is certainly yes, since even the highly experienced usually find it necessary to at least sketch out even a modest list of questions. Most people find that the writing process helps stimulate the thinking process, so it's a good idea to do so. At least by writing out most important questions, this reveals where the difficulties are likely to arise, and what, if anything, we can do to avoid or minimize them.

Good trial lawyers are particularly adept at lulling the witness before he goes after them with hammer and tongs. They do write out their questions by the dozens. He may repeat this process numerous times in a long examination. If we were to make a graph of how he organizes softball and hardball questions, it would look like a series of bell curves or peaks and valleys. The soft ball questions are intended to put the witness at ease and off guard. Of course there is a limit to how many times one can repeat the cycle before even an idiot will catch on, but we shouldn't underestimate how relieved a subject becomes when the hard questions cease so he is very amenable to once again being lulled by easy questions. Thus, in organizing an interrogation, we first make a list of our hard questions, the ones we believe the subject will not want to answer. Then we can create a list of softball questions, probably questions that don't even need to be asked. After the two lists are made, the questions are then reordered according to the effect we wish to achieve. One does not much experience to apply this technique, although one might need a bit of effort to keep a straight face when applying it.

Here's another important reason for preparing our questions by writing them down: if the questioner is so preoccupied with thinking of the questions that he is going to ask, then he's probably not fully listening to the answers. We can see this with television interviews all the time where the questioner hardly even stops to wait for the answer before asking the next question. The subject may give an astonishing answer, but it goes right by him. With a prepared list, one can ask the question and then make a conscious effort to turn away from the list and listen.

Learning to use these techniques yields a double benefit; not only do your interrogations produce better results, but when the time comes that you end up on the witness stand as the witness, you'll have a solid understanding of how the opposition lawyer is trying to manipulate you and you'll not fall victim to his devious designs.

Golden Silence

Many, if not most, people have an unconscious need to fill all silences with words; they are uncomfortable with silence, particularly in the presence of others. If that describes you then you'll need to get over it. Silence is one of the most important tools in the interrogator's kit. Not only does silence give you the opportunity to listen and consider, but can also be used as a technique toward other ends. For example, you ask a question and the subject gives an answer that you feel is only part of the truth. While he was answering, you were looking down at your list, but now that he's finished you look up at him but say nothing, as if you expect him to continue. The look you give him may be questioning, or it could be an utterly blank expression. You might be surprised at how many times an answer met with silence provokes the subject to talk some more. Notice here that silence is not synonymous with no action; silence and facial expression (or lack of it) are the planned action that almost inevitably will produce a response in the subject. Keep that in mind and try practicing it in normal relations with others.

Another tool in the interrogator's kit is the axiom that a liar always feels the need to embellish the lie. A famous line from Shakespeare illustrates: "The lady doth protest too much, methinks"[3]. When the lie is suspected, it should not be met immediately with another question, but a pause of 15 seconds or so, an encouragement to go further. The embellishment of a lie more often than not just makes the lie more incredulous. In some instances, the embellishment will actually prove the lie as a result of conflicting statements. In this situation, the direction of your attention is important; if you are looking at the subject, this is seen as challenging; if you are looking elsewhere, that will have a different effect, so control your gaze accordingly.

During an interview, the interviewer needs to be prepared for the unexpected. Few people are so skilled that they can instantly recover from the unexpected. It takes time to react properly to the unexpected, and the only way to get that time is by keeping quiet and the thinking turned off. One does not need to be a brilliant interrogator, for this is a race that goes not to the fastest but to the plodding and persistent. On the contrary, there are good reasons why it is better to appear to be dumb, or at least not terribly bright, than smart. People are much more at ease around people that they perceive as not the brightest bulb on the string. Being *consistently* slow establishes a pattern that is normal in the eyes of the interviewee, so that when you do need the extra time to consider an answer, this does not appear abnormal. Keep in mind that with yacht claims, the people you're dealing with will usually be on the above average side of intelligence, so it's not a good idea to attempt to lock intellectual horns with them.

Know the Answer before You Ask

This is the rule used by lawyers to avoid being surprised by unexpected answers, or the revelation of information that they don't want disclosed. It is not a rule that we need to apply rigorously, but it certainly does help. What is meant by this is that the order and preparation of our questions will be predicated on the answers we expect to obtain. All we can do is anticipate what the answers will be. But if the answers are not what we expect, our carefully planned questions are now disrupted and we have lost some control.

In other words, don't plan a string of questions which depend upon a certain answer to an earlier question because, if you don't get the expected answer, the whole string becomes invalidated.

To avoid this, anticipate this result and make a plan B. That is, don't lead yourself down a dead end road of carefully prepared questions that is suddenly ended by an unexpected answer that leaves you looking foolish and grasping for questions. This situation will happen frequently and we need to be prepared for it. It will be all our investigation work up to this point that provides for this preparation, giving insight as to what is likely to happen.

No Response to Answers

Most of the transcribed interviews that I have read contain responses by the questioner to answers given by the subject. "Okay," "I see," "Alright," and so on. And then there are the inevitable "Ah's" and "Ums," of which there are far too many. There is no need to give any kind of response to an answer, which is just the response of normal conversation. Train yourself to not do this because it looks very unprofessional in transcriptions.

There are appropriate exceptions to this rule which the reader is surely familiar with. When an answer is given, one which the questioner believes is incomplete or evasive, if he responds with "Okay" or "Alright," this has the effect of inducing the subject to expand on the answer. This does not always work, so be alert to the effect and use it sparingly.

New Information

Freshly discovered evidence of which the subject is not aware can be another tool in the investigator's kit, but only if he knows how to use it skillfully. Say, for example, that a piece of physical evidence is later found that contradicts the subject's earlier statements. If this evidence is revealed — either intentionally or accidentally — too soon its value will be lost. If the subject in earlier questioning (not in a formal interview) has made statements contrary to the new evidence, then the investigator will want to get the subject to commit himself to that earlier statement. If he does go on record with that statement, which is apparently untrue, one will then need to decide whether it is necessary to reveal the new evidence to him. In most cases it is wise not to do so because he will just attempt to revise his testimony to fit your new evidence. Better to just let the lie stand.

On the other hand, the new evidence could be another witnesses' account, so that now it's one person's word against another's. Theoretically, the one cancels the other and we're at a stalemate and we need to move the evidence basket off the balance scale. Do we confront the subject or insured with the other's statement or not? Certainly the subject will deny or dispute the other's testimony, so we need to consider where that will leave us when he does so. Can we craft our questioning in such a way that it will reveal the lie?

Detecting Untruth

No doubt the reader has noticed that the oath a witness takes in court is rather lengthy, and not merely *Do you swear to tell the truth?* That's because failure to tell the whole truth is no different in effect from the utterance of an overt lie. The end result is the same, the intentional misleading away from the truth. Skilled liars will weave their answers around the truth and then leave out the critical element.

A good interrogator becomes an expert lie detector by means of learning to identify the many signs that untruthful witnesses unconsciously give. Some people are excellent liars and are impossible to detect, but this does not describe most people. Some few can look you straight in the eye while telling a lie, and never blink or look away before you do. In other words, they'll stare you down with the lie. This is not the behavior of normal people but forceful and accomplished liars.

Polygraph machines have to be calibrated to a witness's foundational or normal responses simply because all people are different. And even then, these lie detectors are far from completely reliable since accomplished liars can defeat them. The point here is that the interrogator needs to size up a witnesses behavior before he starts asking questions to which he may receive untruthful answers. In other words, how does the person behave when he's telling the truth, or at least not lying. What physiological reactions occur when he is lying that don't occur when telling the truth. It is only by means of noting the differences of response between the two states that one can reliably come to conclusions about whether an individual is being truthful.

For example, blinking and refusing to make eye contact are commonly considered as indicators of untruthfulness (as seen on TV and read in novels). But how can this be squared with the many people who normally blink a lot and avoid eye contact? It can't, so we have to understand how a person normally reacts before we can judge what is not normal, as when they are lying.

People who are not prone to dishonesty are the easiest to read simply because they are not accomplished liars by means of lots of practice. The most common indicators are:

Prolonged lack of eye contact when normally they will make eye contact.

The voice weakens, sometimes to the point of inaudibility.

Excessive clearing throat, coughing.

Sweating.

Excessive blinking when blinking is not normal.

Repeating the question before answering.

Covering the mouth with a hand.

Efforts to distract themselves or the interrogator.

Obvious diversion of attention to papers or other objects.

Evasiveness, answering questions that aren't asked.

Again, the above behavior is only relevant when we can establish that these are not normal behavior. Needless to say that to be able to make all these observations one needs sufficient time with the person. The Columbo technique will provide that time and many other opportunities as well.

The Dumb Cop or Columbo Technique

The good cop - bad cop technique has been around since long before Arthur Conan Doyle invented Sherlock Holmes, and is no worse for wear because of its age, though we will rarely have occasion to make use of it because it takes two interrogators. But we can make use of a variation on the theme which is called the dumb cop or the Columbo technique. This technique is used *only* for informal, non recorded interviews because it looks totally ridiculous when transcribed and reflects badly on us.

The tremendously successful TV series character Lieutenant Detective Columbo played by Peter Falk was so successful, in part, because that character was not an entirely fictitious fabrication but employs sound elements of good detective work; the methods employed by Columbo are often used by detectives. The TV version of the technique is high drama, and of course we would only apply a much scaled-down version lest we appear absurdly obvious.

The basis of the character is founded on the theatrical act of appearing slightly stupid and non threatening. Here's a guy who, when he adds two plus two, comes up with three — at least that's what he leads his suspects to think. And therein disarms them into believing that Columbo is just too stupid to ever figure out who's done it. But notice that the dumb cop routine is not used constantly, that when it suits his purposes he can be ruthless and display flashes of brilliance.

Guile\ Medieval English: 1. Crafty, cunning, deceitful: **DUPLICITY, DECEIT, TREACHERY**.

Without guile is a term that probably describes the Columbo character best. Although the detective clearly has plenty of it, his act is exactly the opposite of guile as evidenced by both his words, behavior and appearance.

If you have ever had occasion to be interviewed by a police detective who is not very skilled, then what you were faced with was likely a cop who is taken with his authority and presents an over-bearing, decidedly unfriendly, hard-nosed and intimidating presence. Not exactly the best way to elicit cooperation, is it? No, the best way to get cooperation is to do what it takes to put that person at ease and want to cooperate, particularly since marine investigators do not have any authority. In fact, the tools of the interrogation trade are craft and cunning.

The Columbo technique is based on the proven precept that an unthreatening and disarming personality disarms the subject who then drops his guard and hopefully becomes overconfident. Observing the Columbo character closely, we note that his scatter-brained, disheveled act does not stand alone. There is his battered wreck of a car, his rumpled clothing, wild hair, his unconscious bad manners, chewing on an old smelly cigar as if that were the perfectly normal thing to do. Melded into all this an almost fanatical persistence camouflaged by slow wittedness and obviously patronizing friendliness; he appears to be the ultimate jerk (and perhaps he is), but he never gives up; his brain may work slowly but it never stops working. He's like a dog chewing on a bone, like the story of the hare and the tortoise, persistence - not brilliance or speed - gets him to the finish line first. People just can't take him seriously.

However, if we study the character closely, we will observe that Columbo does apply the same act to all people in all situations. Rather, he adapts his act to fit the person and the situation, and therein is the success of the method: adaptability.

Of course I am not suggesting that anyone should attempt to adopt the Columbo personality, but there are many elements of his techniques that, when used with discretion, can be very effective. The reader may not have noticed, but many of these techniques have already been presented, but without reference to Columbo. Once the beginner has had some experience, he will quickly come to identify with the superb and realistic scripting of that TV series and understand the various ways these techniques can be applied to real life situations. Indeed, many investigators apply such techniques in various degrees without making any connection to Columbo. My reference to the TV series provides the benefit of exaggerating and amplifying the techniques, thereby making them immediately comprehensible.

For these techniques to work, they must be applied consistently in the subject's presence, for once the witness catches a glimpse of unexpected intelligence or inconsistency he'll no longer be fooled. If one plays dumb, but then makes the mistake of trying to show how smart he is, his behavior becomes contradictory. We see the very same thing in the Columbo scripting; once he reveals what he knows, the subject becomes defensive and hostile, whereupon Columbo drops his act. Care must be taken to conceal our knowledge unless there is a good reason for revealing it.

Make no mistake about it, good investigators have to become good actors. But it is critically important to develop an act that fits with your own personality. This is because it is very hard to be other than we are; by making the act part of our own personality, it becomes far easier to be consistent without losing sight of who we are what we are doing.

Of course Columbo carries this technique to dramatic extreme, which we should not. Above all things, we need to learn to husband our knowledge and never reveal it except by design. So what makes Columbo appear stupid? *Not revealing what he knows.* By acting somewhat dim, slow and disorganized two things can be accomplished, (1) the appearance of disorganization buys extra time which is important for many reasons, not the least of which it gives us time to evaluate responses and form new questions, questions we probably wouldn't have thought of had we less time; (2) in appearing to be without guile, the witness is likely to be less reserved, more responsive and give more detailed answers.

If, while employing this technique, the investigator obtains an answer he is seeking, he should never let on, or display any visible reaction. Pretend that it is unimportant. If this requires a follow-up question that would betray the importance of the answer, you may want to make a note to reintroduce the subject at a later time in the interview, rather than this moment because the revelation will change the chemistry, so to speak. That's where Columbo always pops back in the door as he's making his exit, *Oh, yeah, one more thing . . .* So, we see that this is no mere dramatic TV artifice but a valid interrogation technique with or without the embellishment. Instead of employing the technique on our way out the door, it can be employed while taking statements as a means of reintroducing a line of questioning. *Oh, I forgot to ask you about . . .*

Whenever it is clear that the witness is hostile or reluctant, it is best to try to break up a logical chain of questions that clearly reveals the questioner's intent. When it's clear that the witness is, at best, evasive, it's time to resort to clever questioning. Application of the Columbo technique helps to disguise your intent by scattering the witness's attention. This is accomplished by rapidly changing the line of questioning so that the subject cannot anticipate. If you ever get the chance to watch Columbo reruns, by all means do so. Those scripts are very well conceived and there's much to learn from them. Just one word of caution: think about who you are and what you're doing before you do it.

The Columbo technique also provides cover for repeating questions without being obvious. *Oh, did I already ask that question? Sorry, I guess I forgot,* with hopes of perhaps getting a different answer. Notice how this choice of words reveals not only a rumpled suit but a rumpled mind as well! Repeating questions should only be done long after the original subject has been changed when you believe that the witness is not telling the truth or is evading. This can, and probably should, be used with the technique of asking the same question in a different way.

No one should ever copy the Columbo character because the subject will recognize the tactic immediately. Columbo is a dramatic character that is part fiction and partly based on real investigation techniques. We want to be careful not to adopt the fictional parts.

Things We Never Say or Do

It should be kept in mind that transcribed interviews are very good at conveying a person's state of mind, attitude, intellectual level, education and honesty. Do not forget that the reader of the transcript will be judging the interrogator as well as the subject.

Never directly impugn the subject's integrity. If a witness is lying, get the witness to expose the lie through skillful questioning. Never openly express your doubt unless prepared for the consequences.

Do not reveal to any subject what your true beliefs are, unless you have a sound reason for doing so. If you think fraud or criminal activity is involved, do not under any circumstances suggest this in any way, not even a hint. In fact, the impression we want the subject to have is one of everything being normal.

Never do or say anything that creates a condition of estoppel.

Never lie to a witness or insured. We cannot legally resort to using false statements the way cops do. This is only likely to cause trouble further down the road.

Do not respond in any way to hostile statements of the insured or witnesses. If you stay in this business long enough you will encounter people that will intentionally attempt to provoke you. If you can't control your reactions, you can always just walk away without reacting.

Avoid badgering insureds or witnesses by pounding away at the same set of questions.

(Footnotes)

1. The incident occurred on the high seas and involved persons of South American countries and there never was an official investigation of the incident. The nationalities involved were Surinam and Guyana, both of which were content to ignore the matter.

2. "Subject" refers to the person being investigated who is often, but not always an insured.

3. *Hamlet,* III, ii, 242.

Chapter 12

Reports

The writing of the investigation report involves the work of taking all aspects of the investigation, analyzing and pulling them together to draw a conclusion. How we arrive at these conclusions and present the results of our work is every bit as important as the actual investigation because the report is the only aspect of our work that others will see. We've done the investigative leg work; have come to a conclusion, and in our mind's eye we think we know how it will look. But how will it look on paper? The reality is that the way we conceive it in mind, and how it turns out in the written word, is usually quite different.

With that in mind, in this chapter we will carefully analyze the elements of good reports and the means to achieve professional results. The investigator will want to make sure that his report is as professionally competent as he can possibly make it. A poorly prepared report makes about as bad an impression as showing up in court in a bathing suit and a ring in one's nose.

The bulk of the investigator's work involves cases that are relatively simple, and for which writing the report is not difficult. When investigations are short and simple, the reports should also be. One should not feel the need to fill many sheets of paper with words to be impressive. For many investigations a one-page report is sufficient.

But a certain percentage of our work will involve large, complex cases in which the writing of a good report is a decidedly difficult task, and it is these that we are concerned with here, for the large or complex investigations are the ones most likely to be litigated, though in reality any case can end up in litigation.

Unfortunately, it is usually those cases which we expect to be run-of-the-mill, open and shut cases that catch us by surprise, which we find that we did not do as good a job as we should have, that come back to haunt us. Therefore, we should get into the habit of treating all investigation reports as if litigation will ensue. In preparation for writing this chapter I reviewed dozens of investigation reports of others, culled from my files, in which the vast majority lacked a professional standard of presentation, or were fraught with errors.

Reports were found in which the investigator got lost in his details and became confused; reports that were missing critical information such as dates, and places. Many were marred by excessive wordiness. Reports were found that contained contradictions and unsupported conclusions, and were obviously biased by presenting only favorable evidence while ignoring unfavorable factors. Some contained obvious efforts to discredit the subject of investigation, or gratuitous and irrelevant remarks. But, by far, the most common fault was that the investigator simply did not know how to present his findings in a comprehensible and professional manner.

Surveyors working for insurance companies on claims, or for other clients, tend to be a bit too casual and informal, often creating reports that read like personal letters. The basis of the professional investigation report should be the presentation of evidence that is supported by documentation, with the understanding that the information contained therein will have a profound effect on other interests. That is, purported statements of fact must be backed up by solid evidence such photographic or physical evidence, and not merely the assertion of the investigator. In other words, evidence cannot merely be alleged because a qualified expert says so. The evidence must be verifiable and be able to withstand challenge. A report that does not meet this standard presents an invitation to challenge.

A Public Document

We should get this point securely established in mind: the report we write does not belong to us, our client nor anyone else. We may think that it does, but once it is sent off, it is now in the public domain and we have no control over its distribution and use. Not only is it paid for by the client who may use it as he sees fit, but it is also discoverable by subpoena should litigation be initiated.

The essential attribute of the professional report begins with the writer who knows exactly what he wants to say; it is logically constructed; the discourse is precise, with an economy of words; presenting evidence to its best effect and leading to a carefully drawn conclusion without creating unintended elements of doubt. This, of course, is much easier said than done so we will explore some of the things that make for good as well as bad reports.

Personal Bias

Few persons are truly capable of purging themselves of personal bias. We all have them, regardless of whether we are aware of these prejudices operating subconsciously in our minds or not. One need only look at the behavior of the news media to appreciate how pervasive personal bias is. As pointed out in an earlier chapter, the investigator's bias is most likely to result from a loyalty to the client's interest.

When it comes to investigative work, allowing bias to influence our work will not only cause problems for us and our client, but sooner or later will land us in trouble. The investigator therefore needs to diligently work to prevent bias from influencing his work. Note that I did not say that we need to rid ourselves of bias, for that is not possible. But it is possible to guard against it by being aware of our tendencies and prevent them from entering our efforts. That becomes possible only through diligence and practice.

Yet another famous lesson from the O.J. Simpson case comes to mind. Recall when lawyer F. Lee Bailey asked Detective John Furman whether he had ever uttered the n-word, Furman responded with that famous one-word lie, *no*. This question was a carefully laid trap for Furman, one that he stepped right into. The implication of that answer was that Furman was unwilling to admit that he had ever used the word, which only served the purpose of amplifying it, in this case to an astounding result. The n-word is a word that almost everyone has used at least once in his lifetime, so Furman's answer wasn't credible, even if he had never used it. Now, let's consider what would have happened had he answered in the affirmative, or said that he couldn't remember. What would have been the effect of that? It would have sent the signal that Furman was a big enough to own up to his prejudices and the effect would be nowhere near what it was. After all, we cannot overcome bias until we recognize that it exists, at which point we have the option of rejecting it.

Economy of Words

Lawyers who give lectures to investigators at seminars frequently caution against "verbosity", using too many words. Besides being unnecessary, saying too much is likely to result in inadvertent errors or saying things that aren't intended. Lawyers advise that a report should be as clear and concise as one can make it. Precision has little to do with the number of pages a report contains, but rather how many words are used to make a single point. Another common fault of surveyor's reports is the apparent urge to impress by the sheer length of the document, a tactic that everyone but the author of the report clearly sees through.

The tendency to become excessively wordy – at least judging by my own experience – derives from uncertainty about one's facts or one's method of presentation. It bears repeating that if the investigator is certain of his facts, there is little chance for confusion or motivation to engage in excessive explanation. Invariably, he runs into trouble when the facts don't fit what he knows his client wants to hear. The following examples demonstrate this point:

> The color of the sky determines the color of the ocean. When the sky is blue, the ocean looks blue, but when the sky is gray, the ocean also looks gray. Thus, it is the color of the sky that determines what we perceive as the color of the ocean.

> The color of the sky, in part, determines the color of the ocean. When the sky is blue, the ocean looks blue, but when it is gray, the ocean also looks gray. However, the appearance of the color of the ocean is mitigated by yet other factors, such as water pollution, and the depth of the water. The surface condition also has an effect, as with the differences that result when the ocean is calm versus very rough.

The first example makes the clear point that the color of the sky largely determines the color of the ocean. The second example introduces numerous other mitigating factors that only have the effect of complicating an otherwise simple point, leaving the reader uncertain as to what exactly determines the color of water which has no color in and of itself. The reality is that the ocean, as viewed by most people most of the time, is blue. There is little point in introducing needless complexities unless there is a definite reason to do so. The question the investigator must always ask himself is whether the mitigating factors are significantly relevant to change an otherwise cogent explanation. The significance of this example is that the addition of superfluous details can alter the ultimate meaning with unintended consequences, which is why it is best to avoid lengthy explanations that detract from the essential facts. Too much explanation is more likely to cast doubt on a stated fact than it is to bolster the fact.

Composing Reports

Evidentiary Documentation

Photos and video tape are two obvious form of documentation, but less obvious forms include measurements, detailed descriptions, sketches, drawings, detailed illustrations and last but not least, the object itself. Video tape has the attribute of being time consuming and costly to deal with. It is easy to make a video, but not so easy to review and handle it. Generally video is not used except in large cases where it deals with evidentiary problems in a better manner than photos, and where its cost is less of an issue.

Before starting the writing process, take all your materials and lay them out so that you have a clear view of them. Since photos are normally an important component of most reports, a decision will need to be made about how to use them. It is not a good idea to embed digital photos directly into the text as some people do, the reason being that such images are too small to be useful in litigation and actually make their use and the report more cumbersome. Instead, mount the photos separately and refer to them by number in the report as follows:

> The aft bilge pump (photo #13) impeller was found to be tangled with a piece of string (photo #14).

The best procedure is to lay out all the photos, decide which ones will be used and place all others aside. If you adopt the procedure of referring to photos directly in the report, as illustrated above, then they can be glued onto sheets of heavy paper and numbered sequentially so that the photo number can be referred to. This will make handling easier and less confusing if there are a lot of photos. The same goes for sketches, drawings or other reference documents that can be labeled Exhibit A, B, C and so on.

Photos often require an explanation because the viewer may not be able to discern what he is looking at. Photo captions are normally placed on the mounting paper with the word processor for which a special format has been generated such as a text box. However, the creation of photo essays provides other opportunities to create verbal gaffes. Therefore, we must be certain that captions are consistent with, and do not contradict, anything in the report. Be very careful not to include gratuitous commentary.

Logical Structure

Because of the diversity of different types of investigations that are encountered, there is no one standard format that will fit every job. The structure of the report should fit the nature of the investigation. Investigations that involve mainly the actions of people will be very different than that of a sinking, fire or collision investigation. Note that investigation reports should not include information about repairs and or repair costs unless such topics pertain to a causal investigation such as a dispute over repairs and costs. All damage evaluations should be contained in a separate report. There are essential common elements for all reports which should be topical along the following lines:

- Introduction or Preamble
- Identification of vessel, subject and relevant components
- Background
- Persons in attendance
- Description of Methodology
- Presentation of facts
- Conclusion

Introduction or Preamble

This section serves as the opening statement containing the who, what, where, when and why; it details the nature of the investigation, by whom it was commissioned, the reported nature of the casualty, date of casualty, dates and locations involved. The particulars of the vessel may be contained in this section, or may be set out under a separate heading. These should include the vessel owner, vessel description, registration, engines and serial numbers of engines, etc. A typical introduction appears as follows:

> This is to certify that the undersigned investigator was commissioned by (client) on or about (date) to investigate the cause of (casualty) occurring on (date) at (location). This report constitutes the full and complete findings of this investigator to date, and as of this writing the investigation is considered to be closed. The investigator reserves the right to modify any conclusions contained herein in the event that any new information comes to light subsequent to this report.

Vessel and Component Identification

Complete description and identification of the vessel should be provided when the investigation involves a particular vessel and should include: builder and model name if any, principle dimensions, the registration, HIN, engine type and serial numbers, engine drive configuration (inboard, stern drive, vee drive, etc.). Description generally needs to be linked to the nature of the casualty so that the description provides the necessary identification or the subject matter. Example: a report involving structural damage or failure should contain a greater rather than lesser description of general construction; a machinery damage case needs more rather than less machinery description and identification. Use model numbers when available whenever the model number would identify the component, such as the model number of any component that is involved in the cause of a casualty. When doing physical investigations, it is best to get into the habit of recording model and serial numbers because so often it is later found to be needed.

Background

Sometimes it is necessary to provide background information, such as when events leading up to the casualty are unusual. Any mitigating circumstances as would affect the outcome of the investigation, such as vessel having been salvaged and/or moved, pilfered or otherwise disturbed should also be described. The most common mitigating circumstances are lost/damaged evidence due to actions of salvors, conditions of weather as well as late reporting of loss by the insured, so be sure to include these factors if present:

> The vessel reportedly went up on the beach at 1800 hours where it was battered by the surf for more than twelve hours. As a result of this circumstance, much evidence was lost or destroyed.

When including background information we need to be very careful that the information is accurate, and that it does not in any way affect the conclusion. If it does, that is not background, but rather a fact bearing on the conclusion. Background essentially is used to define why something was or was not done; it sheds light on why we did things the way we did them.

Persons in Attendance

This section names those persons who were in attendance during the investigation, including assistants, helpers, etc., the importance of which is to identify potential witnesses of the event and proceedings.

Attachments

Any and all documents relating to the conclusion of the report should be listed here, including drawings, photos, sketches and statements of witnesses. Attachments are specifically named here so that the report cannot be used out of context of the whole by others.

Methodology

A common feature of analytical lab reports of physical evidence is to state the methodology used. This may or may not be necessary in an investigation report but more often methods are described in the body of the report at the point where a particular operation is described. An example would be to describe how and where evidence is found in a fire investigation; it may be necessary to demonstrate that the investigation methods employed did not spoil other evidence. Another example would be with a large fire where it was necessary to cut and remove debris, perform layering and so on. If an investigation was performed with great care and attention to detail, then the report should reflect those facts.

When any kind of component is tested, the means of testing should be described such as when testing the bilge pumping system of a vessel after it sank. The primary purpose of describing methodology is to demonstrate that the correct result was achieved by use of the proper method, i.e., to close off any open loop holes.

Reference to interviews within the report may be relevant in some instances in certain types of investigations. In such cases, the complete transcript of the interview should be attached.

Methodology may be stated at the beginning, or any other appropriate location in the report.

Presentation of Findings

The bulk of the report will consist of the presentation of findings. In a case where there is a large mix of verbal and physical evidence, these can be broken down under appropriate captions, and may further be ordered by subject matter or chronology, depending on what would best fit the particular investigation.

The presentation of findings should include *all* evidence that was used to reach a conclusion, including exclusionary evidence. Keep in mind that evidence is not merely that which supports a positive conclusion, but is also that which proves that it is not something else. It is at this point in the report that we are most prone to fall into the trap of diverging into editorializing, making of non factual statements and unsupported assertions.

In cases where a preponderance of evidence determines the conclusion, it will happen on occasion that three pieces of evidence point toward the conclusion while one piece does not. Nor should one ever omit negative facts just because they cast doubt on what would otherwise be a clear-cut conclusion. Omitted negative facts have a way of coming back to haunt the writer. The way to handle this is to make the case that the three positive pieces overwhelm the single negative piece. But to omit the negative is to leave the door open to the charge that the investigator has ignored important evidence.

With some types of investigations, the inclusion of a time line of events is critical. Yet a large number of such reports that I have reviewed were lacking an adequate time line. This leaves a report wide open to attack when the order of events is not properly established.

In laying out the findings we are seeking to do it in such a way as to eliminate all doubt about how we reached our conclusion. If elements of doubt exist then the conclusion cannot be drawn and the result is inconclusive. It should be born in mind that because up to half of our investigations will not be conclusive, elements of doubt cannot be ignored. If evidence exists that leads to inconclusiveness, then this evidence should be included. If a firm conclusion is reached, make sure that the written presentation does not inadvertently accentuate elements of doubt, but put them into proper perspective.

When discussing exclusionary evidence, it is best to say less than more, to make broad statements rather than detailed ones so that we don't inadvertently leave an opening for challenge. It is fine to simply make a list of what was considered and summarize that no other relevant evidence was found among them, rather than provide a detailed explanation of why.

The Conclusion

The final section is the conclusion and should reiterate how the facts lead to the investigator's conclusion. If there is but one direct cause, this section will be quite short. In simple cases, a single, short paragraph will often suffice. However, when there are contributory causes or conflicting evidence, how these factors influence the conclusion should be explained. This section will therefore tie all the disparate facts together to form the whole, and will necessarily outline the actions of persons over time that have come to bear on the conclusion. It is of critical importance that the investigator conveys his conclusion clearly and concisely.

There are three possible levels of conclusion that we could reach, each of which means that we treat the written conclusion in a different manner:

Preponderance of Evidence – This degree of opinion leaves some element of doubt, for what it is really saying is that a *majority* of evidence supports a conclusion, but not all evidence. It evinces that a cause is probable, but not beyond reasonable doubt. This standard of evidence is ordinarily not sufficient to deny a property insurance claim and would be very risky using as evidence in plaintiff litigation, but would be very useful in non insurance defense cases.

Clear and Convincing — This degree of evidence leads one to a conclusion without doubt, in which case we can write *Based on the evidence presented above, it is this investigator's opinion that such and such caused the casualty.* Period, end of story. No further justification need be given.

Undetermined — This term means that there is insufficient evidence from which to draw any conclusion; it doesn't mean that there isn't any evidence, but that sufficient evidence is lacking to reasonably infer any particular cause. If the cause is undetermined due to insufficient resources, then that should be so stated.

The conclusion doesn't necessarily have to state that the conclusion is an opinion since that may be self-evident, but it should state the conclusion's degree of certainty. With the preponderance of evidence conclusion, what constitutes a *majority* of evidence is essentially an estimate of the weight of each item of evidence, and how we weigh each item is certainly a matter of opinion, albeit a professional opinion.

In cases where there are contributory factors or negligence, it need be spelled out how that evidence is weighted in drawing the conclusion. For example, in some instances a loss will involve more than one potential cause, or even a contributing cause or factor — a common situation in sinking losses and collisions. When we are drawing a conclusion from a preponderance of evidence, we need to spell out the reasoning behind favoring one cause over another, and to do this without excessive argumentation.

In liability cases we will be dealing with issues of contributory negligence as a matter of degree that may be used to proportion settlements.

Conclusions should be written with an economy of words that are clear and direct, for this is the one place where a bad choice of words could be terminal. A conclusion may be properly supported and summed up by a statement as simple as the following:

Based upon the above findings, it is the undersigned investigator's opinion that preponderance of evidence is strongly supports the conclusion that . . .

In cases where conflicting evidence exists, further discussion may be necessary to explain one's reasoning. But in all cases one should err on the side of less rather than more discussion.

Dos and Don'ts

Investigation of Persons

The behavior or persons is vastly different than physical evidence, for it involves the problem of the investigator's bias to a far greater degree than his assessment of things. With persons, the moral dimension, and the investigator's feeling about that, is a constant underlying factor. Therefore, with the investigation of the actions of persons it is necessary for us to be much more diligent with self-censorship of personal bias or emotion. This is especially true when one finds oneself judging the actions of a subject as morally reprehensible, for it is extremely easy to allow one's feelings to creep in.

A writer need not express his feelings directly in order for those feelings to be transmitted through his written words. Instead, it shines through in the tone of the report with the choice of words we use, often unconsciously.

The correct method of reporting the actions of persons is to state the action in direct words with an economy of adjectives. *Smith was seen boarding his boat by witness Jones one hour before the fire* instead of *Smith was seen* furtively *boarding his boat by witness Jones one hour before the fire.* The use of the word *furtive* is judgmental unless the meaning of that word can be explained. Perhaps Smith was seen moving around on his boat in a sneaky manner, but it is inappropriate for the investigator to use that adjective. Contrast the word *furtive* with the following:

> Smith was seen moving toward his boat in what was described by Jones as a low crouch. At one point he stopped behind a tree and seemed to be looking around to see if anyone was observing him.

Now, it's a different matter if Jones uses that word to describe Smith's movement, in which case the adjective should be attributed to Jones. The investigator needs to be careful about the use of such pejorative words for his own attribution lest it be perceived as bias.

Care should be taken to always set the time and place of the actions of persons. Don't make the mistake of saying that Smith did something without telling where and when and according to whom. News reporters can get away with saying, *Witnesses stated that* . . . but we cannot. State the fact in as neutral a tone as possible and do not embellish. If the evidence is sound, it will speak for itself and doesn't need any editorializing or embellishment.

Mixing the actions of persons with the presentation of physical evidence is problematic from the standpoint of tying both together. In this case it's best to create two separate sections and then tie the two together in the conclusion. This is due to the frequent need to create time lines when the actions of persons are involved. An example is a case in which three brothers, whose fishing business was going broke, conspired to sink their large fishing vessel in order to pay off a large mortgage. Proving a conspiracy was important because three owners were insured, and if only one of them could be implicated, the others could still collect the insurance (My brother did it, not me). The investigation involved extensive investigation of the brothers in which a precise time line of actions had to be presented. But this had to be tied into a large amount of physical evidence as well.

In such a case the only way to accomplish this is to present the evidence by category and then tie it altogether in the conclusion, which was itself lengthy. To attempt to do it any other way will result in a confusing mix of a hard-to-follow evidentiary story. Note that large investigations of persons essentially amounts to story-telling by the presentation of who, what, where and when in a logical order of time. The physical evidence then serves as back up or supporting evidence. But instead of a writing a short story, what we are doing is giving a presentation of evidence point by point in such an orderly fashion as it would lead to the reasonable conclusion that we will ultimately render. So long as the facts are presented in orderly fashion, it does not matter whether the basis of the conclusion is immediately apparent to the reader, only that the conclusion is supported by the evidence.

False Theories and Misleading Evidence

Rare is the complex investigation that does not produce at least one false theory or misleading evidence. It is the nature of investigators to get an idea or hunch and then attempt to follow it through, but often these don't pan out. So too, with pieces of evidence that seem to lead in one direction but are later found to be misinterpreted or not relevant.

The thing to be mindful of here is that if you came to such conclusions, isn't it also likely that someone else might come to the same conclusion? It is the essence of legal defense work to find other possibilities and to use them in an effort to sow seeds of doubt. False theories and misleading evidence does not need to be proven false, but we do need to be prepared to explain in testimony why these are false. To discuss them in a report is to sow the element of doubt no matter how much we try to explain them away. Don't forget that all the defense side need do is to create reasonable doubt.

Discussion of Conflicting Evidence

The easiest way to go off course with the presentation of findings is to engage in explanation of conflicting facts in this section. In the presentation section, facts should just be stated, not debated. If there is any doubt about the fact, then perhaps it is not really a fact after all, or a fact that has no bearing on the conclusion. The place for discussing how the facts were evaluated is in the conclusion.

Unsupported Allegations

It is very easy for unsubstantiated assertions to slip into a report. This is something that, once again, stems from uncontrolled bias:

> In a recent case an investigator asserted, without providing any supporting evidence, that an engine being out of alignment caused an exhaust hose connection to separate. On the face of it, the assertion seems unlikely, but in deposition the investigator was unable to support that statement and ultimately admitted that he was told by someone else that the engine was out of alignment. He made the mistake of accepting hearsay as evidence without bothering to verify it as fact.

The important point here is that he did that for one of the two most common reasons detectives, investigators and prosecutors get into trouble; they allowed ulterior motives or bias to creep into their work, whether based on laziness or other motivations.

> In another instance an investigator asserted that a component was old, without stating how he knew it was old. At trial it turns out that the part was not old and the opposition was able to prove the point with an invoice for the part; the investigation was impeached because the investigator did nothing to establish the age of the part other than to form an opinion that it *looked* old simply because it was dirty. He did not question the boat owner as to the age of the part. Had he done so he would have been told the correct age of the part and his conclusion would have been different.

Whenever a condition is critical to determination of cause, it is imperative that all assertions as to fact be supported by proof of that assertion. If we assert that something is not right, then we need to be able to prove why it is not right. The editing of reports should always be done with a view toward ferreting out such mistakes by self-critiquing ourselves.

Opinions and Editorializing

Editorializing is the act of adding an opinion along with a statement of fact that may rise to the level of an unsupported allegation. There is only one place for editorializing in an investigation report and that is in the conclusion. Editorializing becomes even more egregious when it involves the nature of a person. It is one thing to state a fact about a person, such as he said or did this or that. But we have to be very careful about drawing conclusions as to that person's motivations or mental state, as well as writing in a tone that suggests a personal bias, bearing in mind that the opposition will seize on anything that they think can be used to defeat one's credibility.

A recent federal appeals case turned on an editorial comment by the investigator when he attributed a boat owner's actions to an opinion of his mental state. This ill-considered comment sunk the investigator's client's case because it not only suggested a bias, but was not a proven fact from which the investigator drew a conclusion. It also made for some very spirited and embarrassing questioning at trail. I have no doubt that had the investigator taken the time to carefully edit his report, he would have recognized and stricken that comment because he was not a novice but had a great deal of experience.

An opinion is a belief that can be rooted in personal prejudice, or it may be the result of a concerted effort to understand an issue. That being the case, opinions may or may not have merit. Opinions of experts are acknowledged by courts only to the extent that the expert can *demonstrate* that his opinion has merit. His opinion doesn't have merit simply because he's an expert. It follows, then, that in drawing conclusions it is a valuable exercise to present whatever evidence or logic on which one's opinion is based.

Analysis of a Bad Example

On the face of it, editorializing, unsupported allegations and prejudice seem like easy things to avoid. The reality is that, based on our usual mode of conversation, it is all too easy for these errors to creep in unconsciously. In the following examples, all taken from a single report, such errors are painfully obvious to us, but they were not obvious to this investigator, either because he didn't edit, or because he lacked experience. This was a case in which the investigator was representing the liability carrier for a marina. The following quote comes from a report investigating a boat sinking that ultimately proved to be a parted exhaust hose connection. It appears under a heading of OTHER RELEVANT EVIDENCE:

> The claimant operated the boat over the 4th of July and up until the date of the sinking on July 16; there was [sic] no problems with leaks that were sufficient to sink the boat. The boat was sunk partially on the port side near the shipping channel with winds 15 to 20 miles per hour and 1' to 3' waves would be hitting the boat from the shipping channel. Excess water could enter the boat because a floating dock moves with the wind and waves and if not tied properly, the port side could dip low into the waves.

Aside from the author's poor grammar, this paragraph is not taken out of context of the whole report; it is as incomprehensible in this extraction as it is in the whole. In the very first sentence, he sows doubt about the statement that *there were no problems with leaks that were sufficient to sink the boat.* The fundamental error here is that the sentence suggests that there were other leaks, but they were not sufficient. It came out in his testimony that he did not find *any* other leaks, which is what he should have said, period. The cross examining lawyer used the investigator's own words to demonstrate that he did have a bias by intimating that there were other leaks, since the major emphasis of the report was to show that the boat was in poor condition.

Next, he mixes opinions with facts: *"Excess water could enter the boat . . . because a floating dock moves . . . .and if not properly tied . . . the port side could dip low in the waves."* Here we have either four unsupported allegations or opinions in just one sentence. And we're left to wonder what "excess water" is.

If this investigator is clear about what he is trying to say, he completely fails to express himself clearly. His assertions were unsupported allegations because he provides no credible evidence. In fact, he is being disingenuous by suggesting that there were "1' to 3' waves" without providing proof of same. Plus, there is a huge difference between a one foot and a three foot wave, so why does he give such a great a range? As it turned out, the answer was that he had no knowledge of what the wave height was; he was not there at the time to personally have that knowledge and again he relied on hearsay. This report ends up impeaching itself when the writer concludes one thing, but tries to give evidence of yet another:

> The bilge pumps were not working at the time because they *should* [Italics mine] have handled the excess water. Had the pumps been working all of the time, the batteries would have been dead.

Here the investigator asserts that the bilge pumping system was faulty because, incredibly, the boat wouldn't have sunk if the pumps were operating. At first glance that statement might seem reasonable, but is the mistake of an amateur. There are other possibilities that could account for this that he does not address. He further asserts that because the batteries were not dead when the boat was raised, the pumps were at fault. Both sentences are non sequiturs. He asserts that the bilge pumps should have prevented the boat from sinking, and the fact that they didn't is proof that the pumps were faulty. In reality, the boat sank due to a disconnected 4" exhaust pipe hose that put the boat on the bottom within minutes. He failed to address the issue of whether the rate of water entry could exceed the capacity of the pumps. Had he done so, he would have either proved his point, or proved himself wrong.

Here's another editorializing statement in the same report:

> It should be noted that the boat was not insured, which is a serious liability issue. Probably the reason for no insurance would be that the insurance company would have required a survey and the boat would not have passed.

The opposing lawyer had a field day with these allegations. Whether the boat did or did not have insurance is not relevant to the cause of the casualty unless he is asserting that the owner is engaging in fraud, something that he hints at here. Then he goes on to assert that the boat would not pass an insurance survey, but fails to give any reason of how or why he comes to this conclusion. In conjunction with other similar comments, it was clear from the report that the investigator had a clear bias and was attempting to discredit the boat and its owner:

> There was extensive corrosion of the electrical connections in the engine compartment. This corrosion is not from a one-time sinking.

That the wire connections were corroded was undeniable, but the investigation was done on July 18, while the sinking occurred on June 6. The investigator could not provide any evidence to prove his assertion that the corrosion was not due to the sinking. Certainly a month and a half is plenty of time for corrosion to occur. The report contains numerous other unsubstantiated allegations as well as presentation of irrelevant "facts" that have no other purpose than to disparage the condition of the boat.

These examples serve the purpose of illustrating how easy it is to go get off-track in a report that becomes completely derailed. Perhaps most surprising is that this report was issued by a large investigative firm with no demonstrable expertise in marine losses, where it is evident that the firm's objective is to protect its client. Yet this report did not protect the client, quite the opposite. That firm ended up losing a large insurance company client when their client was sued by a claimant for bad faith and the insurer ended up settling for an amount far larger than had they paid the claim in the first place.

In this case the allegations and innuendo are intentional but, regardless of whether they are or not, the point to be driven home is that such things do not go unnoticed by others and there will be a price to be paid for such errors whether intentional or accidental.

Attacking an Opponent

It often happens that we are called into an investigation after the other side has already performed their investigation and issued their report. Far too many investigators indulge in attacking the opponent's report directly. This is very bad form in the event of litigation unless the expert is consulting for his client's attorney and the report will not be used as evidence but as advice to the lawyer.

If you are specifically asked to perform this function, then what you are doing is not an investigation but an analysis of another investigator's work. There is nothing wrong with that except when what we are doing becomes mislabeled. Then, when performing the critical analysis, be very careful to use rigorously neutral language; criticize the work product, not the worker. If there are areas where you are in agreement with the other person, by all means say so because this helps remove the onus of bias which is always present in criticism and makes you appear honest.

If you are performing an investigation with the opponent's report in hand, feel free to use it to guide your efforts, but do not attack it in writing by making direct refutations of facts or conclusions drawn in that report. If you can present evidence that refutes the opponent's findings and conclusions, by all means do so but refrain from direct criticism. Present your own facts and findings and draw your own conclusions, but don't stoop to attacking the other investigator. Be confident enough to let your work stand on its own merit. If you don't have that confidence, perhaps you should rethink what you have to say.

Fraud

Fraud is a criminal offense, and for that reason reports that deal with issues of fraud must be very circumspect to avoid the problem of slander. Never make the direct assertion that someone committed fraud. When we suspect that fraud is involved, the best approach is to consult with the client's attorney before writing the report. Barring that, the safe approach would be to state the facts and to fashion a conclusion that falls short of making allegations about intentions. An example might be to simply assert that the basis of a claim is unfounded according to the evidence presented.

When evidence appears to be clear, a statement along the following lines would be in order:

> The manner and location in which the hose was found to be cut with a knife or other sharp instrument is consistent with an intention to sink the boat as no other conclusions can be drawn from the nature and location of the cut hose.

Notice that what this statement does not do is to infer fraud directly attributable to a person. Even if there is evidence that ties the action to a person, it is not necessary to make the accusation as the two elements of evidence will speak for themselves. So long as the facts are the facts, we can be content to let someone else draw the direct conclusion. As private investigators, we have nothing to gain and everything to lose by charging someone with fraud. Notice how the phrase "consistent with" leads up to, but does not actually make a direct charge.

Should evidence be developed that a person had the opportunity, means and motive to commit fraud, again, just state the evidence without directly making an allegation.

Writing

The Process of Writing

The process used by all good writers is essentially the same. No one is ever so adept that he can just sit down and zing out a report with little or no preparatory effort. No, the success of any effort derives from the amount of preparation time expended. It should be noted here that we will either have to spend the time at the beginning or at the end. The easiest and most efficient way is to put the preparation time in at the beginning because while writing is hard, editing is even more difficult.

If we don't already practice the habit of keeping good notes, at report time we rediscover the virtues of doing so, particularly with long, complex cases. The first thing to do is to sit down and review all the information at hand until thoroughly familiar with it. Facts are a dime a dozen, but few are actually relevant; which need to be included? Next, it is necessary to sketch out the order of presentation. The usual way to do this is in outline form. Creating an outline further helps us to get a firm grasp on what we intend to say – and not say. We want to know what we are going to include and not include. What difficult issues need to be dealt with and how to do so?

Consider those false theories that arose and whether they need to be explained or otherwise disposed of. The objective will be to so cover all logical possibilities as to close off all opportunities for the opposition to challenge our findings. Determine what other possible theories exist and utilize the existing evidence to refute them.

It is useful to lay out all evidence such as sketches and photographs, deciding which are to be used, and particularly which are to be referenced in the report.

This is followed by the writing of a first draft. The purpose of the first draft is essentially to get our ideas down on paper and to reveal the flaws in our efforts; never think of it as a final product that merely needs editing. During drafting things flow out of our subconscious that we may not be aware of, thoughts and ideas that will need revision. The first draft is merely one step in the process of creating the final product.

The best way to avoid serious errors is to allow at least twenty four hours between first and second drafts. There is a certain magic that occurs with our thinking with the passage of time that is beyond explanation; it is sufficient to simply say that we need *time* to digest these complex matters. Serious study of the first draft will reveal it's flaws that can then be corrected. With moderate size jobs we should be able get the job done with just a first and final draft; for large jobs a third draft may be necessary.

To do a good job it is imperative that we allow adequate time. It won't help that we are constantly interrupted with phone calls and other matters. Again, it must be restated that the report is the final work product that needs to be as well thought out as we can possibly make it. It's the only aspect of our work that others will see. The specter of possible litigation should always be a motivating factor and, in such cases, we should be aware that the significance of our report goes far beyond our client and it's possible use in court. Exceptionally well prepared reports have an effect that goes beyond the obvious. It sends a signal about the writer as an expert that he is skilled, knowledgeable and someone to be reckoned with. The more one can do to convey that impression, the less likely we are to become a target of the opposition.

Relevancy

At this point we need to once again visit the issue of relevancy since during the report writing phase is the time when we again take a look at the "facts." To avoid going off course, there is a simple procedure that can be used to separate the wheat from the chaff. Take each item and submit it to the following test:

> Is it a supported fact?
>
> Describe what constitutes support or proof

Describe how it is relevant

Is the total proof adequate? Does it eliminate doubt or add to it?

Is the report free of bias?

It is very easy to be indiscrete in making references to others. The following is a good example pulled from a court case, a comment in a report by a marine surveyor that came back to haunt him:

> "Mr. Cooper [fictitious] is basically a nice chap, but I think he is undergoing a delayed identity crisis in his life which may be affecting his judgement. He has a 20 year old girlfriend who he explained has no education and therefore he should possibly prepare her statement for her."

There was nothing wrong with the investigator's intent to advise his client that the insured wanted to prepare a statement for a witness (the girlfriend). What was wrong was the manner in which he reported it. He felt the need to editorialize on the insured's mental health and thereby exhibited a bias, and that provided all the ammunition that the opposition needed to discredit his testimony. He should have just stated the facts and left it at that. The investigator is likely to end up having to explain how it is that he has diagnosed the insured's identity crisis, along with his qualifications to do so. The lawyer might also have a bit of fun by asking him to explain the difference between a "delayed" identity crisis and an identity crisis that is not delayed. Never mind the question of what an identity crisis has to do with the matter!

It is common to find investigation reports that reference the condition of the vessel without linking the reference to the conclusion. As mentioned earlier, in one recent report that I reviewed, the investigator goes to great lengths to disparage the condition of the vessel without in any way linking the cause to the condition.

Very frequently investigations involve vessels that are in bad condition, yet unless this condition bears directly on the cause of loss, one must be careful that the condition of the vessel is relevant if you intend to include comments about it. Conversely, it is okay to state that the vessel was in poor condition, but must go on to say that no evidence was found that linked condition to cause. Otherwise such commentary becomes merely disparaging without relevancy.

It is insufficient to merely state that the condition of a vessel is poor without providing proof of same. If we do not do this, we can be accused of bias, and rightfully so. If the condition is poor, the basis for making that statement must be given. *The basic rule of relevancy is that the relationship of all evidence presented must have a bearing on the cause.*

Hearsay

Hearsay is a verbal statement provided by or through another person. *Bill told me that Jim did it.* Except under rare conditions, hearsay is not admissible evidence. When we receive advice about something someone else said, to be used as evidence this has to be corroborated on a first hand basis, or provide yet other witnesses that such a thing was said. The greater danger in written reports is that conclusions may be drawn from such statements. Don't include hearsay as this will only invite trouble. If one needs to convey hearsay to the client, do it over the phone.

Style and Tone

An investigation report is a semi formal style document. The proper tone for an investigation report is semi-formal, the third person, but avoiding sounding pedantic, arrogant or biased. The third person viewpoint does not reference yourself, for it is understood that the report is the work of the signatory. Avoid the first person pronouns as much as possible. It is bad form to use "I", "me" and "my" in reference to yourself unless absolutely necessary. Most novices will at first make extensive use of them, something that will clearly mark the report as that of a novice or beginner. Eliminating the first person pronouns is easy as the following examples attest:

I inspected the boat on January 28th.

The investigation was conducted aboard the boat on January 28th.
The undersigned returned to the vessel on January 28th.

Next I looked at the port side gizmo.

The port side gizmo was inspected next.

It is not a good idea to attempt to adopt or copy a style, but rather to use your own words and style, but you certainly can use a good example of another expert as a guide. Bear in mind that the report is not a letter, and should not be addressed to any person. Investigation reports do not have an addressee because they are a public document. We don't know who the readers will be.

The tone of a report should be as neutral and unbiased as we can possibly make it. Remember that any bias that is felt will very likely become amplified in the report, which is why it's best to "sleep on it" for 24 hours before doing a final edit. Not only is a spell check necessary, but also a tone and bias check.

Sensor yourself and watch out for the use of pejorative words and tone. We should never think for a moment that someone reading our report cannot discern how we feel about the matter when we allow our emotions to creep in. A well-written report is one in which it is clear that the writer is neutral, but we all have personal feelings and opinions so it's not easy to keep them out of our work. This can only happen when we work at it, and only with practice. Sleeping on a report helps us to better see when wrong choices of words creep in. Keep in mind that it is not just sentences and paragraphs that may convey unwanted sentiment, but the overall tone of the whole report:

In an effort to determine whether any other possibilities were overlooked we did this, that and the other thing. While points A and B do not support this conclusion, neither do they refute it, in that they seem to be coincidental with no direct relationship that we could find.

Consider the net effect of the above statement. This statement conveys the impression of impartiality by demonstrating a willingness to consider other possibilities, that the investigator made a conscious effort to go beyond the bounds of the obvious. It's a good idea to develop a few stock-in-trade clauses such as this for use in all reports.

Right Words, Wrong Words

It is equally important to be careful of the meaning of words that we use. In everyday speech we all more or less use words carelessly without any problem, but to use those same words in an investigation report could have grave consequences. Consider the following string of words and which would be preferred to describe a condition:

Terrible, wrong, bad, awful, inadequate, improper, does not comply with standard.

Always, never, is, did, should, could be, could have, seems, appears to be, maybe, possibly.

The first four in the second set are absolutes and we must be very careful when we use them that we can support that level of definitive statement. Conversely, the later phrases are at the opposite extreme and are indefinite. "Appears to" is the most overused and abused term found in survey reports and what one might refer to as the "weasel word," the word too many surveyors use when they are uncertain. There is nothing wrong with the well-considered and judicious use of the term "appears to." But think of what it means when it is used three or four times in an investigation report. The reader begins to wonder, "Is this investigator certain about anything?" The purpose of an investigation report is not to raise questions but answer them.

The term *"consistent with"* is a very useful term used by official investigators and lawyers to convey that good evidence does not absolutely establish a cause.

Non Sequiturs

A non sequitur is an inference from a stated fact that does not necessarily follow or is not supported by evidence upon careful consideration. It is an assumption that may be based on what the writer believes to be an obvious conclusion, but lacks supporting evidence. Here are a couple of real world examples:

The bilge pumps were not functioning because the wire connections are corroded.

While this is a possibility, it is not a proven fact. Corrosion on wire connections does not mean that the connection is broken. Simple testing would prove the point, so the statement should read:

Continuity testing of the bilge pump wires determined that corrosion of the wire connections caused an open circuit.

Here's another statement that got an investigator in trouble:

Inspection revealed that there was blue colored sealant around the manifold which indicates that previous work had been performed and that there was a problem with the gaskets.

In this instance the investigator makes two assumptions without evidence or adequate knowledge. First, he assumed that blue silicone gasket sealant was evidence of a repair when in fact the sealant was used by the manufacturer and the engine had never been repaired. The investigator simply assumed that manufacturers do not use gasket sealant (most don't) when in this case the sealant *was* the gasket. This automatically negates the second assumption, compounding his error. The veracity of the second point hinges on the truth of the first point.

We need to be extremely careful when a conclusion is based on a chain of facts, when each fact is dependant on the veracity of the others. This is especially problematic in the issue of proximate causation wherein a sequence of events is presumed to be set in motion ultimately leading to the casualty. If one event in the sequence proves to be in error, then the whole theory of causation falls down. Therefore, in a sequence, we need to take care that every minor fact can be proved.

Non sequiturs often result from erroneous beliefs that we've held for a long time and are more or less unconscious. These assumptions will often appear repeatedly in an investigator's work because he has never taken the time to validate that assumption. There is only one way to avoid falling into this trap and that is by taking the time to critically evaluate what you write during the editing process. Is every assertion we make true?

No Disclaimers

Disclaimers of any kind are not to be used in investigation reports. Neither should any assertions to objectivity or "without prejudice." If your report truly is without prejudice, that fact will speak for itself. Disclaimers and assertions serve mainly to produce the opposite effect of what was intended.

Editing

The single most important thing we can do to ensure that we issue the best work product possible is to edit, edit, edit. Yes, editing is tedious, time-consuming work but there is no way around it. We're not just talking about spelling and grammar here, but the content of the entire report. There can be little doubt but that the primary reason for so many badly written reports is not due to the writer's ignorance, but having been short on time by the pressure of other work. I can assure you that there is nothing more painful than to come face to face with a bad example of your own work in a litigation case. This has happened to me on many occasions until I finally vowed that I'd never let it happen again.

Editing is not merely a process of checking spelling and grammar, but is the process of analyzing what we have written to ensure that what we write is what we intend to say, with the proper selection of words, and is stated clearly and without dissembling. Badly worded statements may convey meanings that aren't intended. Conversely, what is intended may not be comprehended when wording is awkward.

One of the most important aspects of editing is allowing time to pass before the final edit, the proverbial "sleeping on it." Time has a way of putting things into proper perspective, revealing errors and poor wording. It is truly magical how the passage of a few days can open our eyes to errors that we would not have recognized had we performed the editing on the same day the report was written.

Novices will probably wonder how long does it take someone with years experience to do a report? I now spend more time than in the past because experience teaches that I will get my nose rubbed in my mistakes in court or deposition. Mistakes are just too embarrassing. A four-to-five page report takes me about eight hours total time, including editing, spread over several days. For years I dictated reports on tape for a secretary to transcribe, but was always unhappy with the results. I found that reports that I banged out on the word processor were much superior to dictated reports. Contrary to what we might think, this does not take longer than dictating if we have decent typing skill.

Hone Your Writing Skills

It is hard to overemphasize the importance of developing good writing skills because the written report is the only work product that will be seen by others and will go a long way toward establishing your reputation one way or the other.

One of the best marine investigators I know is also one of the worst writers I've ever seen among professionals. This fellow writes reports that are so bad as to be almost incomprehensible. Everyone who comes in contact with his work is aware of that but the man himself. Some of his clients have told me that they find his work embarrassing. But he is not alone, for I find more poorly written investigation reports than good ones, probably because good writing skills are a rarity amongst the general population. Even worse, once we develop bad writing habits, it's hard to change them.

It takes a lot of practice and effort to become a good technical writer, particularly a technical writer who has to explain things to laymen in a language they can understand. If you intend to reach the top of your profession, then you have no choice but to take a technical or business writing course unless you are already so trained, or make a concerted effort to teach yourself.

Actually, it is not difficult to teach oneself since all that is needed is a study of what makes for good writing versus bad. This we can do with our daily reading. Ask, why is something easy to read and comprehend compared to something that is difficult. Is it not because the writer makes his point without the reader having to dissect or second-guess the meaning of the sentence? When we write with short, simple sentences, it's hard to fail to convey our meaning concisely. The longer a sentence, the more *qualifiers* are introduced into the subject. And that makes for confusion.

Another element of good writing begins with knowing your subject thoroughly along with what you intend to say. Outlining is the common method used by most writers to keep themselves on track. Outlines need not be formal, structural outlines, but can be more along the lines of a sketch or brief summary of intent. With an investigation report it is really as simple as A+B+C = D where A through C are the facts and D is the conclusion. Anything that we write that does not directly lead to or support the conclusion is irrelevant.

A good dictionary and a thesaurus are necessary tools that should be used constantly. If you didn't do well in your writing courses in school, this is going to cause you problems because written reports are the work product by which you are judged by everyone who comes in contact with your work. Of course, you want that product to be the best you can possibly make it. If you recognize that your writing skills aren't what they should be, pick up a good text book on writing. Then improve you skill through practice and taking the time to analyze other good writing. Notice the differences between what constitutes good writing and bad. The following are some points to be aware of:

- Avoid overly long, run-on sentences.
- Make sure that paragraphs are confined to a single point or idea.
- Avoid overly long paragraphs.
- Don't say more than need be said.
- Edit, edit, edit

The best writers in the world become so by virtue of their dedication and persistence at editing because editing is a form of self-education where we learn to see and correct our mistakes. Not even the best writers can deliver a finished product with a first draft.

Additional Factors

Incomplete Investigations

It is best to do everything possible to avoid issuing investigation reports that are incomplete. Information contained within preliminary or status reports is likely to be wrong, and when it is we can be sure that it will be used as a weapon against us in litigation. It was mentioned previously how early theories of causation can be wrong so that to put such into writing plays into the hands of the opposition.

If it becomes necessary to issue a written preliminary or status report to the insurer (there will be times when a claims review committee will require this, or it is necessary to put a complex situation into writing that it can be analyzed and understood by the client), put this report under the caption of an investigation *status* report, never as a preliminary report. This report should be in the format of a letter, and should contain a statement similar in effect and intent as this:

> Evidence and information contained herein is based upon an incomplete investigation and may be subject to error in fact and in conclusion. It's only purpose is to keep the client appraised of the status of the investigation. The facts and opinions expressed herein are subject to change based on new evidence. Only the issuance of the final report should be taken as conclusive.

Even so, this will not prevent the opposition from attempting to use preliminary information against us so it is better to avoid written status reports whenever possible. Keep the client up to date with phone calls. Also be aware that everything in the insurer's file is subject to discovery, so nothing should be said that we don't want disclosed to others.

In an actual case, a surveyor issued a report and made the statement, *"The actual cause of the fault was not determined at this time."* Then the report went on with much speculation and finally drew an uncertain conclusion anyway as to the overall cause of the casualty, in essence contradicting the earlier statement. We need to get it firmly established in our minds what a good lawyer could do with such a terrible mistake; the contradiction utterly destroys the credibility of the investigator. How could such a dramatic error happen? Such mistakes happen frequently because the writer failed to analyze and edit his own work.

At some point a final report will have to be issued whether it is felt that the investigation is complete or not, as when an investigation terminates for lack of funding. The investigator should never feel compelled to draw a conclusion if he feels he has inadequate evidence. We may occasionally run into problems on smaller casualties or cases where the client resisted spending money for a laboratory analysis or other experts that was felt to be critical. We can be pretty certain that we know the cause, but we need the lab analysis to prove it and the client is refusing. Here's another instance where we're torn between loyalty to the client, doing the right thing, and protecting ourselves. We're left with a decision of whether to make our client look bad or leaving ourselves vulnerable. We should always assume that an opposing lawyer is as smart or smarter than we are, so that if we see the need for another expert or lab work, so will he. If the client declines to pay for more costly expertise, then so be it; that is his decision and one need not assume any responsibility for the client's error.

The experienced reader will certainly know where I'm headed with this line of thought. If we do not make it clear in our report that we recommended the use of other experts, and a suit follows, that lawyer is going to hang us out to dry, for it boils down to a question of who is going to hang, us or our client. We can attempt to ameliorate the situation by explaining to the client that it is our obligation to include this point (lab analysis recommendation) in our report so that the client clearly understands the risks to himself of not doing the lab work. Moreover, the client or claims supervisor may not have the final word on that decision, so he or she will have the opportunity to cover themselves as well.

It often happens that an insurer with a relatively small loss is unwilling foot the bill for costly forensic analysis when it is needed. In such cases, the insurer is essentially saying, "I am willing to make a decision based on inadequate information." Unfortunately, a lot of investigators will cover for their client by failing to address the issue in their report. The net result is that the investigator now assumes responsibility for that omission. Do that often enough and sooner or later it's going to come back to haunt you when such a case unexpectedly goes to litigation. The author has sunk many opponents' efforts by pointing out that their investigator failed to perform obviously needed technical analysis. It may not have been his fault, but the fact that there was no mention of it in his report left him wide open to the charge.

If the client has made the decision not to perform the analysis or engage in additional work, the client should be prepared to live with the consequences. To protect himself, the investigator must include the recommendation in his report which, lacking same, will be inconclusive.

Other Experts

Investigators routinely use other experts to deal with technical issues that are beyond our means, but the manner in which the work of other experts is incorporated into our report and conclusion must be carefully crafted. Typically the work of the expert is referenced in the body of our report and the expert's report attached thereto. Our conclusions may be based in whole or in part on that of the forensic expert. Therefore, lest our own work become compromised, it makes sense to make sure that our expert renders a proper report, and not merely assume that it will stand up to scrutiny. Many experts, particularly in the marine field, have little litigation experience, and we will find that they often manage to compromise their own work by saying things they shouldn't.

The expert's report should be analyzed in the same manner that we analyze our own work. If the expert is called in to evaluate a narrow question, something that is only a fragment of the overall question, care should be taken that the expert's report stays within bounds of his area of expertise, and that the expert does not stray into drawing conclusions as to overall causation where that expert has no basis for doing so. Straying beyond the scope of his expertise or engaging in speculation can end up being grounds for discrediting his own work. It is up to us to make sure this doesn't happen. After all, we hired him and don't want his mistakes reflecting on us, making us look bad in the eyes of our client.

Many experts simply do not know how to prepare a report that will stand up to close scrutiny under litigation. For this reason the commissioning investigator should: (1) counsel the expert to confine his comments only to his area of expertise, and (2) carefully review the expert's report and if there are problems with the manner of presentation, to help him edit it properly. We have a right to do this; we do not have a right to induce him to materially change his findings and conclusions. So long as this rule is adhered to, we are on solid ground.

Chapter 13

Deposition & Court Testimony

Because boats and yachts have a tendency to produce litigation, the marine surveyor as investigator inevitably ends up being a witness in such cases. The frequency with which investigators are involved in litigation is fairly high so that it is prudent for him to improve his testimonial skills in order to better serve his clients. Since the American judicial system is an adversarial system, it is a fundamentally hostile environment; it's a place where well-trained lawyers are presented with unsuspecting witnesses whom they do their best to discredit, humiliate and make fools of. Some have likened it to the Roman Coliseum where unarmed Christians were offered up to do battle with the lions. The good news is that this one-sided affair only exists if the witness is untrained and inexperienced, and that is something that we can change.

We would have little need to educate ourselves as professional witnesses if the purpose of taking our testimony was to simply derive the truth. But getting at the truth of the matter is a partisan competition and we are partisan witnesses. That is, we are witnesses *for* one side or the other. There will be much that we have to say that the other side does not want to hear, and will therefore seek to discredit our testimony and resort to trickery to try to trip us up.

Our objective in self-education is to come to an understanding of the process and the tricks of the legal trade so as to avoid becoming victims of clever tactics that are designed to discredit our testimony.

Material Witness vs Expert Witness

There are two types of witnesses in litigation, the material or fact witness, and the expert witness. The material witness comes to his possession of fact by way of coincidence; that is, he either just happens into a knowledge of facts surrounding a case, or is hired as an investigator, typically for an insurance company.

The expert witness, on the other hand, is hired after the fact either as a consultant to an attorney or to review a case and render his expert opinion in court. In many cases he will actually perform both functions, including case review. Expert witnesses may also engage in investigation to some degree, usually concerning the veracity of facts proffered as evidence by the other side. For example, if an investigator for the other side has a laboratory analysis performed on a piece of evidence, the expert may question that evidence and have his own analysis performed. He may also engage in all types of investigation work, the results of which may or may not make of him a material witness also, depending on his client's legal strategy. See more on expert witnesses later in this chapter.

Discovery

It is a principle of American jurisprudence that all witnesses and material evidence to be presented at trial are discoverable by the other side. One of the very first processes of formal litigation is called "discovery" wherein both sides are required to disclose their evidence and witnesses to the other side. Any information developed by an expert that is hired as a consultant to a lawyer is considered privileged and is not discoverable unless the attorney wishes it so. The consultant expert however cannot testify as to any of his work that is claimed as privilege.

When it comes to documents, virtually anything in a witness's possession that relates to the case is discoverable, including his entire file, unless documents are privileged attorney documents. This is why I caution in other chapters to be extremely careful about what is kept in files. Let this serve as a special warning to those who have never been through the litigation experience before: the usual kind of notes that we are prone to making and keeping will often contain information that, in the hands of the opposition, will be used against us. And it's hard to understand how this is so until we've had the unfortunate experience of shooting ourselves in the foot.

> A brief example is that I once had a file subpoenaed that contained a number of telephone messages taken by my secretary. During discovery my entire file was copied and during deposition, the opposing lawyer questioned me in detail about every one of those telephone messages. In another instance a note made to myself caused me a great deal of trouble because the note was contrary to what I was testifying about other evidence.

Differences between Depositions and Trials

Even though the procedures are similar, there are important differences between depositions and trials. Deposition remains part of the discovery process, its primary purpose is to discover and lock down the witnesses testimony, though not absolutely so. It is also for the opposing lawyer to size you up as a witness. Trials, of course, except for bench trials, have juries, a factor that turns them into something of a theatrical event where appearances are very important. In depositions, the significance is primarily in the spoken word, though the attitude of the witness will certainly affect the interrogator and vice versa. Never-the-less, the advice given in this chapter more or less pertains to both events with noted differences.

Clarify Your Role

Contrary to what one might think, actual court testimony time for the expert witness accounts for only a small percentage of his time. The greater part is spent in case review, investigation, consulting and preparation for testimony.

It often happens that when an attorney hires an expert, he fails to clarify the role he expects the expert to play: it may be consultancy, expert witness or both – frequently both. A great deal of trouble can arise when the expert writes reports or correspondence not knowing whether such documents are discoverable or not. Reports containing advice are likely to involve speculation and mere commentary. If such a report is not properly understood as advisory, and ends up being provided to the other side during discovery as evidence, then both the lawyer and expert are likely to find themselves in trouble.

Therefore, the expert should always make it a rule that before ever writing anything, he should review the matter with his client; is this document to be provided as evidence? If so, the report should contain nothing but supportable evidence, never speculation or commentary. If the document is a matter of advice and consultancy, it should be captioned: CONFIDENTIAL TO: (Lawyer's name).

What to Bring to Deposition or Trial

First, ask your lawyer. Under no circumstances ever bring your entire file. Generally it is best not to bring anything, but you may, without much difficulty, bring anything that has already been produced during discovery, including all your reports and photographs.

Qualifications

Your Qualifications

Marine surveyors often run into problems with their qualifications, not because the qualifications are inadequate, but because they do not derive from formal training. There is a widely held assumption (certainly by lawyers) that formal education is better than experience or self-teaching. Sometimes this is true, sometimes not. Opposing counsel will likely attempt to discredit the witness based on a lack of formal training, which is fairly easy to do if the witness lets him get away with it, but a good witness won't. When preparing a resume, be sure that you don't exaggerate or misrepresent your training and experience. Any attempt to impress is likely to be viewed as just that; an attempt.

This is the one area where a witness should have a well-prepared and rehearsed answer. After all, there is nothing more important than the witness's credentials which do not reside solely in college diplomas. You may be asked to give your entire work and education history from high school onward, and you should be prepared to give it without hesitation.

Don't hesitate to take your time giving the complete answer. If you are being attacked based on a lack of formal credentials, it's useful to point out that long before the word engineer was invented, for thousands of years men had been building boats and ships that sailed around the world, all without university diplomas. Before education comes experience; experience is the foundation of all education. In fact, most boats are not designed by naval architects but by men of experience in boat building. An answer like this defuses an attempt to discredit based on lack of formal training. To support this answer, one must be prepared to recite a lengthy description of one's experience.

Resumes or CV's

Resumes are capable of causing witnesses a great deal of trouble, mainly because they are written for the purpose of impressing potential clients. The problem is that this degree of expansiveness provides the opposition with fertile hunting grounds, particularly if the witness has exaggerated. Because of this, I have resorted to creating a separate resume for legal work that contains only sufficient information to indicate that I have adequate qualifications.

Challenges to Expertise

Challenges to one's expertise may come at any time. Marine surveyors provide a wide range of services; certain types of work predominate while others are performed less frequently. A common tactic for challenging qualifications starts with detailed questioning of the nature of the witness's work. This then extends to identifying the specific services the witness provides, along with the percentage of the total that this amounts to. Using an example of a surveyor who's work is 75% insurance claims, 20% surveys and 5% appraisals, our hypothetical litigation involves an appraisal. Obviously, the witness will be attacked on the basis that 5% doesn't give him adequate qualification, or at least that there are others who would be more qualified. This tactic can be used for virtually anyone's work if, in the present instance, the issue at hand does not comport with the majority of the work you perform, so be prepared to answer that.

In the case of the 5% appraisals, if the witness has been doing 5% appraisals for twenty years, this might come to 30 individual jobs annually, that amounts to a total 600 appraisals during career to date. But while the reality of 600 over twenty years isn't much, it still sounds impressive and provides a satisfactory answer.

In insurance defense cases, where you are an expert for the insurer's defense, the plaintiff will probably try to paint you as a hired gun for insurance companies, and will try to attack on the basis of how much work you do for insurance companies. If you do nothing but insurance work, you'll have to own up to that, but if you do other kinds of work, be prepared to explain the various types of clients you have.

Bear in mind that these are questions for which it would be almost impossible to prove the answer true one way or the other and the lawyer has no way of knowing the nature of one's work, so there is plenty of leeway for answering. Never give a vague answer because a lawyer will bore in on that. In my own case, the nature of my work can vary widely from year to year, so the truth is that I've never tallied up a count of the different types of work I do. Since I can't give an exact answer, I revert to answers like "dozens" or "hundreds," even "thousands". When they invariably try to pin me down, I simply relate the constantly changing nature of my work and the fact that I have not kept a 39 year logbook. Or I say that I have performed this type of job for twenty or thirty years.

The questioner may bore in and try to trip you up with a question like:

> Can you give us an example of a recent job you've done?

In a deposition, this might be followed up with;

> Could you provide us with a copy of that report?

Answer:

> No, the report belongs to the client, and is confidential.

The following question presents another common tactic:

> Isn't it true that you've never investigated a boat sinking that occurred in fresh water?

In this instance, the challenger is attempting to show that the witness lacks experience in some particular detail. Challenges to expertise may be valid or not, but whichever it is, it is important for the witness to meet such a challenge not with justification but with facts, and to do so precisely:

> This is true, but the fact of fresh water or sea water has no bearing on this case since the sinking would have occurred regardless of the type of water.

This effective rebuttal involves no dissembling and is most effective by virtue of being the truth.

Challenges to qualifications or expertise may come at any time during the examination. The form that the challenge usually takes involves asking about formal education or training about a particular subject, such as:

> Are you a licensed engineer? Do you hold any diplomas or certificates? Do you have any formal training on this subject?

A good answer is:

> No, the majority of the surveyor's knowledge comes about through experience and sharing knowledge with other surveyors.

When challenged in this manner, I like to point out that there are only several thousand, practicing marine surveyors, and that, since the field is so small, there are few opportunities for formal training.

The follow-up question is likely to be:

> And what is your experience on this matter?

At this point we have to be prepared to give a good answer. We can prepare for this in advance because we know what the subject matter is; then we need to think about it and review what our past experience has been so that we can give a cogent answer. We don't want to be caught flatfooted and have to formulate an answer off-the-cuff since our memory isn't likely to be that good.

> In a recent case I was asked to define the term seaworthy. When I replied that "It is essentially a legal term that was first established as a doctrine of Admiralty Law," the lawyer immediately tore into me about what my legal qualifications were to make a legal determination! *Do you have a law degree? Did you pass a bar exam?* He demanded. This was a very good trap question if one is not prepared for such. I was momentarily blindsided, but my answer was: *A ship's captain, though he is very unlikely to have gone to law school or posses a law degree, would be inadequately trained and incompetent if he did not understand the legal definition of seaworthiness backwards and forwards. So it is with a marine surveyor. Knowledge of the law is not limited to lawyers.*

The lawyer immediately dropped that line of questioning. The point here is to not allow yourself to be thrown off by attacks like this. Take your time about answering when your experiential qualifications are challenged. Give yourself time to recover.

Attacks on Personal Credibility

Once you become a witness to litigation, whether as an expert or material witness, you enter the lion's den and become fair game for the opposition to attack your credibility. There is likely to be a concerted effort to discredit both yourself personally by way of qualifications, and your testimony. It does not happen often in civil cases, but a witness's character is also fair game. These efforts can be personal and vicious. Lawyers have a number of proven techniques for tripping up a witness right at the start. If they can't successfully mar his credibility, they will try to shake him up.

> In one case an expert was suddenly asked, *Are you taking any medications?* The implication of this question is to suggest that he was! When he responded that he was, the lawyer persisted, ending up exploring the witness's medical history and finally asked, *What about alcohol?* This led to an in-depth discussion of the witness's drinking habits and several unfortunate answers were forthcoming. This witness made the mistake of answering a dangerous question candidly.

A lawyer cannot counsel a witness to lie, but understand that in this level of civil case, no lawyer can afford to do extensive background investigations and therefore has no way of knowing something like this. These are fishing expedition questions that are best answered negatively. Similar questions are also posed for educational and work experience issues.

Two Key Elements to success

Expert witness work can be lucrative and enjoyable, but before one gets there one has to attend the school of hard knocks. Giving testimony is a lot like being a soldier at war; no matter how well he may be trained for it, nothing can prepare for the actual experience because every case is different, and usually greatly so.

There are two key elements to successful depositions and court testimony. The first of these begins long before there is any idea of litigation. What every surveyor and investigator must thoroughly understand is that when his work ends up in litigation, even when his work is not the basis of litigation but merely related evidence, it will be poured over in an effort to find faults, often by other experts. Any errors, inconsistencies or even a poor choice of words will be seized upon and used to attack the witness. For this reason, the best litigation preparation a surveyor can do is to perform his daily work with this in mind. Don't let errors or shoddy practice slip into your work. Simply put, perform as if every job will end up in litigation. Of course, none of us can perform our work perfectly, but by maintaining an awareness of the legal implication of everything we put into writing, we can save ourselves a lot of grief and better serve our clients.

The other key to successful testifying is preparation. This includes not only knowing your subject backwards and forward, but also making the effort to anticipate what the opposition's attack strategy is likely to be. The attorney for your side can be a great help in preparing you in this regard. Discover the weaknesses in your work and be prepared to defend them. Look for poor choices of wording, badly explained conditions or any other faults in your work and be prepared to defend and explain without appearing defensive.

The Importance of Impartiality

In the chapter on writing reports, it is stressed at length the reasons why it is imperative to be scrupulously unbiased. That need for impartially will ultimately play its most important role in any case that ends up in litigation, and most especially in court. A trial lawyer will pick up the scent of impartiality — the impetus to defend your client — like a blood hound picks up the scent of a coon, and it won't be long before he has the coon run up a tree.

The fact that someone is paying us for our testimony does not mean that we owe fealty to them to distort or withhold the truth. No lawyer has ever suggested to me that I ought to lie or avoid the truth. The number of times that it has even been covertly *intimated* that I should subvert the truth is very few.

The fact that we will be considered as a hostile witness by the other side does not mean that a jury will see us that way; to them we are an honest witness until we give them reason to believe otherwise — or we permit the opposition to paint us that way. If we expect the jury to believe our testimony, it is imperative to present the *appearance* of honesty and impartiality. It is the attempt to sway or distort the truth that causes jurors to doubt. This most often comes about through attempts to avoid answering questions directly, by being resistant, evasive, argumentative or showing anger. These things are very evident to everyone in the court room.

When the opposing lawyer hits on a weakness in our work, he will sense that and start to bore in on us in an attempt to exploit that weakness. Any conscious effort to deflect questions or conceal the truth will make the interrogator all the more determined to get to it, so instead of deflecting the question what we would really be doing is flying a red flag and the jury will recognize that, too.

The only possible way to defuse a weakness or error in our work is to own up to it immediately, without reservation and without any sense of guilt. Yes, it may hurt your client's case, but not as badly as when a witness persists in either lying or evading. The more he denies, the worse it's going to get. Let's consider how this might play out. Let's say we have conducted an investigation that led to litigation. During the course of that investigation there was a lead that should have been followed up on but for whatever reason we did not. The opposition lawyer has picked up on this and now he pops the question. Keeping in mind that lawyers avoid asking questions that they don't think they know the answers to:

Q. Mr. Witness, isn't it true that you did not inspect the gizmo from the right side? Only the left?

A. Yes, that is correct.

All we do here is to confirm what he already knows, without elaborating; resisting the impulse to justify ourselves in any way[1]. That simple, direct response poses the questioner with a dilemma. The questioner has already scored one point with the admission. Next the lawyer will try to capitalize on that admission; he will bore in on what the effect of that admission will be on the outcome of the investigation. Did it compromise it? Had the gizmo been inspected from another angle, would that have changed the investigator's conclusion? And so on.

But if the witness's answer was, *I'm not sure. I really can't recall,* now look what the interrogator does to him:

Q. You don't recall?

A. No.

Q. Let me see if I understand your answer correctly. Do you recall examining the gizmo from the left side, is that correct?

A. Correct.

Q. But you don't recall whether you examined it from the left?

A. No.

Q. Was it not possible to see the left side? Was there some reason why it couldn't be seen?

A. No

Q. So there you were, having the opportunity to look at both sides but you only bothered to look at one side?

A. Uh, yes.

Q. Perhaps you didn't think the other side was important?

In the above example we see how the witness gets himself in ever deeper as soon as he attempts to evade by saying that he doesn't recall. Now his interrogator starts to tear down the witness's credibility because saying that he doesn't recall isn't credible. The odds are that if we lie, intentionally or subconsciously, or merely avoid or subvert the truth, that lie or concealment will be recognized. People tend to think that juries are a lot dumber than they really are. They probably get this impression based on the occasionally absurd verdicts we hear about. Don't ever believe that unreasonable verdicts are the same thing as stupidity. Such verdicts come from personal bias and not a lack of general intelligence. A little further on I'm going to talk more about observation of jurors and you'll learn just how smart even the dumbest of them can be. Therefore, never assume that you can fool a jury. Everyone in the court room is looking at the witness; but the one person who can least read the witness is the witness himself. We can't see ourselves as others see us; trust the jury to hear truth and evasion when they hear it.

Opposing Attorneys

Opposing Lawyer Attitudes

Good trial lawyers engage in much acting, and the most common act used is that of the "good cop, bad cop." Despite how easily recognizable this tactic is, nearly everyone falls victim to it in some degree. The questioner starts out with a friendly or at least neutral demeanor and simple, easy questions. He maintains this attitude in order to get you comfortable and hopefully to embellish your answers and volunteer as much information as possible. Stated another way, he tries to establish the questioning as a friendly conversation. In court, he'll start out with a cheery, "Good morning, Mr. Smith." In court, if the witness answers with an excessively reserved reply, he will have established in the witness an "attitude," so it's best to give similar cheery reply, as unfelt as that may be.

The friendly demeanor will continue to the point where he perceives a weakness in the witness's testimony, at which point his tone suddenly changes, becoming hard and demanding, thereby startling the inexperienced witness. The advantage in recognizing the tactic is that we are alerted as to what is coming by the tone of voice. The soft ball questions are over for the moment and it's going to get tough. This back and forth will continue in cyclic fashion throughout.

A Trial Lawyer's Most Powerful Weapon

All good trial lawyers develop the skill of how to detect untruth. In litigation there is no such thing as "a little white lie" because all lies have the same effect on the jury. The effect of a witness that dissembles or attempts to justify or cover up the truth even slightly is painfully obvious to everyone in the court room but the witness himself. Nothing a witness says is of any value unless the jury believes it. But if the jury does not believe a witness, that factor becomes extremely damaging to his client's case; he is perceived as a liar.

Notice that what I'm talking about is not blatant perjury, but merely shading or avoiding the truth in any way. Trial lawyers are trained in methods of exploiting a dissembling witness and know how to turn a simple evasion of the truth into a club with which he beats the witness's credibility to death. A witness should never fool himself into believing that he can get away with untruth.

When witness's get themselves in trouble, it usually starts out as something very small and seemingly insignificant, a minor evasion, a slight coloring of truth. Witness's are typically asked a lot of questions. Depositions and court testimony can run to dozens, even hundreds of pages of transcript, which leaves plenty of opportunity for slipping up. When a lawyer detects evasions, his tactic will be to try to get the witness to persist in, and deepen the evasion, even turning it into an outright lie if he can maneuver the witness into a defensive posture. A witness that becomes defensive is defending an untruth. If the lawyer knows what the truth is, then he'll proceed to play the evasion as a direct lie.

Therefore, in preparation for deposition or court testimony, it becomes important to give special emphasis in our review to any areas of weakness in our work.

The Fear Factor

Fear is a powerful weapon in the hands of a trial lawyer examining a hostile witness. But it is a weapon that only the witness can give him. Understand that a lawyer can smell fear on the witness like smoke from a fire and he'll pick up on it and exploit that fear immediately. There is no reason for a witness to be fearful, either in a deposition or at trial, yet my experience is that most witnesses display many of the physical, outward signs of fear. Therefore, let's take a look at fear and where it comes from.

First, what are the physical signs of fear? General nervousness in the form of fidgeting and basic discomfort. Hands that won't hold still, tapping feet, hands to the face, rapid eye movement and the like all send signals of nervousness which is a softer synonym for fear. There are a wide variety of symptoms and we all more or less know what they are. One of the more common signs is weakness in the voice where answers trail off to inaudibility. If the witness is asked to "speak up" this is a sign that his fear is obvious.

Fear results from either of two factors. For those testifying for the first few times, it is the fear of the unknown, basically stage fright. That is something we only get over through experience. But the worst and most damaging kind of fear directly results from bias, the intent to craft testimony in favor of the client. This fear is the fear of being discovered not telling the truth — a very real possibility when facing a skilled trial lawyer. This later type of fear is easy enough to avoid by resolving not to be dishonest or evasive. If we have conducted an honest investigation and have been straightforward with our client, then this should not present any problem. If you find yourself wanting to defend your client, get over it fast! Before testifying, we should have long ago discussed any weaknesses in our investigation with him. The ridding of ourselves of any intent to manipulate our testimony will effectively rid us of that kind of fear.

Stage fright is another matter, and since nearly all people are afflicted with it to one degree or another, general nervousness is not something we need be overly concerned with. We should not make a determined effort to hide nervousness because this will cause more problems. Stage fright is something that most people manage to overcome with experience. A method that I used to train myself was, in depositions, to place my hands on the table in front of me, not clasped, but separated, and to look at them as often as possible. I'm a doodler, so that if I have a pen in my hands, it will never stop moving, even when sitting at my desk alone. Yet, sitting at a conference table with everyone looking at me, I have trained myself so that my hands will sit there as quiet as can be. There are very few people who can hold their hands still without training, but in so doing I am sending a clear signal that I am very confidant even though I'm nervous. On the witness stand I try to place my hands so that they can be seen by the lawyer.

It's a very useful exercise to study the nervous habits of other people, particularly the way they use their hands. In doing so, you'll become more aware of your own nervous habits so that you can better gain control of them in these most critical situations.

Deposition

Deposition Advice for First Timers

Included in this chapter is discussion of some of the more advanced techniques that experienced expert witnesses use. However, novices are cautioned to NOT attempt to use them. Trial lawyers are very well trained in the techniques of witness manipulation and the novice makes a fatal mistake if he gets the idea that he can match wits with them; be assured that he cannot. Before even thinking about attempting to match wits with a trial lawyer, a witness should have considerable experience at depositions and at least three prior courtroom appearances. Only then will he understand the peril of trying to outsmart a lawyer. Never underestimate your adversary.

Before testifying, prepare your educational history and work experience and memorize it. Keep it very brief; this is not a resume. Most likely you will be asked about your prior experience with the issues at hand. If you do not have much experience with the subject, be content to rest on that and do not embellish in any way.

Some lawyers will work to prepare their witnesses more than others, while others won't give you any help at all. Keep in mind that a lawyer is not permitted to coach you on answering questions; his assistance can only be general. It is primarily the witness's job to prepare himself.

The first-time witness is cautioned to concentrate and listen closely to the questions asked: be sure that you understand what is being asked, then, answer the question with the shortest answer possible with frankness and sincerity and not be concerned for how the answer relates to the client's case. Do not attempt to anticipate a strategy behind a question and attempt to foil it.

Many people are in the habit of anticipating a question before the questioner finishes it, and are not aware of that habit. The witness should listen to the entire question, and not start answering before the questioner is finished. Make a habit to allow a brief pause between question and answering. This will give you time to make sure that you understand it fully.

Concentrate on using proper language and avoiding sloppy language, not using "yeah" for "yes," "un uh" for no. Use "yes Sir" and "yes Ma'am". Answer with words, not gestures.

Do not expand on answers, launching into longer explanations, even if you perceive that the simple answer doesn't fully address all ramifications of the question. The reason is this: the more you say, the more opportunity you provide the enemy to attack your response.

It is difficult for witnesses without experience to perceive how obvious character and attitudes can be on a transcript, but they are just as evident on paper as they are in a court room. One should strive to comport oneself to the best of his ability, using language as correctly as he possibly can, and to keep his attitude as neutral as possible. You may *act* friendly, but do not *be* friendly; be on guard. If you are more comfortable being reserved, that is fine.

Avoid the temptation to justify. The lawyer will attempt to discredit you in various ways, but most witnesses find it very difficult not to respond with self-justification and explanations. Again, to do so just provides the lawyer with more opportunities to attack you. The more yes or no answers you can give, the better off you will be. Stick with the shortest answer possible.

Do not answer a question which you don't fully understand. Ask for it to be repeated or simply say that you don't understand what is being asked. This may happen often because the questioner is trying to trick you.

If you do not know or remember the answer to a question, say so directly, don't beat around the bush. The opposition may ask a question by referring to something you said or wrote in the past that you do not recall. In this case, be sure to say so and refer back to that document for the exact context of the quote.

The witness will be repeatedly asked about his qualifications at various times and on various subjects, so be sure not to embellish in any way. If the lawyer bores in with a line of questions that stress a lack of formal education on many subjects, one can respond with the point that experience is the primary education of the marine surveyor/investigator. Don't go beyond that brief statement.

As a first time witness, you will make plenty of mistakes, and will have opportunity to learn from them. If you make a mistake during a deposition, such as saying too much, it's better not to try to correct it, but let it pass. If you recognize that you gave a wrong answer, feel free to interject and correct it, but do it with as few words as possible.

Depositions are stressful and may stretch for several hours, during which time you will become mentally fatigued and out of focus, or even irritable. You have the right to ask for breaks and should have a minimum five minute break at least every hour. This will give you the opportunity to refresh and regroup.

When you are finished, you should demand the right to read and sign your deposition; do not waive that right. Your copy of the deposition will serve as an excellent learning tool for you as you read and study your performance.

Depositions

The purpose of taking a deposition is to nail down the witness's testimony; it is part of the discovery process to make all facts available before trial with the objective of trying to get the parties to the dispute to settle without a trial which, in most cases, they do. The deposition therefore is a very important aspect of pre trial work. Since the vast majority of cases never get to trial, the deposition is, in a sense, *the* trial.

Since the purpose of a deposition is to obtain testimony in advance of trial where instead of having juries the lawyers will be sizing up their own, and their opponents, cases. Therefore, it is important to make as strong a showing as a witness as we can, maintaining a composure the same as if it were a trial because the opposition is sizing us up as a witness. If he senses weakness, that weakness will be exploited at trial to an even greater degree than at deposition.

The subpoena for deposition will come from the opposition as each side deposes the other's witnesses, and therefore the deposition is also a search for "information," a fishing expedition. The opposing attorney will employ a strategy to "box in" or "nail down" the witness's testimony since, having testified under oath once, it's rather difficult to change one's testimony later. The lawyer is likely to employ many tricks, either to get him to give wrong answers, or weak answers that he can exploit later at trial. Once all the depositions are taken, the lawyers will review the evidence and make a decision whether to settle or go to trial. This makes the deposition as equally important as court room testimony. Other purposes are:

- To gather new information, refute or confirm existing facts
- Lock the witness into a position for trial
- Trick the witness into a false or weak position
- To size up the witness, search for weakness
- To develop what appears to be a lie or an inconsistency and then use that point for purposes of impeachment
- Examine qualifications, credibility

From this we can see why it is essential that we be well prepared. All the rules that apply to being a good trial witness apply to depositions. The better we perform at deposition, the better it will be for us at trial. Depositions are good training grounds for testifying at trial but for the fact that there is no jury. Because of this, opposing lawyer's behavior and tactics will be different. There will be no posturing and theatrics for benefit of the jury, so his main line of attack will be your testimony. He's testing you and searching out your weaknesses.

Here's one rule that we should never forget: *When witnesses get into trouble it is almost always because they brought that trouble on themselves.* We cannot get into very much trouble by telling the truth; trouble comes in the form of either being inconsistent or dishonest to any degree. Dishonesty here doesn't just mean telling an outright lie, but even slight shading or evasions of the truth. A lawyer that senses dishonesty is like an eagle that spots a rabbit in an open field. However, the lawyer will also attempt to manipulate you into being inconsistent, so be alert for attempts to get you say something you don't mean. Watch out for those strings of questions that require one-word answers which is a common tactic.

More often than not, depositions are rather informal, often intentionally so. Don't be fooled by this, for that informal civility will soon evaporate as opposing counsel bores into the witness's credibility. In deposition, the hostile lawyer will not be using his voice for the benefit of the jury such as to express disbelief. Here only the meaning of words count. Don't be lulled by a tone of voice that sounds friendly; all questions on cross examination contain hostile intent.

The procedure for depositions is that the side that subpoenas the witness for deposition starts the direct questioning first. Then comes cross examination by the other side, then possibly redirect and recross. It is important to be aware of this, particularly when you get in trouble (as you inevitably will). If there is trouble, it is your attorney's job to clean up the mess, so to speak, and get you out of the problem, which is usually a matter of having been misled by the other lawyer. Recross provides the opportunity for your lawyer to straighten things out. However, some lawyers prefer to avoid getting involved other than to make objections, so you may not get any help.

Don't expect not to make mistakes, and when you do don't become desperate to try to correct the record. If your attorney is astute, he'll review the trouble spot on cross, or at trial, and attempt to repair the damage at that time. If you make a misstatement, and suddenly become aware of that, it is appropriate to interrupt the current line of questioning and correct or clarify the point.

Notice of Deposition (Subpoena)

It isn't always necessary for a subpoena to be issued; a witness may voluntarily agree to submit.

The notice of deposition will inevitably contain a demand for the witness to produce any and all documents and records. The following list is a common one:

1. All documents reflecting or relating to any communication between the expert and opposing counsel, including such things as engagement letters.

2. All documents reflecting any communication relating to the engagement, including any communications with witnesses.

3. All documents reflecting or relating to any preliminary opinions or conclusions.

4. All documents consulted or relied upon by the expert in connection with the engagement including those he consulted or relied upon in forming his opinions.

5. All documents relating to his educational, employment, and professional history and any other documents reflecting or relating to his qualifications to testify.

6. Copies of all professional publications to that he has written or contributed to.

7. All documents reflecting other cases in which he has testified as an expert, including any documents, including transcripts, that reflect the substance of his testimony, the terms of his engagement, the court in which the action was pending, or the outcome of the case.

8. All other documents relating to the engagement, the opinions he expects to give, or the opinions he was asked to consider giving.

Some states even allow the demand to produce all electronic records that essentially amounts to a demand to produce the hard drive of your computer(s). Obviously such demands go way beyond being reasonable, and because of this unreasonableness, it is largely ignored. Clearly we have an obligation to produce all documents in our possession relative to the case. Should one decide to withhold anything, be very certain never to make reference to that in testimony. Particularly note that item #3 is discussed in the chapter on writing reports. Also note how items #5 & 6 relates whatever is included in our curriculum vitae.

Claims supervisors love to get correspondence from their service providers, but we don't want to discover the hard way why we should be very circumspect about everything we put in writing. Be doubly on guard using e-mail where the tendency to say too much is higher due to its ease of use.

Mistakes, New Evidence & Changed Opinions

It is not unusual that between the time an investigation was conducted and a case goes to trial, that new evidence is introduced that may change or alter the opinions of the witness. It is quite common that during the discovery process the investigator is exposed to new information that was not developed during the investigation. The net result could be anything from blowing his original opinion to pieces to confirming his opinion — and everything in between. This is more likely to occur during the discovery deposition process and less so at trial.

There is only one way to deal with this eventuality and that is with complete frankness for all the reasons expressed earlier. Don't make the mistake of thinking that a modified opinion is deadly to the client's case because very often it is not.

Hypothetical questions are a tactic used by lawyers for a variety of reasons. At deposition, it often signals that the opposition thinks it has information that you don't know about, so he's testing you. Be very, very careful about such questions, and consider your answer carefully. Consider whether the facts presented in the hypothetical are reasonable; if the facts are not reasonable or possible, decline to answer the question by saying that you can't answer a hypothetical based on irrational facts. If the question is reasonable, you have to answer it.

At trial, a hypothetical may be used to merely make the witness look weak. But more often it is an attempt to box the witness in with information that he is unaware of. The question is commonly presented as, *would it change your opinion if ... ?* Consider the question carefully and answer truthfully, even if it appears that your answer would change everything. It's not wise to try to anticipate what lies behind the hypothetical and answer in a manner designed to defeat the question:

Q. Would it change your opinion if I told you that the boat was maintained by a professional captain?

A. It would.

Q. And why is that?

A. Because in most cases the captain will have more knowledge and experience than the boat owner.

Note that in this instance, the hypothetical is nearly undeniable. But now consider:

Q. What if you were told that a person with no experience whatever had repaired the hull of the boat?

A. My opinion is that is not possible.

Here we see that the facts presented in the hypothetical are not reasonable or even possible. The witness could have said that a repair made by an inexperienced person would have produced certain results, but that is playing into the questioners hands. Instead, he defeats it by denying the possibility of the hypothetical itself.

Another tactic that we frequently encounter is when the examiner reads something published by another expert, and then asks whether we agree with it. Usually, this will be something that is contrary to what we have said. It doesn't much matter whether you agree or not, what the lawyer is doing is simply interjecting the opinion of another expert without actually having him testify. In other words, the lawyer is testifying. In this case, just answer the question honestly because there's nothing you can do about it.

Publishing History

At deposition, the witness is likely to be asked whether he has ever published anything such as magazine articles, where and when. Accessible published articles (such as on the Internet) can cause problems because a lawyer will search them out for statements that the witness has made to use against him, but this is likely to happen only with larger dollar value cases. There's nothing like having something you wrote 15 years ago being used to refute something you say today. But it happens! I have published a great deal and these writings get used against me constantly, though rarely does the lawyer score points. It is unlikely that we have any memory of what is being quoted, but the lawyer will have a copy which you can ask to see. If not, you can say that you don't recollect the piece, or the context in which the quote was written. If he has a copy, one should read it thoroughly; for this will give you time to formulate your answer. Check the context and make sure the statement is relevant. If the lawyer has scored a point, then give it to him; it's not the end of the world.

Documents

When handed a document by the opposing attorney and being asked a question about it, don't be certain that you know exactly what it says, even though you are familiar with it. You may be set up for a trick. Take the time to read that part of the document that is applicable; there is no reason to be in a hurry.

Review and Signing Depositions

When finished giving a deposition the court reporter will ask whether you wish to waive reviewing and signing it. Perhaps you will be encouraged to waive because it costs extra time and money. There are several reasons why we should not waive this right. The first is that it may well contain errors that we have the right to correct. But perhaps more importantly, it gives us the opportunity to review our testimony while still fresh in mind. Here we get a firsthand opportunity to see how well we performed and where we may have been tripped up. Plus, there is so much to be learned from our own depositions that this is a major learning experience that ought not be passed up.

Court Testimony

First Time Court Testimony

There is a first time for everything, but the first time testifying in open court is not unlike an actor's first time on stage before an audience. It's not an easy thing for anyone, but for those prone to stage fright (which includes most people), it is a very upsetting experience that brings out nervousness, sweaty palms, weakening of voice and so on.

For inexperienced witnesses there will be a tendency to rehearse the whole thing in the mind starting even days beforehand. He will want to be well-prepared, so he rehearses everything he can think of. But, as every old pro can relate, all those wonderful responses that he rehearsed in his head are usually answers to questions that are never asked. Once one has gained a lot of experience, it may be possible to anticipate the kinds of questions we will be asked, and even where the trouble spots are. But as a beginner, there is no basis by which to anticipate, so don't waste your time and clutter you mind doing that.

Before testifying as an expert, one should thoroughly review one's work, but avoid rehearsing answers. It becomes very easy to identify a witness who has rehearsed his answers by his tendency to provide answers to questions that aren't asked, so eager is he to put forth the fruits of his rehearsal. Don't do it! Thoroughly review the file and leave it at that. If you find yourself rehearsing, it's because you have the intention (consciously or otherwise) of directing or influencing the case though your testimony. There is no need to rehearse because you are being asked to testify about a subject no one knows better than you do, not to give fabricated answers. It's not just you, but almost everyone who tends to do this.

It often happens that some points of information or evidence that the witness thinks are crucial to the case are never even brought up at trial. The witness may be astounded that such important information was never even considered, though he shouldn't be. This happens because the witness is second-guessing the case, putting himself in the position of the lawyer. He leads himself astray because he has no idea of what the trial strategy is, and therefore cannot know what evidence lawyer either considers relevant or intends to use. It very often happens that a lawyer avoids dealing with critical pieces of evidence because these are not helpful to his case, leaving that for the other side to develop. But, then, maybe the other side doesn't find that evidence beneficial either, so both sides end up skirting the issue. Yet there is the witness, staying up all night worrying about answers to questions that will never be asked!

It's not until about the third time that we testify that we really begin to understand what's going on. The novice witness should never attempt to do battle with a lawyer; he's trained and the witness isn't. It would be hard to overstate just what a poor impression this makes with a jury when the witness becomes argumentative. Do not engage in verbal fencing and certainly don't try to out-fox him. Answer the questions as briefly as possible. Avoid the urge to give expansive answers. If you've made work-related mistakes and are caught, do not attempt to justify or defend, simply admit to them quickly and without dissembling. You will not be crucified for admitting a mistake, but you will be crucified for trying to cover or justify it.

When responding to your own lawyers direct examination, there will be a tendency to be more friendly and expansive, and much less so with the lawyer for the other side. Make an effort to be consistent. Don't be effusive when your lawyer questions you, but then clam up for the other lawyer. In other words, try to show the same level of reserve for both sides. Opposite of a deposition, at trial you will be called as a witness and questioned first by your attorney. You will not, of course, be asked hostile questions and so you'll become more comfortable and forthcoming. But this will be followed by the hostile lawyer and your demeanor will suddenly change, a change that is obvious to everyone but the witness. It will be easier and more effective if you treat your own attorney with a similar measure of reserve, than to try to be friendly with the enemy.

Patience is a key word here for novices; the opposing lawyer will quickly discover that you are not an experienced witness and will try to exploit that. He'll try to get you frustrated and angry by picking at things in minute detail, by intimidation and treating you like a child or a liar. You must maintain a calm, open, forthcoming attitude while at the same time only answering the question without embellishment. Don't allow yourself to get angry with him and as soon as you start to feel anger, squelch it. Take a deep breath, smile. The first couple times your only goal should be to just get through it without committing any major blunders. The only serious mistake you can make is to lie or attempt to conceal the truth.

Give careful study to your deposition for it provides clues as to how your testimony will be attacked. Read it over completely at least twice, taking note of possible trouble areas.

Pretrial Conference

When a lawyer hires an expert witness, almost certainly he will have a pretrial conference with him before he testifies. That may not be the case if one is a material witness, though most often it is. However, a lawyer may have a reason for not wanting to discuss issues with him at all before testifying. Before the trial, the lawyer already has your deposition which pretty much nails down the way you have to testify; that is, of course, unless something has come up which changes how you will testify. Perhaps the lawyer is simply too busy to speak with you before hand. As you review your own deposition and file before trial, you will likely find a few problems with your work and testimony as *you* think it will affect the case. The time to deal with that is *before* testifying. Be sure to advise the attorney of any problems with your work or anything that has come up that would change your testimony. In that way you spring no surprises on him and he will be afforded the opportunity to try to mitigate the damage, if any. It is not for the witness to attempt to cover up mistakes.

A lawyer is not permitted to "coach" a witness, which means that legally he cannot in any way advise him on *how* to answer questions. A lawyer may inform the witness of what questions he will ask, and what questions he thinks the opposition will ask. Almost invariably the opposing lawyers will probe the witness about the nature of his conversations with his lawyer. Keep your answer brief and avoid details as much as possible.

Preparation for Court Testimony

Before testifying in court we will have given a deposition. The opposition lawyer and his experts will have carefully reviewed that deposition along with our work product, searching for weaknesses to exploit. At this point in time the events of the trail are partially carved in stone. On direct examination, our attorney will review the salient points of evidence that we have developed. On cross examination, the opposition's primary interest will be: (1) any weaknesses he perceives in either work product or our deposition testimony, (2) inconsistencies of our work versus other evidence or experts, and (3) problems concerning qualification.

A careful review of the deposition we have given will provide some clues as to what questions might be asked. Note, however, that the opposition has already gotten answers to questions already asked and he's not going to ask them again unless they are helpful to his cause. It is usually easy to spot problems with our deposition testimony so we should be prepared for more of the same.

On reading over our depositions we should take note of any questions where we gave evasive or argumentative answers. If asked these questions again, we have the opportunity to correct our posture, since this is the first time the jury hears it. If the opposition has scored a point, then give him that point, don't try to take it back.

You have a right to discuss your work and testimony with your lawyer. You can ask what areas he thinks you'll be attacked in, what he thinks your weaknesses are, and how you should prepare. Be alert that your court testimony does not conflict with deposition testimony. It is not unusual that some new information comes to light before trial time that may change our views. If something has changed in the interim, be prepared to account for the reason in a most convincing fashion.

What if we have made a mistake in our deposition by giving a wrong answer? At trial there are two opportunities to correct this. The first and best method is to bring it up with your lawyer and let him handle it. If we don't have a chance to do that, then we may ourselves make the correction *if the question is raised.* All we have to do is to say that we were mistaken or did not understand the question as it was asked. If it is not raised, then simply let it go since it is not being presented to the jury.

We should never prepare ourselves by rehearsing answers, first because prepared answers are obvious to everyone, and second because the questions you think will be asked usually aren't, so we've wasted a lot of mental effort. This is not to say that we shouldn't attempt to anticipate the general questions that will be asked. A good investigator analyzes his work for weaknesses, knowing that if any exists they will be exploited by the opposition. This is why I repeatedly stress that the best approach to all investigations should be with a view toward litigation.

It is unlawful for an attorney to rehearse a witness's testimony; it is not unlawful for an attorney to review the witness's answers so long as the attorney does not suggest what those answers will be — in any way. Under cross examination, a lawyer is likely to ask this question and attempt to make it appear that the answers are rehearsed. Don't worry about this, it's up to your attorney to set the record straight and should do so on redirect.

It's best to start reviewing the file several days before the trial. Read through all material, paying attention to dates. Make note of any trouble spots; if they're serious enough, you may want to discuss or mention it to your attorney. What looks to you like trouble may not be a serious problem for your attorney. Bear in mind that *we do not know the importance of our testimony to his case* — it is not our case, nor should we attempt to influence it in any way, even though his client may be your client. As far as being a witness is concerned, the proper attitude is to let the chips fall where they may; it is up to the lawyers to handle the chips.

Rare is the occasion that I have ever testified in court where the opposition didn't score at least a few points. There is a grave danger of becoming defensive, argumentative or evasive once we start making judgements about how these points affect the client's case. The proper attitude to take is one of unconcern. Your lawyer has already gone over all of this and he should be prepared to deal with it. If he has not, then it still is not your problem.

The courtroom process of witness testimony rotates between the lawyers from direct to cross, then r*edirect and recross.* Redirect or recross gives our attorney the opportunity for *rehabilitation*, a term that means the opportunity to patch up or correct any problems with our testimony. It often happens that the opposition lawyer manipulates us in such a way that our answers do not express the truth. For example, he may confine us to yes or no answers, and since few issues are black and white, we have no opportunity to explain. When we attempt to override his efforts to manipulate us is when we begin to appear argumentative. We need to be careful about that.

Maintaining Consistency

One of the most important things a witness must do is to maintain consistency with his facts and opinions:

- Between all documents that he has produced

- Between deposition and trial testimony

- Between the current issue and past publishing and/or writings

The most important of these is being consistent with one's deposition testimony at trial, which is why it is so very important to study one's own deposition in depth. Yet it is equally important to examine all of one's communications with others regarding the case at hand, especially with insurance jobs where the witness is likely to have produced troublesome correspondence.

Spotting an inconsistency in one's past statements isn't necessarily fatal, but the results will surely be disastrous should the witness fail to spot it. Keep in mind that the opposition will go to considerable length to try to impeach the witness. When inconsistencies exist, these should be brought to the attention of one's attorney, and then endeavor to formulate the best answer possible. You may know that trouble is heading your way when faced with questions like these:

Do you remember having your deposition taken on (date)?

Do you remember having been sworn to tell the truth?

Did you tell the truth on that date?

Any question beginning with "do you remember?" is likely to be a harbinger of a rocky road ahead.

Court Trials

Court trials often seem to bring out the worst in people, particularly lawyers, and appear to be mean, vicious affairs. People associated with court trials tend to scoff at the idea that any kind of justice results, but for all the lying, scheming and maneuvering a kind of justice does emerge, at least if not in one particular case, then in the aggregate. The truth is that litigation is a business with no repeat customers. As far as the lawyers are concerned, there's nothing personal about it. Though trials may be ugly affairs, it helps to avoid becoming angry by realizing this, that these attacks on our character, professionalism and integrity are not personal, but merely the business of litigation.

We must not take any of these attacks personally. Notice that if we permit ourselves to become sympathetically aligned with the client's cause, or take personal offense at the attacks against us, we lose objectivity and will inadvertently be drawn into a partisan attitude of self-defense. This we must not allow to happen.

On The Stand

Once sworn in and seated in the witness box, he is the star and all eyes are on him. That's enough to make anyone, even a seasoned pro nervous. It is best that one should learn how to comport oneself sooner rather than later. You know what they say about first impressions, and since we only have a short time in front of the jury, that impression is all important insofar as credibility is concerned. If we should be concerned about anything, it is how the jury sees us.

Obviously, dress and grooming are very important. Manner of dress should be consistent with our line of work; if you don't normally wear a three-piece suit on the job, don't wear one to court. A conservative sport coat and pressed slacks are appropriate. Shoes without socks aren't. Rumpled clothes, pony tails and ear rings won't make a good impression for a witness that purports to be a serious professional. There is no jury at a deposition so it doesn't matter what you wear at this event.

The physical comportment of the witness is equally important. Sit up straight, don't slouch and don't cross a leg over your knee. It is better to be stiff and formal than overly casual, but something in the middle is ideal. An extremely important aspect of witness perception is his manner of speaking. Inarticulateness is the worst offense. Answers and mannerisms such as "yeah," "uh huh," "you know," "its, ah, like . . " and so on. In other words, avoid sloppy. There are many people who, when under stress, have the bad habit of inserting "uh" several times in each sentence. This looks terrible in depositions and sounds just as bad in court. If you are one of them, you will need to break yourself of this habit. It is okay to leave silent spaces in your speech while the mind considers what to say, but it's not okay to say "uh" several hundred times.

Your lawyer will be sitting at a table in front of you. If you get into trouble, don't stare at him looking for help because he'll avoid making eye contact with you. He doesn't want to give the appearance of communicating with you in any way. At this point, the witness is completely on his own.

You are going to be questioned by lawyers who are standing more or less in front of you. However, it is a mistake to direct your answers only to the lawyer asking the questions, as though this were only a conversation between he and you. Your answer is to the whole court, particularly the jury. But that is the way it happens 99% of the time, as if the jurors, who are sitting off to the side, are merely eavesdropping on an interrogation. If you were to watch 100 witnesses testify, of those only the seasoned experts will address their answers to the jury. All the rest will be looking at and answering the lawyer directly. It is the jury to whom you should be speaking, and the jury whom you are looking at least part of the time.

If we want to be believable in the eyes of the jurors, how much better it is to establish eye contact with the jury, not by eye-to-eye contact with individual jurors, but as actors do on the stage by looking at the audience as a whole. This doesn't mean to do this all the time, but to at least turn to them occasionally, signaling that you acknowledge their presence. If the questioner is on your left and the jury to your right, it will be necessary to actually turn to face them. If in an advantageous position, look at them more often. Obviously, if we're swiveling around all the time — that is, having to turn our body — this won't look so good. Therefore, only turn occasionally.

If you learn to do this right from your first experience, you will find that soon you will easily be establishing a contact with the jury without even thinking. This will establish a relationship and credibility that cannot be had by just talking to the lawyers. You will observe their expressions, whether you are boring them to death, and whether they understand your answers and believe you or not. When they believe you, they tend to establish eye contact with you; when they don't, they tend to look away. Some few will be so bold as to even express their disapproval by glaring at you or making faces.

In contrast to a deposition, it is somewhat less of a maxim to keep your answers as brief as possible. Here, more emphasis should be placed on the "whole truth" simply because you must be convincing to the jury. You must be sure they understand the import of your question, while you understand the fine line between saying enough and too much. It is not, for example, saying too much when being expansive while explaining technical details.

Most of the time you will be giving technical answers so it is extremely important that the witness be able to gauge whether the jury is comprehending. When they don't, they usually either frown or mentally drift off. If you are observant, you can't help but notice that they aren't understanding you. It is doubly helpful that when you speak directly to the jury, you are not merely talking to them, but are also getting feed back from them and when you see that one or more don't understand the answer, you have the opportunity to rephrase your answer in another way. When appropriate, take the opportunity to be a teacher. Once you begin to gain experience in this way, your credibility with the jury soars; of all the witnesses — and often there are dozens — you are going to be the one, or among the ones that they remember most when they go into deliberations.

> In one case I arranged for a blackboard in the court room because I knew I would be faced with explaining issues of hydrodynamics and trim that would be impossible to bring out with words alone. Pre-rehearsed when asked a question, I went to the blackboard and drew a simple diagram and labeled it with nautical terms. The jury watched with rapt attention, whereas before they were bored and dozing off, because now they had someone who was talking to *them*. Then on cross, I was once again able to refer back to my drawing to illustrate my answers.

> On more than one occasion I noticed several members of the jury with looks on their faces that said that they didn't understand my answer, so playing the role of teacher I said: *I can see that some members of the jury didn't understand what I said, so let me explain that another way.*

Should it be necessary to create an illustration to get your point across, take advantage of that. Juries are essentially very bored. They are sitting over there with no one paying any attention to them and they will *love* the attention that the witness gives them. If you know in advance that you have a difficult explanation to make, discuss with your attorney in advance about using a blackboard or easel to make a drawing. It is better to make a drawing in the court room than to bring one, if you are capable of that. I'm speaking here about making a sketch to illustrate a point that was the result of a question, not a preplanned exhibit. Crude sketches made by you are probably more effective than those made by professional illustrators because *you* become the center of attention.

So, the rule is this: When asked a question you will turn in your seat and directly address the jury at a minimum of 25% of the time, which should be for questions that involve substantially more than a yes/no answer, and especially when an explanation is involved. This applies to both direct and cross examination. An opposition attorney, when seeing that you are astute enough to address the jury directly, is going to be very wary of you. He'll understand immediately that you know what you're doing and are not afraid of him. This is one very formidable weapon you have against his attempts to manipulate you.

Here's another rule: never make faces at the jury, show emotion or attempt to be personal or friendly by expression or gesture; always maintain a professional posture.

Look at Your Lawyer Occasionally

It's not good to stare at your lawyer with a plea for help when you feel you are in trouble; the jury will see that. Yet it's a good idea to let your eyes scan across the room to try to pick up any signals he may be sending you. However, lawyers don't often do this because they are sitting there in plain sight, as are you.

If your lawyer voices an objection, STOP SPEAKING. If the objection is sustained, you don't have to answer; if over-ruled you do, but wait for the ruling.

Humility vs. Self Confidence

When it comes to making an impression on the jury, the worst possible attitude is one of arrogance. The problem with overt displays of self-confidence is that there is a fine line between confidence and arrogance. And since arrogance is usually a cover for insecurity, an insecure person has no idea that he is perceived as arrogant. It is therefore best to err on the side of humility, even if slightly faked. This means to avoid making any effort to appear very confident to a jury by not putting on any kind of act. Acting cannot be maintained consistently and it soon becomes evident that the witness's demeanor has changed. We should strive to achieve a consistent demeanor throughout. Note that a naturally self confident personality is more at risk of being perceived as arrogant so that if any acting is to be done, "toning it down" may be appropriate.

Excessive over confidence takes the form both of putting on an act and a degree of certainty that is improbable. There are few things in life that are absolute and to take a rigidly certain attitude too frequently is sure to raise this impression. This is particularly relevant to the expert witness who will be challenged on the basis of his opinions. Admissions of doubt at the appropriate times are more likely to be helpful than harmful.

Proper Attitude of Expert Witnesses

An expert witness may have prior involvement in a case as investigator or some other function, or may be hired to render expertise in the form of a consultant who may or may not testify. As a consultant, one may think like a partisan and exercise loyalty to the client *before* testifying, but not *while* testifying. As a witness, one should shed all loyalties as well as concern for the outcome of the case. The role of a witness is only to give accurate testimony insofar as his knowledge affects the case at hand.

As a consultant, one has an obligation to give the best expert advice possible to his attorney client. But if his role is as an expert witness to give testimony at trial, it is still fitting and proper that he provide his attorney/client with any information that one thinks he needs to know, including pointing out problems with evidence. If we have knowledge of evidence that seems to be very harmful to his cause, we should tell him of it and not avoid the issue and hope it doesn't come up, for it probably will.

It is plain from my observation of the performance of dozens of professionals in court, both material and expert witnesses, that many have overblown opinions of themselves that produces an attitude that is readily detectable by jurors and therefore sits very poorly with them. This was determined not by my opinion of their attitude but by watching how jurors respond to them. Jurors do not sit in the jury box stone-faced all day long; they are ordinary human beings that are prone to expressing emotions on their faces so that if we want to know how they feel, all we have to do is watch them.

Juries

Jurors should never be underestimated, not necessarily for their intelligence, but for their ability to detect truth or untruth. Amongst all the people in the courtroom, jurors are usually the least biased. If you've ever served on a jury, then you know that most of them make sincere efforts. However, that statement can't stand without qualification for clearly a jury's lack of bias is based on the type of case at hand. We're all aware that people generally have prejudices on certain subjects that may be conscious or unconscious. One of these is insurance companies, whom many people hold in contempt, and usually unreasonably so. Then there is always the little guy versus big guy bias; we Americans tend to root for the underdog and this frequently carries through into the courtroom. Hence, there are certain groups who have a tough time getting a fair trial, corporations especially.

The vast majority of people feel that it is okay to be dishonest about insurance claims, for a myth has grown up around insurance companies that *they* are dishonest because they sometimes refuse dishonest claims. Those denied then blame the company for their own corrupt behavior and the myth of the dishonest insurance company continues, as does the myth that all corporations are mean and evil. Thus, in insurance cases, the plaintiff will nearly always paint the insurance company as the big, bad and evil corporation that tramples the rights of the little guy and charcoal broils newborn babies for dinner.

Being an expert on behalf of insurance companies, I've been in front of juries who were just dripping with hostility toward the defendant insurance company, even though it was plain to me that the policy holder was an outright crook. Of course his lawyer painted him as one of the poor, oppressed and downtrodden masses (a doctor with a $300,000 yacht, condominium in Palm Beach and summer home in Martha's Vineyard and Vail, Colorado) but the jury was buying the proletarian angle hook, line and sinker. The jurors were either glaring at me with contemptuous eyes or refused to even look my way. One woman in particular appeared to be trying to send hate-rays at me.

When you run into a situation like that — it won't happen often — there is really no hope; what you have is a badly biased jury. This case was, mercifully, later declared a mistrial when one of the jurors reported to the court of overhearing a conversation among other jurors about how they intended to vote before the trial was half over. It is difficult not to be affected by things like this, but it is the lawyer's job to handle these situations; the witness must ignore them as best possible and stick to his role of testifying honestly.

Hostile Examinations

All interrogations by the other side are hostile to some degree, but some lawyers will take it to extremes, and your lawyer may or may not come to your defense. In my opinion, witness abuse occurs all too frequently. Judges should preserve civility in court, yet judges themselves often are not shining examples. Some people have thick skin, while others will be deeply affected by a lawyer's insulting hostility. The abuse is intentional and by design, the purpose being to get the witness confused, riled up and angry; in other words, get him off-balance and out of control of himself. Combative witnesses, those who tend to argue with the examiner, almost always look bad to a jury. The impression given is one of defensiveness. And if you are defensive, you must be hiding something. That is the picture the other side is trying to paint for the jury.

How should one handle this situation, especially if you don't have much experience? If you find yourself in this situation, the easy way out is to just give in to the point. You lose far less by conceding a point than to angrily defend it. Bear in mind that, despite the apparent personal hostility, that nasty lawyer is not being personal; he's just acting and bears no personal animosity toward you. We need to be acting also, and should we feel a personal insult or anger, we must gather our wits and suppress such feelings. If you can't control yourself in such situations, then you're not going to make a very good expert witness and won't have much of a career ahead of you. People with military service tend to handle this very well because they've got a lot of experience with verbal abuse which is, or was, a way of life in the military. But for the rest of us, this sort of self-control is something we have to learn, the sooner the better.

Avoid the temptation to play mind games with your tormentor. Bear in mind that you are on stage and the jury is watching YOU. Should you resort to such tactics, they will see it and probably formulate an opinion of you that you'd rather they didn't. The lawyer can get away with this behavior only to a very limited degree, beyond which the jury begins to develop a negative impression of him. If you're going to play any role, let it be that of a victim.

When the questions start to get ugly, take a deep breath while pausing. Once you're gained enough self control, you'll find yourself in a position where you can completely defeat attempts to humiliate you. Pause and then smile at the lawyer, as if to say. "I know what you're doing and I'm not falling into your trap." Do this and you'll stop that tactic almost immediately. If there's one thing a lawyer hates, it's a witness who's wise to his tactics. It makes a fool of him, instead. Be careful though and don't get carried away with this. If there's anything worse than a dishonest witness, it's an over confident and arrogant one. One should strive to maintain a neutral attitude.

Body Language

A good way to learn how to become a good witness is by observing as many television trials (real ones, not dramas) as possible. This chapter can't begin to teach you everything you can learn from television for free. In watching a trial one can observe the importance of body language, composure and attitude. By far the most powerful and convincing manner of comportment is that of humility combined with confidence. Arrogant confidence is self-defeating, but understand that arrogance is usually born of fear, an attempt to disguise fearfulness usually by over compensating. Whether it is arrogance or not, the problem is that people perceive it as arrogance.

Bob Hope at the anniversary of his 50th year in show business said that though he had gone on stage ten thousand times, his stage fright never left him. This should help put the issue of fear in perspective. Bob Hope can cover it up with jokes, but we cannot. Unless we are unusually good actors, feigning confidence is likely to be perceived as something else, so the best advice is to be yourself as much as possible:

- Look at your questioner when he is asking the question.
- Frequently look at the jury when answering.
- Sit upright and avoid slouching; place hands in your lap.
- Keep your hands away from your mouth.
- Don't cross leg over knee.
- Pause and breathe deeply when feeling emotion.

Gaining real confidence is mainly a matter of experience and developing effective techniques. After having testified, take a moment to review your performance. If you were nervous, what signs of nervousness did you exhibit? The obvious signs are these:

- Bouncing feet
- Nervous hand movement

- Weak voice

- Hands on face

Paying close attention to your questioners and what is going on around us serves to take our attention off ourselves and relieve nervousness. If your hands are fidgety, play with a pen. Nearly everyone does that and it won't look unusual. You should be taking with you to the witness stand a file containing your casework documents, the ones that have already been entered into evidence, and only those. I usually just take an ordinary clip board with a minimum of documents attached. My main reason is that I just don't have to sit there staring into space when there are delays. The lawyer can ask to see what you have, so don't bring anything you don't want him to see.

The purpose of the clip board is for its transparency; it's not hiding anything and is rarely questioned. Instead, I review the documents, not that I haven't already read them many times, but it's something to absorb my attention instead of letting my mind wander to what's going to happen next. Like the TV news anchor at the end of his script, he sits there pretending to being doing something with pen and papers when we all know that he's just waiting for them to turn the camera off so he can get the heck out of there!

A great many people have a tendency when fearful to let their voices trail off. Be very vigilant about this because speaking with a weak voice does not play well. Besides the fact that he can't be heard, it clearly indicates that he is nervous. If you are asked to "speak up" know that you're slipping into trouble. Rather than trying to force it, take a deep breath or two and try to relax a bit and the voice will return to a normal level. Taking a deep breath is a good weapon against nervousness, but do it through the nose and not the mouth because that way it's not visible. Allow the deep breath to lift your head up and cause you to sit up straighter. This technique also works well against anger.

The experienced witness will learn to develop whatever techniques work for him. The most important point is that he be able to recognize the warning signs that tell him he's heading for trouble, and then use whatever method that will get him out of it.

Recovering From Mistakes

Everyone makes mistakes, but when you're on the witness stand, the opposing lawyer, upon discovering that you are merely a human being, will try to make it appear that you are the only person in the whole world that has ever made a mistake, and that mistake will cause his client irreparable harm. One of the most critical skills of the expert witness is the ability to recover from exposed mistakes.

The biggest mistake that witnesses make, expert or otherwise, is the attempt to gloss over or deny mistakes. The expert is likely to be overly concerned about how his mistake will affect his client. The mistake is already made and we cannot undo it, but attempting to cover it up is far worse than the mistake itself. Most of the mistakes we make are relatively harmless, and sometimes we can recover from them and other times not. In the chapter on report writing I recite a case in which a witness has said something in his report that he should not have, viz:

> "Mr. Smith [fictitious] is basically a nice chap, but I think he is undergoing a delayed identity crisis in his life which may be affecting his judgement. He has a 20 year old girlfriend who he explained has no education and therefore he should prepare her statement for her."

A good lawyer had a field day with this comment, yet the witness could have completely defuse the issue by saying, "You're right, I never should have made that comment. Frankly I have no basis for that conclusion and should never have said it." But that is not what he said; instead, he tried to justify it. The examiner probably won't want to let it go, and will continue to dig at the witness:

> "But this reflects your true opinion about my client, doesn't it Mr. Jones?"

Now that the witness has admitted his error, he can respond by being evasive:

> "Oh, I think it's fair to say that most people would come to such a conclusion when they see a middle aged man sailing off into the sunset with a twenty year old girl. The important point of that comment is that Smith wanted to prepare his girlfriend's statement for her."

> "You didn't answer my question. Didn't this reflect your true opinion about my client?"

> "Sure, it did."

Notice how this takes the wind out of the examiner's sails because the witness did not allow himself to be placed on the defensive. In this revised scenario, the witness made a serious mistake, but did not compound it by trying to cover up. Secondly, that was a two-part statement that the lawyer was not careful to separate and the witness used the opportunity to emphasize second sentence: *the insured concocted the witness's statement.*

In another instance we may get ripped over a poor choice of words that is being twisted by the lawyer. Here, again, the best way to recover from mistakes is to own up to it and then clarify:

> Yes, I can understand why one might see it that way. That was a bad choice of wording on my part, so let me clarify . . .

Notice that the response is not defensive but conciliatory; the witness is not jilted but remains at ease. At this point, the lawyer is likely to try to prevent the witness from clarifying, by cutting him off abruptly or use some other tactic. The witness should not allow himself to be deterred; he was asked a question and has a duty to tell the *whole* truth. He might respond with:

I just took an oath to tell the whole truth, but you seem to be trying to prevent me.

This is a devastating answer for the lawyer and is one of the best responses that a witness can give in any situation where the questioner is trying to prevent the witness from clarifying an answer.

Loose Lips Sink Ships

Witnesses need to be careful about discussing ongoing cases with others. On more than one occasion a witness sank his own ship by making inappropriate remarks in the corridor outside the court room.

> Once during a trial at lunch break, we went out to lunch at a hotel restaurant where it happened that the opposition was also having lunch. I went into the men's room where I happened to overhear a conversation between two men who were witnesses for the other side; they were coordinating their testimony in a loose sort of way. Even so, I made notes on what I heard discussed in the restroom and passed it to my lawyer. The next day when I was called to testify, I was asked about what I had heard. My lawyer later briefed me on the results: both witnesses were completely discredited and the plaintiff's case fell apart, all because two important witnesses said things they shouldn't have, in a public place where they could be overheard.

There will be times when we're left waiting in hallways with other participants in the trial for hours with nothing to do and the temptation will always be there to make casual remarks. Make it a rule that you do not ever discuss a case at trial time with anyone other than your lawyer. You can have a conversation with other witnesses but never about the case.

Dealing with Tricks and Traps

Opening Questions

Whether at deposition or trial, the opening questions will be from the opposing side and will cover your current occupation, background, employment history and education. Then it will move on to what you did in way of preparation for this testimony. You will be asked what documents you reviewed and, most especially, about any conversations you had with your attorney. The gist of these questions is an attempt to show that you have been coached on what to say. Your lawyer has the right to know what your testimony will be; he can inform you of areas of questioning you might be exposed to, but he cannot influence your testimony in any way.

Feel free to recount your discussions with your lawyer, but be careful how you state the matter. It is wise to offer as little as possible without appearing evasive. Let the opponent ask questions without you volunteering much.

The same applies to that which you reviewed. Cover the basics but refrain from going into detail by giving long lists. Don't say: *Everything in my file,* because he will then ask to see everything in your file. Never give him that opening:

> Q. What did you talk about with lawyer Jones this morning?

> A. He asked me about what I had reviewed for today's testimony. Then he explained that I should listen to all questions carefully and not answer before the question was finished. We only spoke for about ten minutes.

> Q. Anything else?

> A. That's all I can think of.

Following is the list of common opening questions by the opposing lawyer's that are likely to start off tricky:

Education

Qualifications

Trial history

What you did to prepare for today

Discussions with your lawyer

Are you taking any medications

Do you understand the oath? What does it mean?

Are you feeling okay?

Testing your recall

Your fees

Relationship with client

When did you get this assignment?

Specifically, what were you asked to do?

Current nature of your work

Many opening questions by their personal nature are intended to make the witness mad so that he comes across as angry, hostile and uncooperative.

Trick Questions

Over the years I have asked numerous lawyers questions about how to deal with trick questions. Invariably, their answers are glib responses that the witness just has to muddle through as best he can and none of them has ever given me any specific advice. I don't know whether this is because they don't want to reveal the tricks of their trade, or they simply don't want their witnesses trying to match wits with the opposition lawyer. Perhaps it's both, but my view is that they run just as much risk of having an unprepared witness that's going to fall victim to these tricks. However, I do agree with them that a witness should not try to match wits with his interrogator as this can lead to unfortunate consequences; that it is imperative that he appear forthright and cooperative regardless of how badly he is being treated.

A witness is making a big mistake when he thinks he can defeat a lawyer that has lots of training and experience at what he does. He does this sort of thing almost every day; we do it only occasionally. There is little likelihood that he will be defeated by a witness, for he is trained to defeat you if you try. There's nothing he'd like better than to lock horns with you, get you angry and argumentative. As will be pointed out elsewhere, most trick questions are intended to trip up dissemblers and deceivers and will therefore have far less effect on the witness who is scrupulously honest. Many of these traps can be easily, if not completely, disarmed with only moderate vigilance on our part.

Being alert to lawyer's tricks allows us to avoid falling into their cleverly designed traps. This is not matching wits with them but rigorously guarding our testimony, which is all we have control over. It is a mistake to attempt to outsmart his strategy, or try to head off the direction of his questions.

Questions that appear to be straightforward should be answered accordingly, but when presented with tricky questions we have a duty to listen carefully and avoid being tricked. Most trick questions are fishing expeditions intended to get the witness to say more than he intends to say, for the lawyer automatically assumes that the witnesses is a liar. The first troublesome question is the "tell us everything you know" question:

> Mr. Baker, please tell us everything you did regarding your investigation.

Such a question is obviously frustrating for it is asking the witness to immediately recall everything about an event that happened long ago. Be very patient and go ahead and answer it just as asked, starting at the very beginning;

> I received a phone call from . . . I set up a file, made a phone call, set up an appointment with...

and so on. Since he expects this question to be exasperating, it's easy to turn the tables on him by being very patient and detailed. Take your time and don't be in a hurry to get through it. Make the answers as mundane as possible, for that is not what he wants to hear. He will soon interrupt you with another question and that will put an end to it because he expected you to cut to the chase and get to the heart of the matter, whereupon he launches his attack. If asked to continue, go on in the same vein.

Because such a question is so broad, our answer will inevitably leave much out. This is what he is expecting so that he can come back and hit you with the omissions in order to make you look like you're being evasive. The only harm this does is if you become defensive about your omissions, so we say:

> Yes, sure, I did that also.

Agree with thy adversary. Or:

> You are asking me to remember all the details of an event that covered many days and happened two years ago. I'm not capable of doing that.

Here's another one:

> Q. Mr. Smith, did you read my client's deposition?"
>
> A. Yes."
>
> Q. What is your understanding of what he did?

A question like this would be objected to in court, but probably not a deposition. The pitfalls of trying to answer this are obvious, and one should not do it. A good answer would be along the lines of:

> A. Your client's deposition was over 100 pages long, and covers many things. I can't recite everything he said, so you will have to be more specific.

Chances are the lawyer will rephrase the question, but narrow it down only slightly, still leaving you in a bind. If so, respond with a partial answer, such as "He went fishing and his boat sank." Don't recite the whole story. At this point you have turned the tables on him and now he has to try to drag the answers out of you, so he becomes forced to refine his own questions.

Consider the above issue carefully because you will face it repeatedly. The purpose of such questions is to get you give an expansive answer. Giving an exceedingly short and precise answer (which is by no means easy to do) defeats the lawyer's attempt without in any way being evasive and yet honestly answers the question. That answer is likely to be followed with, *Anything else?* At this point you've won the battle because he's now reduced to dragging an answer out of you piecemeal.

Sometimes lengthy, convoluted questions frequently cause witnesses quite a bit of trouble and are difficult to deal with. Such questions sound like short speeches rather than questions and are an opportunity for the lawyer to testify to the jury. Then, when we say that we don't understand the question and please say it again, the question is rephrased in equally lengthy and confusing form. Asking him to repeat more than once is playing into his hands because we start to look evasive. Don't do that; instead, try to take the statements/questions apart and answer only one part of the question. If you don't answer all of it, that is his problem, not yours. Again, you are forcing him to take apart his own speech. Be alert that the monologue is likely to contain an erroneous statement of fact, hoping to get you to agree with it. Sometimes the speech/question is designed, by its seeming unintelligibility, to bait the witness into argumentation or anger.

One insidious lawyer technique is to cleverly plant a false fact into a question that otherwise is true, and then get you to confirm it:

> Q. So on March 7th you obtained that piece of evidence and took it to the lab to have it completely analyzed, is that right?
>
> A. Yes.
>
> Q. [Picking up the lab report] Looking at the lab report, it says here that they performed a micro structural analysis. Is that right?
>
> A. Yes.
>
> Q. But they didn't perform a gas chromatograph, did they?
>
> A. No.
>
> Q. And they didn't perform EDAX, did they?
>
> A. No.
>
> Q. But you told me earlier that you had a *complete* analysis performed?

This may seem like a minor thing that is easily corrected, yet the lawyer has effectively challenged the witness's credibility before the jury. The witness agreed to the original *complete* description but now he has to take it back.

Good response:

> "If you used the word "complete" then I missed that. I did not intend to say complete, only that a microstructure was done."

Prompt admission of the mistake effectively neutralizes it.

Note: Getting caught by trick questions is one reason it is so very important to study your deposition carefully before testifying at trial. If you can pick out the mistakes, it becomes much easier to correct at trial by virtue of the fact that you are now prepared for it. The lawyer will surely use that mistake against you at trial. Your answer becomes:

> I'm afraid that I didn't fully understand your question when you asked it. It was not my intention to testify that . . . My testimony is . . .

The no-win question is the classic:

> Have you stopped performing your work in this faulty manner?

Never answer this question with a yes or no answer. The correct answer is:

> I disagree with your premise that the way I do my work is faulty. That is the way most of the professionals in my field work.

Wearing Down the Witness

Wearing down a witness by the use of detailed and trivial questions is effective after the witness has been testifying for a while and he's getting tired. The objective is to get the witness eager to get it over with because he'll be more prone to agree with the lawyer's questions, or get frustrated and angry. This tactic is common and is most easily defeated with patience. When you see it coming, it's easier to sit back and settle in for the duration. If you are really loosing focus, control or are getting angry, ask for a break. In court, turn to the judge and say:

> Your honor, I'm getting tired and would like to request a ten minute break.

You won't be refused.

Repetitious Questions

A lawyer doesn't have the right to badger the witness by repeatedly asking the same questions. When this happens, just say;

> I thought already answered that question.

This makes the lawyer look foolish. Repetitive questions are usually phrased in such a way that they appear very different; the objective is to try to get two different answers to the same question.

Silence Is Golden

After giving a short answer to a long question, the lawyer may try to get you to expound further by expectantly staring at you. This preys on the tendency of most people to fill all silences with words. Meet this tactic by staring right back at him.

Interrupts with Another Question

The lawyer may try to cut off a long answer with another question. Don't let him get away with this.

> You asked a question and I was trying to answer but now you cut me off with another question

Or,

> You didn't let me finish.

Keep in mind that throughout such exchanges, we must never allow ourselves to slip into a hostile or anything other than a completely cooperative, friendly or at least neutral manner. Maintaining this neutral attitude when under attack is not easy, but it is something we have to train ourselves to do. The ability to remain calm while under attack is very impressive to a jury, but should be practiced in depositions as well.

Testing Recall

Testing recall is a device to try to cast doubt on the witness's memory. Mostly it's worked by asking questions that the lawyer knows the witness won't be able to remember, questions that are often trivial. Thorough file review helps to minimize "I don't remember" answers so don't overlook the trivia. "I don't recall" answers, even if true, can only be used up to a point where it begins to look as if the witness is being either evasive, or has a poor memory.

For example, the lawyer asks how many times, we've testified in court, how many depositions. Then he asks for specific names and dates, questions which he is certain that the witness cannot remember. He'll go on at length this way until he's elicited numerous "I don't recall" answers. Then he hits you with *Your memory isn't very good, is it?* Possible responses are:

> My memory isn't good on those points because I have no reason to remember them. People remember what they need to remember and discard the rest, otherwise our minds would be like a cluttered garage.

When asked questions about things long in the past, give a reason why you can't recall, don't let the memory lapse be allowed to suggest you have Alzheimer's. A typical question will be, *"When was the last time you were involved in something like this?"* then, *"What was the name of that?"* the object being to keep the *I can't recall* answers coming. An example of a good answer that breaks up the intent of this line of questioning is:

> I've had dozens of other cases since then, so there's no reason why I should recall those details. Plus, it was X number of years ago.

This is legitimate use of justified answers which make sense and will not be construed as evasion. Improper justification is making excuses which aren't exactly true or stretch the truth.

"You're getting paid to testify" Question

This loaded question is an attempt to have the witness admit that his testimony is bought and paid for. For example:

> Mr. Jones, how much did they pay you to come in here and testify that my client's boat is unseaworthy?

A suggested answer to defuse the situation might be:

I wasn't paid a penny to testify to that specific conclusion. I was hired to analyze the evidence an formulate and opinion of whether the yacht was seaworthy.

No Zingers, Please

There will come a time when we become sufficiently experienced that we begin to spot the errors of the questioner who gives us an opening to insert a zinger, a barb, or just plain hoist him on his own petard. It is very unwise to do that because you'll probably only succeed in motivating him to retaliate. Stay humble.

Two More Rules

There are an additional two essential rules that witnesses should hold foremost. The first is to think before you answer; the second is contained within the first, that is, to never volunteer information.

Having observed hundreds of people testify, it is clear to me that most witnesses feel the need to answer questions quickly. Apparently they feel that any hesitation signals uncertainty. In so doing, they often say unfortunate things, answering questions that aren't asked, and even answering before the questioner is finished asking the question. If you were to read twenty depositions, you'd find in about half of them, that the questioner reprimands the witness to let him finish his question before the witness answers. If this is happening to you, know that you've got a problem with listening to the *whole* question.

Train yourself to listen to every question carefully. Concentrate on the questioner's voice. As we know even from just watching TV trials, many questions are trick questions; questions are often intentionally long, convoluted and hard to follow. The purpose of this is to mislead you into saying something you don't intend to say, or to give an answer to something that wasn't asked. The lawyer may simply be on a fishing expedition. One should avoid trying to read into the questioner's motivation for asking that question, and instead focus on the question precisely as asked. If you heard the question as asked, but do not understand what is being asked, then say so.

Train yourself to pause before answering. This does not make you appear uncertain; it makes you look thoughtful and careful. I once attended a witness training seminar where the lecturer said that slow responses to questions gave the appearance that either the witness didn't know, or was figuring out how to lie, and therein was suggesting that questions be answered quickly. And recently I read another article by a "jury expert" that said the same thing. I emphatically disagree with that notion. Anyone who feels compelled to answer a hostile lawyer's tricky, convoluted questions quickly is heading for trouble. Firing off an answer without having a moment to carefully consider what is being asked may well lead to misunderstanding the question. Consider this question:

You'll tell me, won't you, if you don't understand the question, or any part of a question?

Cross examining lawyers often lay this trap for witnesses, then he will throw at the witness some very complicated questions designed to trip him up. If the witness answers without detecting the trick question, and he later discovers that he was tricked and tries to correct his answer, the lawyer counters him by saying;

> But you said you would tell me if you didn't understand any part of the question. You didn't do that, did you Mr. Witness?

"Don't volunteer information" means to answer the question fully, but don't go beyond the bounds of the question; don't say more than the question requires for an answer.

Equivocal Answers

"Yes" and "no" are absolute answers which, once given, can be hard to get out from under should we come to realize that we have been mislead, or have made a mistake. In many cases "yes" and "no" answers are unavoidable and proper, but with others the witness may come to realize that he's being tricked. For example:

> Is there anything else about this that you can tell us about?

This type of question is a trap. A "no" answer precludes any later recall. The witness is at a disadvantage when asked to recall a broad range of information over a period of time because he's on the spot with a demand for instant recall. The easy way out is:

> That is all that I recall **for the moment**.

The smart lawyer will respond with, *Take your time and think back* . . . So take some time, think back and respond with the same answer, don't say, "No, that's all."

We can only get away with equivocal answers to a limited degree until it becomes obvious that we are being evasive, so use this tactic sparingly and only when justified by clever questions.

Just Answer the Question

It should be evident from the preceding, that your lawyer's admonishment to, "just answer the question and not volunteer information," is far easier said than done. Nor have I found any lawyer who can adequately explain the admonishment. Ultimately, knowing how much to say or not say is a matter of experience, and is not something that is easily taught. My purpose here is to get the reader to give careful consideration to this issue each and every time he testifies.

As mentioned earlier, some lawyers will try to manipulate us into giving misleading answers. A novice will be sorely tempted to elaborate and explain. This is very dangerous ground as the manipulation may be a conscious effort to get the witness to say more than he intends to say. Until one has had plenty of experience, the admonishment to just answer the question and don't volunteer information is good advice. Even with plenty of experience it is risky to banter with the questioner. If further explanation or clarification is necessary, leave it to your attorney to take care of that.

Conversely, going to the opposite extreme and providing only the absolute minimum of words in answer can lead to trouble. Referring again to the O.J. trial, we saw one of the investigators in the role of the crusty, old, hard-nosed detective, giving answers in clipped, monosyllabic words. The demeanor of this detective was unfavorable to the prosecution's case because he looked unyielding, uncooperative, closed-minded and prejudiced even though he was probably honest. But, it was clear that he intended to say only the absolute minimum necessary, and that made him look uncooperative. Even worse, by his one-word answers the lawyer was manipulating him with near total control. He was giving one-word answers when they were not the "whole truth," but simply the short answer which did not suffice. The end result was that his testimony did more harm than good to the prosecutor's case.

The proper attitude is to act normally, being cooperative but neutral, willing and helpful while at the same time not volunteering any more than what is necessary to answer the whole truth. Yes, it is indeed difficult to discern how much of an answer constitutes the right response. It is a skill that only comes with experience.

Clarifying Answers and The Whole Truth

This leads us to the concept of "the whole truth," as contained in the oath we have to take, that poses some interesting questions and problems. For the most part, testifying is simply a question and answer session. Lawyers can get a witness to distort the truth through a manipulative process of trying to force yes or no answers. Few things in life are black and white but rather shades of gray. The yes or no answer may be only a partial truth, but we have sworn to tell the whole truth. We have the duty and the right to explain ourselves fully even when the lawyer demands a yes or no answer. In many cases this will not seem very important, but later he traps you with the inaccuracy of your simple answer when a more detailed answer was in order.

The purpose of yes and no answers may be to prevent full and complete answers, or to distort the truth. Lawyers will resist your attempts to explain yourself mainly by intimidation and tricks. Here are some examples:

- Lawyer stares at you, refusing to break eye contact.

- Demands a yes or no answer.

- Repeats question as if you failed to answer.

- Raises his hand signaling witness to stop.

- Asks court reporter to read back the question.

- Turns his back on witness as if not listening.

- Complains to judge that witness is unresponsive[2].

Finally, he may say, *That didn't answer my question, did it?* Knowing full well that it did.

Of course there will be times when we are eager to tell the whole truth and times when we aren't. We are sworn to tell the whole truth, but what does the whole truth mean? We are not obliged to volunteer information that is not asked about. The whole truth means a complete answer to the question, but what about when a yes or no answer will provide a satisfactory answer, but doesn't fully tell the whole story and is actually only a partial answer? This is still an adversarial process of partisans. If the lawyers are legally permitted to engage in all sorts of trickery, it is foolish for us to adopt an entirely moralistic attitude toward the "whole truth" when they are doing everything possible to subvert that ideal. When it is to our benefit not to give the whole, definitive answer, we don't, but with the caveat that we must not give the *appearance* of holding back. In short, if a simple answer benefits our side, we give it; if it doesn't, we elaborate. Do everything possible to present the appearance of being forthcoming when advantageous to do so, and when it's favorable to hold back without being obvious, we do that too.

Compound Questions

Among the most frustrating questions for a witness to deal with are compound questions which always involve premeditated trickery. Three questions are melded into one, two of which require a "yes" answer but one a "no" answer. The one requiring the "no answer is the one that isn't true. The lawyer is hoping that the witness either isn't listening closely, or won't take the time to clarify. Listen to compound questions very carefully, taking the time to discern where the trick is hidden. Explain the answer as much as necessary, not allowing the lawyer to try to prevent the answer.

Long, windy and confusing questions that sound like speeches are probably intended to get the witness to say more than he intends. In court, he may be just playing to the jury. Much of what comprises the question is not a question at all, but rather statements which may not be true. Listen carefully and only answer the question that is asked. There may be three or four questions inferred in the little speech, but only one actually phrased as such. Answer that one and the lawyer will probably forget about the rest of it.

If the lawyer is demanding an answer to everything he said, then you'll need to take his question apart, line by line. Whenever a lawyer tries to frustrate a witness, he runs the risk of frustrating the jury, and probably the judge, too. With a bit of experience we can turn the tables on him, especially if the jury is reacting to the question as you are. What do their expressions say? The speech will either contain a single question couched in the speech, or the speech will consist of multiple questions phrased as statements. Much depends on how you hear it.

Mischaracterizing Previous Testimony

Mr. Jones, in your earlier testimony you stated that . . . .

Questions like this may be a setup to get the witness to contradict himself. This is unlikely to happen at deposition since a wrong answer can be later corrected, but at trial it cannot. Once again, this is why the witness is constantly admonished to listen to the question closely. If that is not what you said, then say so emphatically.

The Set Up

Lawyers plan their cross examination of hostile witnesses in groups of questions which are designed to trap the witness. The first four or five questions are seemingly harmless questions that elicit a "yes" answer. The questions are intended to get the witness to affirm points leading up to the "kill" in which the final question is asked, usually a question the witness will not be happy to answer. Anyone who's ever testified before will recognize the pattern immediately and will likely know what's coming. The "set up" almost always comes as a result of some weakness the lawyer has found in our work.

People naturally react to being trapped like this by trying to extricate themselves from the trap by arguing or justifying. This is exactly what the lawyer hopes to achieve. Not only has he exploited the weakness but now hopes to compound it by getting the witness to argue, justify or deny. This, of course, makes a bad situation worse. When we see the set up coming, the thing to do is to resign ourselves to the truth and not play into his hands any further. If he has caught us in a mistake, the only thing we can do is own up to it without justifying, explaining or arguing. If the opposition has scored a point, then give it to them.

Fortunately for us, there is a limit to how much a lawyer can try to manipulate us without making a bad impression on the jury himself. If he goes too far, they begin to see him as a con artist, so this will limit how many trick questions he can ask. Those that he does ask will be on vital points, so be particularly alert when they do come. Normally, there are only a few big pot holes in the road that we have to maneuver around.

Record Keeping

There are pros and cons to keeping good file records for extended periods of time. By that I mean beyond five years or so. Statutes of limitations are variable on differing matters and run three to ten years generally with five to seven being the median. Beyond IRS requirements, there are no laws requiring you to maintain non-tax related business records. Maintaining a lot of old files because some few of them may end up in litigation may result in an extra job or two, but it's more likely to cause excess grief due to shotgun subpoenas in litigation where you will not be paid any more than the proscribed $12.75 witness fee for expenses.

Lawyers have the right to subpoena virtually all records related to their case that includes paper as well as computer files. When the subpoena arrives, the first thing you have to do is to go searching your records to see what you've got. I've received subpoenas that have demanded that I bring my entire computer to a deposition and had a lovely time trying to get around that one! Thus, computer records can be a double-edged sword. Of course you can see how years worth of digital photographs can become a gargantuan problem, which is yet another reason why I discourage the use of digital cameras, for film is ultimately more convenient. Perhaps in the future this issue will be resolved, but for the present it is not.

Due to the excessive numbers of subpoenas I receive, I save files for only five years and then destroy them.

After you've been dragged through the trial experience a few times, you will have painfully discovered that there are things in your files that you'd rather not have others see; you have said things that should have been said another way, as well as having said things that shouldn't have been said at all. It is illegal to cull your file after the process server knocks on your door. Therefore, it's best to learn as quickly as possible about what shouldn't be in a file. Honest notes ironically turn out to be the biggest problem. Notes on your thoughts about an investigation, doubts, things like that. But just as bad are preliminary notes or conclusions. Notes relating to preliminary thoughts or conclusions should not be put in the file. It's okay to make those, notes, but it's not okay to save them:

> I've never been so thoroughly roasted on the witness stand as in an insurance case that ultimately became a criminal case. I performed a lengthy investigation in a far away city when, eventually the state police and FBI were brought in. By the fourth day of the investigation, it seemed like the whole world was involved and it became very difficult to keep track of what was going on. Since I was staying in a hotel, there was plenty of time in the evenings to write up notes. For several evenings I sat down and wrote out everything I could recall, then summarized my thinking at that point and made a list of further things to do. These notes included summaries or comments of law enforcement people I was dealing with. What I was doing was all proper, good procedure, but I made just one mistake.

> Those notes got left in the file indefinitely when I should have culled and destroyed them. These were working notes and not records of evidence. Most of my time on the witness stand involved what I had written in those notes. Early on I had developed a direction of investigation leading to a theory that had soon proved to be false or at least inaccurate. Later, evidence suddenly popped up that proved the case, but there was little need for notes about this because the proof was overwhelming; there was nothing to speculate about.

Therefore, virtually all my notes were about my unproductive line of investigation and wrong theory. Naturally, the defense seized on this like a drowning man a life ring.

This taught me the hard way that these kind of notes should not be kept in the file. It is not illegal to destroy notes before they have been subpoenaed.

The Expert Witness

Although this book is about marine investigation, in this chapter, we have discussed both material witnesses and expert witnesses, because marine investigators generally possess the degree of expertise necessary to qualify in court as expert witnesses. An expert is defined as a person that possesses a high level of knowledge, training or experience on a given subject. By the time a person has had at least fifteen years of experience in his line of work he can be considered "expert." Someone with less than this will likely be less highly regarded. Expert witnesses are, of course, hired by lawyers for assistance in litigation. Another way to describe them is as technical consultants who sometimes, but not always, testify as to their expert opinions after reviewing the facts of the case.

Being hired as an expert witness is the ultimate compliment to the marine surveyor for it signifies that he had reached the top of his profession; it is not something that usually comes to those of average experience and knowledge. People often believe that expertise is something that comes primarily by way of formal education so that expertise that comes by way of experience is, unfortunately, often given short shrift. While it is certainly impressive to have a Ph.D. attached to one's name, it should be understood that before a formal education can be taught, someone had to first gain the knowledge by means of experience or research. The learning of PhDs typically comes by way of books and college professors who also learned from books, so in most cases the knowledge they possess is second-hand, whereas the knowledge of the surveyor is higher in the order of first hand experience. We shouldn't lose sight of the fact that experience is the "first teacher" in the University of Knowledge. The fact that marine surveyors don't have the advantage of significant formal training available to them does not make them less qualified or reduce their standing. We should not ever forget this important fact when it comes time to testify, for it will be necessary to demonstrate and defend our qualifications.

Conflicting Roles of Experts

It often happens that the roles of experts become confused, by both himself and the attorney. As noted earlier, an expert may be both a consultant and a witness at trial, a factor that not infrequently causes trouble. A consultant's advice to a lawyer is privileged information, but if privileged, he cannot testify to that advice:

A recent example of a mistake that I made involved what I thought was an advisory report that I made to an attorney who had hired me as an expert. It was my fault that I failed to clarify the use to which this report would be made because, unknown to me, the lawyer provided a copy of my report to the other side during discovery.

In that report, I made statements that I would never have made in a report for use as evidence. The report contained idle speculation and comments concerning a litigant that ought never to have gone beyond the lawyer's file. During deposition, these comments were used against me to considerable effect.**

Therefore, it bears repeating that whenever writing any kind of correspondence to an attorney or client, it is absolutely imperative to clarify in advance what that report will be used for. If it is to be used as evidence, it must contain only elements of fact, never speculation or idle or suggestive commentary. This is a mistake that you want to be very careful not to make! Do not expect your lawyer client to clarify this for you – it is up to you to find out.

If you are writing a consulting report not to be submitted as evidence, make sure that report is headed with the caption: CONFIDENTIAL: THIS REPORT CONTAINS CONSULTING ADVICE TO____. Follow this rule and I guarantee that you'll save yourself tons of grief.

Curriculum Vitae

It is necessary to maintain a Curriculum Vita for a variety of reasons. Unfortunately, a CV can be a dangerous document in the hands of the enemy. Bear in mind that any background information, such as past employment, can be used as a basis for research on the expert. Say, for example, there was an unhappy stint with a particular employer. Or, he is the author of magazine articles. If one is a witness in a big case, that is, high dollar value, it is probable that the opposing lawyer will use the expert's CV as a basis for investigating him. Be circumspect about what your CV contains; keep it as brief as possible. Another difficulty: say there was a period of four or five years where the expert changed jobs frequently. A lawyer would use this to suggest that he is an unstable person. Keep in mind that a fancy CV is not going to impress anybody, only be used as a weapon against him in litigation. It is best to make your legal CV as brief and as vague as possible, while including the essentials. Avoid using a chronology and dates, unless one can comfortably do so, this because you are then forced to fill in any gaps.

***

** The best way to defuse these errors is simply to own up to them. In this case I was able to extract myself with much less damage by simply stating the truth of the matter, and admitting that my comments were not evidence and not relevant; they were intended to provide advice on avenues for further investigation, not expert advice about evidence. I could have avoided this problem by making sure that I understood what the attorney would use the report for before I wrote it.

Most people have had to take interim menial, or less than ideal jobs at one time or another, but a lawyer will seize on this in an effort to make a witness look bad.

When testifying at deposition or trial, a lawyer may question the witness at length about his educational or employment experience for the sole purpose of trying to find something that casts doubt on credibility. It is advisable to preplan one's testimony as to education and work experience, considering it carefully and thinking it through, pinpointing any sore spots. Areas which do not fit in neatly with one's current line of work will need to be explained, if one intends to mention them. As to what to include, it's best to only touch on the highlights so long as this doesn't leave any major time gaps. For example if you had one stint with an employer 1985 to 1989, and another beginning in 1991, expect to be asked about what you were doing in 1990.

The way that the opposition is likely to get hold of our CV is to ask the witness at deposition for it. Or, your attorney may turn over the one that you provided to him. Therefore, it's probably a good idea to have at least two versions of your CV, one you give to prospective clients and the other strictly for legal cases.

The publishing of articles can result in problems for the expert, so it is best not to include any publishing on one's legal resume. The reason is that lawyers will usually search these articles for things that you have said that could be used against you in a case. This would not necessarily be some kind of factual error, but more likely just something that is beneficial to their case, in which situation you become a witness for the other side! At deposition, lawyers will often ask whether you've published anything. Be careful how you answer. If you have stuff out there in the recent public realm, you'll have to own up to that.

Fees

Material witnesses under subpoena are not entitled to expert witness fees but only the pitifully small fees set up by statute, ranging anywhere from $0.50 to $12.00 per day - yes, you read that correctly, fifty cents per day! And travel allowances won't even cover bus fare. Where we run into trouble is when we are not hired by anyone as an expert, but get a subpoena because we did work for someone not involved in the litigation. For more on this subject see The Non Expert Witness later.

Probably due to the recent spate of high profile celebrity trials on television, a lot of people seem to have gotten the spurious idea that being an expert witness is a ticket to instant wealth. Trust me, it's not. There are more than a few marine surveyors who advertise incredibly high rates such as $300/hour or $2,000/day but I doubt that they have many customers. The vast majority of pleasure craft cases will only support modest fees. The problem with legal cases is that they are tremendously time consuming so that, when setting fees, one needs to be cognizant of how much time will be spent.

Attend any conference of marine surveyors and one is bound to hear of complaints of not getting paid by lawyers. This is a huge problem for surveyors, but one largely of their own making. One should start with the reality that lawyers are among the most difficult people to collect a debt from, because they can defend debt collection efforts at a cost of only their own time and we have virtually no leverage over them.

Never accept a promise or "guarantee" of payment by a lawyer; his promise is about as good as taking advice from a stock broker. Let's consider some of the reasons why we have so much trouble collecting from lawyers. First, it is the problem of contingency fee cases; if the lawyer loses a contingency fee case, he doesn't get paid, and neither will you, despite the promises. When a lawyer hires an expert, he is acting as an agent for the client. It is the client who ultimately remains responsible for such fees and costs.[3] Secondly, lawyers frequently fail to take into account how much time we are spending on a case and are shocked at the amount of our bill. He may have told the client it would be much less.

Except for insurance cases, experience teaches that there is only one solution to this problem and that is to get your money up front. The reality is that if a lawyer isn't willing to pay you up front, the chances of getting paid at all are slim to none. I have personally had a number of instances where the lawyer charged the client for my fee, but refused to pay me, thereby putting the money in his pocket! If you do make the mistake of not getting paid in advance, try checking with the client to see if the lawyer billed him for your fee. If he did, that is fraud, and you can file a complaint with the state bar association; see your local state's attorney about a fraud action, or both; this, in lieu of undertaking costly litigation yourself.

When discussing the money matters with the lawyer, it is important to try to get a good feel for just how much time you will be spending on the case; it is foolish to think that he has an unlimited budget, or that he is wisely managing his own time and fees; if anyone is going to get short-changed, it won't be the lawyer! Therefore, don't just discuss hourly rates but also the likely total amount of time that will be expended. Don't be shy about this because this involves the issue of whether you will be paid for your time or you are working pro bono.

Set a reasonable hourly rate in consideration of the amount of time to be expended and the value of the case. Obviously, $200/hour isn't going to fly on a small case. If you ordinarily make $60.00/hr., it may be necessary to extend this rate to litigation work if it is particularly time consuming. Some experts set a split fee rate, one for case review and another higher rate for testimony time. Since the vast majority of cases are mundane disputes, they won't command high rates, but are offset because there are more of them and offer a much steadier work flow.

When discussing fees, try to review everything he wants you to do so as to get an idea of how much time will be involved. It is in the best interest of both parties that the lawyer isn't hit with an unexpectedly large bill.

Keep in mind that case work often takes place in other cities and states, so that travel expenses are frequently a major component of one's billing. Travel expenses should always be calculated and advance payment requested so that one doesn't end up financing the client's case.

Retention as Expert

Another reason why the expert should get a retainer fee in advance has to do with the kind of games lawyers will play with witnesses, which goes like this: Lawyer A wants to prevent lawyer B from using a particular person or persons from being available as witnesses to the opposition. Lawyer A calls up the expert and feeds him a long spiel that strongly suggests that the expert is being hired. In reality, he does not retain, pay or use him in any way. Often he tries to gain valuable information from the witness who will never hear from that lawyer again, then the layer lists the expert on court documents as "his" witness. This deceitful practice has been used on me a number of times until I finally wised up to what was happening.

This can be avoided by demanding a sizeable retainer and if the lawyer balks, you'll know that he never intended to pay you in the first place and haven't lost anything when never heard from again. A retainer letter does not suffice in lieu of the fee for he can still tie you up without paying you.

Expert Witness Contract

Most lawyers are now used to the idea of signing expert witness contracts. It is advisable that experts should use one and get it signed. The following example outlines some of the basic points covered in such a contract:

Consultant Agreement

This agreement is entered into between Mr. Qualified Expert, consultant, and Larry Lawyer, Esquire, attorney at law, counsel for _____, on March 4, 1892.

The purpose of this agreement is to set out the terms of services provided by the consultant in relation to the case of Sidney Small v. Titanic Operations International, Case number 92-00234567 AD before the U.S. 4th Circuit Court.

Mr. Expert agrees to provide his professional consultant service for the client attorney as an independent professional, and that Mr. Expert is an independent contractor.

Expert agrees that all information disclosed to, and provided to Expert by client attorney, is confidential and shall not be disclosed to any other party or person without the express written consent of the counsel.

Client attorney agrees to pay a one-time, non-refundable retainer fee of ___ to be applied to the hourly charges until exhausted. Client attorney agrees not to list expert as a witness on his behalf until such time as the retainer is paid.

The client attorney agrees to pay to Expert his standard hourly rate of ____ plus expenses outlined as follows:

Purchase of airfares shall be at refundable or transferable coach air rates at consultant's discretion.

Auto mileage at the rate of __

Telephone, courier, etc.

The consultant fee covers compensation for all tasks performed under this agreement, including analysis, calculations, conclusion, preparation of reports, travel time and deposition and court testimony.

Consultant bills on a ninety day basis and client attorney agrees to pay these invoices within 30 days, and shall be subject to a 1.5% per month late penalty for unpaid balances.

There are no other promises, agreements, conditions or other understandings between Consultant and Counsel which are not set forth herein.

This agreement covers essential protections required by both lawyers and experts, and should be modified to fit individual circumstances.

The Non-Expert Witness

By virtue of having involved ourselves in investigative matters for years, there will come a time when the subpoenas start rolling in quite unexpectedly. At this point we have a problem because we no longer have a paying client; or the subpoena comes from a non client, which presents a serious problem of not getting paid. As a material witness, we may only entitled to that puny witness fee. We are faced with a loss of income as well as additional expenses.

The problem of standard witness fees becomes critical after a decade or two of work in this business. At the peak of my career I was getting as many as two unexpected subpoenas per month and with 75% of these being only standard witness fees, I found myself working for free a good part of the time. In reality there is no legal way out of this box; one can make appeals to the courts but they already have too much to do and aren't interested in our problems. In one instance, I walked into the judge's chambers holding sixteen subpoenas in my hand, all from the same year. The response: So sorry, there's nothing we can do about that.

Numerous experts report having to make it clear that they will be hostile unless they get paid in advance, and I've had to do the same thing. The threat is that you anticipate contracting amnesia in the near future. The problem with this is that to do this we are making an illegal threat, but, then it's a standoff that we will probably win because of our threat is to be uncooperative in court. The refusal to cooperate is the only possible solution but, as stated, risks a contempt of court charge. But it's hard to prove that someone doesn't have a faulty memory. If you have to resort to this tactic, it's a good idea to create a separate file and save all our subpoenas so that if we get charged with contempt, we can prove mitigating circumstances.

However, in recent years the tide seems to be turning on this problem. The rules of some states or bar associations now address this issue directly, such as those of Colorado:

> The premise that an expert witness fee is owed only [if] an expert opinion is elicited from the witness is not a valid assumption. An expert who comes into the possession of facts or information solely because of his position as a professional is entitled to receive compensation as an expert when he testifies to those facts in court.

Therefore, be sure to check your state statutes and bar association rules before considering the above.

Case Review

Being asked to review a pending case is one of the more interesting and enjoyable forms of expert work, especially if you don't mind reading through reams of paper and are good at assimilating and organizing large volumes of information. Expert document analysis can be likened to panning for gold in a stream — it takes persistence, patience and determination. Instead of investigating boats and people, expert witness work is usually a matter of analyzing depositions and documents, piles of them. If you don't like paper work, you probably won't make a very good expert witness.

At first the task of reviewing hundreds of pages of documents — and in some cases thousands — seems daunting. The process of reading and assimilating it all is rather like moving a mountain, one shovel full at a time. It just takes time and persistence. My experience has been that I have never managed to assimilate a complex case with a single reading. It takes reading through at least twice.

The purpose of case review is to search for weaknesses in the opposition's case. As marine experts we have eyes to see such things that our client attorney does not. That's why he's hired us. These weaknesses can consist of a wide range of faults from procedural and factual errors to matters of bias, motives and deception. From all my years of investigation and court room experience, I'd have to conclude that there is no such thing as a perfect investigation because all investigations contain errors and weaknesses, and by virtue of our expertise, we are qualified to find them. This assertion begins with the reality that we are nearly always circumscribed by the economics of the case; there's never enough time and money to do all that we'd like to do.

Before getting started, two things should be done. First, we should obtain from the client attorney an overview of the thrust of his case. This is necessary so that we can make decisions about the importance and relevance of facts. Otherwise, we may waste time working with irrelevant (to the attorney) information. Keep in mind that the study of many documents is being delegated to you, the expert.

Secondly, it is necessary to organize our materials – particularly when there is a lot of paper – in the most accessible and easy to locate manner. This means to sort and segregate the documents into categories and file each category separately. This will usually mean revising our normal method of filing things in simple file folders to the use of large indexed files. Moreover, we'll probably need to improve our discipline in scrupulously keeping papers filed in the right place because dealing with a large volume of paper can result in large amounts of wasted time looking for a single document.

As for note taking, a proven method is to use a legal pad and record notes under the heading of the relevant document, and when finished the notes can be placed in the appropriate file. Another method is to establish code numbers and letters for the categories between notes and documents.

Case review begins with reading whatever documents are provided to us. From these we usually discern certain areas or points that require further analysis or investigation, whether of physical evidence, documents or persons. Case review inevitably raises questions that need answers, and this may compel us to do some investigating on our own.

The reports of other experts are usually fertile ground for reaping the opposition's errors. We examine the reports for all the faults that we would not want to make ourselves, trying to get a sense for the expert's degree of knowledge and skill. Is his conclusion reasonable and well supported? Is his evidence weak or strong, does he leave open alternate theories, did he close the door on any other possible or probable causes? Does the wording of the report provide openings for challenge? Are there important questions that go unanswered?

With a defense case the objective is to cast doubt on the plaintiff's allegations. In some cases we are fortunate enough that the plaintiff's case is so weak that there is actually enough evidence available to disprove the allegation. In others, the best we can do is to try to shoot their case full of holes.

With plaintiff cases, the objective is usually to search for faults in both our client's and the defense case, but with the later we will not know what their defense theory will be until the discovery process is well underway. Good lawyers want to know what the weaknesses of their cases are, so we should not shy away from critiquing the client's case and bringing to the attention of the lawyer any problem areas that we perceive. No good lawyer wants to take a bad or even weak case to court. However, we will also run across clients that prefer to ignore bad news, so we need to approach this point with some caution. My policy is to simply ask the client point bank as to whether he wants to hear negative critique as well as positive. Of course, no lawyer is going to say that he doesn't want to hear any bad news, so we need to listen to his answer carefully. Here are two typical answers to the direct question:

Uh, yeah, sure.

Definitely. If you run across any problems, I want to hear about them.

Though both answers are affirmative, the first is far less than enthusiastic while the second is decisive. The way to treat the first lawyer would be to state your case, but don't push it. If he really doesn't want to hear it, that is his problem. We have been hired for our expertise and if the client doesn't want to make use of it, that's his decision. As I write this, I have one client who requested specifically that I play devil's advocate with the facts of his case while another has an attitude that says that he'd rather not hear about it. As a service provider, it's not healthy for me to question the client's decision making.

The best procedure for case review is to do a quick read-through, followed by a more detailed study. Before we can get down to details, it is first necessary to have a good overall understanding of the situation. Otherwise, we risk developing tunnel vision wherein we focus on facts that might be taken out of context or misunderstood as to how they fit into the overall situation. The importance of this point should not be underestimated: Before case evidence can be evaluated it is vital to have a clear picture in mind of the entire subject of contention.

As we go through documents the first time, many areas will be discovered where clarification is needed, but the object is to get a general overview of the case so that a more carefully reading will be more fruitful. It is useful to make notes at this time even if you never look at them again since the process of making notes reinforces points in our minds. On the second reading use a yellow marker to highlight important points for future reference and make good notes if you're going to make a written summary.

Case Summaries

Sometimes the expert is called on to prepare written summaries of his case review. Summaries are not easy to create in an orderly and logical fashion with well-considered comments. Summaries of entire cases are best made in either a chronological or categorical order of events, although chronologies can be further broken down by topic and vice versa. Needless to say, the client already has enough paperwork to wade through, so you don't want to make his job any more difficult with a report that is longer and more wordy than it need be. Keep comments as brief and to the point as possible. We should not lose sight of where our expertise ends and the lawyer's begins and confine our commentary to the evidence of the case and not its importance or how it is to be used.

It's a common failing on our part to come to believe that we have discovered a very important point of evidence, only to find that our client has no interest in it. The client has a litigation strategy so that we will find that at times what appears to us as important evidence simply doesn't fit into the client's strategy. The client won't be pleased with us if we continue to push it.

Case summaries should be prepared with an economy of words; wordy explanations of important points should be avoided. Don't confuse a summary with analysis. When in doubt about whether analysis or editorial comment is called for, the simple solution is to simply ask the client what he wants.

Deposition Review

Many lawyers will request their experts to review depositions for a number of reasons. The main reason is because the expert possesses knowledge that the lawyer does not and therefore is probably better able to understand the veracity of the witness's testimony. Depositions often contain nuggets of pure gold, nuggets that are not always obvious and can be difficult to ferret out. This is where the expert's experience comes into play. The expert may be able to get a sense of when a witness is dissembling and covering up a point that he doesn't want to admit, bearing in mind that the lawyer's knowledge of the subject matter is probably less than the expert's.

Since the purpose of deposition review is to ferret out inconsistencies with other facts and evidence, when we review depositions we need to do so only after we have reviewed all other case documents or depositions. Most of the time we will be comparing the testimony of one witness with another, determining whether they agree on specific points or are at odds. Furthermore, there will be times when testimony can be related to facts contained in other documents.

Expert witness work is not for the faint-hearted or persons who are loath to rock the boat or be critical of others. Even in large markets the marine business world is a small world where most of the players tend to know each other, if not personally, then at least in passing. The most common situation will be reviewing the work of other investigators or experts, evaluating the thoroughness of their work, the validity of their conclusions and even their honesty. We will be up against people such as yacht brokers, boat yard, marina and repair people. This inevitably brings us into conflict with peers, colleagues and possibly even friends. It will happen that we are required to critique the work of personal acquaintances and testify to that critique in court. The way to handle this is to ignore the friendship; this is business, and if the friend were in your shoes, he'd be doing the same.

Document Review

Documents play a leading role in nearly all litigation cases and, like lawyers, we become expert paper-pushers. It is truly amazing how much can be learned from invoices and repair bills, nor is it unusual that key evidence to a case might be found in a repair bill. In a recent case critical evidence was found after careful analysis of parts lists that contained primarily part numbers and no description. It was necessary for the expert to obtain part descriptions for all those part numbers, of which there were several hundred. While this involved several days' worth of tedious labor, the end result was that this effort ended up proving a fraud case in which the boat owner and repairer conspired to cover up the true cause of a casualty. To the extent that these were documents already presented as evidence, the exposure of these hidden facts in court produced a rare moment of civil court drama.

As was discussed in the chapter on fraud investigations, sales documents contain a wealth of information, much of which is gleaned by "reading between the lines". Any document can be as important for what it doesn't say (or omits) as what it does say. There have been large cases where there were so many documents involved that it was necessary to hire a small team of temporary workers to analyze, collate, and prepare breakdowns and summaries. Subpoenas to produce documents in the average case doesn't produce large quantities, but in large yacht cases where good record keeping is the rule rather than the exception, boxes of documents are likely to be involved. If the litigation team isn't prepared to deal with this it will be overwhelmed and important evidence will be lost.

The cost of reviewing large volumes of documents is always a serious issue and so one needs to accomplish this efficiently, if it's going to be done at all. How we will handle this will be highly dependent upon what we are trying to accomplish. It is not possible to perform expert analysis on thousands of pages of documents. Efficiency starts with an understanding of how to do it with good organization.

For example, there was a case in which a million dollar refit of a yacht was in contention due to the owner's failure to maintain control over the contractor. The owner was presented with a stack of invoices that was nearly three inches thick. A brief review of these invoices suggested that the lengthy materials lists and time sheets were heavily padded. To resolve the issue three temporary workers from a quality temp agency were hired and put to work in a rented hotel conference room. These people were instructed on what to look for, and then they entered the data from the invoices onto rented computer spread sheets, after sorting the documents. Here the objective was first to break down the work load into manageable proportions by separating the data into categories. The first task was to make the project manageable. In this way, it was determined that the amount of materials billed for was vastly greater that what was actually used.

Since I was the only expert involved, I was able to utilize non experts to break the task down to size. With a spread sheet containing dates, document descriptions and invoice numbers, the task of analyzing boxes of documents was made possible. In other instances the computer can be used to create lists, chronologies, tallies of totals and comparisons. The ability to perform such analytical work is often invaluable to the client who may not even be aware that it is possible to achieve such results.

The lawyer who hires an expert as a consultant basically has little idea of what the expert can actually do for him; he's really just hoping that the expert can fill in gaps in his knowledge. Our value to the client is largely a matter of initiative and creativity. The more we understand that a pile of documents are a potential gold mine, the more value we can be to the client. All documents, whether invoices or narrative reports, contain an undercurrent of reality that is not overtly expressed by whatever language the document contains. A good analyst is one that can read between the lines where other experts miss the subtleties. Here's a short example:

> Recently the entire file of a competitor was given me in a case that was about to go to trial. Persistent study of this file revealed that dates of certain events were suspiciously missing throughout documents in this file, when it was normal that those dates should have been included. This led to the question of why were these dates conspicuously left out? Continued digging finally revealed that the other investigator was not present when certain things happened, even though his report suggested that he was. Another reading of the report revealed that it was cleverly worded to give the impression of direct involvement in an issue without actually stating so. It turned out that the investigator had assembled his report solely on the basis of the work of others. Thus, he could not be accused of lying, yet he was still wide open to the charge of being intentionally misleading. This finding led to the complete discrediting of this witness and the ultimate collapse of a defense case.

I want to stress how well hidden some of these gold nuggets can be. Sometimes the gold is not a nugget but a small flake. Notice how subtle the issue of a few missing dates is. The discovery of this fact was the result of recognition of an anomaly, something that was not right or out of order. At other times it's nothing more than intuition, a hunch that causes us to search further.

Expert Witness Testimony

This chapter on the subject of being deposed and giving court testimony is intended both for the material witnesses and expert witnesses. However, it should be understood that the expert witness will be expected to possess a higher degree of experience and skill because (1) he is being paid as an expert, not only in his field of expertise, but for his skill at testifying, (2) by virtue of holding himself as an expert, an opposing lawyer has much greater latitude to attack him than he does with a fact witness and, (3) the expert commands little, or at least less, native sympathy from the jury and will expect the lawyer to be very hard on him.

Unfortunately, many people who hold themselves out as experts neglect this aspect of the vocation and as a result end up performing poorly in court. Not understanding how they can be bamboozled and trapped by a good trial lawyer, a single poor showing in court, particularly one that loses a case for a lawyer, is likely to seal that person's reputation for a long time to come. We shouldn't underestimate just how small our individual fields of endeavor are and how rapidly bad news travels along the "grapevine." Bear in mind that both sides of the case are witness to a debacle; conversely, if a person does very well, the good news spreads equally rapidly thus making the first impressions extremely important to one's reputation and career.

It is axiomatic that an expert witness under cross examination will be subject to devious and hostile examination and woe to him who is not prepared for this. It is naive for an expert to assume that professional expertise, diligence and truthful intent will protect him from testimonial harm. Simply stated, to hold oneself out as an expert witness and to be able to give professional testimony as such, the expert needs to be schooled in the ways of trial lawyers. This is not a particularly difficult subject, nor is it time consuming to learn: a full, two day seminar by an expert trainer (of which there are many) will be sufficient. This subject is best learned in a training environment and not from books, but the investment at the beginning of one's career will pay for itself many times over.

A free educational experience can be had by going down to the nearest court house and being a spectator in a trail, an opportunity to free education that I strongly recommend. Choose a civil trial rather than a criminal trial and pay particular attention to the way witnesses comport themselves, and the way jurors react to the testimony of witnesses of all types. Observe those qualities that make for good, credible witnesses contrasted by those who don't; notice how a few will particularly stand out, both good and bad.

Conclusion

As one can see from this discussion, becoming an experienced and effective witness is not easy; it takes time and practice. The good news is that as you gain in experience, the job becomes progressively easier. The better we get at it, the more we are sought out as experts as our reputation spreads. For the beginner who has never testified before, he should get used to the idea that he is in boot camp and that he's going to have to take a few hard knocks. He should not, however, be overly disturbed by mistakes and poor performances since there is no other way to gain experience. Most witnesses make mistakes and such mistakes are unlikely to seriously harm a client's case.

(Footnotes)

1. If there is a legitimate reason for something, then by all means give it, but a reason must never sound like an excuse that lacks credibility.

2. Judges are often not paying attention and will have no idea of whether the witness was responsive or not. He'll probably just say, "Please answer the question." To which we reply, "I just did." If the judge didn't hear our answer, he's in no position to argue.

3. Rules of the Colorado Bar Association, which are similar to those of some other states.

Appendix A
Useful Data

Conversions

Gallons per cubic foot	7.48
Kilowatts per horsepower	1.34
Horsepower per kilowatt	0.7457
Feet per meter	3.048
Feet per fathom	6
Liter per gallon	3.79
Grams per ounce	28.0
Pounds per kilogram	2.2
Cubic feet per cubic meter	10.8 ft³.
Mm per inch	25.4 mm
Kilometer per mile	0.539 Km
Nautical mile per statute mile (knots)	1.1516

Weights

Pounds per gallon water	8.556
Water per cubic foot	64 salt, 62.5 fresh
Gasoline/gal	6.12 lbs.
Diesel oil/gal	7.13 lbs.

Pounds per Cubic Foot

Aluminum	168
Bronze	481
Concrete	144
Iron, cast	485
Lead	700
Monel	556
Diesel oil	53.3
Lube oil	57.5
Loose sand	90-105
Fresh snow, dry	8

Steel	490
Stainless steel	492-510
Whiskey, qt.	3
Plywood	36
Fir, Douglas	32
Mahogany	32-36
Teak	45
White oak	53
Fiberglass 30/70	96
Plate glass	161

INDEX

OTHER BOOKS BY DAVID H. PASCOE

Surveying Fiberglass Power Boats 2nd Edition
Buyers' Guide to Outboard Boats
Mid Size Power Boats

CPSIA information can be obtained
at www.ICGtesting.com
Printed in the USA
FFOW01n1055080517
35302FF